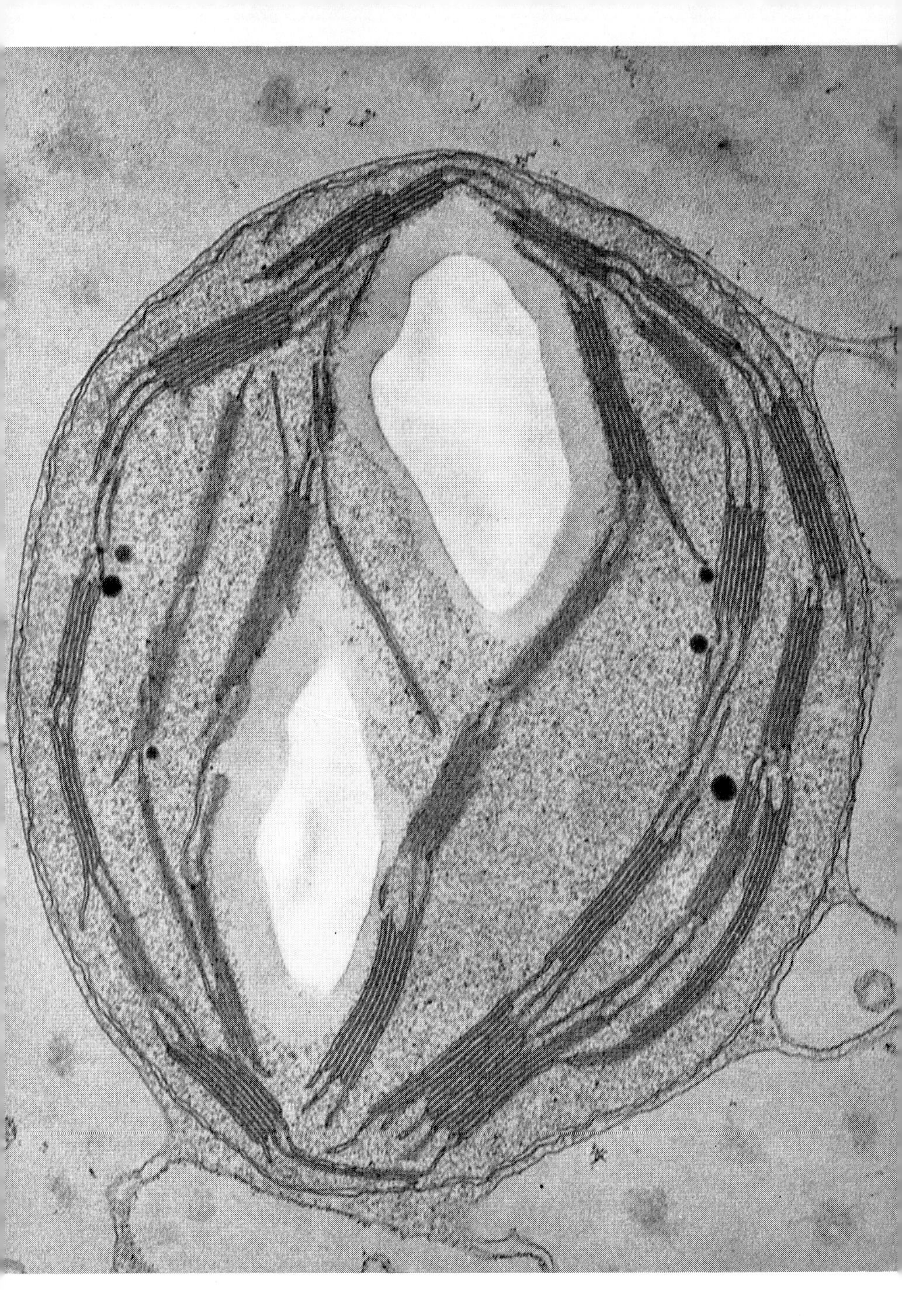

ELECTRON MICROGRAPH OF A THIN SECTION OF A CHLOROPLAST FROM THE LEAF OF *Avena sativa* (OAT). The chloroplast contains two starch grains and shows the lamellae aggregated into grana; cf. Fig. 89. (× 50,000.)

LOWSON'S

TEXTBOOK OF BOTANY

Revised by

E. W. SIMON, D.Sc.
PROFESSOR OF BOTANY, QUEEN'S UNIVERSITY OF BELFAST

K. J. DORMER, B.Sc., Ph.D.
READER IN BOTANY, UNIVERSITY OF MANCHESTER

and

J. N. HARTSHORNE, B.Sc., Ph.D.
LECTURER IN GENETICS, UNIVERSITY OF MANCHESTER

UNIVERSITY TUTORIAL PRESS LTD
9-10 GREAT SUTTON STREET, LONDON, E.C.1

Fourteenth Edition, Revised and Reset, 1966

Reprinted, with minor alterations, 1968

SBN: 7231 0427 1

PRINTED IN GREAT BRITAIN BY UNIVERSITY TUTORIAL PRESS LTD
FOXTON, NEAR CAMBRIDGE

PREFACE
TO THE FOURTEENTH EDITION

LOWSON'S well-known *Textbook of Botany* is intended to serve as a general introduction to the study of the subject, and is designed to meet the requirements of a wide range of students: candidates for General Certificate of Education at the Advanced Level (including Special Papers), for example, will find it suitable for their purpose, as also will Medical, Dental, Veterinary, Pharmaceutical, Agricultural, and Horticultural students, and candidates for certain University Intermediate Examinations. The book has been written with the needs of the student constantly in mind throughout. An attempt has been made to anticipate his difficulties and to present the leading principles of the science as clearly and simply as possible, in a manner which is in conformity with modern ideas, modern teaching methods, and examination requirements.

The Ninth Edition was revised and largely rewritten by Dr W. O. Howarth and Dr L. G. G. Warne and was completely reset. For the present Fourteenth Edition the book has been again rewritten and reset, and many new illustrations are included. There are important changes of emphasis corresponding with modern trends in plant science and with the changing demands of examination syllabuses.

The sections on plant biochemistry and growth physiology have been considerably expanded. The anatomical and morphological chapters have been thoroughly modernised, much greater prominence being given to dynamic and developmental concepts. Taxonomy is approached by way of an unusually frank and informal discussion of the practical problems of classification and identification, and the revised ecology chapter deals with basic problems of ecological observation and experiment. Recent discoveries in the fields of cell structure and molecular biology are introduced in a new chapter on cytology. The systematic treatment of the major groups of plants has been simplified, and the burden of technical terminology has been reduced by the omission of many expressions no longer in general use.

There are many references to economic problems such as food supplies, the production of antibiotics and herbicides, and the purification of drinking water. The results of actual experiments are frequently used to illustrate the discussion, and without attempting to assume the role of a laboratory manual the book adopts a thoroughly practical approach.

The revisers have endeavoured to present not only the known facts of the subject but also the spirit of enquiry in which contemporary investigations are undertaken. Many topics are shown to involve unsolved problems and even controversial issues. We are extremely grateful to our former colleague Dr D. Park, now at The Queen's University of Belfast, for writing the chapter on Fungi, Bacteria, and Viruses.

Our thanks are due to Dr B. Gunning of the Department of Botany, The Queen's University of Belfast, for the Frontispiece.

E. W. S.
K. J. D.
J. N. H.

CONTENTS

CONTENTS

ILLUSTRATIONS

TEXTBOOK OF BOTANY

1 THE SCOPE AND HISTORY OF BOTANY

The life sciences are concerned with the many living organisms that dwell upon the surface of the earth. Botany is one of these sciences, its domain being, broadly, the study of plants. In this introductory chapter we shall consider the nature of living organisms, the ways in which plants differ from other organisms and the various approaches that botanists use in studying plant life.

The Nature of Living Organisms

The most striking characteristics of living organisms are their powers of growth and their ability to reproduce their kind. In addition, they can respond strongly to a small stimulus such as a weak light shining from one side, and most of them have at least some powers of movement. No one of these characters, however, is the sole prerogative of living matter—for a crystal can grow and flames reproduce themselves when fed with wood: a photographic plate is sensitive to differences of light intensity; and movement is the very essence of wind. It is the combination of these characters that is peculiar to living organisms—and also the chemical machinery by which growth, reproduction, and so on are made possible.

When an organism grows it makes more living matter, or in chemical terms it synthesises the many complex organic substances of which the new growth is composed. These syntheses require energy and the same is true of course for any movements that the organism may make. These are the two chief chemical activities of living matter—the synthesis of complex molecules and the consumption of energy provided by the environment. The chemical changes which occur in living organisms are referred to as **metabolism**, and we may say that metabolism is one characteristic of living things that is not shared by the non-living. When an organism dies its metabolism comes to a standstill.

The chemical changes that constitute the metabolism of an organism are subject to a high degree of control and order. They are organised in part by a system of catalysts, the enzymes, each of which promotes a limited range of reactions (or only one) and in part by the extraordinarily complex membrane systems within the cell which effectively divide it into many more or less separate compartments. The machinery of the cell is thus chemical and molecular in nature. Compared with mechanical apparatus it is not very robust and indeed it can only exist and function within a rather narrow range (as seen on a cosmic scale) of temperature, pressure, and radiation.

Plants, Animals, and Micro-organisms

The larger and more familiar organisms fall rather sharply into two groups—the plants and animals, which differ in several respects, most notably perhaps in the source of energy upon which they depend. Animals obtain their energy from the foods they eat; the foods are digested or broken down to relatively simple chemical entities from which are synthesised the organic substances of the animal body. Some of the sugars released during digestion are oxidised (this is the essence of the process of respiration) and the energy thereby released is used for movements and for synthetic processes. This type of nutrition, involving the consumption of organic substances, is termed **heterotrophic.**

Plants have a different type of nutrition and consequently a different type of metabolism. The great majority of plants consume no organic substances, requiring only some of the inorganic materials that are present in their environment, water and inorganic salts found in the soil and gases from the atmosphere. The leading characteristic of plants, the one by which they were first recognised, is their green colour. The significance of the colour is that the green pigment, known as chlorophyll, plays a central role in photosynthesis. This is a process in which solar radiation absorbed by chlorophyll provides the energy necessary for the synthesis of sugars from carbon dioxide and water. Just as in animals, some of the sugar forms the starting point for the synthesis of yet more complex molecules, while some is oxidised in respiration to provide the energy needed for the syntheses. This type of nutrition is described as **autotrophic**.

Another leading difference between plants and animals concerns their growth. Although it is of course smaller, a young animal has many points of resemblance to an adult, having the same general proportions and the same number of organs—two arms, two eyes, one brain, and so on. A young plant on the other hand, bears leaves just like a mature individual—but it has fewer of them. As the plant grows it produces a whole series of almost identical leaves; the longer it lives, the larger it grows, and the more leaves it produces.

We may now summarise some of the differences between a typical animal and a typical plant:

TYPICAL ANIMAL	TYPICAL PLANT
Grows to a definite size and then stops.	Continued and indefinite growth.
Organs in definite numbers.	Indefinite repetition of similar organs.
Heterotrophic nutrition: energy derived from external supplies of food.	Autotrophic nutrition: energy derived from sunlight.
Free-moving.	Static.

With these characters as a guide it should be easy to classify any of the larger organisms into plant or animal, but difficulties arise when we come to some of the smaller organisms. Thus the fungi are heterotrophic but they are static and they have indefinite growth: they do not fall readily into either category—plant or animal. Fortunately the issue is not important and no one to-day insists on this binary classification for *all* groups of organisms. Some people, indeed, prefer to add a third group—the micro-organisms, on the grounds that these organisms (principally fungi, bacteria, and protozoa) show more resemblance to one another than to either the larger plants or the larger animals. In the upshot, what we include within the scope of botany is really more a matter of custom than a question of logical principle or precise definition.

Approaches to the Study of Plants

Early botanical investigations were in the main descriptive, accumulating information about the structure, reproduction, distribution, or chemical composition of plants, but present-day botanical work has passed beyond this phase, concentrating now on an analytic approach. The object of botanical research to-day is not so much to record as to gain some understanding of the way in which plants grow and behave. We now attach less importance to naming the parts of a fruit or the shape of a leaf than to investigating the development of fruits or determining what factors influence leaf-shape.

The student of botany must in some measure retrace the development of the subject because some familiarity with the structure and behaviour of plants is necessary for an appreciation of the more modern work.

Botany is a very wide-ranging study, for plants can be examined in many different ways. The following paragraphs outline the content of each of the main branches of the subject indicating the ways in which they are developing to-day.

Physiology and biochemistry are concerned with the way in which a plant works at the chemical and physical level. Biochemical investigation is concerned with the chemical reactions that go on in cells and the enzymes which catalyse these reactions. Its aim is to examine the many pathways of metabolism that must operate in plant cells and to find out how they are organised and controlled. This is now one of the most rapidly advancing branches of botany, thanks largely to the application of techniques such as chromatography (p. 236) and the use of isotopes (p. 245). One outcome of this work has been the realisation that many of the pathways of metabolism in different organisms are rather similar; the pathway of respiration in a root tip for instance differs little from that in muscle.

While biochemistry deals with events inside the cells of a plant, physiology is concerned with problems that arise at a different level of organisation, such as the mechanisms involved in the movements that plants make and the factors that control growth rate. Another problem is the traffic of molecules into plants and out of them; thus physiologists are interested in the passage of gases into leaves, the uptake of water by the roots, and the transport of solutes throughout the plant. The mechanisms involved here may differ considerably from one type of plant to another; in part because of differences in structure and in part because of differences in environment as between land plants and submerged forms. The accounts of plant water relations (Chapter 9) and of plant growth (Chapter 11) place most emphasis on the flowering plants which constitute the predominant element of our flora.

Genetics is the study of heredity. From observations on the inheritance of characters from one generation to the next geneticists endeavour to deduce what is actually transmitted in the reproductive cells from parent to offspring, and how it operates to produce the characters that we actually see in the offspring. Our understanding of genetics stems from the work of Mendel on inheritance in peas. Although experimental work with flowering plants has continued on an ever-increasing scale, many geneticists have preferred to work with the fruit-fly *Drosophila*, or with fungi or bacteria. Large populations of these organisms can be handled with ease, and their generation time is quite short so that experimentation is much quicker than with a plant that only sets seeds once a year. However, it appears that many of the genetic principles elucidated from experiments with one type of organism apply with equal force to others.

Cytology is concerned with the fine structure of the contents of the cell. Classical cytology as it was developed in the early years of this century dealt with events in the nucleus of the cell. When dividing cells were suitably stained with dyes, a series of threads (the chromosomes) became apparent in the nucleus, and evidence which is related in Chapter 22 led to the conclusion that they were concerned with the transmission of information about hereditary characters. Nuclear cytology therefore has close links with genetics. As regards structures outside the nucleus it has long been evident that the chloroplasts (which contain chlorophyll and are therefore green) must be concerned in photosynthesis. More recently the biochemical activity of some other cell components has come under investigation. We may expect considerable progress in this direction in the next few years from combined efforts with the electron microscope which has revealed a new world of microstructure within the cell and with new techniques for isolating cell components for biochemical study. Here again, as in biochemistry and in genetics, we can say that despite certain differences there is much in common between the cytology of plant cells and that of animals.

Palaeobotany is the study of fossil plant remains. There are two main ways in which fossils contribute to the development of our knowledge. In the older rocks plants are found which differ greatly from anything which is alive now and these extinct plants often lead us to a better appreciation of the living forms. We find, for instance, that *Equisetum* (horsetail) is the sole survivor of a group of plants which formerly played a far more important part in the earth's vegetation. In the later deposits, where the fossils are mostly of plants already familiar to us in the living state, our main interest is in the information which can be gained about past changes in topography and climate. In the clay beds under London we find pieces of palms and other tropical plants, on the bed of the North Sea unmistakable evidence of fresh-water marshes and deciduous forest.

Taxonomy began when primitive man first distinguished some plants from the others, gave them special names, and began to keep (at first by oral tradition) a record of their properties. In making lists and catalogues of the different kinds of plants the human race has been driven by practical necessity, but an important contribution has also been made by the collecting instinct from which few people are entirely free.

Taxonomy, however, is much more than a routine task of indexing. The characteristics by which plants can be recognised do not occur in random assortments, but grouped in an orderly way, so that plants which are alike in some ways tend to be alike in others also. Taxonomy, therefore, is the exploration of a biological system which is just as much a fact of nature as the arrangement of the elements in the Periodic Table. The past history of taxonomy is predominantly one of intuitive working, of skilled guesswork tested by experience, but mathematical and experimental methods are now being adopted just as freely as in other branches of botany.

In dealing with plants which are fairly closely related taxonomists have often been able to apply genetical methods, even to the extent in some cases of duplicating by experimental hybridisation a plant form already known in the wild. There remains, however, a wide field of taxonomic work in which genetics can at present offer little assistance.

Morphology is the study, not only in the mature state but throughout the whole course of growth, of the form and arrangement of the parts of which the body of a plant is composed. It may therefore be considered to include anatomy, which is more specifically the study of internal structures. Morphologists have inevitably begun their work by attempting to distinguish equivalent parts in different plants, giving more exact meanings to such common words as "stem" and "leaf", adding other categories which have proved to be necessary, and cataloguing the variations in the shape and construction of all these parts. This descriptive task is now largely completed, and further work is likely to lead to detailed improvements rather than any major discovery.

The main interest in current morphological work is in the attempt to find out why plants grow in particular shapes. This problem can be attacked by experimental methods; chemical or surgical treatments can be applied in order to change the manner of growth, and it is now common to simplify the situation by working, not with a whole plant, but with part of one in artificial culture. Root systems, for instance, can now be grown indefinitely in flasks of solution without any stems or leaves, and their behaviour investigated under standardised conditions. In some cases it is also proving possible to draw conclusions by direct mathematical analysis of such things as leaf-shapes.

The connection between morphology and physiology is obviously a close one, and indeed when in a physiological experiment we apply some treatment to a plant, the result of the experiment will often appear as a morphological change in the plant; such a result contributes to both sciences.

Ecology is concerned with the relationships between the plant and its environment, which, of course, includes other plants. Many ecological problems are clearly of a physiological character, as when we enquire why some plants can grow upon calcareous soils and some cannot. A great deal of ecological investigation can, however, proceed without any examination of basic physiological processes. It can often be shown, merely by putting up a fence, that grassland from which grazing animals are excluded rapidly turns into some other type of vegetation. This kind of information can be of great practical value, even though the details of the conversion are not understood. In fact a great deal can be accomplished in ecology by systematic surveys of vegetation, by observing the effects of such things as farming operations, flooding, and forest fires, and by performing experiments of a rather simple kind. Ecology being in a relatively early stage of development it is not surprising that vegetation surveys make up a great part of the existing literature.

There is, however, a growing tendency to introduce more refined methods. To take a single instance, it is often important to know whether plants are randomly scattered or whether they tend to occur in groups; to deal with this problem highly sophisticated mathematical tests have been devised.

In the cultivation of a crop the ecological situation is artificially simplified, and in many respects, as for instance in the completeness of meteorological instrumentation, the ecological study of crops is more advanced than that of wild vegetation.

The History of Botany (see also p. 389)

In the earliest times interest in plants was no doubt confined to their useful properties, real or (often) imagined. The first record of any truly scientific study of plants comes from Greece in the fourth century B.C., when Aristotle and Theophrastus worked out a great part of the fundamental morphology of the higher plants. They were able to distinguish between a root and an underground stem, between simple and compound leaves (p. 58), between flowers and capitula (p. 341). Our present distinction between hypogynous, perigynous, and epigynous flowers (p. 332) is taken straight from Theophrastus. The Greek botanists had also some understanding of growth-processes; without any means of magnification they could not, of course, discover how tissues enlarged, but they recognised that the growth of a plant is concentrated in definite regions of its body.

During the Roman period, however, and in the Medieval world which followed, there was practically no scientific study of plants, and indeed very little activity in any of the sciences. At the time of the Renaissance a new spirit of enquiry led quickly to important advances. In 1628 Harvey described his work on the circulation of the blood but any comparable advance in understanding plants required the use of the microscope, and although microscopes were probably made as early as 1580 or so, the instrument only reached a standard which permitted any real progress in plant anatomy much later. In 1665 Robert Hooke discovered the cellular structure of some plant materials. However, there were very definite limits to what could be discovered with the optical instruments of the period, for they suffered from chromatic aberration and produced blurred images. The techniques used to prepare specimens were crude; bits of tissue were cut, or often just teased out with needles, and placed under the microscope, often under poor conditions of illumination. The principal workers were Nehemiah Grew, an Englishman, and Malpighi, an Italian. Both were medical men, and both started with the intention of finding, if possible, structures in plants which would bear comparison with the blood vessels, nerves, lungs, and digestive organs of animals. Grew especially was a man of great ability, who observed for the first time many of the basic facts about the cells and tissues of the higher plants, discovering stomata, chloroplasts, rays, and so on. No understanding of plant physiology was possible at this time as practically nothing was known of chemistry. (Grew, for instance, seeing that pollen was yellow, concluded that it consisted mainly of sulphur.)

By about 1720 it was well understood that the higher plants reproduced sexually, with pollen playing a part similar to that of the sperm in animals, but the reproduction of the lower plants presented another, unsolved problem. The eighteenth century saw many important observations in this field, such as the entry of a spermatozoid into an archegonium, but nobody was able to fit them into a connected life-cycle.

After (and to a great extent because of) the Napoleonic wars, there was very active scientific and industrial development in Germany, and about 1840 German optical factories began to produce achromatic lenses, in which the chromatic aberration that had so long impaired the performance of the microscope was very largely eliminated. Botanically the main result was that proper attention was for the first time given to the contents of the cell. The earlier workers had understandably concentrated on the cell wall, which was about as much as most of them could see, the living contents being passed over as a kind of sap. With the new lenses it was possible to study effectively the growth and division of cells, and within a period of about thirty years the state of botanical knowledge was completely transformed. The origin and development of the tissues of the higher plants were worked out in considerable detail, as were the life-cycles of a fair selection of the lower plants. Hofmeister established the basic facts concerning the alternation of generations in mosses, ferns, and gymnosperms, while de Bary and others made similar progress in the investigation of algae and fungi, showing among other things that many plant diseases were due to parasitic fungi. In physiology the resources available did not permit much examination of the metabolic processes occurring inside a plant, but it was possible with the chemistry of the time to clear up most of the remaining uncertainties about the movement of substances into or out of the plant.

In the early years of the present century the progress of botany was greatly influenced by two ideas drawn from sources outside the main stream of discovery. One was the theory of inheritance due to Mendel, which only became generally known in 1900, though the work had been done nearly forty years before. Mendel's work gave a great impetus to studies of inheritance (genetics) and to investigations on the chromosomes (cytology). The second influence was the evolutionary theory introduced by Darwin in 1858-9. Although botanists were just as quick as zoologists to seize upon the idea of evolution, it was in fact impossible in Darwin's time to arrive at any clear general picture of the evolutionary history of plants, and the evidence for evolution presented in Darwin's writings is predominantly zoological. The balance was restored mainly by the work of Hofmeister and by active work in fossil botany which took place at the turn of the century.

The recent history of the science has been marked by an enormous increase in the volume of research and the number of workers, and by the application of new techniques derived from chemistry, physics, and mathematics.

Applied Botany

We are all dependent upon plants for our food. Not only do we ourselves eat plant products like cereals, vegetables, and fruit, but the animals we eat (cattle, fish, and so on) also depend on plants at some point in the food-chain. Some of us, especially those who live in Africa and the Far East, do not have enough to eat and many indeed die of starvation. The problem of finding enough food for all the peoples of the earth becomes more difficult every day as the number of mouths goes on increasing: at present the population of the world is doubling every forty years. The botanist is one of the few who can give practical help.

Agriculture is based upon the cultivation of plants, of soils, and animals. The investigation of plant growth falls within the province of the physiologist. The special problems that arise in growing a particular crop in a particular environment—potatoes in England, maize in the U.S.A., or rice in the Far East—are studied on the spot, and generally in special research stations or in Universities. A better understanding of the way in which a crop plant grows can lead to improved fertiliser or irrigation regimes and a better appreciation of the consequences of planting early or late, or of sowing densely or not; it can yield information of value to the fertiliser industry (what fertiliser formulations are needed), to the plant breeder (how the crop plant could be improved), to the man who has to apply weed-killers, to the agriculturist who wonders whether to introduce the crop into another area, and so on.

Horticulture is also concerned with food production and here again there are possibilities of improving crop plants and of cultivating them better so as to raise the yield of edible matter. Efforts are being made to develop new types of food, for instance, by extracting the protein from grass and concentrating it into palatable form and by growing unicellular algae in large tanks exposed to the sun. Many foods are now available at long distances from the soil in which they were grown and long after they were harvested. Bananas are transported across the ocean in specially equipped ships where they are exposed to gas mixtures that delay ripening.

The increasing tendency to can, freeze, and dry fruits and vegetables raises problems of judging the best time to harvest the crops, dealing with a glut at harvest time, and preserving the quality of the produce, while at the same time ensuring that it will keep.

After food, comes drink. Tea, coffee, and cocoa are important crops while the fermentation of plant products by yeasts to produce alcoholic drinks is a major industry in some areas. The mention of fermentation brings to mind the other industries in which fungi or bacteria are involved such as the production of antibiotics (like penicillin) and the manufacture of cheeses. Alongside drink we should mention tobacco, still the basis of a large industry in some parts of the world.

We look to the forester for our supplies of timber and for woodpulp from which newspaper and rayon ("artificial silk") are made. The forester is responsible for raising young seedlings in the nursery, managing plantations during the 60-120 years they take to mature, and eventually felling them.

Many plants produce fibres that are useful to us for clothing (cotton, linen) or cordage (jute, hemp) and around each of these has arisen an agricultural industry with problems in both field and factory.

Wherever plants are grown, there are fungi, viruses, and animal pests to assail them. The plant pathologist is responsible for examining diseased plants, identifying diseases, finding out how they spread, and, where possible, suggesting ways of combating disease.

GUIDE TO THE STUDY OF BOTANY

Methods of Study

Bookwork alone can never lead to a satisfactory understanding of botany. Every student should make the most of his opportunities for engaging in laboratory work and work in the field.

Most people find it difficult to acquire proficiency in the examination of specimens, the basic operation of observing and recording the shape and structure of a plant. There are two aspects of the matter which should be kept constantly in mind. In the first place, all textbook descriptions of plants are necessarily incomplete, and lacking in detail. To look at a specimen merely in order to confirm facts which one has already read or been told of is quite insufficient and does nothing to develop the power of independent observation. The student's aim should be to train himself to see features which he did not know about beforehand, and anything but the very simplest object should be made to yield something of this kind before being laid aside.

Secondly, it must be remembered that although the number of different kinds of plants is much larger than any single botanist is ever likely to know one must, nevertheless, endeavour to see a reasonable range of material. Inevitably some things will be studied in far more detail than others. This does no harm, but it is dangerous to let one's thinking centre too rigidly upon a restricted range of standard types or examples. The student who has never prepared himself to meet an unknown plant will draw and describe one of the common textbook examples regardless of the actual nature of the specimen placed before him.

It is doubtful whether anybody acquires much skill in the observation of plants without making drawings. Fortunately there is no need for any artistic talent; the style should be nearer to the engineering diagram than to the photograph. In scientific work there should be no room for sketchy or indefinite outlines, and very little for perspective or conventional shading. What is required is a clear and definite statement of the significant facts, containing no mark which does not carry a botanical meaning. Book illustrations generally place much more emphasis upon realistic appearance than it is necessary or desirable to do in the laboratory, and are generally bad examples to follow. In particular, the laboratory notebook should avoid useless repetition. To draw one cell may, in some circumstances, be enough. To draw two is then a waste of time, and to attempt, as many students will, to draw a dozen or more, is pointless and merely debases the standard of the work. Plants are repetitive in their construction but the nature of the repetition can be recorded without attempting to show all the units in detail.

Many aspects of botanical study to-day are of an experimental nature. Although the professional botanist often uses complex and expensive apparatus to pursue his problems, much can be done with the simplest equipment. Darwin's important work on the movements of plants (Chapter 11) is a fine example of what can be done in this way. The first requisite is an urge to find out for oneself, together with an enquiring mind which can pose problems that could be answered by experiment. Simple, homely equipment and a small garden are sufficient, for example, for investigations on some of the factors that control plant growth or germination. The effect of light intensity on plant growth could be studied by growing some plants in the open and others under a shade, while spacing experiments will provide information on the way in which plants respond to overcrowding. It is not difficult to devise experiments to determine the conditions under which the seeds of a given plant will germinate. Will they, for instance, germinate as soon as they are shed from the plant (or even before?) or do they first require a period of rest, or of low temperature? And is exposure to light necessary—or harmful?

If the resources of an experimental laboratory are available it should be possible to assess photosynthesis rates by determining the change in dry weight when plants are exposed to a bright or a weak light, or are held in the dark; to determine respiration rates, or to investigate some aspects of the water relations of whole plants or their individual cells. Some mosses exist in very exposed, dry places on the tops of walls, while others live in more humid places. The student should be able to plan the experiments necessary to determine how long mosses from various habitats could survive in a desiccator and to assess whether the power of survival is a factor governing the natural distribution of mosses.

The Names of Plants

Plants which attracted enough attention at a sufficiently early date have names in the ordinary spoken languages of the world. Because these names vary in different countries, and because their application to particular plants is often not very precise, their suitability for scientific use is limited. Among English speakers we need not be so pedantic as to exclude such well-established names as those of some of the common trees, crop plants, and familiar flowers, but the vernacular names of plants can never go very far towards meeting the needs of scientific work.

Every plant has a scientific name (treated as Latin, though really drawn from a wide range of sources), and most plants have no other name of any real utility. Each sort (or **species**) of plant has a name consisting of two words, the first indicating a **genus** or group of species, the second a particular species within that genus. It is a system not unlike that of surname and Christian name, but the "surname" (that is, the generic name) comes first. So *Iris pseudacorus* and *Iris pumila* are two species of the genus *Iris*. We can also use the generic name by itself, to include all the species at once. Specific names cannot be used alone.

So far as possible, scientific names should be adopted from the outset. On meeting a plant which is completely new to one, it is as easy to learn the scientific name as any other, and most people begin with a useful stock of familiar generic names like *Iris* and *Narcissus*. The number of plants encountered even in the early stages of botanical study may be quite large, and reference books will be needed (p. 440). There are large numbers of "English" plant names which it is advisable to ignore entirely. Some are dialect forms, which may have a quite different meaning a few counties away, while others are gardeners' whimsies. There is also a substantial class of book-names, which have never had any currency at all, but were invented by people who hoped to make botany more popular by eliminating Latin. It is often reasonable to use standard English words like barley, potato, yew, and beech, but names like "Busy-Lizzie" or "Broad-leaved mud sedge" are of no value to the scientist.

The Major Divisions of the Plant Kingdom

The distinctions between the principal groups of plants are much less obvious than those between such animal groups as fish, birds, and reptiles. Until he has some knowledge of plant anatomy and of reproductive processes a student cannot usefully attempt any general survey of the plant kingdom. It is necessary from the outset, however, to refer to certain broad categories of plants; exact definitions are not required at this stage, but the following scheme will be helpful:

1. **Algae.** An alga is a plant of relatively simple bodily construction, usually pigmented, though not necessarily green, and obtaining energy from incident light by photochemical action. The group includes the plants commonly known as seaweeds, as well as many smaller forms.

2. **Fungi.** A fungus shows the same simplicity of organisation as an alga, but differs in nutrition, being dependent upon the absorption of organic material, as are animals. The objects recognised as "fungi" in common speech are reproductive structures, and are much more conspicuous than are most of the fungi. Along with the fungi are often grouped the bacteria and certain other groups, the inclusion of which among the plants is largely a matter of custom and convenience.

The algae and fungi are sometimes known as Thallophytes, a term which refers to their simplicity of bodily form.

3. **Bryophytes.** A group including the true mosses and some other less familiar forms.

The three groups above are described as **non-vascular**, because they do not produce specialised internal tissues for the conveyance of materials from one part of the body to another. The following groups are **vascular**, these special tissues being present in most of their organs.

4. **Pteridophytes.** A group including the ferns and horsetails.

In the plants so far considered the typical reproductive unit is a single detached cell known as a **spore**. Plants with this type of reproduction were formerly known as cryptogams, a term now passing out of use. In the groups which follow the characteristic reproductive structure is a seed, a much more complicated thing than a spore.

5. **Gymnosperms.** A small group of seed plants including the conifers.

6. **Angiosperms.** The dominant group of vascular plants in the earth's vegetation—the flowering plants. The angiosperms fall into two main series, the **dicotyledons** and the **monocotyledons**. The nature of the distinction may be roughly indicated by pointing out familiar examples such as oak, dandelion, and cabbage (dicotyledons), and daffodil, iris, and grass (monocotyledons). Only by experience, however, can one learn to distinguish the two with certainty.

2 CELLS AND TISSUES

A knowledge of the detailed structure of plants, as well as being of considerable interest for its own sake, is important in almost every branch of botany. It will be found, for example, that the parts of this book dealing with metabolism, classification, reproduction, and inheritance all include references to structural features, an understanding of which is essential for the topics concerned. Such features are often too small to be seen with the naked eye. A simple hand-lens giving a magnification of $\times$ 10 or so may help considerably to reveal important features of structure, but for many purposes the use of the compound microscope is unavoidable. This instrument is standard equipment for any botanical laboratory and every student of botany should seek to become adept in using it at an early stage in his training.

One important feature which even a microscope of only moderate power can show clearly is that the parts of most plants, whatever their differences of shape, colour, and texture, all share a common type of structure (see Plates 1 and 2). Each part is an aggregate of small units known as **cells** which appear as compartments bounded by distinct walls, and generally shaped to fit closely with neighbouring cells. The size of these cells is so variable, even within the same individual, that any brief generalisation about cell dimensions which attempted to be comprehensive would be vague to the point of uselessness. At this stage, therefore, we shall simply observe that many of the cells of higher plants do not exceed 50 microns* in any dimension. At the other extreme, cells which do not exceed 10 μ in any dimension are uncommonly small for higher plants.

The use of the word cell to describe the unit of plant structure is not greatly different from its use in describing the structure of a honeycomb or a monastery: in all cases the walls give strength to the whole erection, while the spaces they enclose are used for the vital activities of the organisation or organism.

* The micron (μ) is the standard unit of measurement for objects in this size range. Its relationship to other units is shown in the following table:

UNIT	FRACTION OF METRE	
Centimetre (cm.)	1/100	$= 1$ m. $\times 10^{-2}$
Millimetre (mm.)	1/1,000	$= 1$ m. $\times 10^{-3}$
Micron (μ)	1/1,000,000	$= 1$ m. $\times 10^{-6}$
Ångstrom unit (Å)	1/10,000,000,000	$= 1$ m. $\times 10^{-10}$

Multicellular construction is a feature of almost all macroscopic plants, that is those visible to the naked eye, and many microscopic ones besides. However, the plant kingdom includes some species in which each individual consists of a single cell. Many of these unicellular plants are extremely small (e.g. *Chlorella*, p. 495), so that the single cell which constitutes the entire organism is of the same order of size as a typical cell in a multicellular plant. Others, however, attain a considerable size. Many fungi (e.g. *Mucor*, p. 547) and some algae (e.g. *Vaucheria*, p. 518) have a body which consists of branched, tubular threads which together make up a mass several centimetres across when well developed. The threads are not subdivided into separate cells, so each individual may be regarded as a very extensive single cell.

The presence of cells in a multicellular plant can be verified quite simply by examining some thin and reasonably transparent organ with the low power objective of the microscope. The root of a cress seedling or the leaf of a moss would be a convenient object. For more solid and opaque parts of the plant thin sections would need to be cut and examined. Although an investigation of various plant parts in this way would confirm their basically similar structure, it would also emphasise the diversity of size and shape among the cells themselves. This diversity is related to the specialised functions of the various types of cell, and will be discussed later in this chapter.

The Origin of Cells

The only known method whereby new cells are produced is the division of existing cells. It is common for a parent cell to divide into two daughter cells, but the process takes various forms differing in whether the daughter cells resemble each other in size and shape or are dissimilar; whether the components of the parent cell are exactly replicated in the daughter cells; and so forth. Examples of various forms of cell division will be found in several later sections of this book: for the present we shall simply recognise that the ability to divide is a property of many cells, and that every cell is the product of division of a pre-existing cell. Once division has been accomplished, each daughter cell, now enclosed in its own cell wall, may either become completely separate from the other, or the two may remain attached. This is an important distinction. For example, in an organism like *Chlorella* (p. 495), where each individual consists of a single cell, cell division is followed by separation of the daughter cells which then become new individuals. In this case, therefore, cell division is the basis of reproduction. The reproduction of multicellular plants may also depend on cell division followed by immediate separation of the products if, as is common, the life-cycle includes the formation of unicellular spores or gametes. A familiar example is the formation of pollen grains by higher plants.

Cell Aggregates

Cell division which is not followed by separation of the products forms a basis for growth rather than reproduction. This is the situation which occurs in the development of any multicellular plant, and the final form of the plant depends very much on the spatial relationships of the daughter cells in successive divisions. Consider the development of a new individual from a single cell, which is in fact what most new individuals do develop from. The first division leads to two cells side by side. Suppose that each of these cells then divides again in such a way that the new dividing walls are parallel to the first. The result is a chain of four cells. If this process continues, with all new dividing walls parallel to the earlier ones and with appropriate lengthening of cells when they are formed, the fully developed individual will consist of a long chain or filament of cells such as is found in many algae (e.g. *Spirogyra*, *Oedogonium*, *Cladophora*, and *Ectocarpus*) and fungi (e.g. *Aspergillus* and *Penicillium*). It is true that in most of these examples the filaments are branched, but this can easily be explained by occasional dividing walls being formed obliquely to the axis of the filament, followed by divisions with the more usual orientation.

The simple unbranched filament is a one-dimensional development from the unicellular condition which indicates a method whereby multicellular plants may have evolved from the unicellular ancestors they are assumed to have had. Branching of the filament is a further development towards a two- or three-dimensional structure, but so long as the filaments remain separate from one another except at basal points of attachment there can be no development of any coherent bulk, nor of any sizeable structure able to stand erect without support. For this to be possible in an organism composed of cells in filaments, there must be some lateral bonding of the filaments. The point may be illustrated by a comparison between the tail of a horse, which hangs downwards since the hairs are separate from one another, and the horn of a rhinoceros which is a mass of compacted hairs and stands erect. The fruiting bodies of the larger fungi are constructed on a similar principle: the common mushroom is a felted mass of threads which is not only bulky, by fungal standards, but also able to support its own weight.

The formation of a macroscopic plant body by the aggregation of filaments is a method of construction not found in groups other than the fungi and algae. The development of most multicellular plants involves cell divisions which are less restricted in orientation, giving a truly two- or three-dimensional aggregate of cells. There are a few plants which illustrate a full exploitation of only two dimensions, such as the alga *Porphyra*, a common seaweed which is collected in parts of Wales to produce the delicacy known as laver bread. The adult plant consists of a flat sheet of cells, several square inches in extent but only one cell thick. This is the result of cell divisions occurring in various directions but always in the same plane. Comparable structure is found in other algae such as *Ulva* (sea lettuce) where the sheet is two cells thick, and *Enteromorpha* where the sheet, one cell thick, is in the form of a hollow cylinder.

The most usual construction of macroscopic plants is completely three-dimensional, and results from cell divisions in all directions. This is not to say that orientation of cell divisions is haphazard in these plants. Far from it. The production of new cells is generally restricted to particular parts of the plant, such as the apices of the roots and shoots. Towards the extreme tip of one of these apical growing points the cells may appear to be busily occupied with a cycle of enlargement—division—enlargement—division . . ., and so on, without any obvious orientation of the divisions. But only a short distance removed from this active centre of cell production it can be seen that the cells have a distinct pattern related to their destined position in the fully developed plant. There can be no doubt, therefore, that the cell divisions at the growing points are integrated with the development of an orderly arrangement of organs each with its characteristic and regular internal structure.

The Shapes of Cells

When the cell is first formed it is enclosed in a wall which is generally thin and plastic. Under these conditions the shape taken by the cell is determined by the forces acting upon the wall both from inside and from outside. The pressure in a cell is usually higher than the pressure outside, so that the wall is under tension and the cell may be compared to an inflated balloon. Assuming that the wall is equally flexible over its whole area and that it is not in contact with any solid object, the cell will be a regular sphere. These conditions are occasionally met in nature, as, for instance, in the egg of the seaweed *Fucus*, which is released into the water. However, single cells floating in water are not necessarily spherical. The wall may be thickened so that it can resist the internal pressure of the cell without distortion. This is a very common situation, and the range of shapes shown by planktonic (floating) unicellular algae is almost unlimited (see Plate 17).

In a multicellular plant, the shape of a cell is influenced by contact with neighbouring cells as well as by internal pressure and the properties of its own wall. This additional factor is minimal in the case of a free (*i.e.* not aggregated) filament, where each cell is in contact with other cells only at opposite ends. In such a case the end walls are flat and each cell is either cylindrical (Fig. 279) or barrel-shaped.

In a three-dimensional aggregate, the shape of each cell is much more influenced by adjacent cells. The simplest situation within this category concerns a closely packed mass of cells similar in size and age, each with thin, elastic walls. This situation is approached fairly closely in many stem apices, in the flesh of some fruits, and in the pith of plants such as *Sambucus* (elder). Its analysis is comparable to that of a foam composed of uniform bubbles, and similar mathematical techniques have been used in the two cases. The wall of each cell is acted upon by opposing forces; the internal pressure tends to force the wall outwards, but this is restricted by pressure from surrounding cells. Under these conditions the cell is moulded into a shape with maximum volume and minimum surface area, and will be a polyhedron, that is a facetted solid like a cut diamond. The shape which is found mathematically to satisfy these requirements is a fourteen-sided polyhedron for a cell completely surrounded by others of similar size and properties, or an eleven-sided polyhedron for a cell at the surface. These expectations are closely fulfilled in some cell aggregates, at least in so far as the *average* numbers of faces per cell are concerned. One frequent reason for which individual cells deviate from these expectations is that an aggregate very rarely consists of cells of uniform size. In an aggregate with cells of various sizes larger cells will tend to have more faces and smaller ones fewer faces than the expectations given.

Aggregates of cells with this foam-like geometry generally account for only a restricted part of a plant. In most parts the shapes of cells are further modified by growth in particular directions. For example, many cells elongate in the direction of growth of the organ to which they belong. But growth often involves cell division as well as cell enlargement, and the balance between these two processes may be very different in different groups of cells. One group may undergo rapid elongation, giving cells many times longer than broad, while neighbouring cells will show frequent divisions to produce vertical series of cells, with each cell no taller than broad.

This difference in behaviour is closely connected with functional considerations, as will be explained later in this chapter.

The rate at which individual cells elongate is not always equal to the rate of elongation of the organ to which they belong. Where growth of individual cells is more rapid, there must be a sliding movement of some cells between others. These movements are difficult to observe directly, though it is often possible to deduce that they have occurred by considering the shape and disposition of certain cells in relation to what is known of their origin and development. Conversely the growth of some cells may fail to keep pace with growth of the organ of which they form a part, and they will therefore be subject to stretching. This can sometimes be recognised by the distorted shape of the cells, as in the pith of a large *Helianthus* (sunflower) stem.

In summary, therefore, the shape shown by a cell is the product of many interacting factors which include internal and external pressures, the thickness and elasticity of the cell wall, and the rate and direction of growth both of the cell itself and of the organ in which it is situated.

Intercellular Spaces

When first formed, each cell fits among neighbouring cells with such precision that there is little or no space between. This arrangement may persist to maturity, particularly among cells upon which the strength of the plant depends. In this case adhesion between adjacent cell walls over their entire surfaces produces a coherent aggregate which is not easily torn apart. Elsewhere in the plant, however, the need to allow exchange of gases with the atmosphere is a factor of major importance. As these parts develop the constituent cells become more separate from one another and at maturity much of their surface area is in contact not with other cells but with spaces between cells. The three-dimensional network formed by these **intercellular spaces** can be visualised by considering a box full of glass marbles; the air spaces between the marbles are continuous throughout the aggregate, and also continuous with the air outside. If in place of marbles we think of cells, whose shape can be altered by compression, then the total volume of the intercellular spaces is reduced if the cells are forced together by extra pressure, and increased if the cells are very loosely packed. In some plants the cells are shaped or arranged so as to give exceptionally large intercellular spaces. This is a common condition in submerged water plants where atmospheric gases are less accessible, but it is frequently found in terrestrial plants also. The pith of

Juncus (common rush) shows this construction with beautiful regularity: each cell has a number of protruding arms which make contact with similar arms of other cells (Plate 1). The intercellular space thus greatly exceeds the cells themselves in volume.

The Parts of a Cell

So far the only features of cells which have been mentioned are the walls which enclose them. Inside the walls of living cells is a miscellaneous assembly of substances, some organised into recognisable structures, others in suspension or solution. Some of these components are directly responsible for the vital activities of the cells and together constitute **protoplasm.** Other components are raw materials for or products of these activities. The word protoplasm has some value as a general term for the essentially living part of the organism, but it cannot be defined with precision and is frequently misused (*e.g.* as a synonym of cytoplasm, see p. 24). Now that there is much detailed information about the various ingredients of protoplasm, such as cytoplasm, nucleus, plastids, and mitochondria, the collective term is losing favour. However, there is still much value in referring to the contents of each cell as a **protoplast**, thereby recognising that the contents are integrated in structure and function.

The several parts of the cell will now be considered. All the parts mentioned below are of common occurrence, but it should be clearly understood that few cells have all these features, and some cells may, when mature, consist of a cell wall only. The descriptions given refer primarily to the cells of seed plants, pteridophytes and bryophytes; that is, the great majority of green, land plants. The cells of algae and fungi are similar in many ways to those of other plants, but they also show some exceptional features which will be referred to in the appropriate chapters.

The Cell Wall

Even when it is newly formed, each cell is bounded by a distinct wall continuous over its whole surface. In a region of active cell-production, such as a shoot apex, the cells are so closely packed together that each protoplast appears to be separated from its neighbours by a single wall. But it can be shown quite simply that the partition is in fact double, each cell having an individual wall not shared with neighbouring cells. This is demonstrated by the technique of maceration. If a small piece of the apex is shaken in 5 per cent. chromic acid the cells fall apart and can be examined individually. Each one is still surrounded by a complete wall:

the chromic acid has therefore dissolved the cement which holds the cells together but has left the wall proper intact. The cementing layer is called the **middle lamella** and is chemically different from the wall proper, which regularly contains a high proportion of cellulose. Although the wall surrounds the cell completely and provides a visible distinction between different cells, it does not represent an impenetrable barrier. In fact each cell is not only in close physical

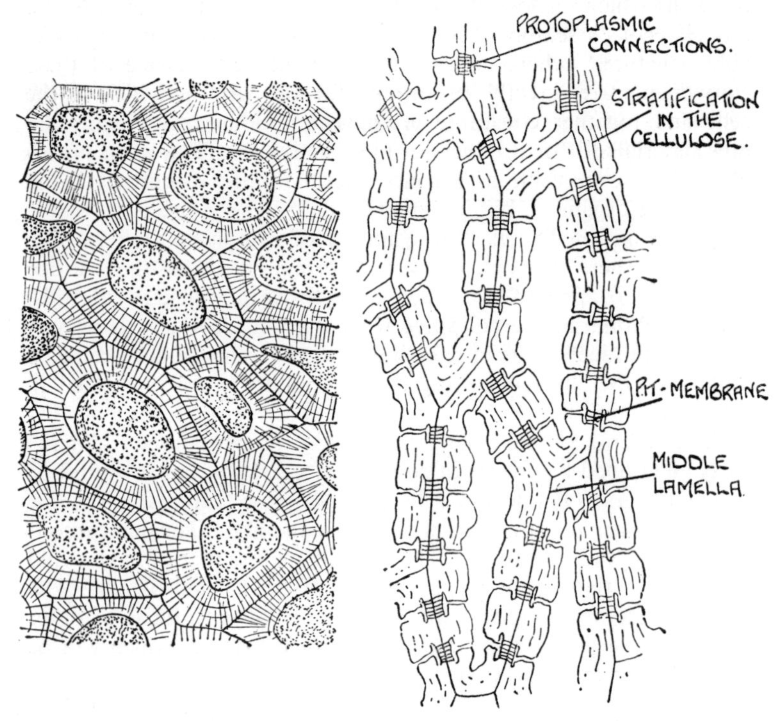

Fig. 1. CELLS FROM ENDOSPERM OF *Strychnos nux-vomica* SHOWING THICK WALLS WITH NUMEROUS PLASMODESMATA.

Fig. 2. CELLS FROM ENDOSPERM OF DATE SHOWING CHARACTERISTIC PITTING.

contact with its neighbours but is in communication with them by cytoplasmic connections known as **plasmodesmata** which pass through the cell walls. It is probable that in thin-walled cells the plasmodesmata occur over the whole of the wall area which is in contact with other cells.

As the cell matures and takes its place in the fully developed parts of the plant, its wall may become thickened by the deposition of more cellulose, sometimes supplemented by other substances such as cutin (p. 30) or lignin (p. 36). During thickening of the wall, however, provision is made for the maintenance of direct communication between the protoplasts of adjacent cells. Sometimes the thickening is interrupted by numerous fine channels, uniformly distributed in the wall, each of which contains a long plasmodesma. These channels are often so fine as to escape notice under the microscope, but in a few tissues they are particularly conspicuous. The endosperm of *Strychnos nux-vomica*, the plant from which strychnine is obtained, is a good example of this (Fig. 1). More often, however, plasmodesmata are preserved in clusters when thickening of the wall takes place. Wherever such a cluster is situated, thickening of the wall is much less marked than elsewhere and the depression so formed is called a **pit**. In its simplest form a pit is no more than a circular depression, but in some cells there are more elaborate types of pit (see pp. 36 and 46). Each pit usually faces a corresponding pit in the wall of the adjacent cell, so that at this point the two protoplasts are separated only by a thin partition which has the cluster of short plasmodesmata passing through it. The thick-walled cells of the endosperm of *Phoenix dactylifera* (date palm) show an unusual structure intermediate between the extremes just described. There are pits which extend in depth from the inner surface of the wall to about half-way through, where they open out into wider cavities. From these cavities to the outer surface, the wall is penetrated by plasmodesmata (Fig. 2).

The Nucleus

The protoplast of every newly-formed cell and of many mature cells also contains a prominent, more or less spherical body called the nucleus. In apical cells, whose average size is small, the nucleus occupies a large part of the cell volume (Fig. 3), but any subsequent enlargement of the cell is usually not accompanied by enlargement of the nucleus, so that in many mature cells the nucleus is far less conspicuous. In most cells little of the structure of the nucleus can be seen with an optical microscope, except that it has a regular shape maintained by a **nuclear membrane**, and that it may contain one or more spherical **nucleoli** which differ from the rest of the nucleus in their affinity for the stains used to accentuate the contrast between different structures (p. 160). The rest of the nucleus, which can be stained very easily, is known to consist of a number of long and greatly intertwined threads called **chromosomes** lying in the **nuclear sap**. The recognition of chromosomes depends on observations made on cells undergoing division, during which process the nucleus passes through a series of characteristic changes in appearance. The process of cell division is briefly discussed on p. 16, and the nuclear changes associated with it are described in Chapter 8.

The function of the nucleus is most important. The chromosomes constitute a "set of instructions" which determine the potentialities of the cell and control most of the chemical activities taking place inside the cell. Thus the nucleus controls not only how particular cells behave but also how the whole plant behaves, since it is probably fair to regard the plant as simply the sum of its constituent cells. Plant characteristics of many different kinds,

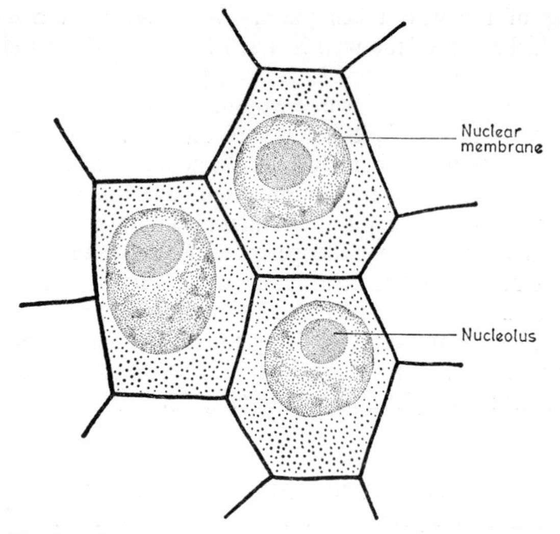

Fig. 3. GROUP OF CELLS FROM ROOT APEX OF *Vicia faba.*

including size, shape, colour, structure, chemical constituents, rate, direction, and duration of growth, are all influenced by the instructions present in the chromosomes, though the degree of control exercised by the nucleus should not be overrated. The features listed are also subject to external influences such as light, temperature, and soil conditions, and the final form of a plant is the result of interaction between internal and external factors.

The Cytoplasm

Some of the space enclosed by the wall of every living cell is filled with cytoplasm. In some cells this behaves as a viscous fluid in which the nucleus and other cell contents lie. Its fluid nature is particularly clear in many leaf cells where the chloroplasts, which are solid bodies suspended in the cytoplasm, may be seen to move around the cell as though swept along by a stream. However, it is equally clear that it is an over-simplification to regard the cytoplasm as simply a liquid. Recent studies with the electron microscope have shown that in cells of many types from a wide variety of organisms the cytoplasm has an elaborate structure of membranes which constitute the **endoplasmic reticulum** (see Chapter 8). It is difficult to understand how the cytoplasm can both contain an extensive system of membranes, which would seem to imply some rigidity, and have the property of streaming which is deduced from the visible movements of cell contents. Further research may provide a fuller understanding of the structure and properties of cytoplasm.

Plastids

Apart from the nuclei, the largest solid inclusions in the cytoplasm of plant cells are the plastids, which are classified for convenience into those containing pigments (**chromoplasts**) and those which are colourless (**leucoplasts**). This distinction is not always related to any fundamental difference of structure since a change in conditions, such as from darkness to light, may be followed by conversion of leucoplasts into chromoplasts.

The chromoplasts about which most is known are those containing the green pigment chlorophyll, and which are therefore called **chloroplasts**. These are responsible for the familiar green colour of most plants, which, contrary to appearance, is not uniformly dispersed through those parts of the plant which look green, but concentrated in these discrete particles. In most flowering plants each chloroplast is a flattened sphere or rather thick disc with a diameter of 3-5 μ, but among the algae there is much greater variety in size and shape. Chlorophyll plays an essential part in photosynthesis, and the structure and function of chloroplasts are considered in more detail in Chapters 8 and 10.

Other chromoplasts are comparable in size with chloroplasts but contain different pigments, usually red or yellow carotenoids. In some books the term chromoplast is reserved for these pigmented plastids which do not contain chlorophyll, thereby recognising chloroplasts as something quite distinct, which, from a functional point of view they undoubtedly are. A function for the carotenoid-containing chromoplasts is known in some instances, but in others the function, if any, is uncertain or completely obscure. The yellow and orange pigments in petals of *Cheiranthus* (wallflower) are carotenoids concentrated in chromoplasts, and they contribute to the pollination system by making the flowers conspicuous. On the other hand, there is no obvious explanation for the presence of carotenoids in the root of *Daucus* (carrot). The carotenoid-containing chromoplasts are far more irregular in shape than chloroplasts, and individual chromoplasts may show variation in shape during a period of continuous observation.

Leucoplasts are a varied assortment of bodies, some of which may simply be undeveloped chromoplasts. For example, there are plastids in the outer layers of a potato tuber which remain colourless while the tuber is underground. If the tuber is dug up and exposed to light it turns green, due to conversion of leucoplasts into chloroplasts. Other leucoplasts appear to be fully formed functional units, such as those involved in the formation and storage of starch, which are called **amyloplasts**.

Mitochondria

Mitochondria are cytoplasmic inclusions of great physiological importance, but much smaller in size than plastids. They are not uniform in shape, but are often spherical or rod-like with a maximum dimension of the order of 1 μ. This means that they can be detected with a good optical microscope as minute particles, but no details of structure can be seen with this instrument. Only recently, through the use of the electron microscope, has it been shown that they possess a regular internal structure made up of folded membranes. Mitochondria are of particular importance in respiration (see p. 229).

Vacuoles

A vacuole is a body of aqueous fluid enclosed in the cytoplasm. Each apical cell may contain the primordia of several vacuoles, and when the cell enlarges the increased volume is mostly taken up by enlargement of these vacuoles. During this process the several separate vacuoles usually coalesce. Hence if a fully formed cell has ten times the volume of the apical cell it grew from, almost nine-tenths of its internal space may be occupied by a single vacuole. In such a case the cytoplasm and its inclusions (other than the vacuole itself) are mostly confined to a thin lining inside the cell wall, though there may also be strands of cytoplasm extending across the vacuole.

The vacuole is separated from its enclosing cytoplasm by a membrane called the **tonoplast** by which the contents of the vacuole are controlled. Certain solutes pass in quantity from cytoplasm to vacuole where they may accumulate, while others are prevented from passing through. The tonoplast can therefore maintain considerable differences (*e.g.* of acidity) on either side of itself. The fluid contained in the vacuole is known as the **cell sap.**

Ergastic Substances

This is the name given to cell constituents which are products of metabolism rather than parts of the metabolic machinery of the cell. They are poorly represented in apical cells, but may be very plentiful and conspicuous in mature cells. Thus starch, which is frequently found in plant cells as a product of photosynthesis is an ergastic substance, but chlorophyll, which is an essential component of the photosynthetic system, is not. Starch grains develop within plastids, so starch is an example of an ergastic substance found in the cytoplasm, as distinct from being deposited in the vacuole. Vacuoles may contain soluble ergastic substances such as anthocyanin pigments which cause the red, blue, and purple colours of many flowers and leaves. The most universal of ergastic substances are the materials of the middle lamella and the cell wall, which qualify for this description since they are not metabolically active. Further examples of ergastic substances are given in the section on storage tissues (p. 45).

Differentiation

In unicellular plants, the single cell which represents the whole individual must be concerned with growth, nutrition, storage, reproduction, and any other property of the organism. There can be no separation of functions between one cell and another. Even in some of the smaller multicellular plants there is little, if any, specialisation. The filament of *Spirogyra* (p. 503), for instance, is a chain of cells similar to one another and each capable of carrying out a wide variety of functions. The only exception is that in some attached species of *Spirogyra* the basal cells have the special function of anchoring the plant. This represents, in the simplest degree, a division of labour between parts of the plant. In most multicellular plants, however, and particularly in the largest, there is a very considerable separation of functions: one part is concerned with the intake of nutrients, another with storage, another with reproduction, and so on. For greatest efficiency this requires the development of highly specialised types of cell. A familiar example of this specialisation is provided by the underground parts of the potato plant. The young roots are covered, towards their tips, with cells which elongate into root hairs. These penetrate between soil particles and have very thin walls, so that both in their position and their construction they are well suited for the absorption of water. The bulk of the potato tubers, on the other hand, consists of spacious, rounded cells in which starch is stored as a food reserve for the plant: again, the cell structure is in keeping with the function which is performed. Despite the difference in form shown by these two types of cell, both of them are developed from apical cells which are very similar when first produced. This development of dissimilar, specialised types of cell from newly-formed cells of uniform appearance is the process of **differentiation**. Regular differentiation into the complex pattern of cell types which make up a higher plant, in such a way that the whole is an integrated and functioning organism, is one of the marvels of the natural world. It also provides the botanist with some of his most difficult problems. What, for example, makes a cell elongate, and why should elongation occur in some cells but not in others? Why, at certain intervals during growth, should a certain group of cells begin to develop into a leaf or a branch, and what controls the orderly differentiation of cells within each of these organs? Problems such as these fall within the province of **morphogenesis** which is currently a subject being vigorously investigated. Answers to the problems stated above are far from complete, but they are at least being approached.

Generally speaking, cells with related functions occur together in groups. It is customary to recognise certain groupings as constituting particular **tissues**. Thus, in young roots the outermost layer of cells which produces the root hairs (the **piliferous layer**) can be spoken of as an absorbing tissue, while the internal cells of a potato tuber represent a storage tissue. Sometimes a tissue may be composed of a single type of cell, but this is not implicit in the concept of a tissue, and examples will be given of tissues each of which consists of a variety of cell types. We shall now consider some of the most common tissues found in higher plants.

Meristematic Tissues

A tissue in which a high proportion of the cells are undergoing division, and of which the main function is the production of new cells, is called a **meristem**. **Apical** meristems are characteristic of all the flowering plants and occur both in the shoot apices from which the aerial parts are derived, and in root apices where they are responsible for growth in root length. Other meristems may occur elsewhere in the plant. Increase in height of many grasses is partly due to the apical meristem, but this is supplemented by cell divisions in meristems lower down the plant, in the stem and in the leaf sheaths. These meristems, which have differentiated tissues both above and below them, are described as **intercalary** meristems. Increase in girth of the trunk of most trees is due to the activity of the **cambium**, a meristem which lies between the bark and the wood. In keeping with its position and with the direction in which it adds new cells to the plant, the cambium is described as a **lateral** meristem.

It is difficult to generalise about the structure and contents of meristematic cells. The cells from many apical meristems are almost isodiametric (having all dimensions more or less alike), with thin walls enclosing cytoplasm in which the only prominent inclusions are the nuclei. But this description would not fit the cells of a cambium, which are frequently much longer than broad and which may contain inclusions such as vacuoles more typical of differentiated cells.

The ability to divide is, of course, an essential property of meristematic cells, although a meristem may not exhibit cell division at all times. In temperate climates the annual growth cycle of plants includes an active period and a dormant period. During dormancy cell division may be completely lacking, but it is still correct to refer to the apices, the cambium, and other similar tissues as being meristems.

Epidermal Tissues

The outermost layer of cells in the younger parts of the plant constitutes the **epidermis**. As the plant grows older, the epidermis may be replaced by other tissues, as in the formation of bark by the trunk of a tree, but it is permanent in organs such as leaves. Because of its position, the epidermis must possess a variety of properties. It has a protective function, since it is the plant's first line of defence against injury by would-be parasites or predators, by abrasion, and by weather. In the aerial parts the strength needed to fulfil this function must be combined with suppleness and elasticity to allow flexibility and growth, and with transparency to allow entry of light for photosynthesis. At the same time it must permit the interchange of gases with the atmosphere, but prevent excessive loss of moisture under conditions of drought. The epidermis of the root has to satisfy a different set of conditions. Transparency is not required and desiccation is not such a serious hazard. But there must still be strength to avoid damage from abrasion by soil particles and permeability to allow absorption of water.

The aerial parts with their more exacting requirements have the more complex structure in the epidermis. A leaf or a young stem generally has an epidermis consisting of an impermeable layer perforated at intervals by **stomata** (singular: **stoma**) which provide pores of variable aperture. The cells of the impermeable layer usually appear square or rectangular in a section cut at right angles to the surface (Fig. 4), but when seen in surface view each cell may have a wavy outline reminiscent of a piece in a jig-saw puzzle (Fig. 5, A). Epidermal cells shaped like this are found in many dicotyledons. The comparison with a jig-saw puzzle is appropriate, since the cells fit closely and exactly into one another, giving coherence to the layer of cells and an absence of intercellular spaces. But the analogy must not be taken too far: the cells are rarely "fully interlocking". The epidermal cells of most monocotyledons are rectangular in surface view with the long axis of the

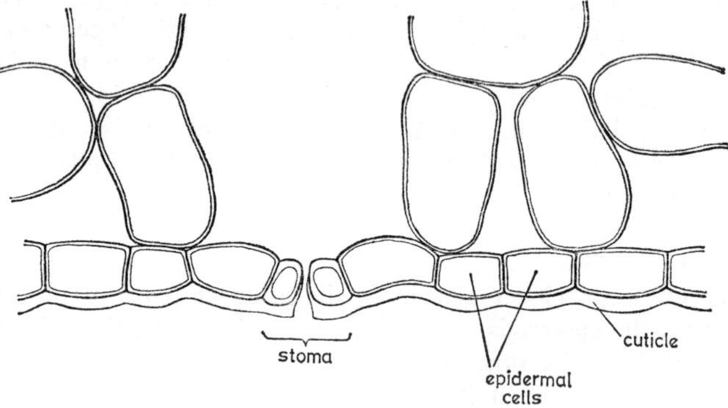

Fig. 4. LEAF OF *Rhododendron*.
Part of section cut at right angles to surface, showing lower epidermis.

rectangle parallel to the leaf axis (Fig. 5, B). These also fit closely together and there are no spaces between them.

Impermeability is assured by the addition of a fatty substance, **cutin,** to the outer walls. This is an ergastic substance produced by the protoplasts and deposited in the cellulose wall where it appears to move outwards and accumulate on the surface. Thus the outer walls of the epidermal cells have on the outer surface a layer of cutin alone, forming the **cuticle** (Fig. 4). Inside this is a region of cellulose heavily impregnated with cutin, forming the **cutinised layer,** and on the very inside the wall is mostly cellulose. The cuticle formed by each cell merges with that of neighbouring cells, forming a continuous waterproof sheet which can often be stripped off in considerable pieces. Although a cuticle is a regular feature of the epidermis in aerial parts, the extent to which it is developed varies. Plants which face a serious and frequent risk of desiccation, such as those growing in hot, dry places, often have a very thick cuticle which may be supplemented by a layer of wax. At the other extreme plants which grow in damp, shady places have an extremely thin cuticle.

There is usually nothing very outstanding about the contents of the cells which make up the impermeable layer. The cells are vacuolated and the cytoplasm occupies only a small part of the volume. Plastids are not common, but plants which live in deep shade may have chloroplasts in the epidermis of the leaves. Anthocyanin pigments are dissolved in the cell sap of epidermal cells in many petals and in leaves of such plants as the copper beech and ornamental varieties of *Coleus*.

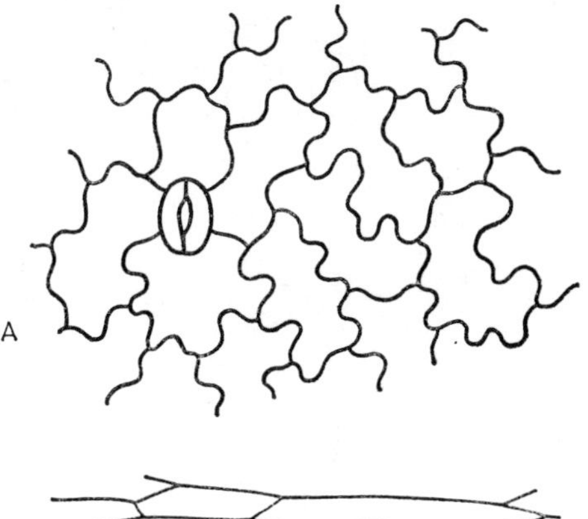

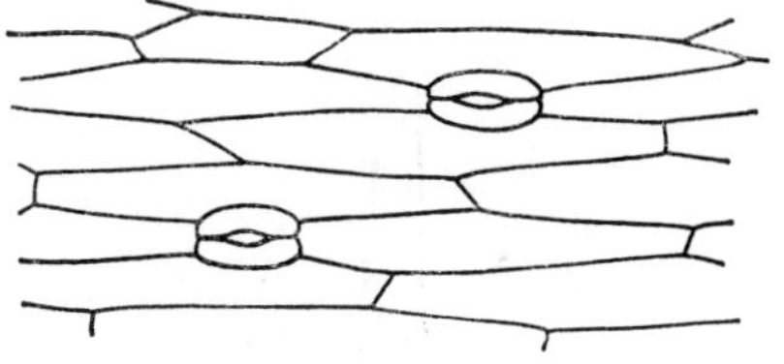

Fig. 5. SURFACE VIEW OF LEAF EPIDERMIS. A, *Lycopersicum* (a dicotyledon); B, *Iris* (a monocotyledon).

Stomata provide the system of controlled ventilation which is essential in the green, aerial parts of the plant. Each stoma consists of two **guard cells** lying side by side, which may be closely pressed together along their length, or which by an alteration of their shape may have an aperture or **pore** between them (Fig. 80). This alteration of shape depends on changes of pressure within the guard cells, the underlying mechanism of which is discussed in Chapter 7. The guard cells lie either in the same plane as the other epidermal cells or somewhat recessed below the general level. Unlike other epidermal cells the guard cells regularly contain chloroplasts. The group of cells immediately surrounding the guard cells may be dissimilar in shape from other epidermal cells, in which case they are called **subsidiary cells**. A regular pattern of subsidiary cells is characteristic of certain species or groups of species. This pattern can be related to the formation of the stoma during leaf development. Each stoma originates in a superficial cell which divides to produce a central cell and several cells around it, all in the plane of the epidermis. The central cell divides into two, and these sister cells become the guard cells of the stoma.

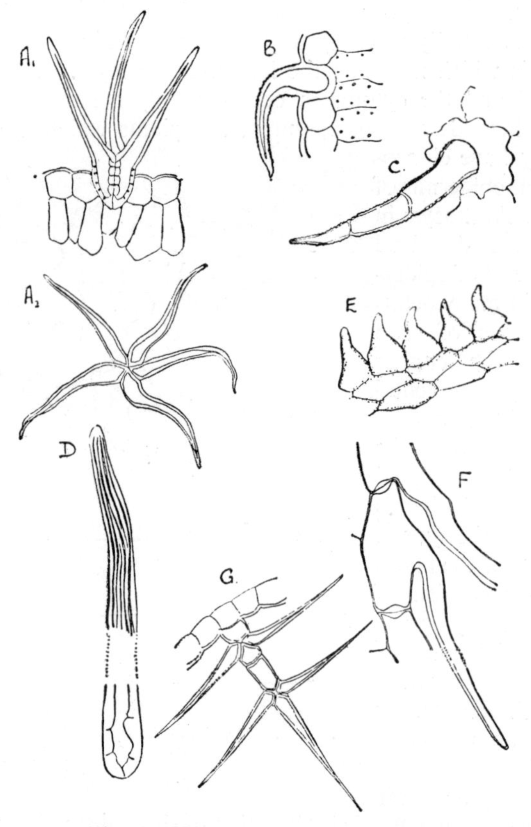

Fig. 6. VARIOUS KINDS OF TRICHOMES.

A_1 and A_2, leaf of *Hamamelis*; B, leaf of *Cassia*; C, leaf of *Datura*; D, testa of *Strychnos nux-vomica*; E, petal of *Arnica*; F, testa of *Strophanthus*; G, leaf of *Verbascum*.

A very common feature of the epidermis is the possession of outgrowths which are collectively referred to as **trichomes.** A trichome is strictly an outgrowth of the epidermis alone and is distinct from excrescences of a more substantial nature including some of the inner tissues, which are called **emergences.** A familiar

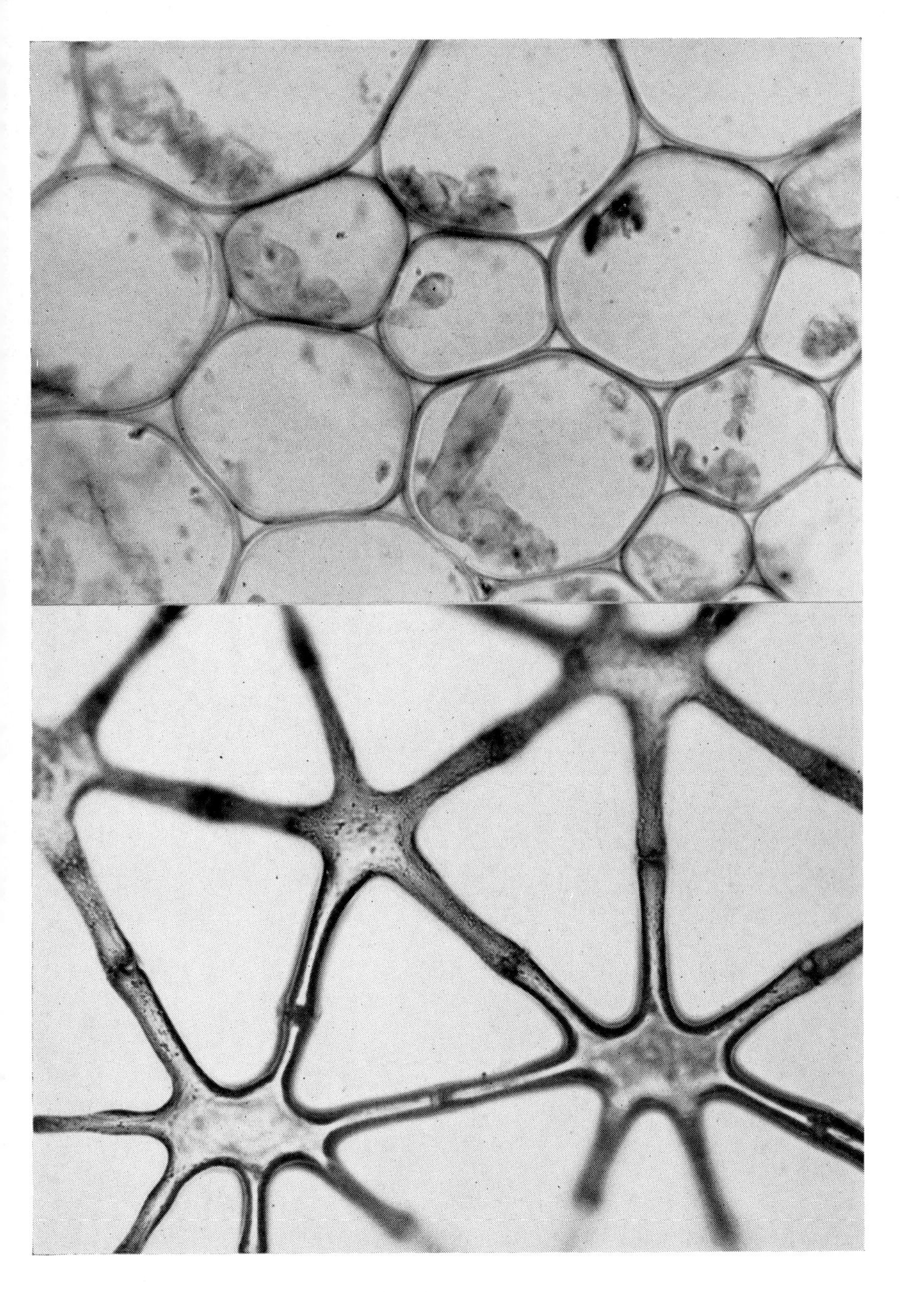

PLATE 1

TYPES OF CELL SEEN IN TRANSVERSE SECTION OF STEMS. (× 550.)
Above: PARENCHYMA CELLS FROM THE PITH OF *Astrantia*.
Below: CELLS FROM PITH OF *Juncus* (COMMON RUSH).

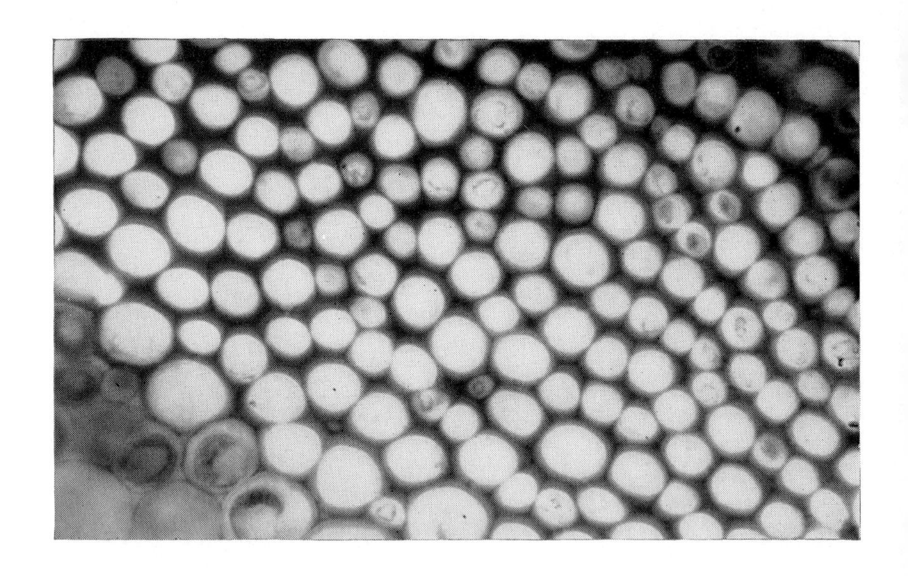

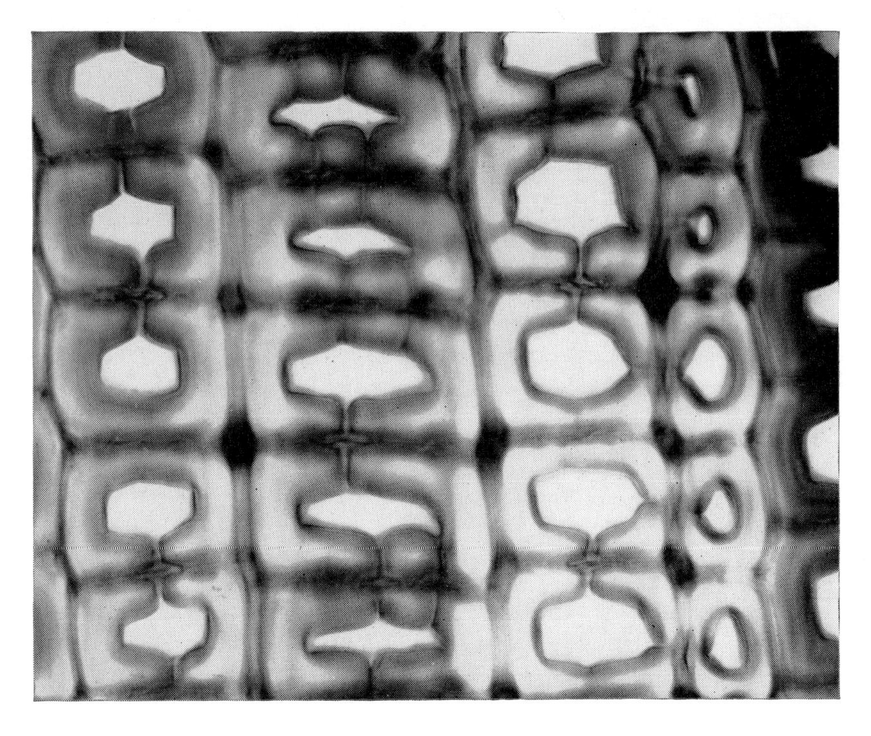

PLATE 2

TYPES OF CELL, SEEN IN TRANSVERSE SECTION OF STEMS. (× 500.)

Above: COLLENCHYMA CELLS FROM CORTEX OF *Senecio* (GROUNDSEL).

Below: SUMMER-WOOD TRACHEIDS FROM SECONDARY XYLEM OF *Taxodium* (SWAMP CYPRESS).

example of an emergence is a prickle on a rose plant. Trichomes show great diversity of form from simple unicellular hairs to elaborate multicellular structures. The simplest type is also the commonest, for epidermal cells of most young roots develop into root hairs which are unbranched, unicellular, and have thin walls without any cuticle (Fig. 62). The function of these hairs is clear. They provide a large surface area of easily permeated cell wall through which the plant takes in water from the soil. Other trichomes produced elsewhere on the plant may also be of obvious functional significance. For example, the epidermal hairs on the seed coat of *Gossypium*, which constitute the cotton "fibres" of commerce, assist in seed dispersal. The stinging hairs of *Urtica* (nettle) provide an effective deterrent against destruction by animals. Other hairs incapable of inflicting injury may also afford protection, in this case against smaller animals. For instance, many virus diseases of plants are transmitted by aphids which pierce the outer tissues of the plant to obtain food, introducing pathogenic viruses as they do so. A dense mantle of hairs on leaves and stems can prevent this by keeping aphids at such a distance that their mouth parts cannot reach the epidermis proper.

Many trichomes are glandular, secreting substances which are by-products of metabolism. The volatile oil which is responsible for the characteristic flavour and scent of mint, for example, is secreted by multicellular trichomes. The functional significance of this and similar secretions, if there is any, is not clear; but at least there is in these cases knowledge of some activity associated with the trichomes. There are other instances of trichomes, sometimes of great structural complexity, which have no known function or purpose. Fig. 6 shows a selection of trichomes characteristic of certain genera or species, the significance of some of which is quite unknown.

Photosynthetic Tissues

The ability to photosynthesise may be the property of cells which have some primary function other than the synthesis of organic compounds. For example, the guard cells of stomata contain chloroplasts, but the importance of guard cells as sites of chemical synthesis must rank second to the part they play in controlling the pore aperture. On the other hand, the aerial parts of most flowering plants contain tissues in which photosynthesis is the principal function. Such tissues are generally found just inside the epidermis, where they may be several cells in depth. In flat leaves the greater part of the volume enclosed within the epidermis consists of highly ventilated tissue containing chloroplasts (Fig. 7). This tissue constitutes the **mesophyll** (meso = middle; phyll = leaf) and is the main photosynthetic tissue of the plant. It is usually supplemented by similar tissue just inside the epidermis of young stems and other green parts such as bracts and sepals. The position and structure of this tissue can readily be interpreted in terms of the function it performs. It is very near the surface and therefore well placed for receiving light. Cells nearest to the surface receive the greatest light intensity, and correspondingly these cells show the highest frequency of chloroplasts. In leaves which are dorsiventral, that is flat leaves with distinctive upper and lower surfaces, the

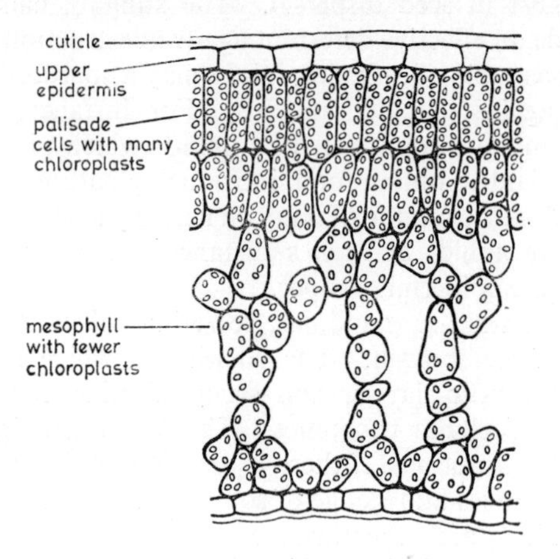

Fig. 7. SECTION THROUGH LEAF OF *Rhododendron* SHOWING DISTRIBUTION OF CHLOROPLASTS.

concentration of chloroplasts is greater towards the upper surface, which more often faces the source of light.

In structure, most photosynthetic tissues are a type of **parenchyma**. This is a name given to all tissues consisting of cells of rather uniform size and shape which are not markedly elongated. Parenchyma cells frequently have vacuolated, living protoplasts and thin cellulose walls, but there are exceptions to this. For example, the pith of some higher plants consists of parenchyma cells which have lost their protoplasts and have lignified walls. Cell shape is very variable among tissues classed as parenchymatous. In some tissues the cells are closely packed and have angular walls; in others the cells are very loosely packed and are rounded or lobed with large intercellular spaces. The parenchyma which makes up typical photosynthetic tissue is of the loosely packed type. The intercellular spaces are necessary for the diffusion of gases to and from the cells where photosynthesis occurs, and they form a continuous network of diffusion channels, connecting with the atmosphere through the stomata.

Vascular Tissues

In an organism where division of function between the parts is as extreme as in a flowering plant, there is a need for an efficient vascular system to translocate the raw materials and products of metabolism from one organ to another. Two functions of the vascular system are particularly evident. Firstly, water is taken in through the roots but it must be supplied to the aerial parts also: there must therefore be a system for the upward translocation of water. Secondly, the aerial parts synthesise carbohydrates which are needed for respiration and growth by the roots: there must therefore be some means of translocating organic compounds downwards. These two examples of the need for efficient translocation do not by any means give a complete picture of the functions carried out by the vascular system, but they provide a sufficient introduction at this point. The two types of translocation referred to are carried out by two tissues which differ from each other in several important respects, and they will be dealt with separately. Before doing so, a few words about terminology are necessary. The terms "transport", "conduction", and "translocation" are all used to describe movements within the vascular tissues. Some authors tend to restrict a particular term to a particular type of movement, but these personal preferences are not generally shared and do not carry the weight of definitions. To avoid any unintended implications, the term translocation will be used in this chapter to cover all movements within the vascular tissues though, as will become clear, at least two radically different mechanisms are concerned.

Upward translocation of water is the responsibility of the **xylem**. In essence this tissue is a system of pipes extending from very near the root tips, upwards through the whole root system and into the stem, and branching out into the extremities of the aerial parts. Just as in the pipes of a public water supply system, the channels in the xylem are made up of short sections of piping arranged end to end. Each section is the wall of a single cell. These walls are usually strengthened and thickened during the differentiation of xylem by the formation of a secondary wall inside the primary wall. The secondary wall consists partly of cellulose but this is mixed with another substance called **lignin**, the chemical composition of which is uncertain. Lignin is deposited not only in the secondary wall but also in the primary wall and middle lamella. The process in which the cell wall becomes impregnated with lignin is called **lignification**. Once the secondary wall is fully developed the cell loses its protoplast, at the same time losing the ability to divide, to respire, to add further thickness to its wall, or to perform any of the dynamic processes associated with an intact living cell. Such cells are often, and quite properly, referred to as dead cells, but it should be remembered that even after their death they perform

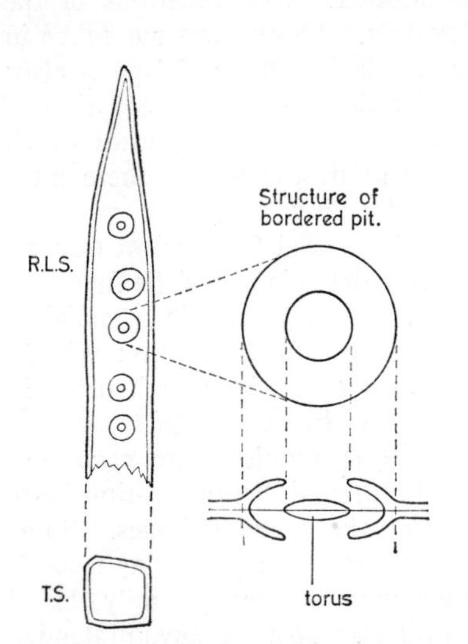

Fig. 8. PART OF A GYMNOSPERM TRACHEID. Note the prominent bordered pits characteristic of these cells.

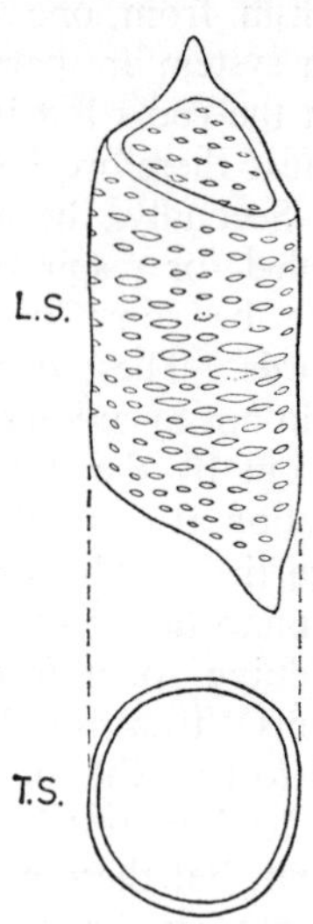

Fig. 9. VESSEL SEGMENT FROM *Quercus* (OAK). Note the open end and the pitted side walls.

a vital function in the living organism. The fact that an organism has a considerable bulk of these dead cells is not an indication that it is moribund.

In the gymnosperms and in lower groups of vascular plants, the translocating cells of the xylem are many times longer than broad, and the passage of water from cell to cell takes place through pits. A pit on the wall of one cell usually faces a corresponding pit on the wall of a neighbouring cell, an arrangement which clearly assists water transport. Translocating cells of this type are called **tracheids** (Fig. 8 and Plate 2). In angiosperms, however, it is common for the translocating cell to show little or no elongation but to have expanded to a considerable breadth. During differentiation the side walls become thickened and lignified, but the walls at the top and bottom usually disappear almost completely leaving only a narrow rim. After loss of the protoplast, therefore, the fully formed cell becomes like a hollow cylinder with the ends removed. These cells occur in vertical series along which there can be uninterrupted flow of water, each series being referred to as a **vessel**, and each component cell as a **vessel segment** or **vessel element** (Fig. 9). Vessel segments which are short and broad, with complete breakdown of end walls, such as have just been described, represent an extreme type found in those angiosperms with the widest vessels. In other angiosperms the vessel segments may show more similarity to tracheids: that is, each segment shows some considerable elongation, and breakdown of the end walls may be incomplete. The essential difference between tracheids and vessel segments is that there is always some breakdown of the end walls in vessel segments giving continuity between the cavities of neighbouring segments, whereas in tracheids the primary wall remains intact and passage from cell to cell occurs by way of pits.

The absence of end walls in vessel segments and the occurrence of pits make it clear that formation of the secondary wall is not simply a uniform deposition of lignified cellulose by the protoplast around itself. On the contrary, thickening of the wall usually follows a precise pattern which may differ from cell to cell of the same plant. Xylem which is differentiated nearest to the apices (the **protoxylem**) has thickening arranged in separate rings or in a continuous helix [the **annular** and **spiral** arrangements, respectively (Fig. 10; A, B)]. This is important since these xylem cells are differentiated in a region of cell elongation. The primary wall can be stretched, but a heavily thickened secondary wall cannot: by having thickening in the annular or spiral pattern, cell elongation remains a possibility. In regions further from the apex, where cell elongation does not occur, differentiation of xylem can involve more general thickening of the cell wall. There may be a network of thickened strips separated by chinks of unthickened wall [the **reticulate** arrangement (Fig. 10, C)], or the secondary wall may be deposited in a uniform layer broken only by pits [the **pitted** arrangement (Fig. 10, D)].

Any pattern of extensive thickening gives considerable strength to the cells, and xylem, apart from its importance as translocating tissue, contributes greatly to the strength of the plant. This point emphasises that a classification of tissues on the basis of function, such as is used here, is likely to be an over-simplification. Many tracheids and vessel segments have walls of considerable thickness enclosing a substantial cavity (the **lumen**), and these cells can satisfactorily combine the twin functions of translocation and mechanical support. In some vessels, however, the lumen is very large and the wall not thickened proportionately: translocation is here the primary function and strength negligible. In such cases the vessels are associated with cells which have specialised in the other direction. These are much elongated, have very thick walls and small lumina,

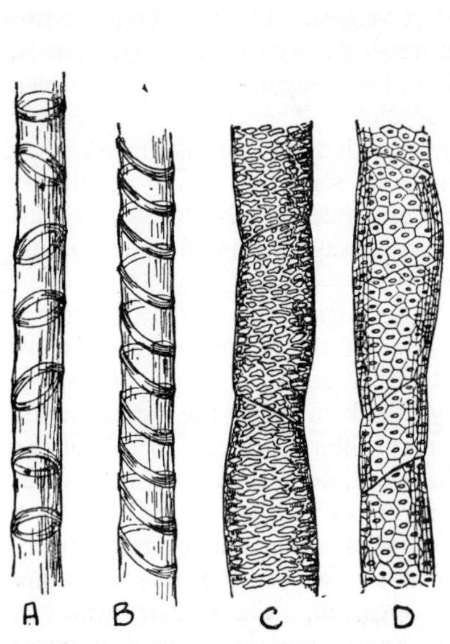

Fig. 10. XYLEM, TYPES OF VESSEL.
A, annular; B, spiral; C, reticulate; D, pitted.

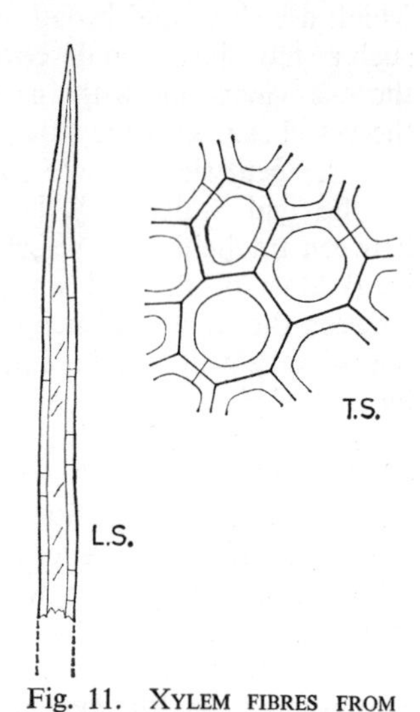

Fig. 11. XYLEM FIBRES FROM *Quercus* (OAK).
Left: Part of one fibre as seen in longitudinal section. *Right:* Group of fibres as seen in transverse section at higher magnification.

and are called **fibres** (Fig. 11). They provide great strength but are useless in translocation. Because of their position, these cells are called **xylem fibres** and are regarded as part of the xylem. Xylem usually contains some parenchymatous cells also which are apparently concerned with storage and secretion. This **xylem parenchyma** is variable in quantity, in cell shape, and in presence or absence of living protoplasts.

The translocation of organic substances from one part of the plant to another is carried out in the **phloem**. This tissue is often associated with the xylem in position, but it differs both in structure and in the mechanism of translocation. Like the xylem, phloem consists of a mixture of cell types only some of which are directly involved in translocation. The actual channels of translocation are elongated cells, but unlike tracheids and vessel segments they have protoplasts which persist at maturity and which appear to play an active part in translocation. Thickening of the cell wall may occur, but if so the thickening is of unlignified cellulose. The translocating cells are of two types. The first type, characteristic

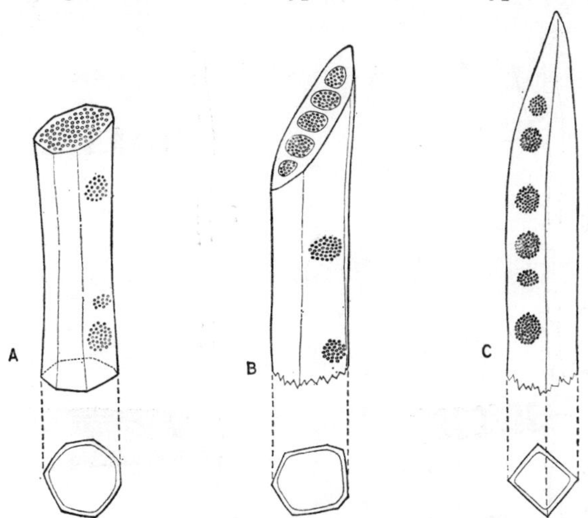

Fig. 12. TRANSLOCATING CELLS FROM PHLOEM.
A, sieve tube member from an angiosperm, with end wall forming a simple sieve plate; B, part of another type of angiosperm sieve tube member with the oblique end wall forming a compound sieve plate with several sieve areas; C, part of a sieve cell from a gymnosperm. Note absence of distinct end wall. In this example sieve areas are confined to one pair of opposite walls, but this is not always so.

of angiosperms, occurs in regular vertical series with either transverse or oblique end walls. These end walls are perforated and resemble sieves: hence the vertical "pipelines" are called **sieve tubes**, and each component cell is a **sieve tube member** or **element** (Fig. 12). When the end walls are more or less transverse, the perforations are uniformly distributed over the whole wall, which is known as a simple **sieve plate**. With oblique end walls of greater area, however, there are several clusters of perforations. The whole wall is therefore a compound sieve plate and each cluster of perforations is a **sieve area**. In addition to the sieve-like end walls, sieve tube members may have some sieve areas on lateral walls.

In gymnosperms the translocating cells of the phloem are not arranged in such regular vertical series. The cells are long and tapering with no clear distinction between lateral and end walls, and sieve areas are distributed over the whole wall area. These are known as **sieve cells** (Fig. 12).

The perforations in both sieve tubes and sieve cells give complete continuity between the two adjacent cells. There is no persistent

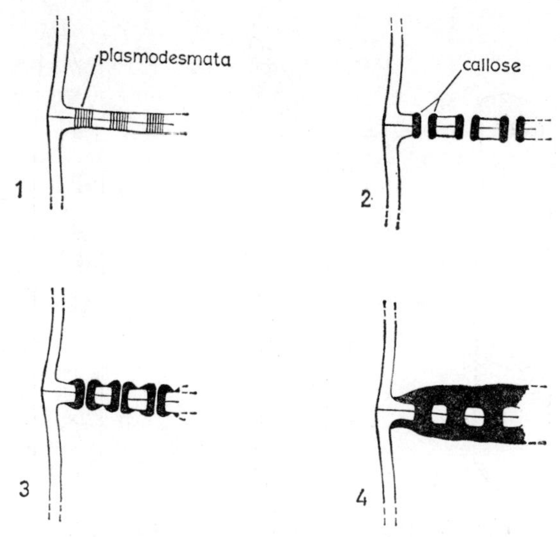

Fig. 13. LONGITUDINAL SECTION OF PART OF A SIEVE TUBE SHOWING DEVELOPMENT OF A SIMPLE SIEVE PLATE.

1, adjacent sieve tube members connected by plasmodesmata; 2, formation of large perforations lined with a callose; 3, further deposition of callose reduces size of perforations; 4, complete occlusion of perforations and formation of callus on surface of sieve plate.

primary wall so it is not correct to refer to the perforations as pits. The continuity is clearly of importance in the mechanism of translocation in the phloem, but the details of this mechanism are not known. It is uncertain, for example, whether it is the cytoplasm or the vacuoles of adjacent cells which are in contact through the sieves. The perforations themselves show an interesting sequence of changes during their useful lifetime, particularly in sieve tubes. At an early stage of development the portions of wall which are destined to become sieve plates are perforated by fine plasmodesmata. The large perforations of the fully developed sieve plate are probably formed by local breakdown of the cellulose wall and coalescence of groups of plasmodesmata. Each perforation in the sieve plate is lined with a carbohydrate called **callose** which is closely related to cellulose, and the initial lining of callose is probably derived from the cellulose of the young cell wall, but later the lining increases in thickness without further inroads into the cellulose wall, and this seems to be the result of direct deposition of callose by the protoplast (Fig. 13).

Callose eventually obstructs the perforations completely, and when this stage is reached, the sieve tube loses its function as part of the translocating system. The plugs of callose may extend outwards at the rims of the perforations so that they coalesce with neighbouring plugs and this leads to a prominent accumulation of callose on the surface of a defunct sieve plate which is known as a **callus**. Obstruction of a sieve plate by callose may be only temporary, during a period of dormancy. In this case when active growth is resumed, perforations reappear in the callose plugs and continuity between sieve tube members is re-established.

In the sieve cells of gymnosperms the perforations do not develop to the same extent, and the sieve areas of mature sieve cells are often perforated by connecting strands no larger than normal plasmodesmata.

It has been pointed out that sieve cells and sieve tube members retain their protoplasts, at least while they are actively concerned with translocation. However, during differentiation the nucleus degenerates, and when fully functional the cell has no nucleus. This is probably connected with the fact that in angiosperms each sieve tube member is associated with one or more smaller cells called **companion cells** (Fig. 14). The association begins early in development of the phloem: a single primordial cell will divide into two longitudinal parts, one of which develops into a sieve tube and the other into one or several companion cells lying alongside. A typical companion cell is slender and elongated with dense cytoplasm and a prominent nucleus. It seems likely that the sieve tube member and its associated companion cell (or cells) are closely integrated in function, with the nucleus of the companion cell doing service for the sieve tube member also. Phloem in gymnosperms does not contain companion cells though some cells in the rays may have a similar function.

As with the xylem, phloem frequently includes fibres and parenchyma cells which play no direct part in translocation, called **phloem fibres** and **phloem parenchyma** respectively. Phloem fibres often have walls of great thickness which may or may not be lignified.

Before leaving the vascular tissues it is interesting to make a brief comparison between the two major groups of seed plants, the gymnosperms and the angiosperms. In both xylem and phloem the gymnosperms have less specialised types of translocating cell than have angiosperms, which are regarded as being more highly evolved. The tracheids and sieve cells of gymnosperms are both

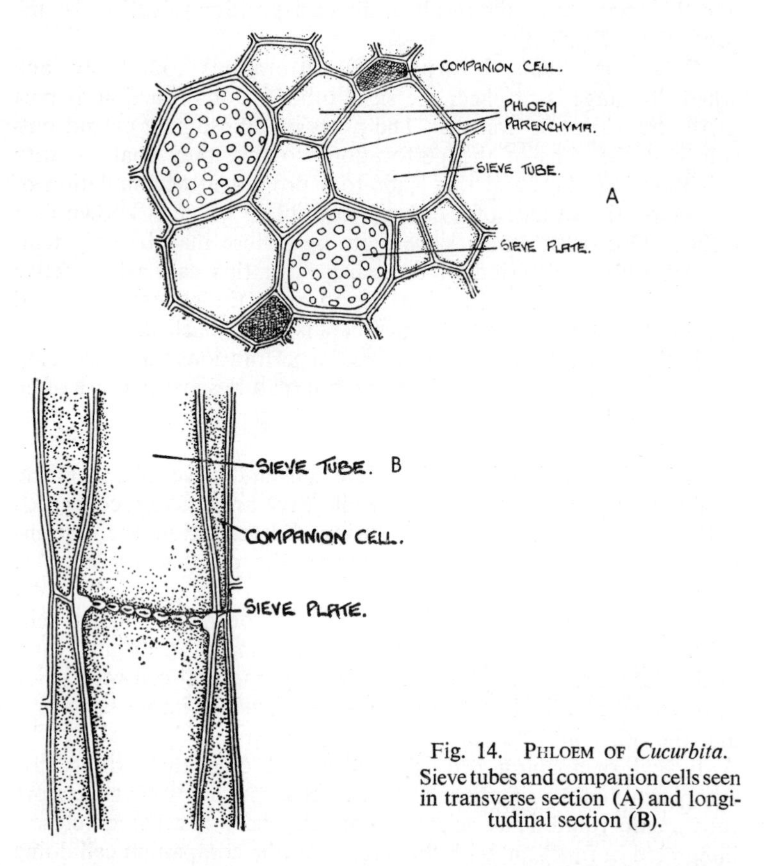

Fig. 14. PHLOEM OF *Cucurbita*. Sieve tubes and companion cells seen in transverse section (A) and longitudinal section (B).

many times longer than broad and connect with neighbouring cells by pits or very small perforations. The corresponding cells in angiosperms which comprise the vessels and sieve tubes, are generally shorter and fatter and their walls have large perforations. This combination of features would seem to allow much more efficient translocation, though the gymnosperms are not noticeably handicapped by their more primitive translocating cells. For example, the gymnosperms include the giant redwood trees of California (*Sequoia* spp.) which reach heights of over 300 ft and are the tallest trees known.

Strengthening Tissues

The larger the size of a plant, the more vulnerable it is to damage by physical forces. This generalisation is particularly true of the aerial parts which must not only be able to withstand climatic hazards such as wind, rain, and snow, but also must be sufficiently robust to support their own weight against gravity. It is not surprising, therefore, that almost all macroscopic plants are equipped with tissues whose principal function is to provide strength. This is achieved by thickening of the cell walls. Two main types of strengthening tissue are recognised differing in whether the thickened walls are all primary, or whether there is a secondary wall also. The important distinction is that the wall produced while a cell is still growing is the primary wall, whereas any further addition after the cell has reached its full size constitutes a secondary wall.

Strengthening tissue in which the wall thickening is limited to the primary wall is called **collenchyma**. This is a living tissue of particular importance in giving strength to parts of the plant which are still growing, and which may also take part in photosynthesis. The walls are thickened with a mixture of cellulose and pectic substances, and they have a high water content. The tissue is often recognisable by the presence of living protoplasts, perhaps with chloroplasts, in cells whose walls are conspicuously thickened (Fig. 15 and Plate 2). In many cases the thickening is uneven, being greater on tangential than on radial walls, or being concentrated at the angles of the cells. There is greater development of intercellular spaces than is usual in thick-walled tissues. Collenchyma occurs in layers of strands closely underlying the epidermis in stems, petioles, and other aerial parts. In such a position it is closely associated with the photosynthetic parenchyma, and there may be no clear distinction between the two tissues. Only the extreme cell types will be clearly recognisable for what they are—the parenchyma cells being thin-walled and isodiametric, the collenchyma thick-walled and elongated parallel to the axis of the stem.

Where wall thickness is largely due to formation of a secondary wall, the strengthening tissue is called **sclerenchyma**. The wall is usually lignified and mature sclerenchyma cells usually have lost their protoplasts. One type of sclerenchyma cell of frequent occurrence is the fibre, examples of which have already been given in the accounts of xylem and phloem. Although these cells were referred to as xylem and phloem fibres because of their position, it is equally correct to refer to them as sclerenchyma fibres because of their structure. Sclerenchyma fibres show all degrees of association with the vascular tissues. They may be in small clusters intermingled with the conducting cells, or in bundles lying alongside the vascular tissues but distinct from them, or in bundles or sheaths showing no close association with vascular tissues. In all cases the cell structure is generally similar. A characteristic fibre is greatly elongated with its ends gradually tapering to fine points. The cell wall is thick and the lumen small. Pits may be present in the wall, but they have small apertures and probably serve no useful purpose. Fibres which are less specialised have a

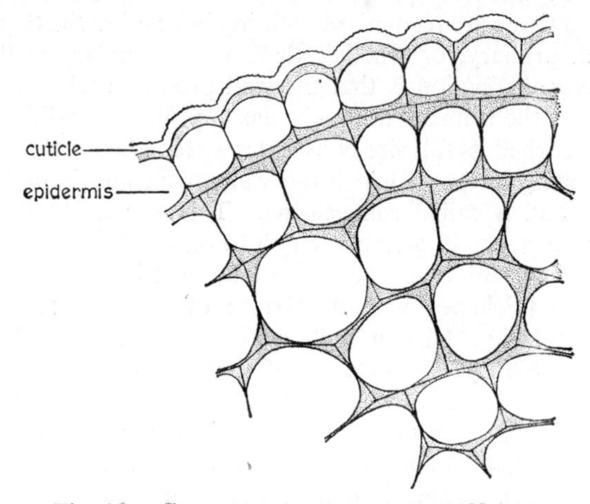

Fig. 15. COLLENCHYMA FROM STEM OF *Nepeta*.
Cell contents not shown. Note localisation of thickening on tangential walls.

structure approaching that of tracheids: the lumen is larger, the wall thinner, and the pits wider. In fact it is not possible to make a clear separation between fibres and tracheids, although the extreme types are quite distinct in structure and function.

The grouping together of fibres into bundles makes a tissue of great mechanical efficiency. Within each bundle the individual fibres lie parallel to one another, overlapping at their ends with other fibres above and below, and forming part of a long strand running the whole length of the plant, which possesses both strength and flexibility. The length and strength of these strands makes them valuable raw materials for the textile industry. Linen thread is made from the phloem fibres of *Linum usitatissimum* (flax), while

Cannabis sativa (hemp), and *Corchorus capsularis* (jute) also yield phloem fibres of commercial importance. The strength of the thread produced is partly due to the length of the constituent fibres. Fibres from flax may be as much as 4 cm. long, which is well above average for plant fibres. But even this seems modest by comparison with the fibres from *Boehmeria nivea* which may reach 22 cm. in length. The textile thread produced from *B. nivea* (ramie) is thus extremely strong, though it is troublesome to produce, and therefore not a serious competitor for the more established textiles.

Some confusion exists about the use of the word "fibre". In correct botanical usage a fibre is a single cell with the properties described above. In everyday speech and in the textile industry, however, the word is often used to refer to any thread or strand which may or may not be of plant origin. In this sense a bundle of fibres (botanical sense) extracted from a flax plant is referred to as "a fibre", and reference is commonly made to cotton "fibres" which botanically are not fibres at all but epidermal hairs.

A second type of sclerenchymatous cell is the **sclereid** or stone cell. These possess the essential characteristic of sclerenchyma, namely, a thick secondary wall, but are less uniform in shape than fibres. If they are elongated at all their length does not exceed their breadth by more than a few times. Many sclereids are more or less isodiametric, and some are contorted or branched into very irregular shapes. They are sometimes associated in clusters or even large accumulations, but solitary sclereids are also common. For example, the hard shell of many "nuts" consists of large numbers of sclereids united into an almost solid tissue, and the gritty texture of pear fruits is due to small groups of sclereids mixed with the parenchyma of the flesh; on the other hand, tea leaves contain solitary, branched sclereids in the mesophyll (Fig. 16).

Storage Tissues

A close analogy can be made between plant metabolism and a manufacturing industry: in both cases there are likely to be times when production exceeds demand. Plants are equipped to meet this situation by the provision of storage tissues where the surplus products of metabolism can remain until required for growth or respiration. Storage tissues are usually parenchymatous with cells sufficiently spacious to contain the substances deposited in them, and are so arranged in relation to other tissues that these substances can conveniently reach them and be removed from them. As is the case with other functions of the plant, cells concerned with storage may not be exclusively devoted to this purpose. The mesophyll of leaves, for example, although primarily a photosynthetic tissue, may also act as a temporary store for the products

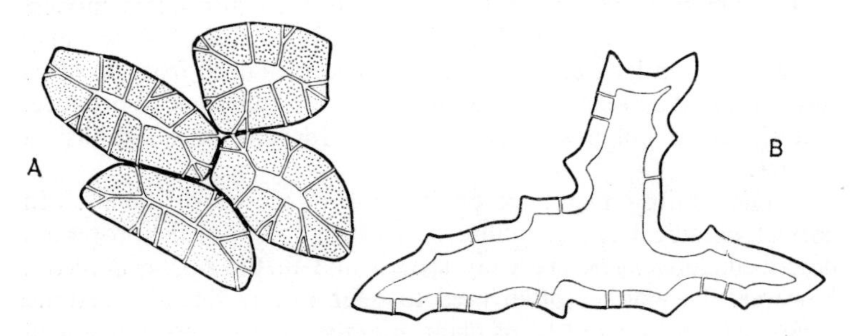

Fig. 16. SCLEREIDS.
A, group of sclereids from flesh of pear fruit, broken off from a much larger cluster. Note branched pits. B, solitary sclereid from mesophyll of tea leaf.

of photosynthesis. However, most plants contain other tissues in which storage appears to be the primary function.

Some of the more frequent and recognisable substances found as reserve foods in storage tissues are the following:

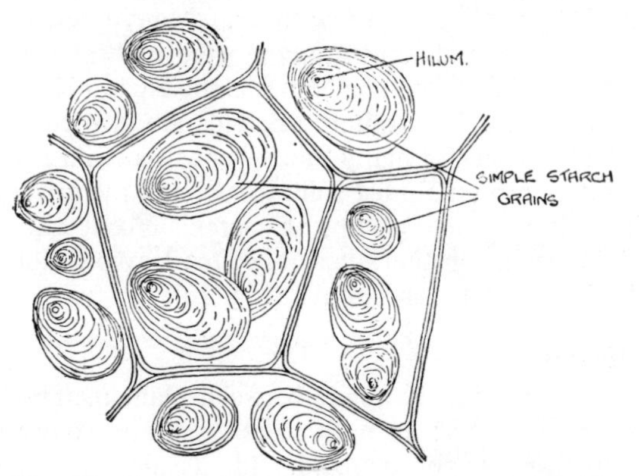

Fig. 17. STARCH GRAINS IN CELLS OF POTATO TUBER.

Starch. This, the commonest form in which reserve food is stored, is found in many plants in the form of insoluble grains in the cytoplasm. In spite of the chemical similarity of the starch itself, the starch grains found in different species may have characteristic differences in structure and appearance which are useful in recognising the composition of powdered foods and drugs.

Fig. 17 shows the type of starch grain found in the potato tuber, in which each grain has a layered structure. The point around which all the layers are arranged (the **hilum**) is characteristically eccentric. Each grain is a single and separate structure, and is therefore called a simple starch grain. Other types of starch grain are found in

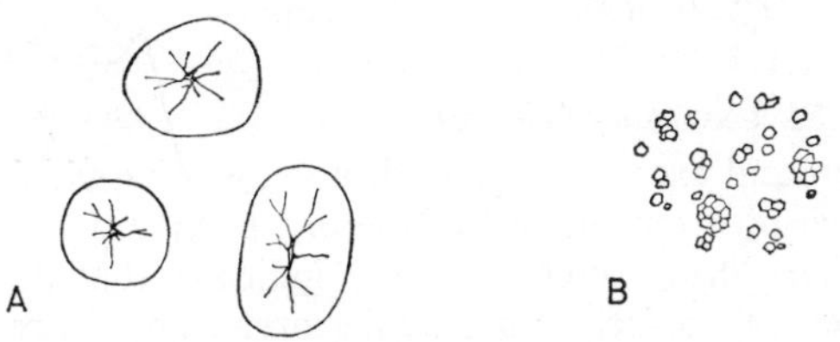

Fig. 18. STARCH GRAINS FROM COTYLEDON OF KIDNEY BEAN (A) AND FROM ENDOSPERM OF RICE (B).

Phaseolus vulgaris (kidney bean), which has simple grains with a central hilum, or *Oryza sativa* (rice) where granules are clustered into compound grains (Fig. 18).

Proteins. Proteins are among the major chemical components of the protoplast in all living cells, where they form an essential part of the metabolic machinery. In addition, some cells contain reserves of protein which may appear either amorphous or as crystals. Wheat, for example, stores not only starch in its seeds but also the protein gluten which is responsible for the coherent dough produced from wheat flour, and which therefore helps to give wheat its valuable baking qualities. This protein is stored in an amorphous form. Crystalline protein is found together with starch in the outer cells of potato tubers. In many seeds proteins are stored in more complex **aleurone grains** which are concentrated in a layer of cells underlying the seed coat, known as the aleurone layer. Each aleurone grain in *Ricinus communis* (castor bean), for example, has an outer membrane enclosing a matrix in which is embedded a crystalline body (the **crystalloid**) and a spherical body (the **globoid**) (Fig. 19). The globoid consists of a derivative

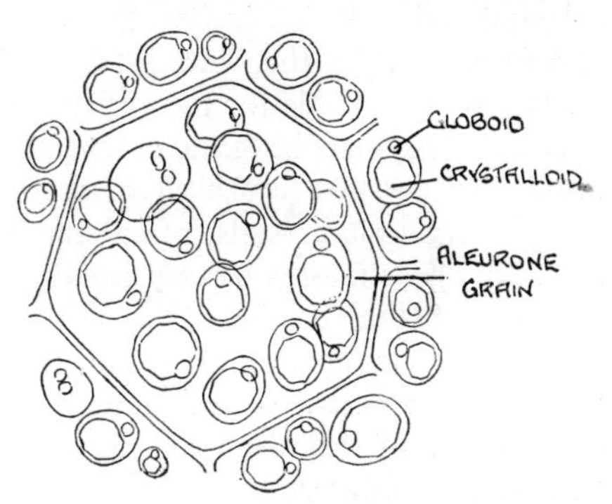

Fig. 19. ALEURONE GRAINS IN ENDOSPERM CELLS OF CASTOR-OIL SEED.

of phosphoric acid, but both the matrix and the crystalloid are proteinaceous.

Fats and Oils. Globules of fat or oil are commonly found in plant tissues, and are particularly prevalent as food reserves in some fruits and seeds, e.g. *Cocos nucifera* (coconut), *Theobroma cacao* (cocoa), and *Myristica fragrans* (nutmeg).

Secretory and Excretory Tissues

Secretion and excretion are both processes by which substances are separated off from the rest of the organism and accumulated or expelled. The term excretion clearly indicates that the substances produced are of no further use to the organism, whereas secretion can include the production of useful substances such as nectar or the digestive juices of insectivorous plants. Since the significance of some substances commonly found in plants is not known, it is not always possible to distinguish between the two processes, so the tissues concerned are here discussed together.

Cells in which by-products of metabolism accumulate are often not distinctive except in their contents. For example, the parenchyma of the pith and cortex of many plants contains crystals of calcium oxalate which has no known metabolic importance except as a form in which the plant disposes of surplus calcium. Calcium oxalate is remarkable for the variety of forms in which the crystals appear. They may be found as single prismatic crystals (Fig. 20, *a*), needle-like crystals (**raphides**) arranged in bundles (Fig. 20, *b*), complex multiple crystals, often star-shaped and known as **druses** (Fig. 20, *c*), or masses of very small crystals resembling clusters of sand grains (Fig. 20, *d*).

Similarly tannins are frequently deposited in isolated cells in various plant parts. These tannin cells may be recognised by the dark colour of their contents, but they are otherwise no different from neighbouring cells.

Alternatively, cells which act as depositories of by-products may be specially enlarged. **Lithocysts** are large cells containing deposits of calcium carbonate, occurring sporadically among epidermal and parenchymatous cells of leaves. Each lithocyst contains an amorphous mass of calcium carbonate known as a **cystolith**, attached to the cell wall by a stalk (Fig. 21).

Other secretory or excretory tissues consist of multicellular structures which may discharge their products externally or internally.

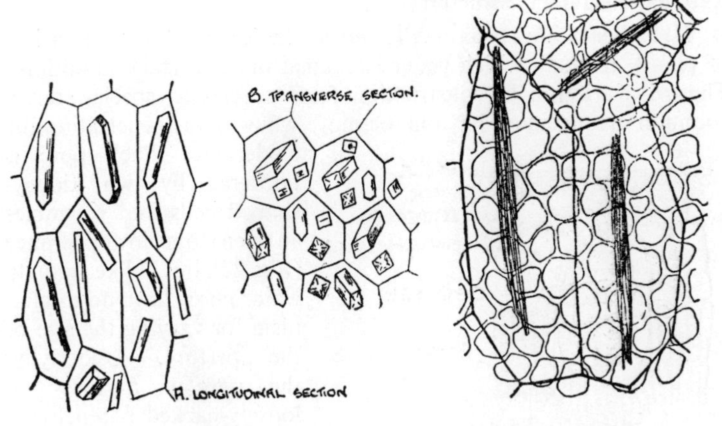

(*a*) Prismatic crystals in the phloem of *Quillaja saponaria*.

(*b*) Raphides in leaf cells of *Circaea lutetiana*.

(*c*) A and B, druses in *Rheum* and *Begonia*.

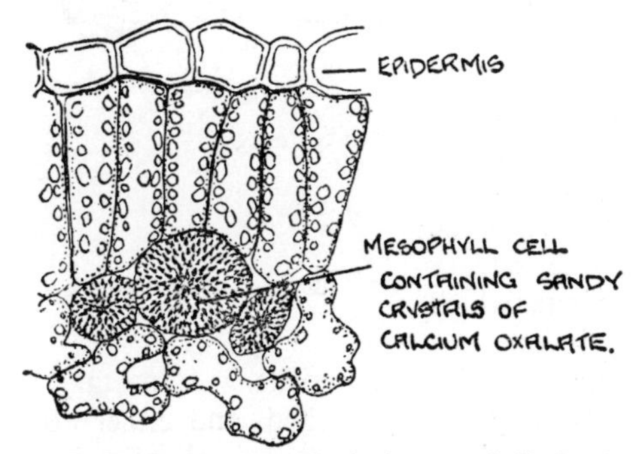

(*d*) Sandy crystals in leaf of *Atropa belladonna*.

Fig. 20. TYPES OF CALCIUM OXALATE CRYSTALS.

External Secretory Structures

Hydathodes are structures found in the leaves of a wide variety of plants, through which water is exuded under certain conditions. There is variation in construction from species to species, but a common arrangement has one or more water pores penetrating the epidermis. Each pore is bordered by two kidney-shaped cells and resembles an open stoma in appearance (Fig. 22), but unlike stomata water pores have no mechanism for varying the size of the aperture. Underlying the pore is a mass of loosely-packed parenchyma called **epithem** in contact with xylem cells which are ultimate branches of the vascular system. Under conditions of plentiful soil water, active growth, and low transpiration, water is secreted from the xylem cells into the intercellular spaces of the epithem and thence through the water pores. This exudation of water, known as **guttation**, is particularly common in plants growing in places where transpiration is restricted by high atmospheric humidity. The water may contain minerals in solution, which become deposited as an incrustation on the leaf surface.

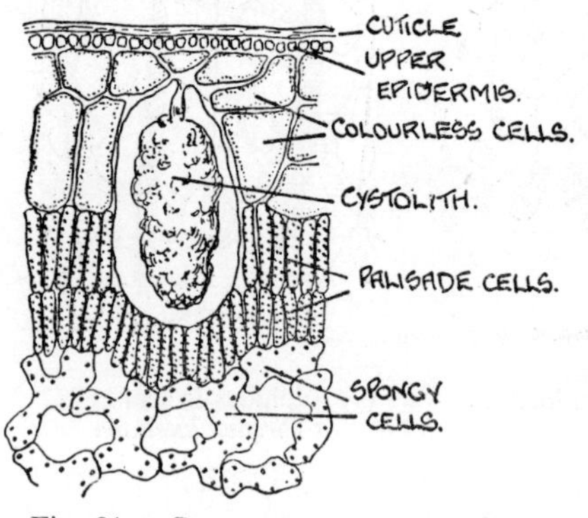

Fig. 21. CYSTOLITH IN LEAF OF *Ficus*.

Nectaries are secretory structures which occur in many insect pollinated plants, either in the flowers or in the vegetative parts. They secrete the sugary fluid known as nectar which is collected by insects and provides an incentive for their visits. A nectary consists of a patch of cells, usually closely packed, and either confined to the epidermal layer or including sub-epidermal cells also. The whole nectary may consist of cells which are roughly cubical or elongated at right angles to the surface, and have dense cytoplasm.

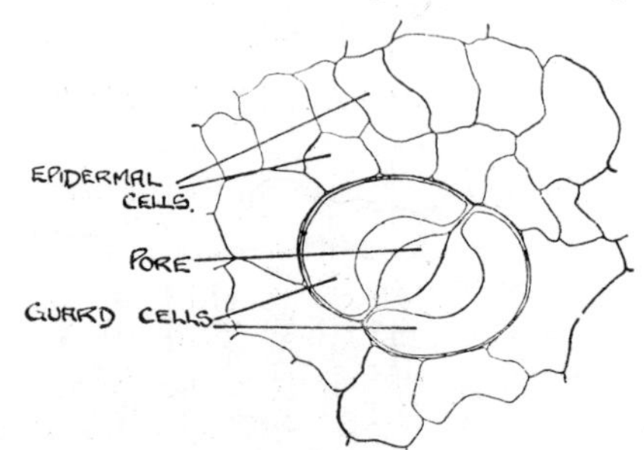

Fig. 22. EPIDERMIS OF *Lobelia* WITH HYDATHODE.

Alternatively the nectary may be more similar to a hydathode, with modified stomata through which the nectar is secreted. Like hydathodes, nectaries are associated with the extremities of the vascular system, but in this case the vascular supply includes or may be confined to phloem cells.

Digestive Glands. Some plants are partly carnivorous and have special devices for catching insects and other small animals, and for extracting nutrients from them. Species of *Drosera* (sundew) and *Pinguicula* (butterwort) are the commonest among the native flora of Britain. In both these genera the leaves bear multicellular outgrowths (Fig. 23 and Plate 10) from which are secreted sticky substances which trap the animals, and proteolytic enzymes which assist in decomposing them (p. 269).

Other secretory outgrowths are referred to in the section on epidermal tissues (p. 33).

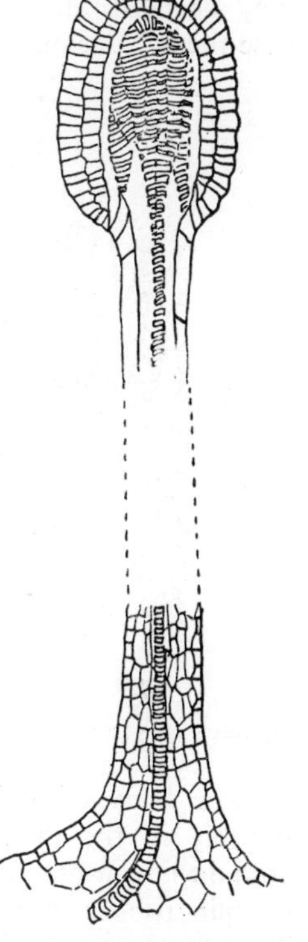

Fig. 23. DIGESTIVE GLAND OF *Drosera*.

Internal Secretory Structures

Laticiferous Tissues. Certain families of flowering plants include species in which the plant body is equipped with a system of tube-like cells each with a thin lining of cytoplasm and containing a fluid called **latex**. This may be watery in appearance [e.g. *Taraxacum* (dandelion)], or milky [e.g. *Euphorbia* spp. (spurges)], or brightly coloured [*e.g.* the vivid orange latex of *Chelidonium* (greater celandine)]. In all cases the latex is an emulsion containing a complex mixture of both organic and inorganic compounds, some of which are useful reserves, and others waste products of metabolism. The latex-containing (or laticiferous) cells may therefore be regarded as combining the functions of storage, conduction, and excretion.

There is considerable variation in cellular construction between the laticiferous tissues of different species, and two principal types are recognised. In one the system consists of separate **latex cells**, each of which may be greatly elongated and branched but still an undivided cell not connected with other latex-containing cells

(Fig. 24, A). During differentiation these cells grow rapidly, and the branches intrude between the cells of surrounding tissues. Latex cells are multinucleate and are therefore examples of **coenocytes** (*i.e.* each cell equivalent to numerous protoplasts within a single wall). In other laticiferous tissues each branched network of tubes is multicellular. In these cases the network extends and branches by connection between distinct cells, rather than by intrusive growth of single cells. The walls where different cells are joined may be perforated or almost completely broken down, in which case the multicellular network is a **latex vessel** (Fig. 24, B).

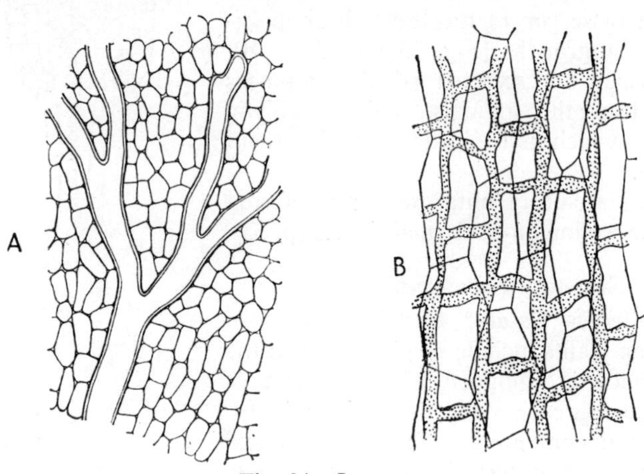

Fig. 24. LATICIFERS.
A, latex cell from stem of *Euphorbia*; B, latex vessel from stem of *Lobelia*.

The latex of a few plants is of great economic importance, notably in the production of rubber. Many laticiferous plants contain no rubber at all, and of the plants whose latex is known to contain rubber, only a small minority have any quantity of it. The major source of natural rubber is *Hevea brasiliensis* (Euphorbiaceae) in which the rubber content of whole latex may be as high as 60 per cent. The latex of *Papaver somniferum* is the source of opium.

Multicellular glands. Some plants contain cavities of considerable size in which secretions accumulate. These glands are classified according to their origins:

(*a*) **Schizogenous** glands are enlarged intercellular spaces enclosed by intact cells which have simply separated during development.

Common examples are the resin canals of some conifers (Fig. 25, A), and the oil-containing **vittae** in the fruits of *Carum* (caraway), *Pimpinella* (aniseed), and other members of the Umbelliferae.

(*b*) **Lysigenous** glands originate from the breakdown of groups of cells, and each cavity is therefore surrounded by the remnants of

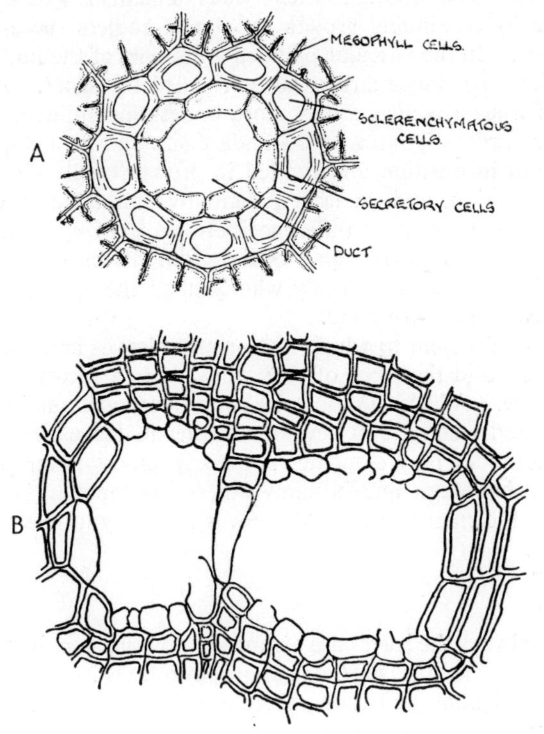

Fig. 25. MULTICELLULAR GLANDS. RESIN-CONTAINING GLANDS. A, *Pinus* (schizogenous); B, *Copaifera* (lysigenous).

these cells (Fig. 25, B). The oil cavities in the leaves of citrus fruits are of this type.

(*c*) **Schizolysigenous** glands begin by separation of intact cells, but further enlargement occurs by cell breakdown. This method of formation is found in the oil cavities of the peel (pericarp) of citrus fruits.

3 THE SHOOT IN VASCULAR PLANTS

One of the most striking characteristics of plants is their tendency to produce by continuing growth an almost endless succession of similar parts. In the vascular plants a great part of the body arises by repetition of a single structural unit called the **shoot**. A shoot consists of a **stem**, which grows more or less indefinitely, bearing **leaves** which ordinarily grow to a standard size and then stop. The leaf is lateral in position and limited in growth, while the stem is central in position, and, at least potentially, unlimited in growth. There is no other constant difference between stem and leaf. It is true that there are usually also obvious differences in shape and structure, but it is unsafe to rely wholly upon these. Some stems look like leaves and *vice versa.*

The part of a stem to which one or more leaves are attached is called a **node**, and the piece of stem between two successive nodes is an **internode**. A **bud** is a shoot with short internodes and immature leaves. If and when a bud develops further its leaves will enlarge and its internodes may elongate, but many shoots never progress beyond the bud stage, and in many others development is concentrated upon the enlargement of the leaves with very little elongation of the stem.

Phyllotaxy

Almost always the leaves are arranged upon the stem in a regular pattern known as the **phyllotaxy** (= **phyllotaxis**). Setting aside some rare and abnormal types, there are three principal forms of phyllotaxy:

1. Verticillate phyllotaxy includes all cases where two or more leaves arise at each node. Ordinarily the leaves at one node are spaced equally round the stem, and every leaf at one node bisects the angle between two of the leaves at the node below (Fig. 26, A). By far the commonest form is that in which each node has two leaves. This is called **decussate** phyllotaxy, but is more commonly expressed by saying that the leaves are **opposite**. Leaves in **whorls** can usually be taken to mean that there are more than two leaves at each node, for in dealing with foliage leaves it is not customary to speak of whorls of two. Opposite leaves are very common, but whorls of leaves are rather rare, and some common plants which appear at first sight to have whorls are not really constructed in that way (*Galium*, p. 93).

2. Distichous phyllotaxy is a type in which each node bears a single leaf, the leaves of a shoot standing in two rows upon the stem, one leaf in one row, and the next in the other. The shoot as a whole has then a flattened form, though in many distichous shoots the two rows of leaves are not exactly in the same plane, but make a blunt V-angle (Fig. 26, B). Distichous phyllotaxy is no more than moderately common, and is rather sharply restricted to particular groups of plants. Unfortunately many writers have failed to distinguish it clearly, merely saying that the leaves are

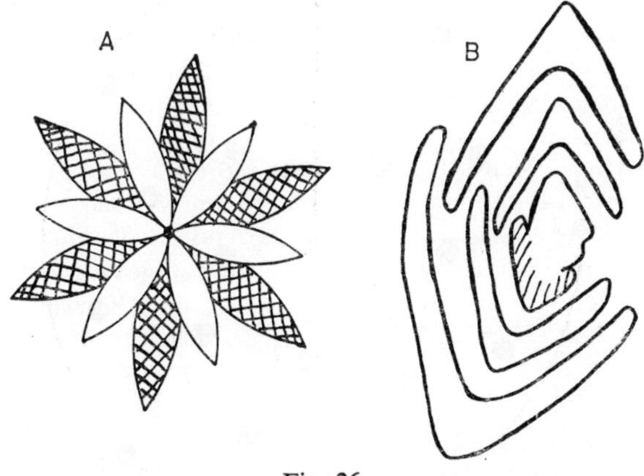

Fig. 26.

A, plan of two successive whorls of leaves, with six leaves in each whorl; B, distichous phyllotaxy as seen in a section through a shoot apex, the shaded area representing a young leaf not completely separated from the stem.

alternate, and thereby confusing it with spiral phyllotaxy (following). Distichous phyllotaxy must be carefully distinguished from the **complanate** condition, in which the free parts of the leaves of a shoot are brought more or less into one plane by twisting and curvature of the parts, regardless of the phyllotactic pattern formed by the bases of the leaves. A yew shoot, which is complanate but not distichous, will make this distinction clear.

3. Spiral phyllotaxy arises when there is one leaf at each node and each leaf follows upon the one before at a fixed angle which is a good deal less than 180°, so that the points of attachment of successive leaves mark out upon the stem a helical (screw-like) line (Fig. 27).

The investigation of spiral phyllotaxy, which is the commonest type of all, offers considerable difficulties. Everything depends upon the exact size of the **angle of divergence** between any two successive leaves. Direct angular measurement is hardly ever possible because the centre of the system cannot be located with sufficient accuracy. The traditional method is to take one leaf as number 0 and to follow the spiral up the stem, numbering the leaves in order, until another leaf is found which stands exactly above 0. If we decide, with a particular specimen, that 8 is exactly above 0,

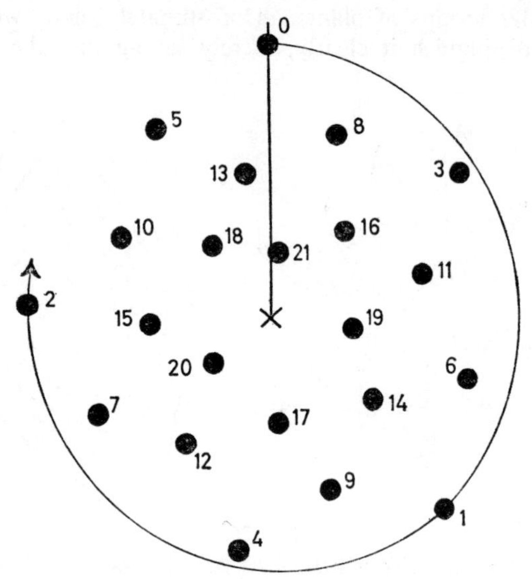

Fig. 27. PLAN OF A SPIRAL SYSTEM OF PHYLLOTAXY, THE DIRECTION OF THE SPIRAL BEING INDICATED BY THE ARROW.

Notice how 3, 5, 8, 13, and 21 oscillate about the radius through 0. Note also the special position of 17, which is half of 34, the next Fibonacci number after 21.

and that in passing from one to the other we have been round the stem three times, then our estimate of the divergence angle will be $\frac{3}{8}$ of 360°, or 135°.

When large quantities of assorted plant material are examined in this way, some numbers, including 3 and 8, occur very frequently among the observations, while others, such as 7 and 11, are rare. The common numbers are members of the **Fibonacci series**, which goes:

$$0, 1, 1, 2, 3, 5, 8, 13, 21, 34, 55, 89, \ldots$$

Each term is the sum of the two preceding terms. Estimates of divergence angle mostly involve fractions formed from **Fibonacci numbers**:

$$\tfrac{1}{2}, \tfrac{1}{3}, \tfrac{2}{5}, \tfrac{3}{8}, \tfrac{5}{13}, \tfrac{8}{21}, \ldots$$

This fraction-series has a very simple and important mathematical property. The fractions are successive approximations to a final or limiting value. Upon calculating the Fibonacci fractions as decimals it will be found that the values converge fairly rapidly, so that the difference between, say, $\frac{21}{55}$ and $\frac{34}{89}$ is very small indeed. It can be shown that the final value is actually $\frac{1}{2}(3 - \sqrt{5})$, which is 0·3819660.... or, expressed in degrees, for we are concerned with fractions of a circle, it is $137\frac{1}{2}°$ very nearly.

Many writers have taken their estimates of divergence angle to be accurate, and have reported one shoot as having "$\frac{3}{8}$ phyllotaxy", another as having "$\frac{2}{5}$ phyllotaxy", and so on. Most of these differences certainly are not real. If a shoot has long flexible internodes the observer is in a very bad position for the detection of small angular discrepancies, and is likely to rest content with some early Fibonacci fraction such as $\frac{3}{8}$ or even $\frac{2}{5}$. If the internodes are short and stiff, then these fractions will be visibly unsatisfactory, and the observer will pass on to some later (and therefore more accurate) fraction such as $\frac{13}{34}$. The presumption must be that in most cases of spiral phyllotaxy the divergence angle is very near indeed to the final value of the Fibonacci fraction-series. It is not yet fully understood why plants should behave in this way, but the matter is discussed further at p. 148.

The surface of a stem is sometimes smooth and featureless but usually there are distinct ridges, and sometimes lines of hairs or bands of colouration, running downwards from the base of each leaf, and forming a pattern which is closely related to the phyllotaxy.

Branching of the Stem

All the higher plants branch, one shoot giving rise to others, and these very often branching again to give shoots of a still higher order. It is a peculiarity of the seed plants, for which no satisfactory explanation has ever been offered, that branches are almost always **axillary**, arising in the angle or **axil** between a leaf and its parent stem. This relationship is often a powerful aid in the identification of organs. Upon observing a branch one looks for its **axillant** leaf, and anything in the right place is usually taken to *be* a leaf, whatever its appearance; conversely, a structure which stands in the axil of a leaf is presumably a shoot. This geometrical relationship does not extend to the lower plants; in ferns, for instance, most branches are not axillary at all. It is important also not to over-simplify the situation. There is no constant one-to-one relationship between leaf and branch. A leaf may have no axillary branch, or it may have a whole cluster of them (p. 137). The rule is merely that branches do not ordinarily arise anywhere else than in a leaf-axil.

Parts of the Leaf

Most plants produce more than one kind of leaf, and it is convenient to make a distinction between **foliage leaves**, which are photosynthetic and usually the most elaborate leaves present, and **cataphylls**, in which photosynthesis is at most a secondary function.

The parts commonly seen in a foliage leaf are the **lamina**, which is the flat green portion, the **petiole**, which is the stalk, and the leaf-base. The leaf-base may be developed in several alternative ways. In a few families of plants there is a **pulvinus** (plural, **pulvini**), which is a kind of swollen joint (see French or runner bean). In many plants the leaf-base is expanded into a sheath which is wrapped round the stem and which is sometimes of great size. Another common feature is the production of **stipules**, which are projections from the sides of the leaf-base. Most stipulate leaves have one stipule on each side, but there may be more.

Any leaf in which the lamina is a single expanse of tissue is a **simple leaf**, no matter how complicated its outline may be. A **compound leaf** is one in which the lamina is divided into several portions (**leaflets**) held together by stalks. It is important to distinguish compound leaves from specialised lateral shoot systems. Basically there are two ways of compounding a leaf. In the **pinnate** form (Fig. 28, A) the petiole continues as a **rachis** upon which there stand two rows of leaflets, and usually also a terminal leaflet. In **palmate** leaves (Fig. 28, B) several leaflets stand in a fan-like manner upon the end of the petiole. Higher degrees of compounding can occur. A **bipinnate** leaf, for instance (Fig. 28, C), is one in which each lateral unit or **pinna** is itself a pinnate assembly of **pinnules**. Although the rule of axillary branching does not apply to the branching of a rachis, the relationship between leaflet and rachis is in some respects similar to that between leaf and stem. Some leaves even have little projections called **stipels,** which are to a leaflet as stipules are to a leaf.

The Description of Leaf-shapes

The shapes of leaves are important in the recognition of plants, and a very large vocabulary of special descriptive terms has grown up. This technical language is convenient in the routine identification of specimens, but it leads to no scientific principle of any importance. We need only take a few examples to see how the terms are defined and applied.

Some words describe the general shape of a whole leaf or leaflet. The leaf shown in Fig. 28, D, for instance, is **lanceolate**. This is the shape of the head of a lance, and must have a sharp point. The curvature of the sides diminishes upwards until they become almost straight, and the widest part is well below the middle. Fig. 28, E

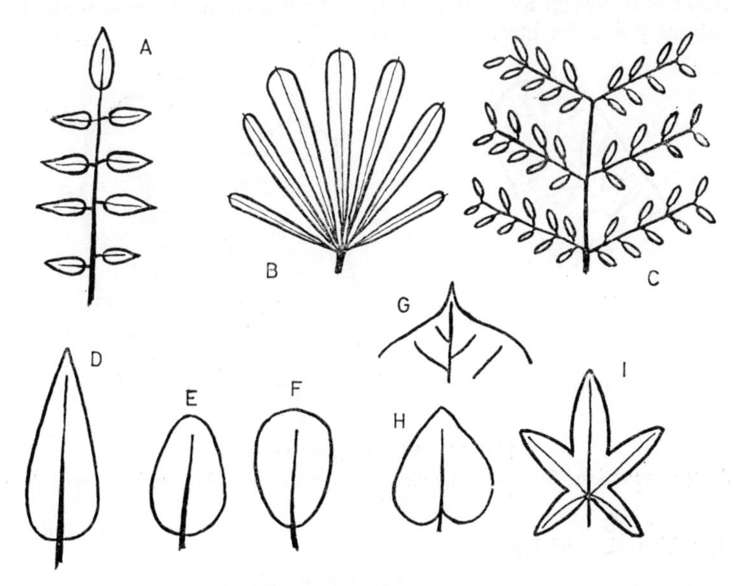

Fig. 28. VARIOUS SHAPES OF LEAF.
A, pinnate; B, palmate; C, bipinnate; D, lanceolate; E, ovate; F, obovate; G, acuminate; H, cordate; I, palmatifid.

shows an **ovate** leaf, shaped like the side view of an egg; its lower part is very much like the lanceolate form, but the upper part is rounded. An ovate leaf is understood to be attached by its wider end, but the prefix **ob-**, which can be attached to a variety of words, has the effect of turning things upside-down, so that an obovate leaf will be as in Fig. 28, F.

Other terms apply only to a specific part of the leaf. An **acuminate** leaf has its tip drawn out into a sharp point, as in Fig. 28, G, but this tells us nothing about its lower part, which would have to be separately described. A few words are variable in their application.

A **cordate** leaf, for example, is shaped like a conventional heart (Fig. 28, H) but one also encounters such expressions as "leaf cordate at base", in which case the upper part may not be like a heart at all.

For some of the commoner conditions there are many alternative forms of expression. Leaves like that shown in Fig. 28, I are palmately lobed, palmatifid, palmatisect, or palmatipartite. At one time these words had slightly different meanings, representing different degrees of lobing and dissection of the leaf. The modern trend is to sweep away these fine distinctions and to deal with the subtler points by mathematical analysis.

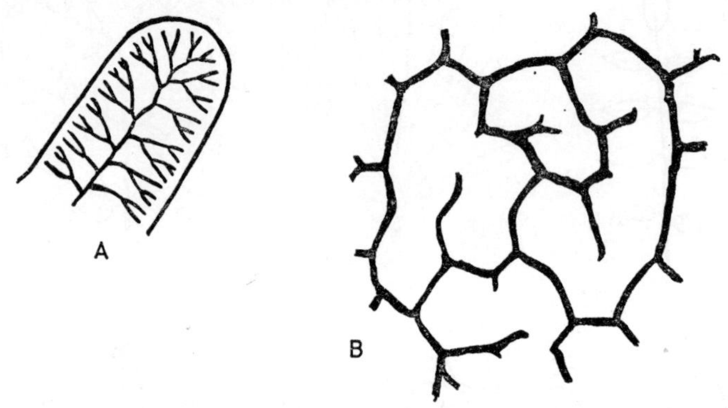

Fig. 29. VENATION OF LEAVES.
A, open venation; B, large-scale view of the finest veins in a leaf with reticulate venation.

The Venation of Leaves

The lamina of a leaf contains a number of vascular strands known as **veins**, **ribs**, or **nerves**, and collectively making up the **venation** of the leaf. Venation may be studied by holding a leaf up to the light, or by examining a skeletonised leaf. In either case the finest strands are liable to be overlooked. The larger veins often project upon the lower surface, and one of them may be specially prominent as a midrib, but the finer veins run in the normal thickness of the lamina and may only be revealed by anatomical investigation. In **open** venation, seen mainly in ferns, the veins branch but do not join up again (Fig. 29, A). In **reticulate** venation (Fig. 29, B) the smaller veins form a network, usually with a large number of blind endings. In **parallel** venation the greater part of the lamina is traversed by strands of equal status running parallel to each other, and linked at intervals by fine cross-connections.

Although there is a close relationship between the venation of a leaf and its general shape there is a strong tendency for the principal veins, instead of running out to the edge, to curve round, and form loops some distance from it. Only rather exceptionally is the relationship between shape and venation as direct as in clover and elm, where the main lateral veins run straight to the edge and influence the details of the outline.

Life-form, Habit, and Duration

It is not enough to consider the structure of the individual shoot; in the bodies of most plants we have to deal with a **shoot system** which has characteristics of its own quite separate from those of the units of which it is composed. A shoot system may grow straight upwards, or sprawl along the ground, or burrow into the soil. It may have short internodes or very long ones, many lateral branches or hardly any. Some shoots live a thousand years, others only six weeks. In the actual business of living these things are probably much more important than differences in phyllotaxy or the presence of stipules.

Among plants it so happens that resemblances in general shape do not at all reliably indicate close family connections. In this respect the higher plants are different from the higher animals; a word like "fish" implies a way of life and also a family relationship, but a word like "tree" carries only the one message without the other. This is developed further at p. 386.

When the shape of a plant is considered in the broadest possible way, just to see what position it occupies in the landscape, we are dealing with its **life-form**. Expressions like "large tree" and "small shrub" are definitions of life-forms, and if made more precise ("trees over fifteen metres", etc.) they will do very well for purposes of vegetation survey.

The general appearance of a plant, considered mainly with a view to recognising it, is its **habit**. The idea of habit includes everything which might be considered under life-form, and much more besides, everything in fact which will make an immediate impression upon the eye of a botanist. In describing the habit it will be necessary to say whether the leaves are opposite or alternate, simple or compound, stipulate or exstipulate, because these are obvious and essential parts of the mental picture by which the plant is recognised. But features revealed only by chemical test or anatomical examination are no part of the habit, no matter how important they may be.

One important aspect of a plant, which enters into every assessment of habit or life-form, is its **duration**, the length of life of the individual. The recognised duration categories are as follows:

1. Annuals are plants which naturally die after less than one year of independent life, survival of the race depending entirely on the production of seed.

2. Ephemerals are annuals with a very short life, sometimes as little as six or eight weeks from seed to seed.

3. Biennials are plants which devote their first year of life to the development of a massive body with large reserves of nutritive materials, and then flower and die in the second year. In cultivation, where growth is artificially accelerated, it is common for some individuals of a nominally biennial species such as sugar-beet to "bolt", that is to flower in the first season. **Bolting** is hardly ever seen in the wild.

4. Perennials are plants which exceed in varying degrees the life-span of the biennial. In many of them the individual appears to be potentially immortal. Perennials vary in their flowering behaviour. There is a small class of **monocarpic** perennials (mostly monocotyledons, mostly in warm climates) in which each individual flowers only once, at the end of its life. A monocarpic perennial in fact behaves like a biennial with a longer period, which may be as much as ninety years. Most perennials, however, flower every year once they have reached maturity; there are great differences in the age at which flowering commences.

Woody and Herbaceous Plants

Although the distinction is not absolutely sharp it is useful to draw a line between **woody** plants, in which there is an upright stem rising well above the soil and persisting for a term of years, and **herbaceous** plants, in which no stem rises far above the soil except as a temporary structure, to serve for one season only.

All annuals and biennials are herbaceous, and there are also many herbaceous perennials or perennial herbs. Woody plants are always perennial, and this is so obvious that one rarely talks about "woody perennials". The woody plants are divided into **trees**, in which each individual has a single erect stem or trunk, and **shrubs**, in which several woody stems rise from the surface of the soil. Again this is only a rough distinction; the behaviour of a woody plant can almost always be modified by pruning, and some species are naturally variable in their shape.

Seasonal Growth

Even in an equatorial climate, where physical conditions are favourable for the growth of plants all the year round, uniform continuous growth is rarely maintained for long. Physiological changes in the plant itself tend to cause distinct interruptions, periods when growth stops or is at least very much reduced in tempo. Resting periods often follow reproductive activity, and in the absence of any distinction between the seasons of the year even different shoots of the same individual may take their rests at different times.

Resting periods in tropical plants often do not involve any conspicuous structural variation in the shoot. A palm, for instance, will sometimes be producing leaves in rapid succession, and sometimes it will stand for months without producing any leaves at all. But all the leaves will be alike, and on looking at the trunk of the tree there may be no way at all of drawing a boundary between the nodes and internodes formed in one period of growth and those resulting from the next. In regions where the weather shows seasonal fluctuations, however, most plants show a definite seasonal organisation of the shoot. Usually the stem apex passes the unfavourable season as a **resting bud** enclosed in cataphylls. There is therefore a steady alternation between the production of foliage leaves, for photosynthesis in the good season, and cataphylls, for bud protection in the bad season (Fig. 30).

There is often a very high degree of preparation for the events of the growing season. The degree of anticipation naturally varies in different cases; investigations in October or November, for instance, will show that in buds of horse-chestnut or laburnum the foliage leaves are well-developed, with distinct leaflets, while the flowers, though recognisable as such, are extremely immature. A hyacinth bulb, on the other hand, contains at the same time of year fully formed flowers with pollen-grains almost ready for dispersal. This pre-packing of organs is of the greatest biological importance. It makes possible extremely rapid growth in spring, this growth amounting in some cases to little more than the expansion of tissues which already have their full complement of cells.

To sustain rapid spring growth a plant must have **reserve materials**. In most woody plants these are stored in the parenchymatous tissues of ordinary stems, but in herbaceous perennials storage often proceeds to such an extent as to require obvious enlargement of particular organs, stems, cataphylls, or roots as the case may be. Reserves are often built up well in advance; a daffodil bulb, for instance, has completed its reserves by early August.

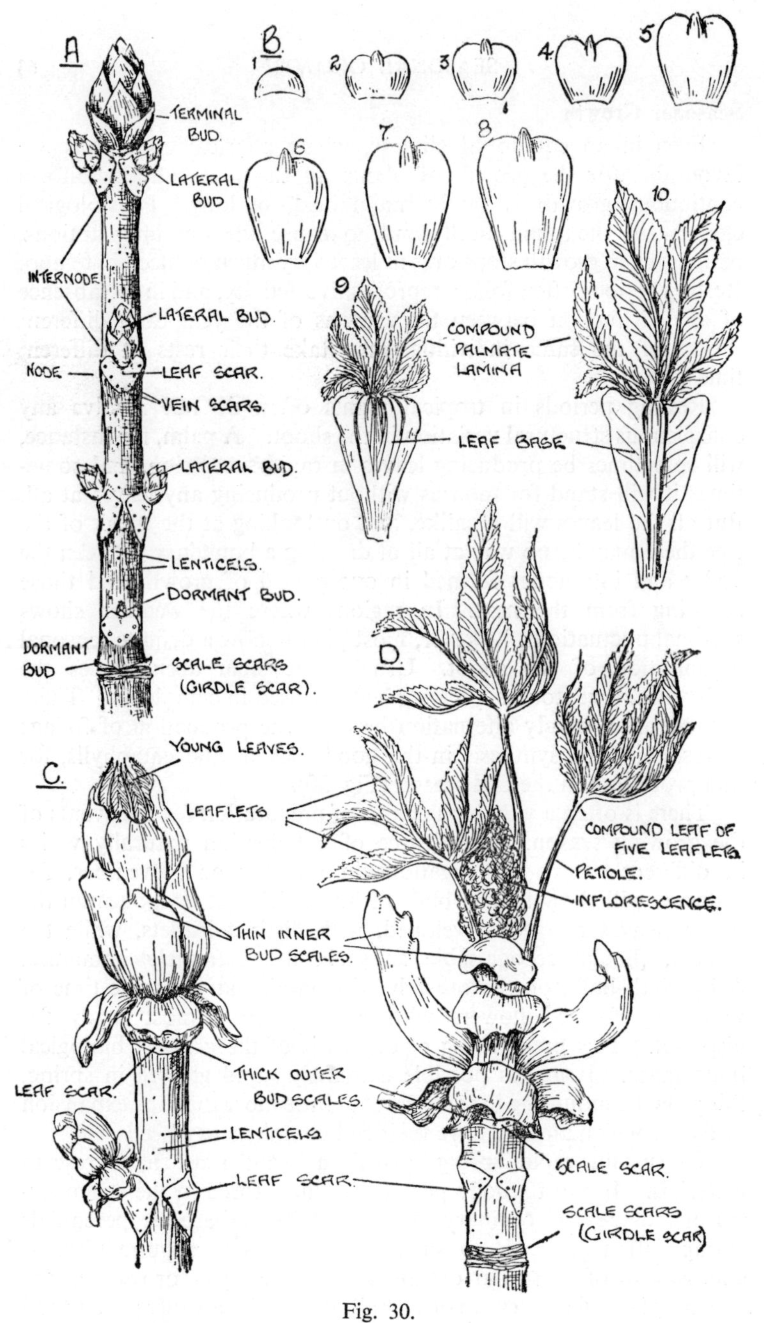

Fig. 30.
A, twig of horse-chestnut; B, terminal bud dissected to show transition from bud scales to foliage leaves; C, bursting bud; D, opened bud.

PLATE 3

Above: PNEUMATOPHORES OF *Avicennia* EXPOSED AT LOW TIDE.

Below left: "TRUNK" OF *Ficus infectoria* FORMED BY NATURAL GRAFTING OF AERIAL ROOTS.

Below right: AERIAL ROOTS OF BANYAN (*Ficus benghalensis*).

PLATE 4

LONGITUDINAL SECTION THROUGH THE APEX OF A SHOOT OF *Zea* (MAIZE). The stem apex appears as a small dome in the centre of the picture, and is flanked and overarched by young leaves in various stages of development. The solid stem at the lower edge of the picture contains several vascular bundles which appear darker than the ground-tissue. There is no cambial activity, but the mature stem is much wider than the apical dome.

Every student should examine a series of plants differing in their behaviour relative to the passage of the seasons. At one extreme are the bulbs, where the activity of one season results in the production of a resting structure (really a giant bud) which may contain *everything*, except water, which is required for the full development of foliage and flowers in the following year. Near the other extreme we may place plants like ivy and *Fuchsia*, which do little more than grow straight on until the weather stops them, without making any visible preparations for winter at all.

The Shoot System in Woody Plants

In woody plants an internode may survive, barring accidents, as long as the plant itself. Usually each piece of stem becomes thicker as it gets older, and this process of growth is associated with changes in the surface tissues. At an early stage, within the first season in many plants, there comes a change in colour, often from green to brown or grey, resulting from the death of the surface cells (p. 105). At the same time **lenticels** are formed, appearing on the surface as warts or pustules and serving as channels for the movement of gases (p. 106). The twig now has a **bark**, though only a thin one. When the leaves are shed, which happens at the end of the first season in **deciduous** plants and after no more than two or three seasons in **evergreens**, the positions of the leaves continue to be marked by **leaf scars**, of which each species has its characteristic design, and also by the axillary buds.

For a few years the pattern of leaf-scars, lenticels, and axillary buds remains recognisable, but in time the bark increases in thickness, coarsens in texture, and undergoes processes of breakage and weathering. The bark of an old stem is a fissured, scaly, or sometimes fibrous mass from the outer surface of which all leaf-scars and dormant buds have long since disappeared. The surface markings of young twigs offer a very complete record of the plant's growth. It is often possible to work back three or four years, dating each leaf, bud, or scar to the season in which it was produced.

Generally the stem apex of a woody plant is capable of growing on almost indefinitely year after year. This is **monopodial** growth. For various reasons, however, the stem apex may cease to be available, and then any further growth of the system can only come from the lateral buds. This replacement of the main apex by a lateral one is **sympodial** growth. Apart from accidental damage or deliberate pruning there are two principal ways in which sympodial growth occurs in woody plants. In some species which are monopodial as long as their activity is vegetative, the formation of an

inflorescence or flower-cluster puts an end to the growth of the stem which produces it. This can be seen in horse-chestnut, where the inflorescence is terminal, and growth is continued sympodially, usually by a pair of branches with a big saddle-shaped inflorescence-scar in the fork. A few woody plants, however, seem to be inherently incapable of maintaining monopodial growth even in the absence of flowering. The only common instance of this is *Tilia*, in which, at the end of each year's growth, the terminal bud is always lost, growth being continued by the axillary bud of the last foliage leaf of the year.

The Tree Habit

A seedling normally starts life with a single upright stem. If this situation be maintained, and if the plant lives long enough, there can be only one result—the plant will become a tree. The tree habit is much more common than a study of British plants would suggest.

The exact shape of a tree is highly variable, and even in a single species astonishing differences can be produced by varying the distance between one tree and its neighbours, by wind action, or by artificial pruning. In the early stages of growth a tree will usually produce some lateral branches, which are necessarily formed near the ground. On a tree which stands alone these branches often persist, so that the fully grown plant has a canopy of foliage sweeping right down to the ground. Large trees in ornamental grounds often show this well, but where grazing animals are admitted the foliage is often cut off sharply at the height to which they can reach. Trees growing close together tend to lose their lower branches through the effects of shading, and have tall, bare, unbranched trunks. A similar condition is brought about in garden trees by careful pruning and training in early life.

The form of a tree is determined to a great extent by the angle which the branches make with the main stem. At one extreme is the **fastigiate habit**, in which the branches stand almost upright, giving a very tall and narrow crown, and at the other extreme is the **weeping habit** in which the branches spread widely and hang down. The angle of branch growth is genetically controlled, and a number of common trees which are naturally of intermediate form can be obtained in fastigiate or weeping varieties.

Trees vary also in their degree of branching. Most European species branch over and over again to produce enormous numbers of slender twigs carrying rather small leaves. In warmer climates with high humidity the trees, on the average, branch much less, their twigs are stouter, and their leaves larger. The limiting case, with a single unbranched stem carrying a crown of very large leaves, is especially characteristic of palms and tree-ferns, but is also found in a few gymnosperms and dicotyledons.

In addition to the normal trunk and crown of branches, some tree species are capable of producing other shoots. **Sucker shoots** arise directly from roots; the ability to form shoots from roots is quite uncommon, but in some poplars and elms the suckers are numerous enough to make dense thickets about the base of the trunks. The foliage of suckers is often very different from that of the main crown, to the extent in some cases of looking like a different species altogether. **Epicaulic shoots** arise from the bark of a mature trunk or large branch. This is a much more common effect. In European trees it leads usually to the production of brushwood partially clothing the trunk, as in many elms and limes. In *Gleditschia* (to be seen in most botanic gardens and some parks) the epicaulic shoots form spine systems, quite different from the foliage shoots. Epicaulic shoots attain their greatest importance, however, in many trees of warm climates where they are sometimes the principal means of producing flowers and fruit. A cocoa-pod, for instance, hangs from a stalk which comes straight out through the bark of the trunk of the tree. As a mature trunk has lost its original surface tissues every epicaulic shoot is necessarily formed from internal tissues, and bursts its way out in a manner more typical of roots.

In a small proportion of trees the root system is modified in ways which significantly alter the form of the plant. In Europe we often see at the base of a trunk a small buttress-like projection which merges into a large root exposed upon the surface of the soil. In some trees of tropical forests this effect is greatly exaggerated; the buttresses may be quite thin and plank-like, but with an outward projection of several feet. At the base of the stem in some plants, even herbaceous ones such as groundsel and maize, roots may emerge a little above ground level and grow down obliquely into the soil. In tropical areas subject to periodic flooding some of the woody plants (*e.g.* mangroves) produce **stilt roots** (or prop roots) of great size, and sometimes the lower part of the stem is lost, so that the plant is entirely supported by a great cage of roots. In some swamp-dwelling trees the root system forms **pneumatophores** (Plate 3). These are portions of root, sometimes an upturned tip but often a sharp upward U-bend, which rise above the water and act as channels of gaseous exchange. The anatomical structure of a pneumatophore is essentially that of a giant lenticel.

The genus *Ficus*, which includes the banyans, is remarkable for the vigour of its roots, which not only grow very actively but have the power of grafting together wherever they touch (Plate 3). These are the roots which are seen in so many pictures in the act of engulfing ruined temples, etc. Often the plant begins life as an epiphyte (p. 622), growing perhaps in the axil of a palm-leaf many feet above ground. Soon thread-like roots descend to the soil, become thick and woody, and graft together into a cage which ultimately strangles the host palm and forms a false trunk standing in its place. Other roots grow down from the branches, and so a whole grove of the banyan is formed from a single seed (Plate 3).

The Shrub Habit

A shrub is strictly a plant with several woody stems rising from the soil, though in common speech dwarf tree-forms are often treated as shrubs. Although some shrubs (*e.g.* bamboos) have a definite rhizome system (p. 70), the shrubby condition usually arises in an almost accidental manner. In most species all that happens is that some of the lower branches come to lie along the surface of the soil, mainly because of the weight of their own upper portions, and there take root, and are gradually covered over with soil and litter. Where this tendency to bury and root the bases of lateral branches is at all pronounced it naturally leads to a gradual spread of the plant. All true shrubs spread to some extent.

Because the stems of any truly shrubby species necessarily produce roots with great facility, most of these plants are readily propagated by cuttings, which is not necessarily the case with trees. Also, any drooping branch which touches the soil is likely to take root, even at a distance from the main stock. Vegetative spread by rooting at the tips of arching branches is common in brambles.

Longevity in Woody Plants

An old gnarled tree presents an appearance of great antiquity, and particular individuals, especially oaks, are often linked in local tradition with historical personages from Julius Caesar onwards. In reality the greatest known ages (obtained by counting growth rings, p. 100) for British trees do not greatly exceed 200 years, and we may safely say that the great majority of our largest trees lie in the age-range 150-250 years. Contrary to the popular impression, the oak is probably not a particularly long-lived tree. The very great ages sometimes assigned to churchyard yews are estimates based on the diameter of the trunk; people making such calculations are often unaware that in this species it is common for several stems to fuse into a single trunk.

The primary cause of death in British trees is almost always storm damage. A large branch is broken so as to expose the **heartwood**, a central core which is completely dead even in the living tree; the heartwood is attacked by fungi and decays, and the whole tree becomes hollow, and eventually collapses. This sequence of events, once started, is quite automatic. The British climate is therefore unfavourable to the attainment of great ages in three distinct ways: tree growth is rapid, winds are strong, and the high humidity encourages the growth of fungi. Ages of 4,000 years and more have been reliably determined in coniferous forests of America, where trees of compact form (*Sequoia gigantea*, the "big tree") meet a climate in which gales are rare, and also in semi-desert areas where the decisive factor seems to be an extremely low growth rate.

In shrubby species the life of an individual stem is often rather limited, but the spreading clump as a whole may be potentially immortal.

Herbaceous Plants

In annuals and ephemerals there is little elaboration of the shoot system, a very moderate degree of branching usually being sufficient for the production of leaves and flowers. These plants must constantly re-establish themselves from seed, and flourish only where a bare soil surface is available year after year.

Biennials form a single central tuber which carries over reserve materials from the photosynthesis of the first season to the reproductive activities of the second. The tuber is usually an expansion of the main root or **tap-root**, as in carrot and parsnip, though some stem tissue is also involved. The biennial habit is quite rare, and almost confined to some groups of dicotyledons (*Umbelliferae*, thistles) which grow in grassland. The efforts of growers and breeders have brought about great increases in the size of tuber in the cultivated biennials, and have induced a similar process of tuberisation in plants like radish which are not naturally biennials at all.

Most herbaceous plants, however, are perennials. In many of these the shoot system is not highly specialised. Some common garden plants (*Sedum*, saxifrages, pinks, *Aubrietia*) merely sprawl upon the surface of the soil, rooting casually in the manner already seen in shrubs. Many of these plants are evergreens, with little seasonal variation in the behaviour of their shoots, and they cannot be sharply separated from the dwarf shrubs.

In many perennial herbs, however, the permanent part of the body assumes a more distinctive form, and may indeed be so greatly modified as to present considerable difficulties of interpretation. To the more specialised variants such names as "bulb" and "tuber" have been applied, often not very consistently. There are two requirements which must be met in every case, the need to provide a shoot apex which will produce the next season's foliage, and the need to store reserve materials. Provision for **vegetative propagation**, that is for spreading the plant across country and multiplying the total bulk of living material, is less fundamental. In many species vegetative propagation is only of limited extent; in others it has become one of the main functions of the shoot system.

Very few herbaceous plants can produce shoot buds from their roots. A good example is the common British thistle *Cirsium arvense*, which produces sucker shoots very freely and thereby achieves both the perennial state and a most efficient means of vegetative propagation, whereas all the other British thistles are biennials spreading only by seed.

Ordinarily buds can arise only from pre-existing shoots, the simplest possible type of herbaceous perennial being then a body like that of a biennial but with a greater expectation of life. This is a **rootstock** (an unfortunate name, for it consists largely of stem), a short stout body standing almost upright, with its upper end flush with the surface of the soil. If monopodial, as most of them are, a rootstock constantly tends to grow out of the ground. The typical rootstock, lacking any mechanism for depth-control, and almost totally ineffective as a means of vegetative propagation, is not a very common type of construction. Examples may be seen in *Primula*, *Geum*, and some ferns.

Any tendency for the underground stem to turn over and grow horizontally affords an opportunity for the plant, by producing longer internodes, to spread rapidly. It also simplifies the problem of depth-control, though horizontal growth is not in itself a complete solution; underground shoots are perfectly capable of maintaining their proper distance below a sloping soil surface (p. 292).

Any underground shoot which is roughly horizontal may be called a **rhizome**; this is by far the commonest type of perennating structure in herbaceous plants. Most rhizomes are subterranean, but a few lie in the soil surface like that of many *Iris* species. It is perfectly practicable to work a rhizome system upon a monopodial plan, the leaves and flowers being carried aloft either upon their own individual stalks or upon temporary lateral branches. This, however, is not the commonest arrangement. Most rhizomes are sympodial; each shoot apex spends the early part of its life adding to the length of the rhizome and then turns sharply upwards to become an aerial shoot, the rhizome being continued by a lateral bud (Fig. 31). No matter whether the single line of advance be a simple monopodial shoot or a compound sympodial assembly, a rhizome usually produces enough additional branches to form a spreading system advancing in all directions.

Rhizomes produce cataphylls, which may be important in the protection of the apex but which are usually of little biological importance from any other point of view, and roots, which are sometimes generally distributed, sometimes more or less strictly confined to the nodes. There is a shifting balance between the

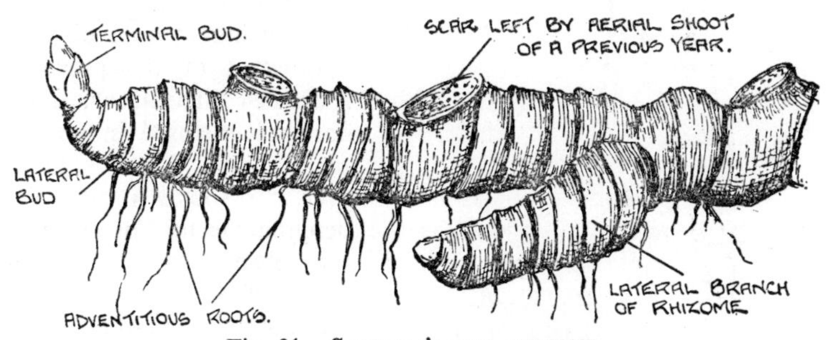

Fig. 31. SOLOMON'S SEAL RHIZOME.

elongation of the internode and its enlargement as a storage organ. Some rhizomes are short and stout, others long and slender, and in some rhizome systems there is a differentiation into distinct parts. The potato is an example (Fig. 32); each tuber is the swollen end of a thin rhizome. In a very few cases the leaves are longer-lived, and more important, than the common type of rhizome cataphyll. In *Lathraea* the rhizome is covered with fleshy scales, each containing a cavity in which there are glandular hairs. The significance of this structure is obscure, but it may be related to the fact that the plant is a total parasite (p. 268). There are also cases, of which *Lathraea* does not appear to be one, in which a scaly rhizome stores part of its reserves in the cataphylls. Another variant is found in the monopodial rhizome of *Oxalis acetosella*, where there is storage in the persistent bases of discarded foliage leaves.

The diversity of structure and behaviour in rhizomes makes nonsense of any attempt to define precise categories of perennating organ. Short, sloping, little-branched rhizomes intergrade with the typical rootstocks, and some scaly rhizomes cannot be sharply separated from the bulbs. Where a rhizome system concentrates the storage of reserves into short thick portions of stem these units are conventionally known as corms or stem-tubers. The truth is that all these structures form a great continuous field of variation, in which the commoner types of rhizome occupy a central position.

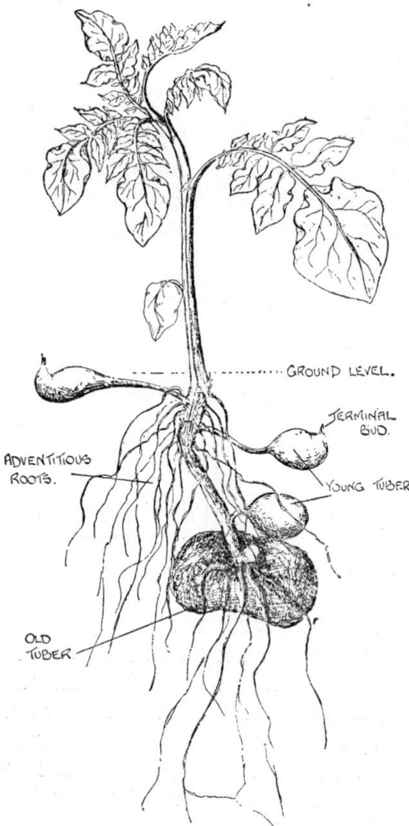

Fig. 32. FORMATION OF NEW TUBERS IN POTATO.

In a **corm** (Figs. 33, 34) the reserves are stored in stem tissue. The examples commonly used in teaching are sympodial, each new corm being formed directly upon that of the previous season. Moreover, each corm is enclosed in papery scale-leaves. There is, however, no sound reason for denying the title of corm to the naked monopodial stem-tuber of *Cyclamen*, and in montbretia and some other plants each new corm arises at the tip of a long rhizome.

In a **bulb** (Fig. 35) most of the reserves are in cataphylls. It is possible to draw a distinction between tunicated bulbs (onion, daffodil, etc.) in which there is an outer papery covering, and scaly bulbs, like those of lilies, in which the storage cataphylls are naked. Most bulbs are sympodial. Sometimes the scales are complete cataphylls which have no foliage function; sometimes they are bases of foliage leaves, the upper parts of which have been lost. Some bulbs have scales of both types.

It is in bulbs, and in the more compact kinds of corm, that the problem of depth-adjustment becomes most acute. Many of these

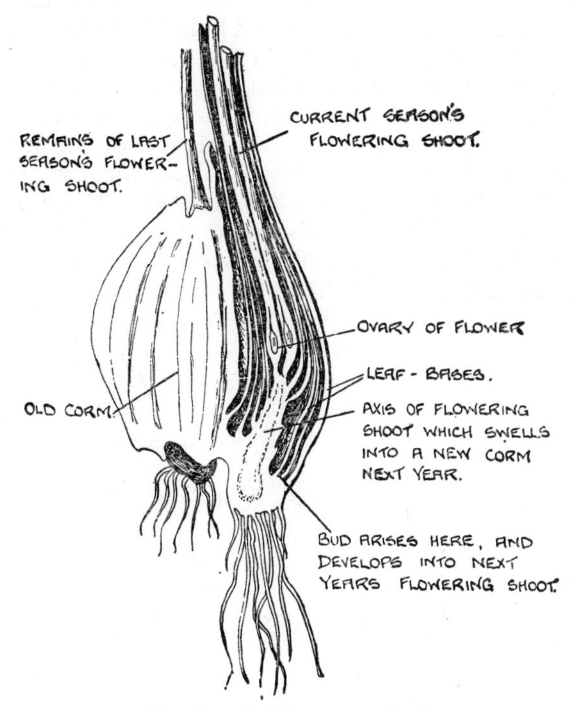

Fig. 33. *Colchicum autumnale.*
Longitudinal section.

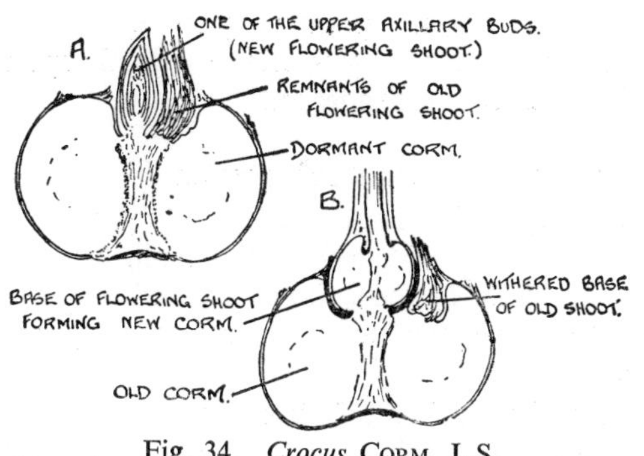

Fig. 34. *Crocus* CORM, L.S.
A, dormant; B, at time of flowering.

plants go much deeper than the average rhizome, and as the seedling always has to start at the surface it is a little difficult to see how the shoot apex ever gets down there in the first place. In fact, the behaviour of young plants is often very remarkable; a typical device is for a leaf-axil to be extended downwards in a deep pocket, a tubular extension which burrows into the soil carrying the axillary bud in its closed lower end. This is called a **dropper**. Once the working depth has been reached it is maintained by the action of contractile roots (Fig. 36). These are quite different from the normal roots and are present only in small numbers. Contractile roots anchor themselves in the soil and then shorten, so counter-

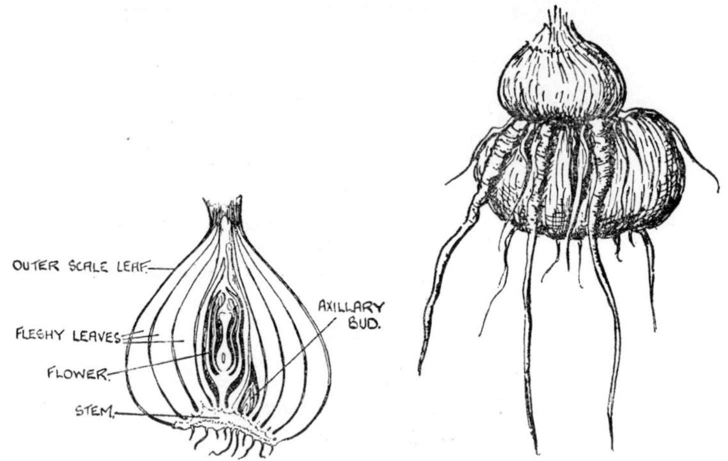

Fig. 35. *Tulip:* BULB IN LONGITUDINAL SECTION.

Fig. 36. CORM SHOWING CONTRACTILE ROOTS.

acting any tendency for the plant to grow upwards. Something similar goes on in the upper parts of a few highly specialised rootstocks, notably that of the dandelion.

Special Methods of Vegetative Propagation

Vegetative propagation is often effectively provided for in ways which are really only incidental to the main business of winter survival. Some shoot systems, however, embody special features which appear to be concerned with vegetative propagation and nothing else.

Stolons (sometimes called **offsets** or **runners**) are branches which grow horizontally above the soil surface and ultimately become rooted at a distance. Examples are seen in strawberry (Fig. 37),

Ajuga, *Ranunculus repens*, etc. Unlike most rhizomes, stolons usually show no tendency to swell or to store large reserves; elongation is the predominant function. Nor does a stolon root all along, as a rhizome usually does, but only at its outer end, where a new stock is to be established. Stolons are not very common, occurring mainly in plants with a rootstock, and making good the deficiencies of that construction as a means of propagation. The development of stolons is often markedly seasonal, tending to follow, often rather suddenly, upon the production of flowers and fruit.

Bulbils are shoot-buds, bulb-like in construction but of small size, which drop off the parent plant and are capable of rooting and growing independently. In size and weight, but not in resistance to

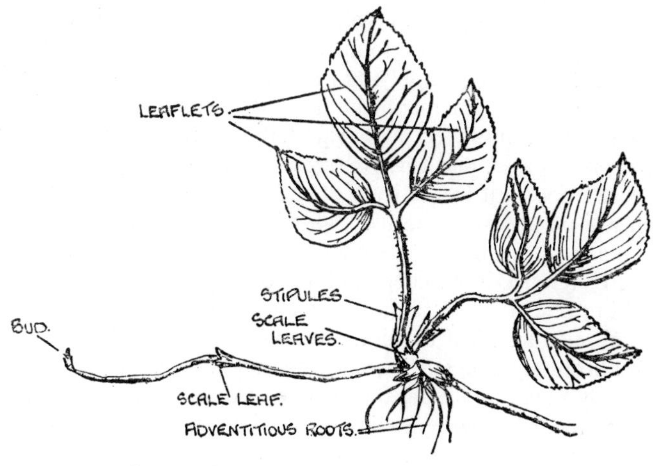

Fig. 37. STRAWBERRY PLANT AND RUNNER.

drought, a bulbil is not very different from a large seed. It is therefore an effective unit of dispersal; the main agency of dispersal is undoubtedly water, especially rain-splash and surface run-off. Bulbils may be formed as axillary buds upon the lower part of the stem (*Saxifraga granulata*) or in the places normally occupied by flowers (some freakish varieties of onion, some non-flowering alpine grass varieties). In a few cases (*Bryophyllum*, *Asplenium bulbiferum*) bulbils arise directly from foliage leaves. Many water plants have separable buds, mostly larger than typical bulbils, which are called **turions** (*Hydrocharis*, *Myriophyllum*).

Regeneration from wound surfaces or from severed fragments is of little importance in natural conditions but forms the basis of some horticultural practices. Some species are very readily propagated by what might be classed as surgical methods. If, for instance, a *Begonia* leaf is pegged down upon a pot of soil, and then its thickest veins are cut through, the **callus** (a wound-healing parenchymatous tissue, not to be confused with the feature of the same name occurring in sieve tubes) which forms upon the severed veins will quite reliably give rise to complete new *Begonia* plants.

Modifications of the Aerial Shoot

In some species the form of the aerial shoots is far enough removed from the average pattern to create special difficulties of interpretation. Many of these cases, puzzling though they may be at first glance, are fairly easily solved upon closer examination. By studying the course of development, by looking for inconspicuous scars and buds, and by applying the rule of axillary branching, it is possible to reach agreement about what is stem and what is leaf. There remains, however, a substantial residue of enigmatic and controversial cases, and of structures, sometimes very conspicuous, and very important in the lives of the plants which produce them, which are of uncertain status. This is hardly to be wondered at. If a plant is to produce some special type of organ such as a spine or tendril, it is understandable that it should often do so by modifying one of the structures which it is already accustomed to produce, such as a leaf or root. But we know of no law of nature which absolutely compels it to follow that course. It may adopt a completely novel and independent line of development, and grow a spine or tendril where nothing stood before. There is also the possibility, in cases of extreme modification, that the clues and landmarks may be lost, so that the true state of affairs can no longer be discovered.

Most spiny shoots are fairly easy to interpret. In *Robinia* and many species of *Acacia* the stipules are developed into spines (Fig. 38). In hawthorn and blackthorn the twigs produce short lateral branches with sharp ends. In gorse also most of the branches end in spines, but here the leaves are spiny as well. In *Berberis* (Fig. 39) the simple foliage leaves are borne on short lateral branches, each of which stands in the axil of a leaf which is itself reduced to a fan-shaped group of spines. A far more difficult problem arises in connection with the spines of cacti. Here there is a thick fleshy green stem, usually devoid of leaves but with structures called **areoles** arranged in a regular spacing. Each areole carries a cluster of spines, and usually various associated bristles as well. Evidently the areole represents a node, but the nature of the spines is in doubt. They cannot be the leaves of the main stem, for in those cacti which do possess obvious leaves (small cataphylls in *Opuntia*, large foliage leaves in *Pereskia*) these are clearly *additional* to the whole scheme of areoles and spines. More probably the areole represents a dwarf lateral shoot, but whether the spines are its leaves or its branches of the second order, or something quite outside the ordinary rules, we are not in a position to decide.

Similarly with **tendrils**, which are special organs by which a climbing plant attaches itself to a support, some cases are easier

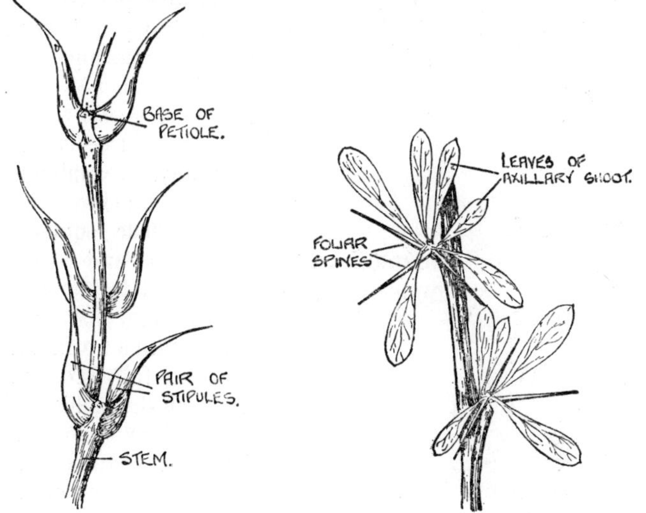

Fig. 38. *Acacia*, STIPULAR SPINES.

Fig. 39. SHOOT OF *Berberis* (BARBERRY), LEAF SPINES.

than others. In *Lathyrus* and *Vicia* there can really be no doubt at all that the tendrils have arisen by progressive modification of the upper leaflets of the pinnate leaf. Another simple case is that of *Gloriosa*, a monocotyledon in which the tip of the simple leaf is prolonged as a tendril. More difficult issues arise in *Smilax* and *Bryonia*; the tendril of *Bryonia* stands above, and a little to one side of, a foliage leaf, and it has been variously regarded as a stipule, an axillary branch, or the first leaf of an axillary branch. There is really no way of resolving the uncertainty. Another famous ambiguity arises in the Vitaceae (Fig. 40) where the tendril is a branched structure standing opposite to a foliage leaf. Perhaps

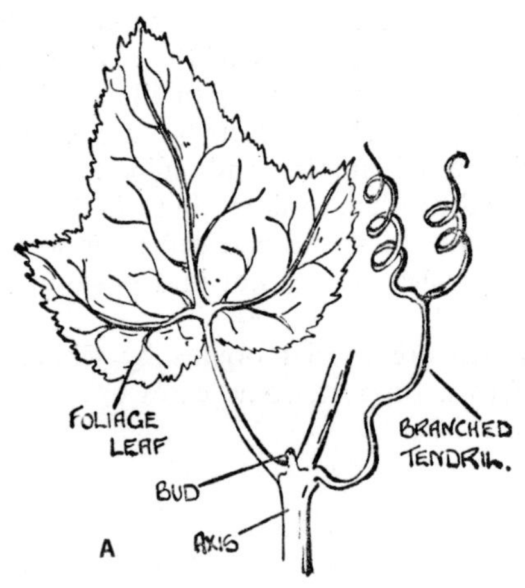

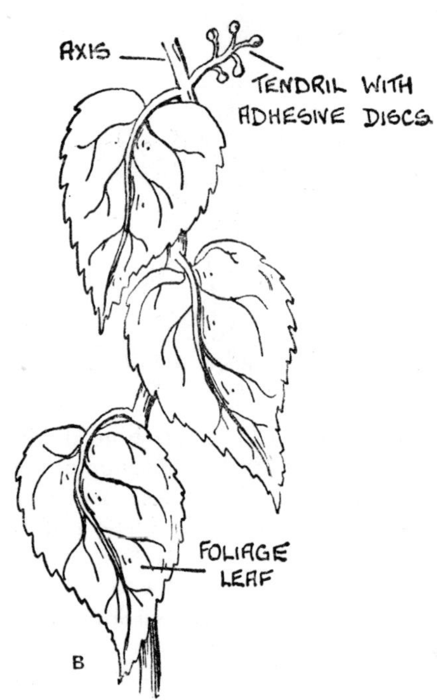

Fig. 40. BRANCHED TENDRILS.
A, *Vitis;* B, *Ampelopsis* with adhesive tips.

this is a case of sympodial growth, the tendril being the apex of the main shoot, the apparent continuation of the foliage shoot being in fact an axillary branch of the foliage leaf. But perhaps the leaves are really opposite, one of each pair being changed into a tendril. Again we cannot decide.

In some plants the photosynthetic organs have undergone perplexing changes. In Australian species of *Acacia* (Fig. 41) the leaf of the mature tree is flattened vertically. Examination of the seedling shows that this is a **phyllode**, equivalent to the petiole and rachis of a compound leaf. The very young plant has bipinnate leaves with a normal rachis; these are followed by others in which the rachis is abnormally deep, but still with leaflets attached to its top edge, and these in turn by typical phyllodes with no pinnae at all. In *Ruscus* (Fig. 42) the photosynthetic organ is a leaf-like structure, but it is vertically flattened, it stands in the axil of a cataphyll, and it produces a cluster of flowers from the centre of its surface. This photosynthetic unit was formerly regarded as a stem, but there is nothing whatever to prevent us from regarding the main photosynthetic

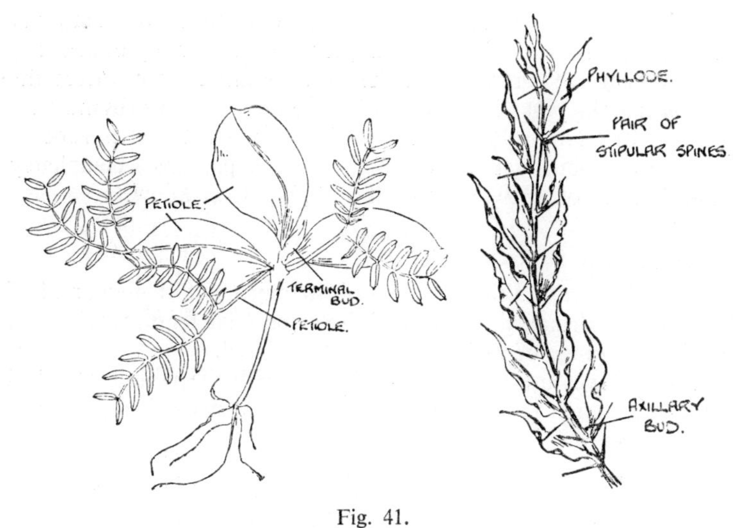

Fig. 41.

The seedling stage of a species of *Acacia*.

The adult stage of a species of *Acacia*.

surface as the first leaf of a flowering shoot which stands in the axil of the cataphyll, and this is in fact the view now generally taken. In some other cases unusual photosynthetic organs have been said, on very slight evidence, to be modified stems. The foliage of *Asparagus* is a case in point. The "frond" here is certainly a shoot system and not a compound leaf, but the nature of the bristle-like ultimate units is really quite uncertain.

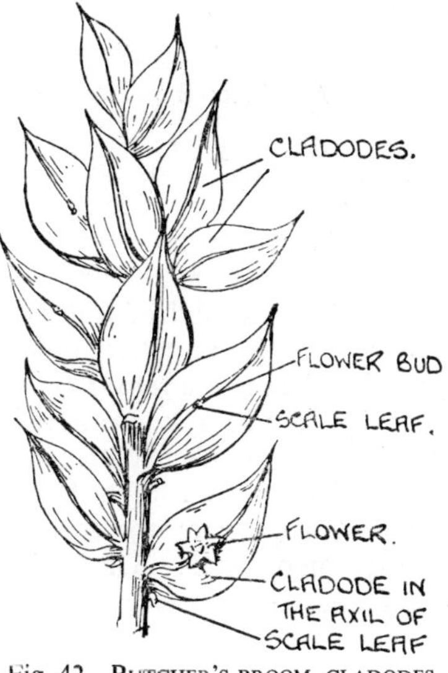

Fig. 42. BUTCHER'S BROOM, CLADODES.

In water plants and parasites, which live in very unusual conditions, there is sometimes an almost total obliteration of the normal distinctions between different parts of the body. In *Lemna*, for instance, the whole body consists of a little green frond with one or more roots. The frond can hardly be regarded as a leaf, for it gives rise to buds and flowers, but neither is there any justification for supposing it to consist wholly of stem; it is an inseparable compound of the two. Similarly in mistletoe the **haustorium**, the part which lives inside the host and absorbs material from it, defies morphological classification; whether it is root or rhizome or some combination of the two, or perhaps a completely novel kind of outgrowth, we shall probably never know.

Some Unusual Forms of Leaf

In some plants, although the basic arrangement of stem and leaf is perfectly normal, the leaf itself shows peculiar features which lie outside the range of variation so far considered.

Some leaves are **peltate** (Fig. 43, A), with the petiole attached somewhere upon the surface of the leaf blade instead of joining it

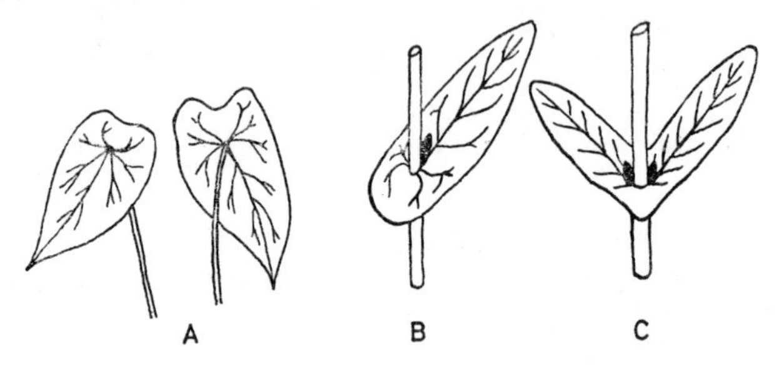

Fig. 43. UNUSUAL FORMS OF LEAF.
A, peltate; B, perfoliate alternate; C, perfoliate opposite.

at its edge. This is a rare type of construction found in isolated members of a rather wide range of plant families; *Tropaeolum* (the gardener's "Nasturtium") is a good example.

A somewhat similar effect is seen in **perfoliate** leaves, where the lamina forms a kind of frill completely encircling the stem. This may occur with alternate or opposite leaves (Fig. 43, B, C). Strongly perfoliate leaves are rare (*Claytonia perfoliata, Dipsacus*).

Many monocotyledons have leaves of peculiar form, some being tubular (onion), others flattened in a vertical, instead of a horizontal plane (iris). In some of the larger monocotyledons of warm climates the development of the leaf involves an actual separation and destruction of tissue. The lamina in a palm, for instance, arises as a continuous but pleated sheet of tissue, and then, as it expands, it spontaneously tears along the folds so as to form a set of apparent "leaflets". When mature, it looks like a compound leaf, but its manner of development has been quite different. A rather similar-looking result may be arrived at when a banana-leaf is torn by the wind, but the palm-leaf is distinctive in tearing itself automatically. In some other monocotyledons, notably in Araceae, spontaneous tears in the leaf do not always extend to the edge. The most extreme development of the perforated leaf occurs in *Aponogeton*, a water plant in which each leaf looks like a piece of green lace.

The most elaborate leaves are those of the carnivorous plants, which act as traps, catching and digesting insects in various ways, some of which call for great structural complexity. These developments are dealt with in Chapter 10.

The Symmetry of Shoots and Leaves

Every shoot system is exposed to the action of an external environment, the properties of which can be measured by meteorological instruments, and which may have a striking effect upon the form and behaviour of the plant. To take a single instance, some *Acacia* species in which the mature branches normally produce phyllodes (p. 78) can be induced to continue the production of the bipinnate juvenile type of foliage merely by keeping them in a humid atmosphere.

Each individual organ, however, is also subject to the influence of what may be called an internal environment, a complex system of physiological processes going on in its vicinity, about which we know very little but which is certain to be affected by the presence of other organs. An axillary bud, for example, develops in a situation where there is a stem on one side of it and a leaf on the other, and it would be very surprising indeed if the development of that bud were completely unaffected by the unbalance in its surroundings.

In reality it is commonplace to find that plant organs display varying degrees of lopsidedness or asymmetry which can be related to the geometrical pattern of which they form part. Sometimes the asymmetry is detectable only by careful measurement, but often it is obvious, and even conspicuous. We need not pursue this matter in detail, but a few examples will show the kind of relationships which are likely to be encountered in the practical examination of common plants.

In every lobed or compound leaf the lower or outermost portions are in a very unsymmetrical position. The lowermost leaflet of a pinnate leaf, for instance, has other leaflets to one side of it but not to the other. The upper leaflets are not affected to the same extent; indeed, if the leaf is symmetrical as a whole the terminal leaflet will have the same number of lateral leaflets to its right as to its left.

Observation shows that the lower lateral leaflets are often very lopsided in outline or in the number of serrations and lateral veins, and that the degree of asymmetry falls off as one passes to the upper and more central leaflets. In bipinnate or intricately lobed leaves this kind of relationship may be carried into the branching of the second or third order.

In a shoot with distichous phyllotaxy (p. 55) there is generally some difference between the two sides or faces of the shoot. Often (e.g. *Begonia*) each leaf has, so to speak, a small half and a large half, and all the large halves of the leaves in both rows point to the same side. This kind of unbalance bears a fixed relationship to the origin of the shoot in an axillary position with stem on one side and axillant leaf on the other. It is also commonly associated with a tendency for the shoot to grow horizontally (notice the asymmetry of the leaves on the horizontal distichous twigs of elm).

Even in shoots where the normal phyllotaxy is spiral, the axillary origin of the shoot (or the origin of the plumule from between two cotyledons, see Chapter 6) produces an initial disturbance. What usually happens is that the first few leaves are in an arrangement which is neither spiral nor decussate, but something in between, and that the decussate component gradually decays until only a pure spiral is left. This can affect not only the angular divergences between the leaves but also the lengths of the internodes. There are many species, for instance, in which the upper part of a shoot has spiral phyllotaxy with internodes of roughly constant length, but in which the first and second leaves of a branch are almost opposite, the internode between them being shorter than those above and below.

It is perhaps a reflection of this situation that in many shoots the first leaves are structually distinct from those that follow. These distinct initial leaves are called the **prophylls** of the shoot which produces them. Although there are many exceptions, it is a general rule that in dicotyledons there are two prophylls standing right and left of the axillary branch, while in monocotyledons there is a single prophyll which stands at the back, often not quite in the middle but somewhere between the branch and its parent stem. The cotyledons themselves are now not usually regarded as leaves at all (p. 132).

However straightforward a shoot system may appear to be, exact measurement almost always reveals a complex system of symmetry relationships.

4 THE STRUCTURE OF STEMS

The Apical Meristem

Although the tip of a growing stem is part of the outer surface of the plant it is never ordinarily visible in an intact specimen, being overarched by its own young leaves. To reveal the apex it is necessary to dissect away a series of leaves of various ages, the youngest being mere primordia in which there is little sign of the characteristic leaf-shape of the species. When uncovered the apex is seen as a body of meristematic parenchyma, sometimes almost flat, but usually rising into a dome. It is soft and delicate, and usually very small. See Plate 4.

Within the meristem there is very little difference between one cell and another except in the timing of their divisions. On the average, in a shoot which is growing actively, each cell will divide about every 3-5 days, but neighbouring cells are not synchronised. At intervals the tissue bulges out to form the leaf or leaves which will stand at a node. In the leaf-primordia, which commonly begin as crescent-shaped ridges running partway round the dome, the rate of cell division is increased, and at the same time the effective size of the stem apex is reduced because part of it has been diverted into the production of leaf tissues. These two factors are responsible for the way in which the growth of the leaf forges ahead of that of the stem tip. The production of leaves involves the apex in cyclic changes; the meristem undergoes a kind of pulsation.

Besides giving rise to leaves the meristem adds to the bulk of the stem on which it stands. By marking stems with waterproof ink and watching the movement of the marks it is easy to find which parts are still increasing in length. In ordinary herbaceous stems several internodes are often elongating simultaneously. The growth of stems is by no means strictly apical; nevertheless the apex, as the principal source of new cells, is really the prime cause of the elongation. Growth in the region behind the apex is mainly due to the enlargement of cells which the apex has provided.

It has long been a matter of interest to discover how much of the apical meristem can be considered permanent. There is a constant flow of cells into the sub-apical region of the stem, but obviously some cells must remain in the meristem to divide again. To discover the number and arrangement of these permanent **apical initials** has been the object of many investigations. The technical difficulties are very great, because one cannot examine the internal structure of an apex without killing it. The course of events must therefore be reconstructed mathematically from great numbers of observations. In the stems of lower plants such as ferns it is often perfectly obvious that there is one apical initial, different in shape from all the other cells, and dividing in a geometrically regular way to give the entire cell output required. Each division leaves the **apical cell** still recognisable, and the other cell which is produced, though it undergoes further divisions, is entirely used up in the production of mature tissues. In seed plants the geometry of the apex leaves no doubt that there must be more than one permanent initial, but probably not, in most stems, a very large number. More like a dozen than a hundred, it seems, and those not distinguishable in appearance from other cells around them which are destined to move out of the meristem.

It was formerly supposed that the apical meristem must contain distinct layers of cells, each giving rise to a particular tissue of the mature stem. The attempt to recognise such layers has decisively failed; the assignment of particular cells to particular tissues, though not a pure random shuffling, certainly involves a considerable element of chance.

The young cell walls are sufficiently fluid to respond to surface tension forces like those which operate in bubbles and foams. We must distinguish between **anticlinal** divisions, in which the new wall is at right angles to the outer surface of the plant, and **periclinal** divisions, in which the new wall is parallel to the outer surface. Mathematical investigation of the effects of surface tension reveals that whereas a cell deep in the interior is equally free to divide in any direction cells near the surface are most likely to divide anticlinally, and in the outermost layers the probability that any new wall which is formed will take an anticlinal position rises very steeply indeed. These conclusions are very well borne out in the construction of meristems.

An apical meristem can usually be divided into an inner **corpus**, in which the direction of division is almost random, and an outer **tunica**, which consists of distinct concentric layers, indicating that periclinal division in the tunica is rare. Once a layer is established in which division is constantly anticlinal, then that layer is self-maintaining, remains uncontaminated by cells from other sources, and must of course have its own initials. In some apices the tunica consists only of a single layer; in others it is up to four cells deep, the outer layers then almost perfectly independent, the innermost subject to occasional exchange of cells with the corpus.

It is possible to obtain a **periclinal chimaera**, a plant in which one or more of the tunica layers are of a different genetical constitution from the rest of the meristem. A common type is that in which the outermost tunica layer consists of cells which are incapable of producing chlorophyll. A plant of this kind will have yellow edges to its leaves, because at the margin of the leaf a considerable part of the inner tissue is produced by periclinal division in the outermost layer. The behaviour of periclinal chimaeras gives us a check upon the stability of the tunica layers. Apart from the peculiar behaviour of the leaf-margins, the degree of stability is in fact usually very high; every branch and leaf repeats the chimaeral structure, showing that the surface layer maintains its integrity through millions of cell divisions. The stability is not, however,

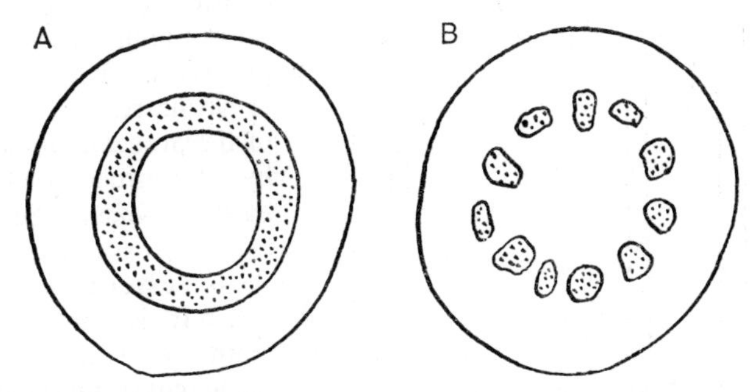

Fig. 44. TRANSVERSE SECTIONS OF STEMS IN THE SUB-APICAL REGION TO SHOW THE TWO PRINCIPAL TYPES OF PROCAMBIAL DISTRIBUTION. PROCAMBIUM DOTTED. A, continuous procambial cylinder; B, separate procambial strands.

quite perfect. Now and then a pure green shoot will appear, showing that the inner tissue has somehow forced its way to the surface; sometimes even a pure yellow shoot may be seen, indicating that the outer layer has divided periclinally to produce a substantial bulk of chlorophyll-deficient tissue.

The Origin of the Vascular Tissues

Within the sub-apical region of the stem a distinction soon arises between the **ground-meristem**, which occupies the greater part of the cross-sectional area, and the **procambium**, which is a localised internal tissue (Fig. 44). In the ground-meristem the cells enlarge, mainly by expansion of their vacuoles, and separate from one another at the corners to form a connected system of intercellular ventilating canals. In the procambium there is little vacuolation, and intercellular canals are not formed. The contrast is sharp, and becomes more pronounced in the later development of the tissues.

Once vacuolation has begun, further division in the cells of the ground-meristem is almost entirely by transverse walls. This is only a passing phase; presently division stops altogether, and the cells of the ground-tissue, without much further change in shape, develop into epidermis, collenchyma, and ground-tissue parenchyma.

In the procambium the division of the cells is predominantly by longitudinal walls. Unlike the ground-meristem, which accomplishes the necessary elongation of the stem largely by transverse division of the cells, the procambium has no such provision. There can be only one result; the cells of the procambium, either by active growth or by the tension which the surrounding tissues exert upon them, must become elongated. It is the procambium which gives rise to the vascular system of the plant, and within this system elongated cell-forms usually predominate.

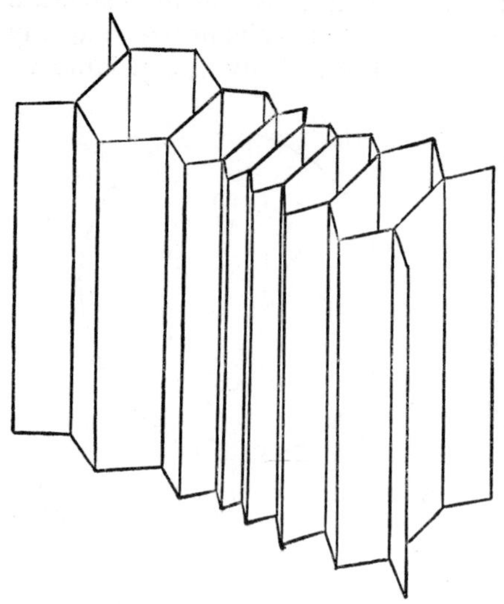

Fig. 45. PERSPECTIVE VIEW OF A SINGLE FILE OF PROCAMBIAL OR CAMBIAL CELLS, ONLY A PART OF THE LENGTH OF EACH CELL BEING SHOWN.

In each species the procambium forms, within the cross-section of the stem, a regular pattern which is related to the phyllotaxy but pays little regard to the boundary between tunica and corpus. In most dicotyledons the distribution of procambium conforms to one of the two alternatives shown in Fig. 44, either a continuous hollow cylinder or a ring of separate strands. The difference is not fundamental, and many species are intermediate or inconstant in behaviour, nor is there any constant relationship between the habit of a plant and the distribution of its procambium. More complex types of vascular construction exist, but their consideration can be left till later (p. 108).

Throughout the procambium a regular sequence of cell division is soon established (Fig. 45). Each new cell wall is not only longitudinal, it is also periclinal; it is a tangent plane to an imaginary cylindrical surface concentric with the outer surface of the stem. This characteristic type of tissue-geometry dominates the whole vascular system. The cells which are produced are in radial rows or files, all the members of one file having arisen from a single parent cell by repeated division. So far as increase in cell numbers is concerned, growth is entirely in the radial direction. Furthermore, the shape of a cell as it appears in tangential section, the outline, that is, which would be seen by an observer looking directly outwards from the centre of the stem, will be the same for all the cells of a file. In other words, the characteristic procambial type of growth is an endless repetition of a particular cell network; we may cut two tangential sections some distance apart, so that no cell occurs in both of them, and yet those two sections will correspond, cell for cell. This system is never found in absolute geometrical perfection. It is, however, the basic pattern of growth, and such enlargements, distortions, and divisions of cells as may be superimposed upon it are never sufficient to obliterate it.

Vascular Differentiation

The maturation of vascular tissue usually begins in the part of the procambium which is nearest to the surface of the stem. Here some of the cells develop into sieve tubes, and this region may be called the **protophloem**. Protophloem sieve tubes are usually very small and of simplified structure, without companion cells. They are formed in small numbers, and their life is short. The adjoining cells enlarge and begin to differentiate, usually into fibres, and the little sieve tubes are soon crushed and digested, finally disappearing without trace. In most stems, therefore, the protophloem, from an early stage, appears simply as a body of sclerenchyma (Fig. 46). Accounts written before the discovery of the protophloem sieve tubes call the fibres pericycle ("pericyclic fibres").

The part of the procambium next to the protophloem, the next layer towards the centre of the stem, develops into more typical phloem which may be called **metaphloem**. Here are normal sieve tubes, with companion cells, and usually also a good deal of phloem parenchyma. This parenchyma is formed from procambial cells which, as their last meristematic function, divide transversely several times.

Soon after the appearance of protophloem sieve tubes functional xylem elements are formed in the **protoxylem**, which is the part of the procambium nearest the centre of the stem. The very first water-conducting elements have usually an annular thickening, but are soon followed by others, a little further from the centre of the stem, with spiral thickening. In most stems the protoxylem is formed before the elongation of the stem has ceased, so that the protoxylem elements are subject to stretching (being dead cells

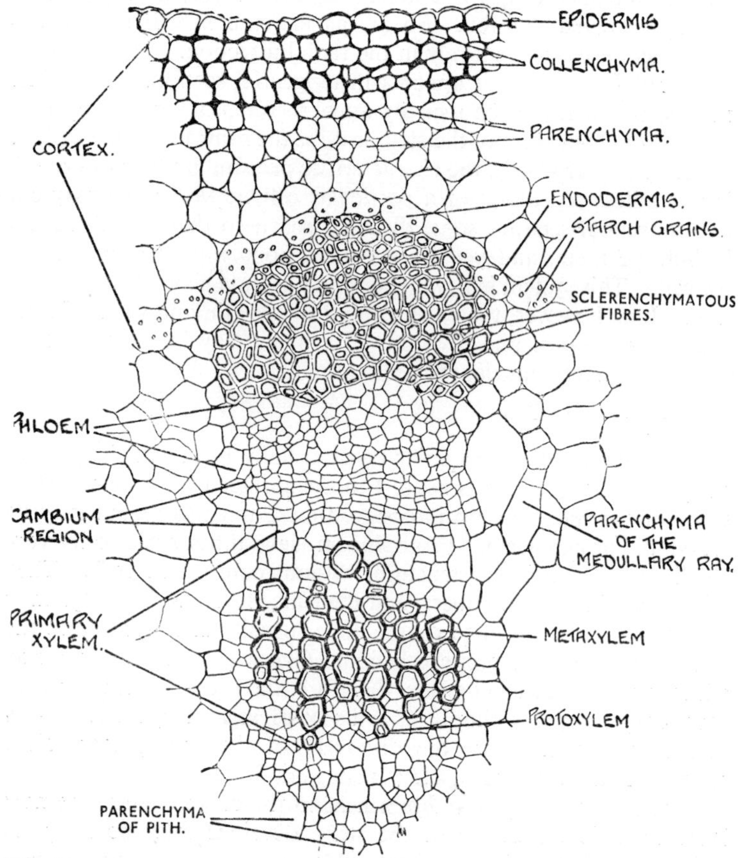

Fig. 46. VASCULAR BUNDLE IN A TRANSVERSE SECTION OF *Helianthus* STEM. THE FIBRES ARE PROTOPHLOEM.
The term "medullary ray" is passing out of use (see p. 91).

they are incapable of active growth). As shown in Plate 5, the amount of stretching varies; the last-formed (outermost) protoxylem vessels, formed only shortly before the elongation of the stem comes to an end, are naturally stretched very little, and their appearance is not much affected. The earliest ones, however, are usually stretched to destruction, and crushed flat by the pressure of the surrounding parenchyma. Unlike the protophloem sieve tubes they do not completely disappear; a careful search upon the inner fringe of the protoxylem of a mature stem will usually reveal fragments of crushed vessels. The thickening-ring of an annular vessel, for instance, is unlikely to break, but is often turned through a right angle so as to present its edge view in a transverse section of the stem.

The part of the procambium adjoining the protoxylem differentiates into **metaxylem**, which is the next layer towards the outside of the stem. In the metaxylem the vessels are of more substantial construction, with a pitted wall which makes no provision for further elongation. Metaxylem often differs from protoxylem also in the greater lignification of its parenchymatous cells. The origin of xylem parenchyma is the same as that of phloem parenchyma, a cell of the procambium dividing transversely into a vertical row of parenchyma cells. Often several adjoining procambial cells will divide in this way so as to produce a patch of parenchyma, but this is not necessarily the case; sometimes one of the vertical files of parenchyma cells stands quite isolated among vessels or fibres.

The Establishment of the Cambium

The early differentiation of the vascular system is a history of two contrasting waves of activity. In the outer part of the procambium development begins with the protophloem and sweeps inwards across the metaphloem towards the centre of the stem. The development of xylem begins at the inner edge of the procambium and spreads outwards. In some examples these two waves of differentiation eventually meet. Mature xylem will then abut directly upon mature phloem, or there may be a little "uncommitted" parenchyma between the two. Meristematic activity is then at an end, and the vascular system is left without any immediate provision for further growth. This is the usual situation in a monocotyledon.

In dicotyledons and gymnosperms, however, the vascular differentiation of most stems never reaches finality. Between the advancing fronts of xylem and phloem a remnant of the original procambium remains permanently active as a meristem called the **cambium**. By custom the vascular tissues produced by the meristematic activity of an established cambium are known as **secondary** xylem and phloem, whereas the protoxylem and metaxylem together are called **primary xylem**, the protophloem and metaphloem making up the **primary phloem**. The vascular differentiation of most young stems is in reality a perfectly continuous and uninterrupted process. The distinction between primary and secondary tissues is then quite arbitrary; between undoubted secondary xylem on the one hand and obvious primary xylem on the other, there is usually a band of tissue in which the wisdom of Solomon could not draw a definite boundary.

The cambium continues the same basic pattern of growth as the procambium, and the secondary tissues contain the same range of cell types as the primary tissues, with the same fundamental geometry. There may, nevertheless, be great differences of constitution between primary and secondary tissues; secondary xylem, for instance, often contains a much greater proportion of fibres than the primary xylem.

Where there is a continuous procambial cylinder the cambium is also a continuous cylindrical layer from the start. Where the procambium arises in distinct strands the primary vascular tissues are similarly arranged in separate **vascular bundles**, with ground-tissue parenchyma between them (see "parenchyma of the medullary ray" in Fig. 46). In most cases of this kind the cambium of each vascular bundle is joined up with that of the next by a resumption of meristematic activity in the ground-tissue. The timing of this process varies. The new cambial activity may begin in ground-tissue cells which have not completed their differentiation and have only just ceased to divide transversely in the manner of the ground-meristem. Sometimes, however, there is a lengthy delay, cambium-type divisions occurring quite suddenly in cells which are fully mature and have shown no sign of meristematic tendencies for a long time.

Cambium formed by resumption of meristematic activity in the ground-tissue is called **interfascicular** cambium, **fascicular** cambium being that in the bundles themselves. In transverse sections the two tissues are similar from the first, but in longitudinal section the interfascicular cambium, because of its origin from parenchyma, lacks the normal elongated cell-shapes. The first interfascicular secondary xylem can only be a kind of lignified parenchyma, and the interfascicular cambium will have to pass through a period of adjustment before it can produce a proper xylem-geometry. Most stems quickly complete this adjustment, but in some there is a permanent difference between the interfascicular xylem and phloem and the corresponding fascicular tissues.

The General Distribution of Tissues in Stems

The outer part of the ground-tissue, between the epidermis and the vascular system, is called the **cortex**. Only in the very simplest cases is this a completely uniform tissue. Immediately beneath the epidermis most stems have a certain amount of collenchyma, which may be spread out uniformly round the circumference but is much more often concentrated in definite ridges arranged in a manner related to the phyllotaxy (p. 57). Most young stems contain also some parenchyma with a specially high level of photosynthetic activity, and this assimilating tissue is found where the development of collenchyma is least. The characteristic pattern is the angular stem with an outer cortex consisting of collenchyma at the corners and photosynthetic tissue on the sides (see Plate 12). The distribution of the stomata is then very uneven, with far more over the assimilating tissue than over the collenchyma. The inner cortex usually shows much less structural differentiation.

In many stems the innermost cortical layer of all, bordering directly upon the protophloem, possesses distinctive properties. This layer, only one cell in thickness, follows one of two alternative courses of development. In most aerial stems it is a **starch sheath**, consisting of parenchymatous cells which contain more starch than those of the adjoining layers. In water plants, and in some other special cases, the layer differentiates as an **endodermis**, the detailed treatment of which is postponed to Chapter 5 (p. 123).

In the centre of the stem is the **medulla** or pith, usually consisting entirely of ground-tissue parenchyma. The pith of most stems seems to be relatively inert; it may have an obvious storage function, with starch-grains, etc., and the cell walls usually become lignified, but otherwise there is little sign of activity.

In most dicotyledons the vascular system, except in very young stems, will appear as a continuous cylinder, and although an interfascicular sector ought in theory to be recognisable by its lack of protoxylem and protophloem it may in practice be quite difficult to decide whether separate vascular bundles ever existed or not. In only a small proportion of dicotyledons do the interfascicular sectors fail to produce secondary xylem and phloem. Some of these plants have an interfascicular cambium which produces only parenchyma, while in others no interfascicular cambium is formed at all. The progressive reduction of cambial activity is an important evolutionary trend, culminating in the great group of monocotyledons, in which interfascicular cambium has never been observed, and even the fascicular cambium has been reduced almost to vanishing-point.

When a stem has separate vascular bundles the ground-tissue of the outer pith meets that of the inner cortex in each interfascicular sector. These regions used to be called the "primary medullary rays", a term which is now passing out of use. In some such stems there is no way of drawing a sharp boundary between pith and cortex, but very often there is a clear distinction between a rather small-celled, often lignified outer pith, and a large-celled non-lignified inner cortex.

Vascular Connections to Leaves and Branches

At every node one or more vascular bundles are drawn off from the vascular system of the stem and diverted outwards into the leaf or leaves of that node. A bundle passing out into a leaf is called a **leaf trace**. The tendency is for each species to have a characteristic number and arrangement of traces. In *Rhododendron*, for instance, each leaf has one trace, whereas a bramble leaf has three, and a rhubarb leaf a large number.

In most stems the leaf traces are structurally different from the other bundles, and this difference may persist for a long way down the stem (Plate 12). The features by which trace bundles may be recognised are: (1) Larger protoxylem groups, and larger protophloem caps, than the other bundles. (2) Traces are often slightly further from the centre of the stem than other bundles are. They tend to be in corners or ridges of the stem; in particular any big outward projection of the pith generally marks the position of a trace. (3) Trace metaxylem has smaller vessels than ordinary metaxylem.

The loss of vascular bundles to the leaves is ordinarily made good by the branching of some of the bundles which remain in the stem. Some species are unusually regular in their behaviour, but on the whole this branching is a rather unpredictable process; one cannot say for certain which bundle is due to branch next, and in most species the number of bundles in an internode is kept only roughly constant.

The arrangement of the bundles in a stem section is determined partly by the phyllotaxy, partly by the number and spacing of the traces to each leaf, and partly by the manner in which the total number of bundles is restored after the departure of traces. The detailed study of these matters is beyond the scope of this book, but a student should from the beginning make a point of noting the different sizes and shapes of bundles and the ways in which his section departs from the circular form.

With few exceptions the vascular supply to an axillary branch arises very abruptly at the node, so that branch traces are not to be seen in internodal sections. A stipule has no independent trace at all, but is served by strands arising from a leaf trace. When leaves are opposite there is sometimes a partial merger between their bases, and in some instances (*Scabiosa*, *Dipsacus*, etc.) there are actually shared leaf traces, bundles which branch in the stem cortex, one half going into each leaf of the pair. Such developments may involve a fusion of the stipules (e.g. *Humulus*). In *Galium* and its allies (Fig. 47 and p. 438) the stipules are leaf-like and form false whorls with the true leaves; the stipules have no direct connection with the vascular system of the stem, but are supplied from girdling bundles

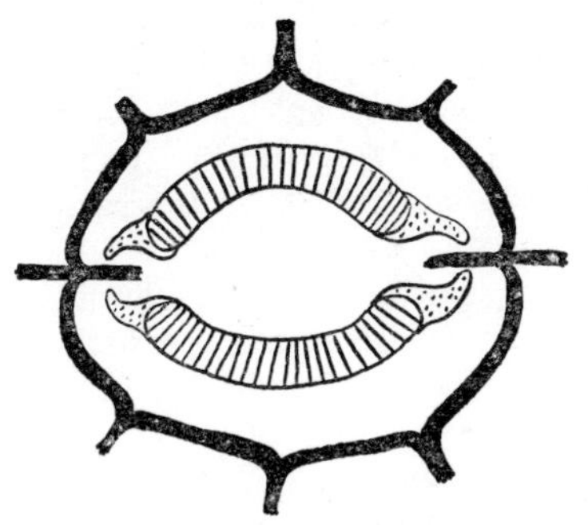

Fig. 47. PLAN OF THE VASCULAR CONNECTIONS IN A NODE OF *Galium*. There are two opposite leaves, each with a single gap in the vascular system (shown striped) of the stem. Each leaf has an axillary branch which draws its vascular supply (dotted) from the edges of the leaf gap. The node has also additional leaf-like outgrowths, of which six are supposed to be present here. These structures are regarded as stipules. They have no direct connection with the vascular system of the stem, but are supplied from loops which run round in the stem cortex between the bases of the leaves. This girdling vascular system is shown in black.

which spring from the traces of the two leaves and run round the node in the stem cortex.

The Cambium

In transverse section (or T.S.) the cambium appears as a narrow band of rather uniform tissue, the apparent thickness of which varies according to the rate of cell division. In winter the cambial zone may be only one cell thick, but at times of active growth it is usually much wider. Perhaps at any moment there is in each radial file of cells only one which is capable of undergoing cambial division, the other "cambial" cells which we see in a section being in fact already committed to a definite course of development as either xylem or phloem. We are not at present in a position to resolve this question, but the existence of substantial amounts of immature vascular tissue adjoining the cambium proper is obvious in many sections, especially upon the xylem side.

The structure of the cambium is best seen in tangential longitudinal section (or T.L.S.). In every normal cambium there are two types of cell, and only occasionally more than two (Fig. 48). One is the **fusiform initial**, the typical elongated cell deriving its shape directly from the course of events in the early history of the procambial strand, or, in an interfascicular sector, achieving a

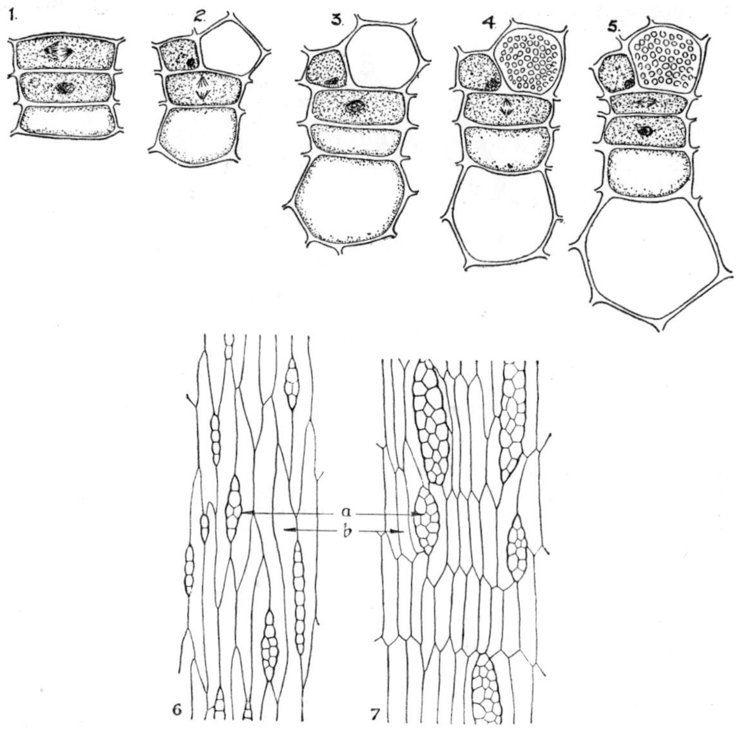

Fig. 48. CAMBIUM.
1-5, Transverse sections showing sequence of divisions in the production of new xylem and phloem, including the formation of sieve tube and companion cell. 6 and 7, Tangential longitudinal sections of stratified and unstratified cambia: *a*, ray initials; *b*, fusiform initials.

similar form by the later adjustment already mentioned (p. 90). The other type of cambial cell is the **ray initial**, formed by transverse division of a fusiform initial. We have already seen in the origin of xylem and phloem parenchyma how transverse division in a cell which has ceased to be part of the cambium produces only a single, possibly quite isolated, vertical file of cells. When transverse division occurs in a cell of the cambium itself, the consequences are quite different, for the whole geometry of the vertical file will be duplicated over and over again by repeated cambium-type division of the cells. The result therefore is a whole mass of parenchyma, extending radially into the phloem on the one hand and the xylem on the other. Such a body is called a **ray** (quite a different thing from the "primary medullary ray" of the older books, see p. 91). The initiation of a ray is an irreversible change. Every now and then a fusiform initial, for reasons which are not understood, divides into a set of ray initials. Ever afterwards that bit of cambium, as long as it continues to function at all, produces ray parenchyma instead of such things as sieve tubes, fibres, and vessels.

There are three things for which the cell division of the cambium has to provide. One is the occasional conversion of a fusiform initial into a group of ray initials. Ray initials, seen in T.L.S., enlarge very little, so this type of division makes no appreciable contribution to any increase in the total area of the cambial layer. The second requirement is the production of new secondary xylem and phloem; this is satisfied by repeated periclinal division, and indeed the overwhelming majority of divisions in the cambium are of this type. Again, there is no addition to the area of the cambial sheet. But the cambium of an active stem is constantly riding outwards on the advancing face of an ever-increasing mass of rigid secondary xylem, so that the area of the cambial cylinder *must* be increasing. How then is this increase in cambial area accomplished?

One might expect the need to be met in the most obvious way, by the occasional division of a fusiform initial by a radial longitudinal wall. In T.S. this would mean that two fusiform initials would stand side by side in the place of one, and when each had expanded tangentially to the size of the parent cell the circumference of the cambium would have been increased by the width of one fusiform initial exactly. This type of division does occur, and leads to the configuration shown in Fig. 48 (7). The fusiform initials here stand side by side in rows, those in each row being derived from a single parent by repeated division, and having their upper and lower ends at corresponding levels. This is known as a storied or **stratified** cambium. Stratified cambia are found in many dicotyledons, mostly woody plants of warm climates. The stratified cambium, however, does not occur in conifers, and it does not represent the majority condition even among dicotyledons. The commoner type of **unstratified** cambium, shown in Fig. 48 (6), has the upper and lower ends of its fusiform initials at different levels, and offers no obvious clue to the way in which the area of the cambium can be increased.

The solution to the problem is a surprising one; the increase is due to transverse division of the fusiform initials. Of course the transverse division of a fusiform initial into two makes no immediate addition to the area of the cambium. The actual increase in girth comes from adjustments which follow the formation of the new transverse wall. We have evidence from many sources that cambial cells are highly plastic; if we could watch a fusiform initial for years on end we should see it stretch and wriggle and undergo all kinds of distortions. To take one simple proof of this plasticity the fusiform initials in a conifer stem twenty years old are several times as long as they were when it was one year old. But by the time it is a year old the stem itself has entirely ceased to grow in length. The cells are actively elongating, although the stem of which they form part is of unchanging length. It follows that the cells must be growing past one another, the upper and lower ends of each fusiform initial extending steadily up and down the stem, and so intruding into planes of T.S. which those particular cells did not originally reach. Therefore the average number of cells in the cambial circle of each T.S. will be increasing, which is what is required to increase the cambial girth. The growth of a fusiform initial cannot be unlimited, so the expansion of the cambium which arises from the enlargement of existing fusiform initials will eventually cease unless new cells can be supplied. Transverse division does exactly that; a long (old) fusiform initial divides into two short (young) ones, and these immediately begin to grow past one another. Other cells elsewhere in the cambium will be doing the same thing, so that the increase will be evenly spread.

In most woody plants the activity of the cambium varies little from year to year, so that the diameter of the cambial cylinder increases by the same amount each season. Notice what this implies in terms of cambial growth. In passing from a diameter of 1 unit to a diameter of 2 units a cambial layer must double its area, an increase of 100 per cent. But in passing from a diameter of 50 units to a diameter of 51, which will take an equal period of time, the increase of area will be only 2 per cent. The problem of cambial extension is more acute in a smaller tree, because there is a smaller stock of cells on which to operate. In general the position appears to be that a young stem must increase its cambial surface at a rate which is proportionately very rapid. In unstratified cambia this is accomplished by enlargement, especially by elongation, of existing cells, in stratified ones by rapid division by radial longitudinal walls. Once a cambial cylinder of either type has achieved a large diameter the demand for new cambial surface, though exactly the same in absolute units, is proportionately very much reduced, and can be met by a very low rate of cell division. In a big fir-tree it can be calculated that it will be enough for each fusiform initial to undergo one transverse division every fifteen years or so.

The Production of Secondary Vascular Tissues

Most cambia produce several xylem cells for every phloem cell. The disproportion between the two tissues is marked even in young stems, and increases with the passage of time, because unlike xylem, which is a permanent and rigid tissue, the phloem is temporary, and its soft parts soon collapse. In most stems a sieve tube functions for only a single season. Sometimes sieve tubes which have been plugged with callose in the autumn are opened for traffic again in the following spring, but two seasons of activity seem to be the absolute limit. Furthermore, there is in old woody stems (p. 107) a constant loss of dead secondary phloem from the outer surface; the tissue is actually cast off. In old trees the amount of phloem (most of it dead) is roughly constant, the loss balancing the gain, whereas the amount of xylem increases every year.

The rate of periclinal division in ray initials is usually much less than that in fusiform initials. In a ray, therefore, the radial diameter of the cells is greater than that of the cells formed in the first instance from a fusiform initial. In radial longitudinal section (or R.L.S.) a ray is like a brick wall, with ray cells in horizontal courses across the stem (Fig. 49). In the rays the geometrical projection of the T.L.S. outlines of the initials is very exact. Only in the simplest cases, however, do the cells arising from fusiform initials complete their development with so little rearrangement.

The closest approach to geometrical stability is found in conifers (Fig. 49), where, apart from the production of an occasional vertical file of parenchyma, every cell produced from a fusiform initial develops either into a sieve cell or into a tracheid, without significant alteration of its T.L.S. form. In all angiosperms additional complications arise, if only through the divisions which produce companion cells in the phloem. The amount of disturbance is, however, usually quite small in plants with a stratified cambium, and the stratified arrangement of cells in these stems is maintained in xylem and phloem without fundamental change.

In dicotyledons with unstratified cambia, however, there is usually extensive rearrangement of the cells. The details are not fully understood, but some aspects of the matter are readily appreciated. For one thing the cells which differentiate as xylem fibres (and in many species these are a majority of the cells of the xylem) reach a final length greater than that of the fusiform initials which produced them. This can only mean that the young fibres grow intrusively, with their ends thrusting through the tissue into places which they did not originally reach. Then again, the cells

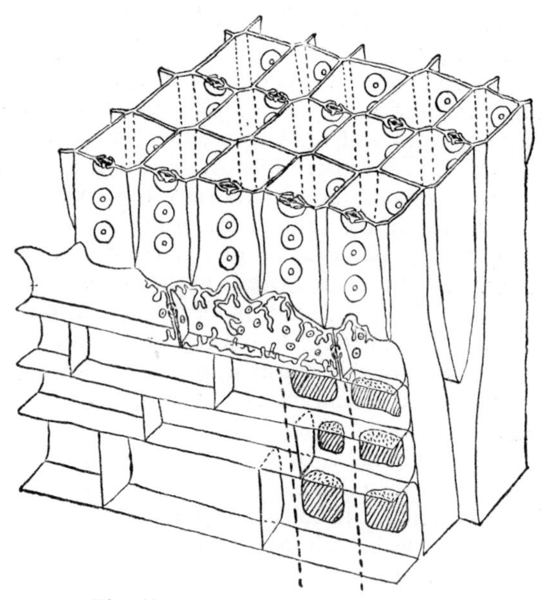

Fig. 49. SECONDARY XYLEM OF *Pinus*.

Three radial files of spring-wood tracheids are shown, those of the middle file having their lower ends within the diagram. The tracheids have large bordered pits on radial walls only. Across the front runs a ray, of which the four top cell-courses are shown. All the ray cells are cut open at the front. The uppermost row consists of ray tracheids, with small bordered pits and elaborate wall-thickenings shown only in part of the row. The ordinary ray cells communicate with the main tracheids by large "window-pits" shown as shaded areas at bottom right only. Some of the walls in this area are treated as transparent; the two broken lines running out at the bottom mark the course of the tracheids curving back behind the ray. The triangular ventilating channels between the ray cells are exposed at bottom right.

which differentiate into vessel elements often increase very greatly in transverse diameter. This also involves intrusive growth, though of a different kind. The very young vessel element is no larger than its neighbours in T.S., and will be in contact with only about six of them. When fully grown it may touch twenty or more of the little parenchyma cells around it; it has forced apart cells which originally touched one another, and bulged out between them to establish new contacts.

When a cell forces its way between others, or slides upon its neighbour, plasmodesmata in the region affected are broken off. If the cells again come to rest while they are very young, connections may be re-established and pits formed in the normal way. But if the movement occurs too late, or goes on too long, there will be a lack of pit-communication between the cells. In general parenchyma cells, ray cells, and vessel elements have a high degree of pit-communication, but fibres are often very largely isolated from one another and also from the rest of the system.

Fluctuations in Cambial Output

So far as appearances go, all the fusiform cells produced on either side of the cambium seem, to begin with, to be completely indistinguishable. The more active the cambium, the larger is this stock of undifferentiated cells from which the fibres, vessel elements, and other standard cell types of the mature vascular tissues are drawn. No plant is known in which the destiny of a cell on either side of the cambium is completely constant. Always there are variations in time, and usually variations in space also. The composition of the secondary xylem arising from any particular piece of cambium is constantly changing, and may in addition be quite different from that of the xylem being formed at the same moment on a different radius of the same stem; similar considerations apply to the phloem.

Much of the variation in cambial activity is of a seasonal character. In temperate climates the cambium makes a new start every spring, and in the larger stems of our woody plants has ceased to make any further addition to the tissues by some ill-defined date which falls in middle or late summer rather than in autumn. The secondary xylem produced in this period is called an **annual ring**, and forms a thin cylindrical shell surrounding the wood which existed previously. The xylem of the first year constitutes the first and innermost annual ring, and in many herbaceous plants the stem is very much like that of a woody plant which produces one annual ring and then no more.

The boundary between two successive annual rings is the surface where the **spring-wood** of one year joins the **summer-wood** of the year before, and is usually conspicuous in sections. Summer-wood is almost always a heavier and harder tissue than spring-wood, even in conifers, where both consist almost wholly of tracheids. Summer-wood tracheids are smaller, with thicker walls, than the tracheids of the spring-wood (see yew and pine in Plate 6; in both these photographs the centre of the stem is above the part shown, so that the summer-wood of each ring, appearing darker, is towards the foot of the page). Upon a deal board the difference in texture is easily observed upon pressing with the thumbnail; the summer-wood here is also more strongly pigmented than the spring-wood. In some dicotyledons similar mechanical differences arise because the spring-wood consists predominantly of relatively thin-walled vessels and parenchyma, while the summer-wood has a greater proportion of thick-walled fibres.

In most woods the change in quality of the xylem during the course of the season is gradual. The photographs of yew and birch (Plate 6) show this clearly. In a limited number of dicotyledons (oak, elm, ash, etc.) there is a more sudden change from a spring-wood with a dense concentration of large vessels to a summer-wood in which the vessels are much smaller. In the photograph of elm (Plate 6) two bands of spring-wood are shown, consisting almost entirely of large vessels. Of the summer-wood one complete band is shown, with parts of two others; during the summer the cambium oscillates between two types of xylem-production, the dark horizontal bands in the picture consisting of fibres, the pale ones of small summer-wood vessels and accompanying parenchyma.

Even in temperate regions it is not an absolute law that a stem shall produce one growth-ring each year. In a drought year there may be insufficient xylem growth to form a noticeable ring. Other circumstances (a rain-drought-rain sequence, or severe insect-damage followed by the outgrowth of new foliage) may evoke the production of two rings in a year. In British conditions age estimates based on ring-counts are subject to only a small margin of uncertainty. The errors are greater in more arid regions. In those tropical climates where there is little distinction between the seasons of the year, many trees produce well-defined growth-marks in their wood, but these are formed at irregular intervals and are often not complete rings at all, the resting-periods of the cambium being unsynchronised even on the two sides of the same stem. Temperate-zone plants transferred to the tropics often do not thrive, and inappropriate periodicity is probably one of the causes of such failures.

Pieces of wood are often associated with archaeological finds, and the fluctuations in ring-thickness which arise from differences between one growing season and the next are often found to correspond in specimens from different places. Tree-rings therefore offer both a system of archaeological dating and a source of information about past climatic changes. By comparing the inner part of one stem with the outer part of another the reckoning can be carried back through the lives of several trees. The method has had some spectacular successes in the arid regions of North America.

The summer-wood of elm (Plate 6) shows that the course of differentiation in the xylem can fluctuate with a frequency much greater than annual. Similar fluctuations are common elsewhere. Some plants, for instance, show an alternation of fibre-bands and soft tissues in the secondary phloem. The waviness of such bands indicates that the synchronisation between neighbouring pieces of cambium is often imperfect. Less commonly adjoining pieces of cambium behave differently for long periods at a time; the summer-wood of oak, in which there are *radial* wedges of fibres, is a good example.

Mechanical Consequences of Cambial Activity

The increase in the bulk of vascular tissue puts a tangential tension upon all the tissues external to the cambium. In epidermis and cortex, and also in the dead parts of the secondary phloem, the tangential stretching of the cells is often conspicuous. Signs of active growth, with anticlinal division of cells, can occasionally be found in the cortex. All such adjustments are, however, of limited scope; long-continued cambial growth always causes a loss of tissue from the outer surface. The living phloem is usually a very narrow band, and can usually accommodate the expansion of the inner tissues by slight distortions which commonly escape notice. In some cases, however, notably in young twigs of *Tilia* (Fig. 50), a critical situation arises from the conjunction of a high rate of cambial growth with an unusually deep layer of functional phloem. In *Tilia* the necessary accommodation is provided by the phloem rays, the cells of which divide and grow actively in the tangential direction.

Stresses in the Inner Tissues

It is noteworthy that there seems never to be any significant compression of the pith, even where conditions in the interfascicular sectors are such as to make such a compression possible. In some of the larger herbs there is indeed an enlargement of the pith (almost certainly a passive stretching); this can be seen well in a large sunflower stem, where the distortion of the cells often makes the lines of stress very conspicuous.

Many stems are hollow. In nearly all cases this arises through a failure of longitudinal growth in the pith parenchyma, a failure which is in the majority of cases confined to the internodes.

The Rays

The initiation of new rays proceeds at such a rate that the tangential distance between adjoining rays is kept roughly constant despite the increasing circumference of the xylem cylinder (Fig. 50 and caption). As to the functions of the rays we have only circumstantial evidence. The radial elongation of their cells, the heavy pitting of many of their walls, the occurrence in ray cells of starch grains and other products, and the fact that the rays are the only

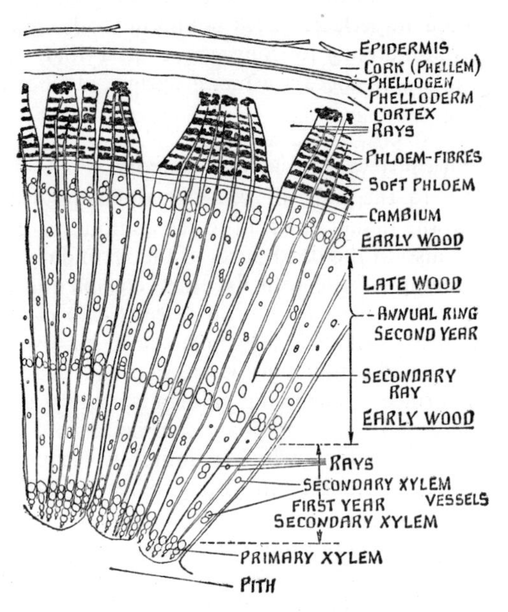

Fig. 50. TRANSVERSE SECTION OF STEM OF *Tilia* EARLY IN ITS THIRD YEAR OF GROWTH.

The term "secondary ray" is sometimes applied to rays which do not extend inwards to the primary xylem. This diagram shows how "secondary rays" are initiated so as to keep the inter-ray spacing roughly constant. Note also the wide phloem parts of some of the rays (see p. 101).

part of the vascular system in which intercellular air spaces ordinarily occur, all suggest that rays are concerned with the radial movement of materials. It is interesting in this connection to find that rays make contact with the other elements of the vascular system much more effectively than a single transverse section might suggest. A fibre, for instance, which in a particular T.S. seems to be as far as possible from a ray, will probably touch a ray in some other

T.S. plane. The distribution of rays makes it likely that they are of considerable physiological importance.

In some conifers, but not in others, and in some dicotyledons, mostly those of warm climates, some of the cell-rows in each ray are structurally distinct from the others. In conifers, for instance, some of the cell-courses in the xylem rays consist of **ray-tracheids**, cells of parenchymatous form but with bordered pits instead of simple ones (Fig. 49). The significance of such developments is quite obscure.

Ordinary rays, though often quite visible to the naked eye, are too small to impart any conspicuous "figure" to the wood in which they occur. In some exceptional cases, however (oak, *Platanus* = lacewood, etc.), very large rays occur, considerable areas of cambium being turned over to the production of ray parenchyma. In R.L.S. such a timber reveals very large patches of ray tissue (the "silver grain" of oak); the slight geometrical irregularities of growth impart an attractive waviness to the outlines, and radial ("quarter-sawn") planks and veneers of these timbers are valued for cabinet-work. All such timbers contain numerous small rays in addition to the big ones.

PERIDERM

Wounds inflicted upon a healthy plant normally heal. Cells adjoining the wound act in such a way as to produce a new covering layer which will protect the inner tissues just as the epidermis did originally. In cases of accidental damage there can be no question of preparing the new protective layer in advance, for the need cannot be foreseen. Many wounds, however, are caused by the plant's own activities, and are predictable. The shedding of a leaf is such a case. It is a very general rule that where the need for a protective layer can be anticipated such a layer is in fact formed some time before it is actually required to operate.

The healing of wounds in soft or parenchymatous tissues almost invariably proceeds by the formation of a **periderm**, an organised system of secondary tissues, with a manner of growth which is in some respects similar to that of the vascular system. In stems where the growth of the vascular system goes on long enough to involve a rupture of the outer surface a periderm appears long before there is any question of an actual break.

A periderm arises in a manner which recalls the origin of inter-fascicular cambium, by the revival of meristematic activity in mature tissue. As in a cambium division is predominantly periclinal

(Fig. 51). The meristem is called the **phellogen** (known as cork cambium in some of the older books). Although it resembles a cambium in T.S. its cells are never elongated; the phellogen and all the tissues derived from it are fundamentally parenchymatous.

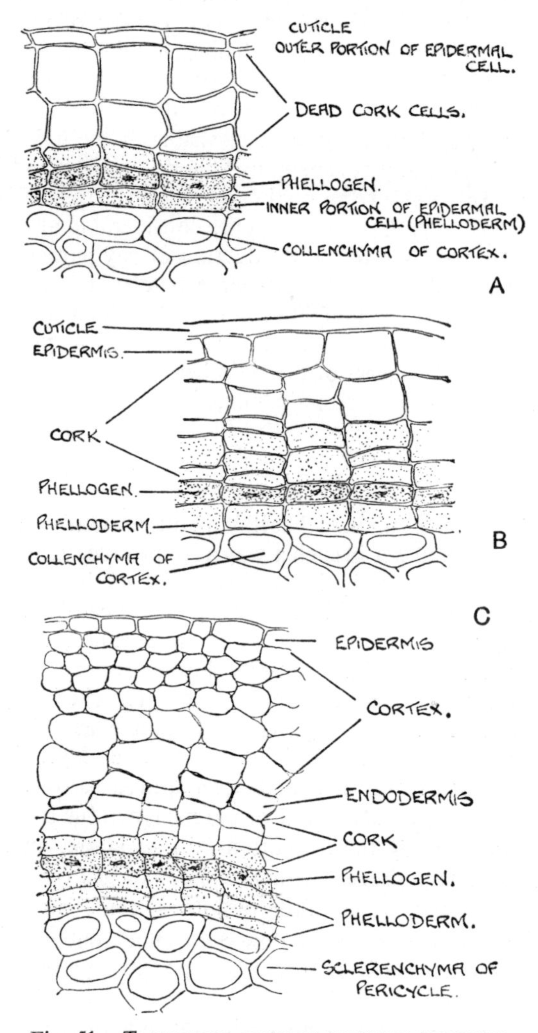

Fig. 51. TRANSVERSE SECTIONS SHOWING PERIDERM.

A, periderm formed in epidermis (*Solanum*); B, periderm in layer below epidermis (*Sambucus*); C, deep-seated periderm (*Ribes*).

The rate of cell division in a phellogen is typically much lower than that in a vascular cambium. Even an active phellogen therefore usually lacks the broad bands of immature product-tissues which commonly adjoin a cambium. The internal product of a phellogen is called **phelloderm** ("secondary cortex" of some older books). Phelloderm is usually a living parenchyma, though in later life its cells sometimes develop collenchymatous thickenings or become sclereids (Fig. 52). It is rare for the phelloderm to be an extensive tissue, and in a high proportion of cases each phellogen cell cuts off only one phelloderm cell in its whole working life.

The external product of the phellogen is the **phellem** (often known as cork, though it does not necessarily resemble commercial cork in

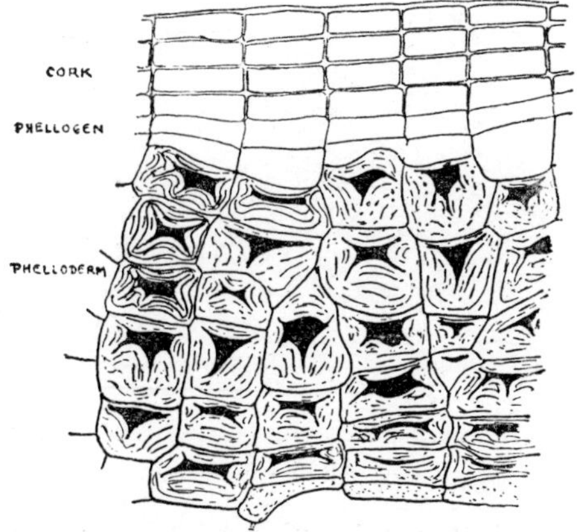

Fig. 52. DETAILED STRUCTURE OF PERIDERM OF *Canella alba*. PHELLODERM DEVELOPED AS STONE-CELLS.

its physical properties). Phellem is devoid of intercellular spaces, and its cells deposit suberin (an impermeable material similar in composition to the cuticle) in and upon their cell walls so as to make a very perfect seal. This is a suicidal process. Even a thin layer of suberin is an almost complete barrier to every substance of physiological importance. Phellem cells are dead cells. What is more, the phellem as a whole is also a complete physiological barrier, so that any cell on the outside of the phellem is also dead, or soon will be.

In young stems the commonest place for a periderm (the whole system of phellogen, phelloderm, and phellem) to appear is in the outer cortex, often in the layer of cells immediately beneath the epidermis (Fig. 51, B). It is possible, though unusual, for the phellogen to arise by periclinal divisions in the epidermal cells themselves (Fig. 51, A). In either case the initial loss of tissue is slight and passes almost unnoticed, the young twigs having a smooth bark. In some plants, however, the periderm arises deep in the stem. In *Ribes* (Fig. 51, C) the first periclinal divisions occur in cells of the starch sheath, and the whole of the cortex, containing substantial strands of collenchyma, is killed at one stroke. The young twigs thus have a stringy shredding bark which is merely the dead cortex.

The activity of the phellogen fluctuates like that of the cambium. Annual zones of growth are usually obvious in commercial cork (phellem of *Quercus suber*). Fluctuations of shorter period can be seen in birch-bark; the phellogen here produces alternate layers of

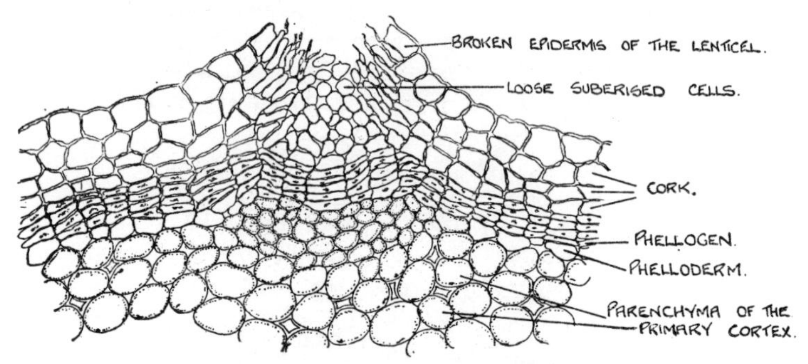

Fig. 53. DETAILED STRUCTURE OF LENTICEL OF ELDER. (As seen in T.S. stem.)

strong and weak phellem, a few of each in a season, and the phellem will tear into very thin papery layers.

Lenticels

Any organ which formed continuous phellem over its entire surface would be cut off from communication with the outside world. In reality some patches of phellogen always behave differently from the remainder, producing distinctive structures known as **lenticels** (Fig. 53) in which intercellular spaces link the internal ventilating system with the atmosphere. The lenticel phellem (or **complementary tissue**) may disintegrate into a powder; in commercial cork it is a chocolate-coloured dust in the irregular lenticel canals. Usually it is more coherent, or at least has firmer layers in it which tend to hold the whole thing together. The rate of periclinal division is higher in lenticels than elsewhere; a lenticel tends to burst out as a kind of pustule, and may also bulge into the underlying tissues. Not all lenticels are conspicuous. Old rough-barked stems, and persistent smooth barks like that of beech, carry lenticels which are not easily detected. Without a practical test (making air bubble out of lenticels under water) it is never safe to conclude that lenticels are absent. Lenticels are usually the first parts of the periderm to appear, and there are some cases where lenticels are formed but the periderm is never joined up between them. The brown dots in the skin of some apple varieties are of this nature.

Bark

The first phellogen of a woody stem usually functions for some years, but in most cases it is liable to be superseded eventually by a new periderm formed in deeper-seated tissue. In old stems this process of replacement is repeated many times. At any given time only the innermost phellogen can be active. Furthermore, whatever the position of the first phellogen the formation of new internal periderms will soon exhaust the supply of cortical tissue present in the young stem. The bark of an old tree, therefore, is a mass of dead tissue in which periderm layers run through secondary phloem more or less crushed and transformed. Given time, every piece of secondary phloem will ultimately become part of the bark, and it is perhaps in the bark that the fibres, sclereids, and crystals which are common in phloem find their main functional significance.

The bark of a tree is important in fire resistance, as a blanket against sudden changes of temperature, and as an insect-repellent layer, and contains substances such as alkaloids and tannins which probably act as preservatives. Barks are accordingly of some commercial value in tanning (oak in Europe, *Acacia* spp. in Australia), as spices (cinnamon), and as drugs (quinine, cascara sagrada).

In most barks each inner periderm covers only a small area, sealing off a scale-like piece of tissue. Where the periderm is mechanically weak (*Pinus*, *Platanus*) these scales are obvious externally. More often, however, the periderm is not distinctive in texture, and the outer bark merely cracks into a system of ridges and furrows. Commercial cork is an artificial product arising from a persistent wound-induced periderm, the whole trunk of the tree being stripped every ten years or so. The diameter of bottle-corks, which have the lenticels running through them sideways, is limited by the thickness of bark which it is possible to obtain uncracked. Large bungs have the lenticels running from top to bottom, and are not watertight unless waxed.

Sapwood and Heartwood

Young secondary xylem (or **sapwood**) is almost white, saturated with water, and contains living cells (xylem parenchyma, ray cells). Sapwood in most species maintains sufficient vitality to show some resistance to infection and to be able, by producing layers of gum, etc., to take at least the first steps in the healing of a wound.

After a period which is often about ten or fifteen years the sapwood is converted into **heartwood**, which is a completely lifeless tissue. At this time any reserve materials such as starch disappear from the cells, and various new substances appear. Any characteristic pigmentation or impregnation such as the colour of mahogany, the oiliness of teak, or the greasiness of lignum-vitae, always arises at the conversion of sapwood into heartwood. There is also a tendency for the vessels of the heartwood to be blocked; sometimes gummy and resinous substances collect in the vessels and solidify into plugs, sometimes **tyloses** are formed (Fig. 54). A tylosis is a bladdery expansion of a parenchyma cell, which bulges into a vessel through a pit. If enough tyloses are formed they fill the vessel as a kind of false parenchyma.

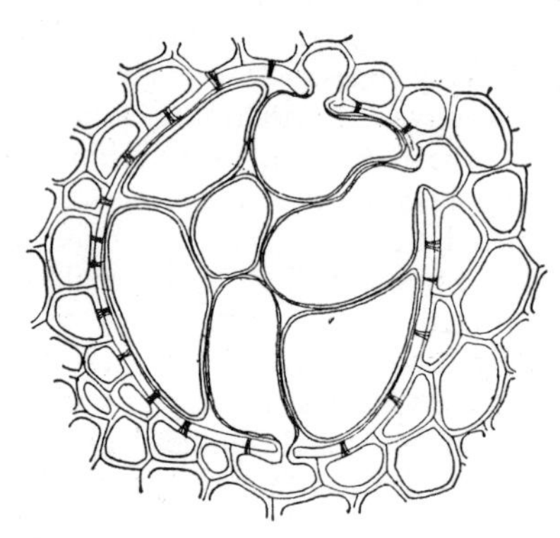

Fig. 54. TYLOSES IN VESSEL OF *Robinia pseudacacia.*

Heartwood is usually a harder, drier, less permeable, more durable tissue than dead sapwood of the same tree. Even the removal of reserve material contributes to this end; many wood-boring insects which live in the sapwood do not penetrate the heartwood because there is no food for them there.

Variations in the Distribution of Primary Tissues

In many seed plants the arrangement of primary vascular tissues differs from the concentric cylindrical pattern (xylem surrounded by phloem) which we have so far considered. The detailed study of these variants is beyond the scope of this book, but it is necessary to summarise the commoner possibilities. Examples are shown in Figs. 55 and 56.

The commonest anomaly of all is the occurrence of internal phloem, with the typical structure of metaphloem, but lying between

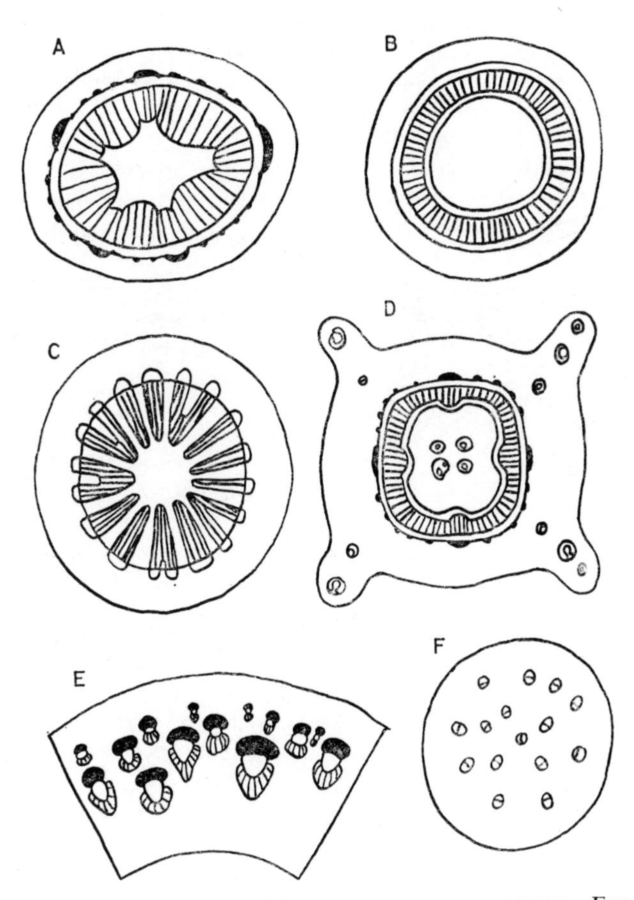

Fig. 55. TYPES OF STEM STRUCTURE IN TRANSVERSE SECTION. FIBRES IN BLACK, PRINCIPAL MASSES OF XYLEM STRIPED.

A, common type of woody dicotyledon (oak, willow, laburnum). B, dicotyledon with almost uniform xylem ring (Onagraceae with internal phloem as shown, Scrophulariaceae without). C, woody dicotyledon with an interfascicular cambium which produces only parenchyma. Mainly in plants of vine-like habit (*Clematis*, *Aristolochia*, *Akebia*), a similar situation with much less secondary tissue in some herbs (*Petasites* rhizome). D, dicotyledon with internal phloem, cortical bundles, and medullary bundles (Melastomaceae). Combination of all these features in one stem is not common, but cortical strands can be seen in *Vicia* or *Lathyrus*, medullary ones in *Tragopogon*. E, a sector of a hollow stem without formation of interfascicular cambium, bundles somewhat scattered, xylem tending to embrace the phloem (*Ranunculus*, *Thalictrum*, some Umbelliferae, many monocotyledons). F, stem with completely scattered bundles (*Peperomia*, *Nymphaea*, many monocotyledons).

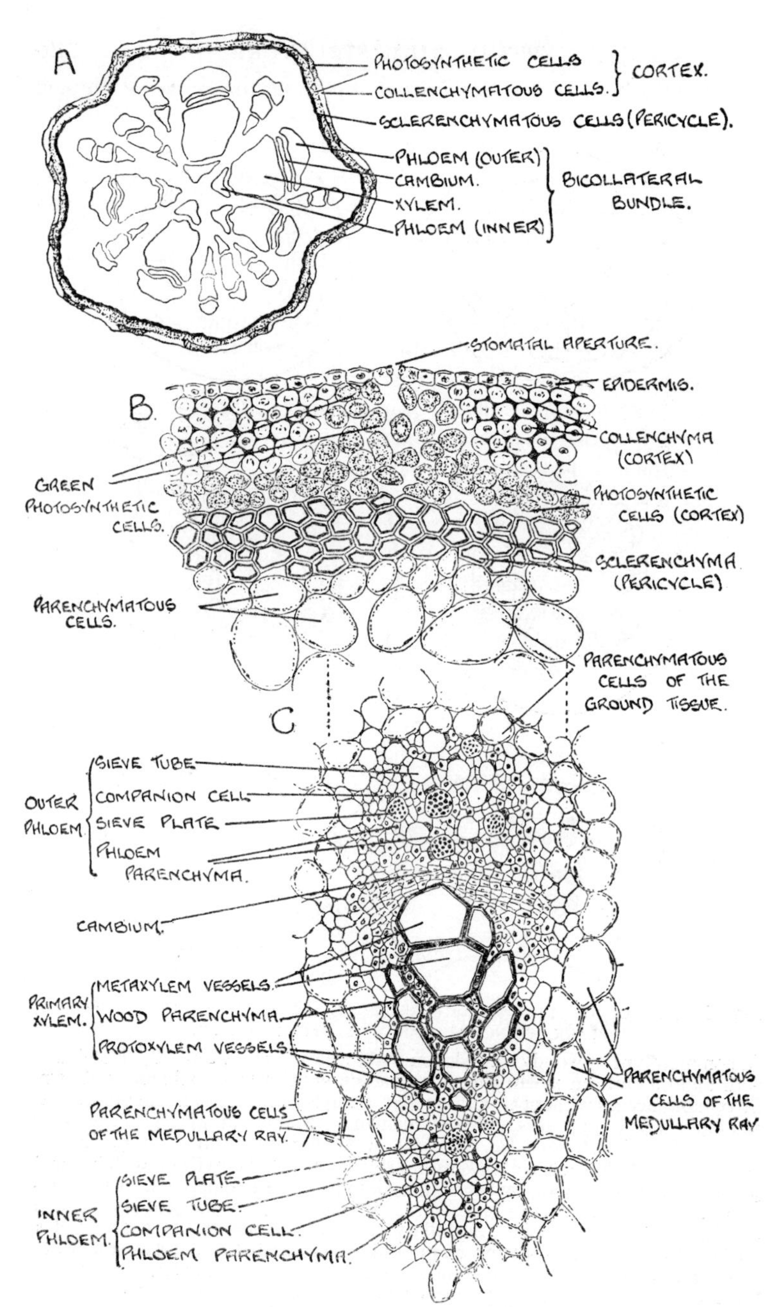

Fig. 56. BRYONY STEM, TRANSVERSE SECTION.
A, diagrammatic; B, detail.

protoxylem and pith. See Fig. 56, but note that internal phloem, in most stems where it occurs, is much less conspicuous than that of *Bryonia*. There are also considerable numbers of stems in which vascular bundles occur in the cortex of the internode. The occurrence of vascular bundles in the pith is also possible, though less common. These anomalies can occur in combination, and it is quite possible to have a stem with internal phloem, cortical bundles, and medullary bundles (Fig. 55, D).

In stems which never develop an interfascicular cambium there is a tendency for the vascular bundles to depart from the cylindrical arrangement. There may be two concentric rings of bundles, but in a high proportion of cases there is a complete scatter-pattern. This arrangement is seen in many monocotyledons; wherever it occurs the bundles near the surface of the stem tend to be smaller, and this gradation is associated with a characteristic course of the leaf traces (Fig. 57). When the activity even of the fascicular part of the cambium is low, so that little secondary tissue is formed, the line of demarcation between xylem and phloem is often strongly curved, the metaxylem of each bundle tending to encircle the phloem (Figs. 55, E and 58).

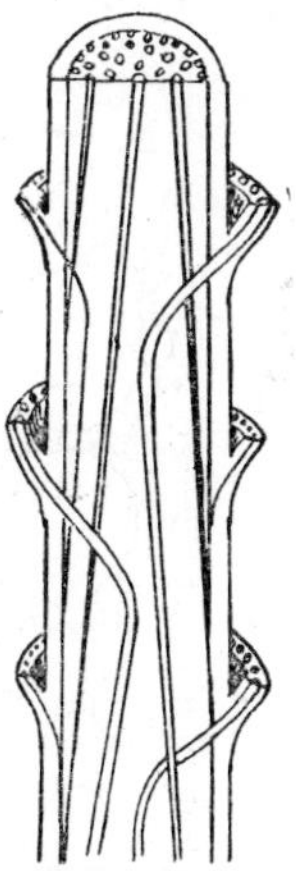

Fig. 57. COURSE OF THE VASCULAR BUNDLES IN STEMS WITH SCATTERED DISTRIBUTION OF THE STRAND.
From the leaf each bundle plunges deep into the stem, then as it is followed downwards it moves outwards again with progressive reduction in size and distinctness.

Variations in Secondary Development

Even a cambial cylinder formed in the normal position may operate in an unusual fashion. Some tropical trees, for instance, have small islands of secondary phloem embedded in the secondary xylem. Cambium may, however, arise in exceptional positions. In some woody climbing plants the interfascicular cambium takes short cuts across the pith, and joins into several cylinders instead of one. In other examples the first cambial cylinder functions only for a short time, and others are formed outside it, giving a system of concentric shells, xylem and phloem alternately.

Many monocotyledons have thick woody stems, and some of them achieve this condition by an unusual type of secondary growth

(Fig. 59). A meristematic layer which produces only a little parenchyma externally forms on its inner side a mass of lignified parenchyma in which complete vascular bundles, not very different from the primary ones, are embedded.

Anatomical Peculiarities of Monocotyledons

The "typical" monocotyledonous stem has scattered vascular bundles in which the metaxylem forms a deep V or Y embracing the phloem, and no sign of cambial activity. It appears very different from the "typical" dicotyledon. In reality, however, there are plenty of dicotyledons which approach fairly closely the

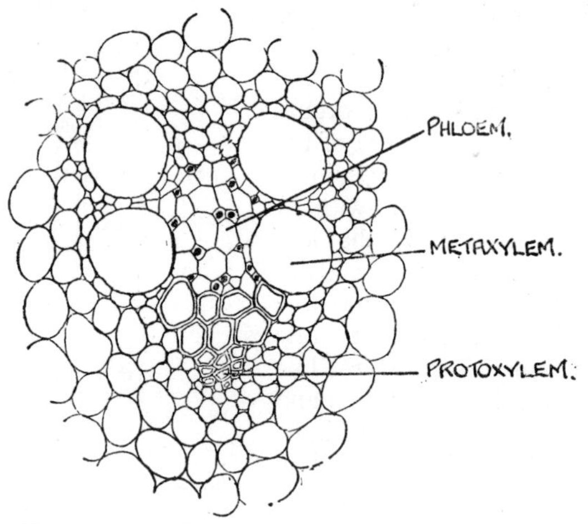

Fig. 58. *Asparagus* STEM, DETAILED T.S. OF VASCULAR BUNDLE.

monocotyledonous plan of vascular construction. Even the strange type of secondary growth seen in Fig. 59 can be found in dicotyledons.

Intercalary Meristems

There is in many plants a tendency for elongation to continue in the lower part of each internode after it has ceased in the upper part. In a limited number of cases this tendency is carried so far that we can recognise an **intercalary meristem**, a piece of stem which retains the power to elongate by the production and enlargement of new cells over the whole cross-section, long after the stem tissues above and below are fully mature. There is a very persistent intercalary meristem in the lower part of most grass internodes.

An intercalary meristem, because it is soft, raises problems of mechanical stability, solved in the grass shoot by enclosing the meristem in a strong and close-fitting leaf-sheath. There is also a problem of vascular continuity, calling for a kind of perpetual protoxylem, and for corresponding adjustments in the phloem.

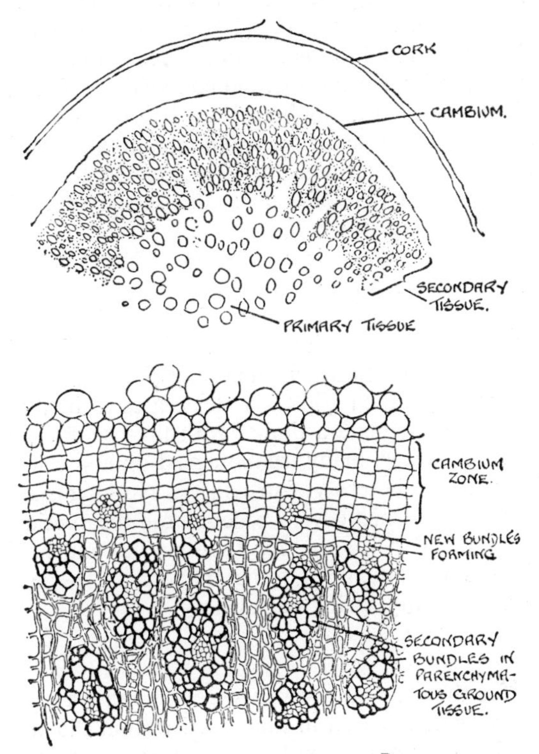

Fig. 59. SECONDARY THICKENING OF *Dracaena* STEM.
(See text p. 111 on secondary growth in monocotyledons.) A similar method of growth is found in some dicotyledons, *e.g.* Chenopodiaceae, Nyctaginaceae, etc.

The Fine Structure of Secondary Xylem

The seed plants display great diversity in the structure of their wood. There are differences in the relative proportions of vessels, tracheids, fibres, and parenchyma, in the way in which these elements are arranged, and in the details of their cell walls. Most timber specimens are readily identifiable. It is very doubtful whether the smaller structural differences upon which identification commonly depends are of any physiological significance. They are, however, of great value as clues in the study of the evolution of the higher plants.

A piece of seasoned timber may as a first approximation be regarded as a mixture of cell-wall substance and air, for cell contents rarely form a large fraction of the total weight. The cell walls of all timbers are roughly similar in their properties. Roughly speaking, therefore, the weight and strength of a piece of timber are directly proportional to the amount of cell-wall material present, and other properties, such as thermal conductivity, follow the same trend. Light and weak timbers like balsa consist largely of parenchyma, hard and heavy ones like lignum-vitae predominantly of fibres. Most are intermediate. The specific gravity of the cell walls is greater than that of water; all timbers sink when water-logged, only the heaviest when dry.

In some respects there is an obvious connection between the structural peculiarities of a timber and the uses to which it is put. English oak, with a complete filling of tyloses, is good for barrel-staves; American red oak, with no tyloses, is useless for this purpose. What fits a timber for one application may disqualify it for another; the impenetrability which tyloses confer ceases to be a virtue when it is desired to impregnate a timber with fire-proofing solution.

There are, however, many technological points which cannot at present be explained in terms of structure. Nothing is known in the anatomy of ash and hickory to account for the special toughness which makes them so suitable for tool-handles and hockey-sticks; nobody knows why dents in some timbers are permanent while those in others slowly spring out again.

Grain

Except for those few timbers in which large rays occur, most of the decorative patterns seen in timber arise from the alternation of spring-wood and summer-wood. On a plank cut in R.L.S. the pattern consists merely of straight closely-spaced parallel lines. On a T.L.S. plank, however, a showier pattern is obtained, in the central part of which the bands of spring- and summer-wood are wide, and meander irregularly (for a trunk is never a true cylinder).

Special value attaches to timber in which the conformation of the annual rings is abnormal. In the angle between two large boughs, for instance, the grain is distorted. Again it sometimes happens that the cambial surface is a dimpled or wavy cylinder instead of a plain one. With skilful cutting such material can be made to yield attractive "figures", almost always used as veneers.

Each annual ring covers not only the trunk of the tree but also its branches, and it follows (Fig. 60) that the earlier rings of the branch-base will be buried in the wood of the trunk, constituting a knot. In normal commercial practice knots are undesirable; they are disfiguring, they are apt to exude resin, which makes painting difficult, and they are points of mechanical weakness. Some trees, such as elm, however, produce **burrs**, large woody bosses with twigs

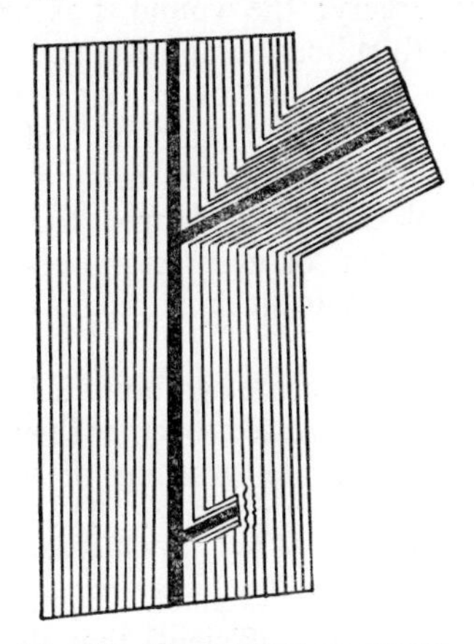

Fig. 60. STRUCTURE OF KNOTS.

A part of a trunk is shown in longitudinal section, the pith black, the parallel lines representing annual rings. There were two branches, one of which was cut off after two years of growth, the other being allowed to remain. When branches are removed from young trees the outer wood of the mature trunk may be completely knot-free; this is an important aspect of forest management. Note that the cambium and bark of a branch are constantly being pushed outwards by growth of the trunk; this sometimes leads to obvious crumpling round the branch-base.

upon them. Burrs are valued because they yield curious figures which are really patterns of small knots crowded together.

Wounds in Woody Stems

Sapwood can usually produce a sufficient seal, mainly by chemical means such as the secretion of gum, to hold off any immediate attack by wood-rotting fungi. Small wounds like those involved in routine pruning of fruit trees are therefore not dangerous in the ordinary way, though trouble will follow if an active parasite such as the fungus which causes silver-leaf disease in plum trees gets in. The cambium at a severed branch-end produces in time a callus-parenchyma, which bulges slowly across the exposed wood surface. Eventually the active tissues join up, cambium is formed right across, and the site of the original wound is buried under layers of new wood and bark.

Even a very small exposure of heartwood creates a radically different situation. The heartwood has no healing power whatever, and is vulnerable to a host of wood-rotting fungi. Callus-formation may be normal, but it will be too late; the tree will be rotting from the core before the join is made. Valued ornamental trees are sometimes saved by surgery; the wound is excavated, plugged with cement, and sealed with rubber compositions.

Anything fixed to the wood of a living tree will in time be covered with wood and bark, the cambium and periderm having an almost unlimited capacity to join up around any obstacle. The inclusion of metal objects is a danger to sawmill machinery. Similarly a scorched patch, or even letters cut into the bark, will always result in some permanent damage, no matter how complete the external healing may be.

In view of the plasticity of the cambium it is not surprising that when stems are accidentally pressed together they sometimes coalesce in a natural graft. Deliberate grafting of woody plants is an important part of horticultural practice. There are many styles of grafting, but all of them aim to bring the cambial layers of the two plants into the closest possible contact. Even then it is necessary (though by no means always sufficient) that there should be close genetical affinity between the two individuals. The grafting of herbaceous plants, especially of monocotyledons, is more difficult, and rarely undertaken except for experimental purposes.

5 THE STRUCTURE OF ROOTS

The root is an organ with remarkable characteristics, and its structure is surprisingly uniform in nearly all the plants in which it occurs. Even the roots of ferns are very similar to those of flowering plants, though the stems of ferns display an organisation fundamentally different from that of angiosperm stems. Almost all living vascular plants possess roots; the only exceptions are a few highly specialised parasites and water plants in which the production of roots has been abandoned, and one or two "living fossils", survivors of ancient groups of plants in which the ability to produce roots seems never to have appeared.

The root is typically a cylindrical organ of small diameter, penetrating the soil and absorbing water and minerals. At its first formation each piece of root is entirely lacking in lateral appendages of any sort. The root apex produces a uniform cylinder of tissue, without any distinction between nodes and internodes, and any branch root or other lateral structure which may eventually appear is an entirely separate and later development.

The examination of the entire root system of a plant is a laborious business, the kind of excavation involved in gardening operations being quite insufficient to reveal the true extent of the system. Often one sees only a few of the principal roots, which may be rather thick; in reality most plants have an enormous total length of root, the greater part of the mileage consisting of delicate filamentous strands (see p. 199).

A seedling begins life with one primary root or radicle (p. 132) and in some cases the entire root system of the mature plant is derived from this. A main root which is specially conspicuous in the mature root system may be called the **tap-root**. In many plants, however, an important part is played by roots which are not derived from the radicle at all. The word "adventitious" is often applied to plant organs arising in places where their appearance is in any way unexpected. Accordingly a root which grows from a stem or leaf is an **adventitious root**, while a bud springing from a root is an adventitious bud. It is difficult to see what is gained by this practice, and it would certainly be quite wrong to suppose that there was anything abnormal about an adventitious root; in nearly all herbaceous perennials all the roots of a mature plant are adventitious.

A few roots swell into storage organs, as, for example, in the tap-root tubers of biennials (p. 62). Tuberous roots occur also in some perennials, notably in *Dahlia, Orchis, Ranunculus ficaria*, and sweet potato. Although these tubers often become involved in vegetative propagation the new shoot does not grow from the root itself; the unit of propagation in *Dahlia*, for instance, is a root-tuber with an associated piece of stem carrying an axillary bud. Storage is in the root, but growth is from a pre-existing shoot. It is in fact very uncommon for a root to give rise to shoot-buds (see pp. 67, 70).

The Root Apex

The rate of division of the cells of a root apex is typically several times that of the cells at the apex of a stem. In actively growing herbaceous plants the time elapsing between successive divisions may be about 24-30 hours in the root tip, but at least three or four times as long in the apex of the stem. The action of the root meristem is also more uniform, with no special areas of increased growth such as are responsible for the first appearance of leaves.

Although the arrangement of the cells in the apical part of a root is often very regular, more so in fact than in most stems, it has not proved possible to trace any constant relationship between the geometry of the apex and the various tissue-layers of the mature root (Fig. 61, B and Plate 7). One universal feature of root apices is the presence of a **root cap**, which is a thimble-shaped mass of parenchyma fitting over the meristem proper. In typical subterranean roots there can be little doubt that the cap is protective in function; as the root advances through the soil the apex is forced between the soil particles, and there is a constant loss of cells from the outside of the cap, balanced by the addition of new cells to the inside. A cap is present, however, even in roots which are not subject to friction or abrasion.

The high rate of nuclear division, and the absence of troublesome enveloping leaves, make the root tip a specially convenient experimental subject. In modern times root tips have been used for studies upon the synthesis of DNA (p. 168), radioactive thymidine (an intermediate in the synthesis of DNA from simpler molecules) being supplied and the distribution of radioactivity in the nuclei being subsequently investigated by laying sections of root against a photographic emulsion (p. 245). This work unexpectedly shows that a root apex commonly possesses a central core, the so-called **quiescent centre** (Fig. 61, B) which lies between the root cap and the main body of the meristem, and which consists of cells almost identical in appearance with those adjacent to them, but with a very much lower rate of division. A newly emerging root has no quiescent centre, but as growth proceeds more and more of the central cells of the meristem, without any significant change in appearance, practically cease to divide, until a substantial mass of inert tissue is formed.

Epidermis and Root Hairs

Behind the apical meristem lies a portion of root which is actively elongating, mainly by enlargement of its cells. This elongating region (Fig. 61, A) is much shorter than the corresponding part of a typical stem, but its length will often be several millimetres.

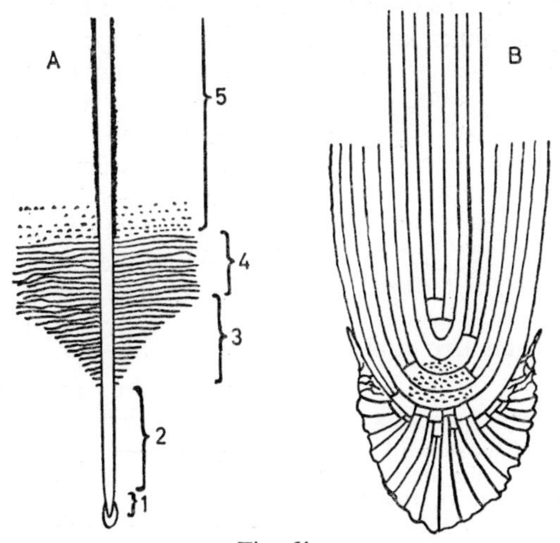

Fig. 61.

A, root tip with cap and hairs: 1, meristem; 2, region of cell-enlargement; 3, growth of root hairs from stationary epidermis; 4, mature root hairs; 5, root hairs dead, surface sealed by exodermis. B, diagrammatic longitudinal section of apex. From the quiescent centre (dotted) radiating lines of cell-flow can be followed into cap and root. In this example there is no independent cap-meristem, though some roots have one. On its outer surface and especially at the fringes, the cap shows crushing and distortion of tissue.

The epidermis of the elongating region is moving relative to the soil particles, and the resulting frictional stimulus is certainly important in the life of the root. Some roots, for instance, have been found to show geotropic responses (p. 290) only when they are frictionally stimulated at the same time. Behind the elongating region the root surface has become stationary. In most roots each portion of epidermis, as soon as it has ceased to slide through the soil, begins to develop **root hairs**. Each hair (Figs. 62, 64) is a simple tubular projection from an epidermal cell, the nucleus usually passing into the hair. In some roots every cell produces a hair; in others there is a very regular alternation between cells which produce hairs and others which do not. The hairs multiply by quite a large factor the total surface area of the root upon which they stand, and there can be little doubt that they are the principal absorbing organs of the plant.

Root hairs are delicate structures with flimsy walls, and the life of each hair is usually less than a week. There is therefore a definite root-hair zone which follows the root apex through the soil, new hairs being produced at the front and old ones dying and disappearing at the back. Death of the hairs involves the loss of the entire epidermis (sometimes known as the piliferous layer) and the outermost layer of cortical cells (the **exodermis** or hypodermis), with some cutinisation of its walls, assumes a protective character which is inconsistent with any large-scale absorption by the older part of the root. The exploitation of the soil by roots is therefore fundamentally a shifting exploitation, and the actual volume of soil upon which a plant is drawing at any moment is much less than the total volume occupied by its root system. In time of drought this may have important consequences (see p. 199). The wilting which often follows transplanting is due to the loss of root hairs, and the time taken to recover is roughly equal to the time taken to grow a new crop of hairs. In water plants, and in plants with a fungal associate (see mycorrhiza, p. 570) root hairs are often not formed at all.

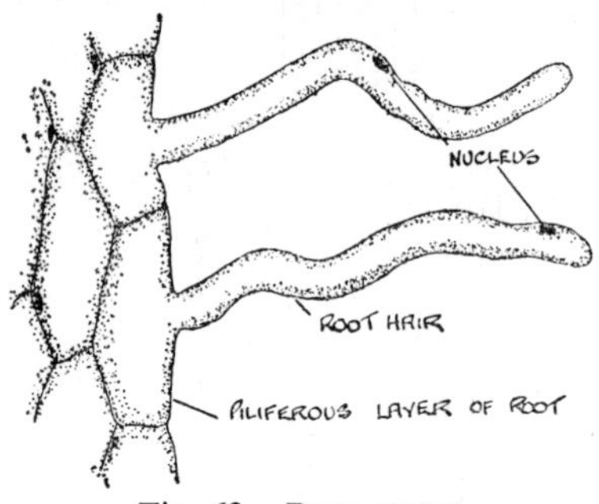

Fig. 62. Root hairs.
The smooth outlines shown here are only found when root hairs are grown in fluid media. In soil the hairs are always kinked and distorted.

Vascular Differentiation

The xylem and phloem of a root are not usually very different from those of the stem of the same plant, but because the elongating region in most roots is so short there is not the extreme and destructive stretching of the protoxylem and protophloem which occurs in many stems.

The distribution of the vascular tissues is quite different from that found in most stems. Usually a root has a single central pro-cambial strand and the differentiation of both xylem and phloem begins in the outer part of this strand. Protoxylem and protophloem groups alternate regularly around the circumference, and the development of both tissues progresses towards the centre. The xylem is invariably in the lead, and in many roots xylem differentiation proceeds to the centre (Fig. 63). Such a root has

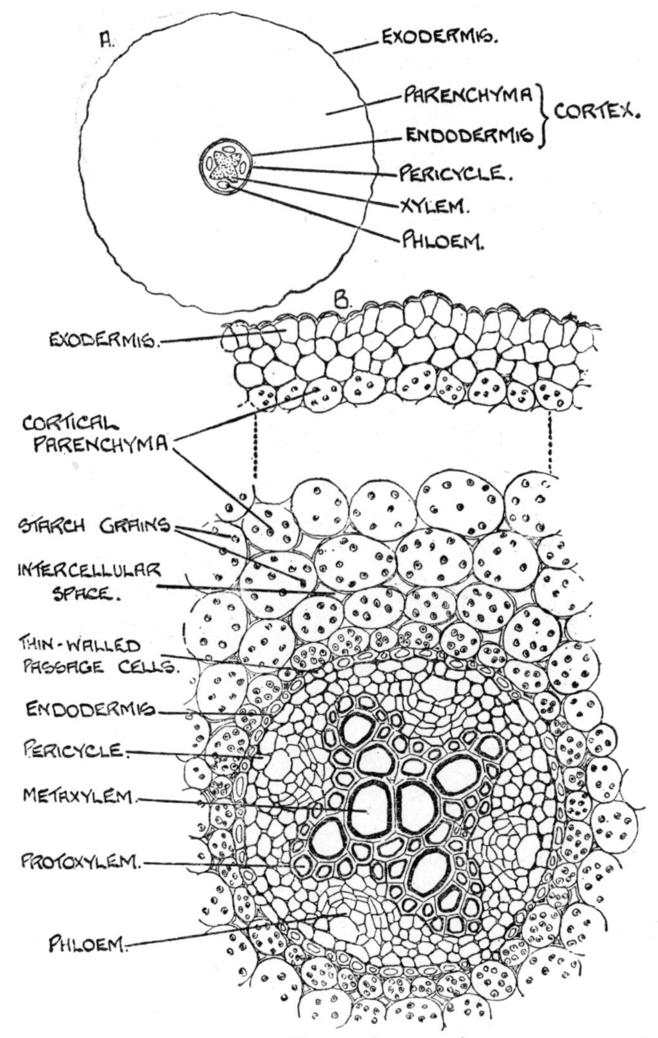

Fig. 63. ROOT OF DICOTYLEDON (*Ranunculus repens*) IN TRANSVERSE SECTION. A, diagrammatic; B, detail.

no pith. Its xylem forms a star, with a protoxylem group at the tip of each arm, and an equal number of phloem groups occupying the bays between the arms. There are, however, many roots in which the central area differentiates into a parenchymatous pith before the wave of xylem development can reach it (Fig. 64).

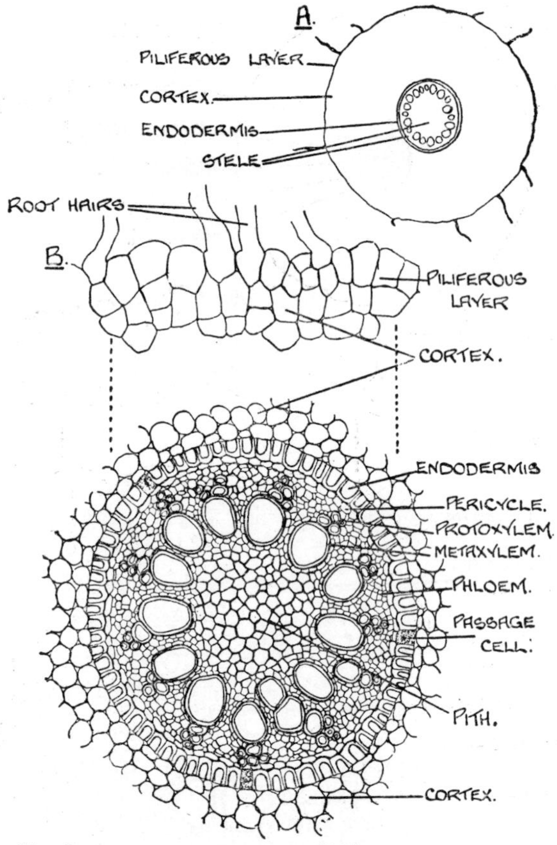

Fig. 64. ROOT OF MONOCOTYLEDON (*Iris*) IN TRANSVERSE SECTION. A, diagrammatic; B, detail.

The vascular development of a young root normally proceeds to completion. No part of the original procambial strand remains meristematic, and any cambium which may subsequently appear will have to be formed in the same way as the interfascicular cambium of a stem, by the resumption of meristematic activity in mature tissue.

The number of protoxylem groups in a root is variable. When there are two the root is diarch, when there are three it is triarch, and so on. Generally the number is related to size, a very small apex producing a diarch root while a better-nourished root of the same plant may perhaps be pentarch, with five protoxylem groups. In many dicotyledonous species five is about the largest number ever found. Most polyarch roots, with numerous protoxylems, are those of monocotyledons. The radicle, the first root of the seedling, is in a special category, the number of protoxylems within

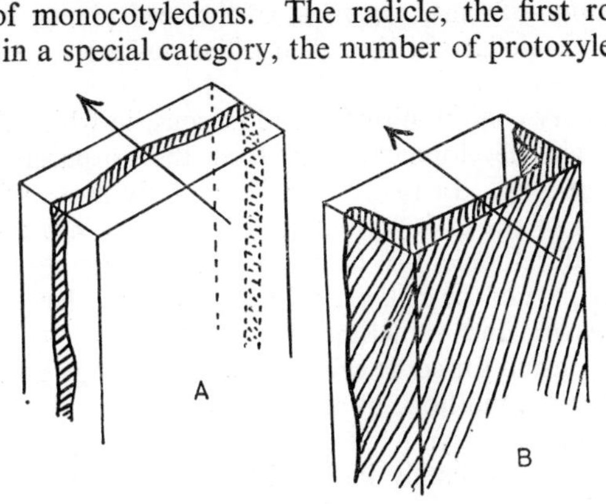

Fig. 65. ENDODERMAL CELLS.
A, top end of cell in primary condition with Casparian strip (shaded). B, portion of cell in secondary condition with heavy thickening burying the Casparian strip. The end of the cell (not shown) would be thickened like the side walls. In each figure the arrow points radially outwards from the centre of the root.

it being usually constant for each species, and most commonly four (tetrarch).

Endodermis and Pericycle

In the great majority of roots there is a single layer of cells known as the endodermis, conventionally regarded as the innermost layer of the cortex, and possessing very distinctive properties. Each endodermal cell has a **Casparian strip**, which is a specialised local impregnation of the wall, involving the production of a material similar to cutin. The Casparian strip runs round all the anticlinal walls and completely encircles the cell (Fig. 65, A). Although the physiological significance of the endodermis is far from clear, the structure is evidently such that any substance passing through the endodermal layer in either direction must pass through the living endodermal cells. It cannot diffuse along the wall between one endodermal cell and its neighbour, for the Casparian strip, which is impermeable, lies in the way. The endodermal cells are therefore in a position to exercise very complete control over the movement of materials between cortex and vascular system. It is interesting in this connection that when endodermal cells are plasmolysed (p. 185) their protoplasts cling very tenaciously to the Casparian strip.

An endodermis is found not only in roots but also in the stems of ferns and other lower plants, and also very frequently in the stems of aquatic angiosperms. In most of the seed plants, however, the stem has no endodermis, though it often possesses a starch sheath in a similar position.

The **primary** condition of the endodermis, in which the cell walls have no special development apart from the Casparian strip, often does not last long. In many roots, especially those of monocotyledons, most of the endodermal cells soon pass into the **secondary** state by the development of heavy lignified thickening which covers all the inner part of the cell, extending outwards at least as far as the Casparian strip, and sometimes further (Fig. 65, B). When this happens it is usual for some cells, known as **passage cells**, to remain in the primary condition, at least for an extended period, if not absolutely permanently.

The tissue immediately inside the endodermis of a root is the **pericycle**. It is usually a small-celled parenchyma of thin-walled cells without intercellular spaces, its principal importance being as the site of secondary meristematic activity. From the situation at the points of the protoxylem it seems clear that the pericycle as first formed must be regarded as a layer strictly one cell in thickness, but in most young roots it is not noticeably different in character from the adjoining **conjunctive parenchyma** which lies between the xylem and the phloem. In most angiosperm stems there is apparently no tissue equivalent to the pericycle of the root.

Secondary Vascular Tissues

The cambium in a root first appears as a system of periclinal divisions in the conjunctive parenchyma between each phloem group and the bay of the metaxylem star. The cambium soon becomes continuous by the initiation of periclinal division also in the portions of pericycle which lie against the protoxylem points. So far as the production of cambium is concerned, pericycle and conjunctive parenchyma behave as a single tissue. The cambium, like that of a stem, produces xylem internally and phloem externally (Fig. 66), and in woody plants the transverse section of an old root is not very different from that of an old stem, though the primary xylem at its centre will, of course, retain its distinctive configuration.

In herbaceous plants it is common for rather large parts of the secondary xylem, especially those which lie opposite the protoxylem points, to consist of parenchyma, often unlignified. Sections of large roots often therefore present a peculiar appearance which can hardly be matched from any stem, but it is only in a small proportion of cases (*e.g.* beetroot, with many concentric cambial cylinders) that there is any fundamental abnormality in the course of development.

Unless the amount of secondary tissue is very restricted the original waviness of the cambial surface is soon evened out so that the woody core becomes truly cylindrical. Although there are exceptions on both sides, most dicotyledons develop secondary tissues in the root while most monocotyledons do not.

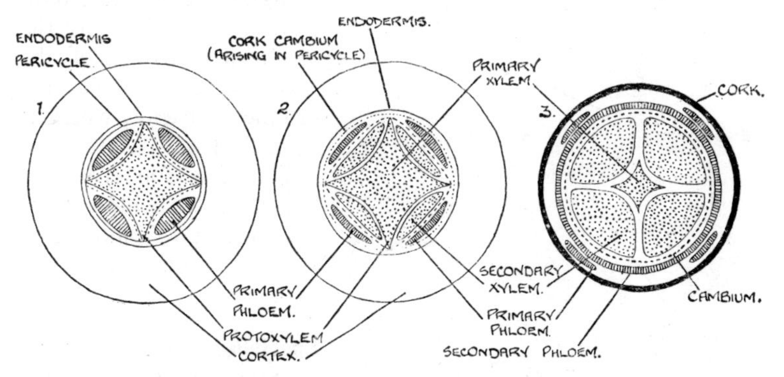

Fig. 66. ILLUSTRATING STAGES IN SECONDARY THICKENING IN A DICOTYLEDONOUS ROOT (Diagrammatic).

Meristematic Activity in the Pericycle

Besides the contribution which the pericycle makes to the formation of the cambium there are two other ways in which periclinal division in the cells of the pericycle can lead to the production of new tissues.

The pericycle is the usual site for the development of periderm in a root, and in large roots a continuous periderm, complete with lenticels, is formed in essentially the same manner as is seen in stems. The origin of a periderm from the outer cortex, which is the commoner pattern in stems, is rare in roots.

Localised periclinal division in the pericycle is also the first stage in the production of a lateral root. A little swelling of the pericycle is formed which gradually organises itself into a root apex, complete with root cap, pointing outwards from the vascular system more or less perpendicular to the endodermal surface. This lateral root then grows independently, bursting and digesting its way through the outer tissues which lie in its path. This internal or endogenous origin is characteristic of roots generally; only in the rarest and most exceptional circumstances does a root arise at the surface of a plant. When a root arises, as many do, from a stem which has no pericycle, or from an old root in which the pericycle has been used up in the production of a periderm, the new root apex is formed from the phloem of the parent organ.

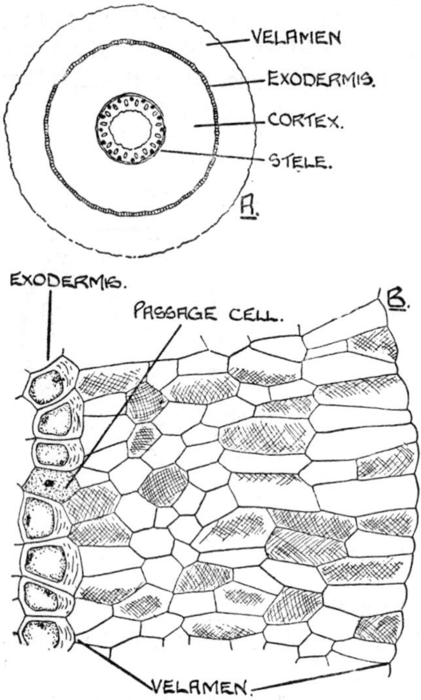

Fig. 67. EPIPHYTIC ORCHID, TRANSVERSE SECTION, AERIAL ROOT.

Although there is no universal law, the production of lateral roots is in many cases concentrated on or near the radii where the protoxylem groups of the parent root lie. Thus, for instance, a carrot, which is formed from a tetrarch radicle, has four rows of lateral roots, while a beetroot, which is formed from a diarch radicle, has only two.

Specialised Forms of Root

Not only do roots display great uniformity in the general arrangement of their tissues, but their capacity for producing detailed refinements of cellular construction is curiously limited. The root is, for instance, the only major organ of the higher plants which is incapable of producing stomata, nor does it ever have anything but the very simplest kind of epidermal hair. The conditions of life are perhaps more uniform below ground than above, but this cannot be a complete explanation for the lack of flexibility in the organisation of roots, because even roots which are unusual in their way of life (photosynthetic roots of epiphytes; spine-like roots growing from the trunks of palms) show in most cases no corresponding elaboration of structure.

The peculiarities of behaviour which we have already noted (p. 67) in the roots of some woody plants involve no very profound structural modification, but call only for the exaggeration of tendencies already present in a wide range of roots. Even the grafting activities of the roots of *Ficus* are really rather commonplace, for we know from experiments with radioactive tracers that in ordinary woodlands adjoining trees of the same species are connected by root grafts more often than not (which may sometimes be important in the spread of disease). The frequency with which roots must find themselves in contact (immovably, we must remember) with the roots of other plants has no doubt been a factor in the evolution of the many parasitic angiosperms in which the connection with the host is effected by the roots.

Almost the only specialisation of the root which involves any real refinement of structure is found in some epiphytic orchids where the surface tissue or **velamen** (Fig. 67) consists of dead empty cells with special wall-thickenings and the underlying exodermis is differentiated into thick-walled cells and passage cells. The velamen acts like a sponge, and the water which it absorbs passes by way of the passage cells into the inner tissues of the root. These roots are aerial, and the cortex is photosynthetic, the whole root appearing white when the velamen is full of air, green when it is saturated with water.

6 SEEDS AND SEEDLINGS

Although vegetative propagation is important in many species and predominates in some, it is very doubtful whether any wild angiosperm has entirely given up the production of seed. In all short-lived species, and in the great majority of perennials as well, the seed is an indispensable means of survival and spread. Every seed is the end-product of a long and complex series of processes which it is unnecessary to consider here (Chapter 12). For the present it will be enough to take the ripe seed as it comes from the parent plant, and to see what is involved in **germination**, which is the first beginning of independent growth, and in the establishment of a **seedling** or young plant.

Every normal seed contains an **embryo** (sometimes more than one, p. 376), which will develop into the seedling, and a supply of **reserve substances** which will sustain the seedling in the early stages of growth before it becomes self-supporting. It is an obvious biological necessity that the contents of a seed should be compact and that they should have good keeping qualities. It is therefore not surprising that a resting seed should have a very low water content and that all its physiological processes should be extremely slow. These properties very largely account for the special importance of seeds (particularly the cereal grains) in the history of the human race. Corn and rice can easily be stored and traded, imported and exported. Under primitive conditions it is impossible to do any of these things with vegetative structures like cabbages or potatoes. Other things being equal, the amount of reserve material present would be proportional to the weight of the seed. In this respect it is important to appreciate that the seeds customarily employed in teaching are quite exceptional. For convenience in dissection such examples as the broad bean and sunflower are usually chosen; they are not in any way abnormal in their structure, but they are gigantic. The average seed is a tiny thing.

In many seeds the reserve materials are contained within the embryo itself, and in that case the embryo will make up the greater part of the total bulk. There are, however, almost as many cases where the reserve substances, or a great part of them, are contained in a remarkable structure known as the **endosperm**, which must be thought of as a kind of freakish, short-lived half-brother to the embryo. An endosperm is present in every developing angiosperm seed; it is just a question of how soon the embryo can digest the endosperm and absorb such nutritive materials as it may contain. When this digestive process is completed early, so that the endosperm disappears before the seed is ripe, the seed is **non-endospermic**. An **endospermic** seed is one in which the endosperm survives at least until the time of germination. Although the balance is variable, most endospermic seeds carry their main reserve in the endosperm, with the embryo making less, and often very much less, than half the total bulk. Few seeds have any significant reserves beyond those contained in embryo and endosperm, but occasionally one finds **perisperm**, which is a parental tissue (persistent nucellus of the ovule, see p. 369).

The embryo and its reserves are always enclosed in a protective covering. In dealing with this it is to be noted that many structures which are commonly known as seeds are in fact one-seeded fruits. The distinction between the **testa**, which is the covering layer of the seed, and the **pericarp**, which is the wall of the fruit, is an important one and must be carefully maintained. When a gardener sows radishes or beans the things he is handling are seeds, each enclosed in a testa. When he sows lettuces or lawn grasses he is dealing with one-seeded fruits, each consisting of a seed (with its testa) enclosed in a pericarp. In cases where it remains attached to the seed the pericarp naturally takes over some of the protective functions which are elsewhere performed by the testa. In the Brazil nut, which is a seed, the hard shell is the testa; in the acorn, which is a fruit, it is the pericarp which forms the shell, the testa being only a flimsy papery layer. Whatever its origin the protective coating is always a highly specialised tissue, often with several very different layers of cells, presumably with different functions, about which very little is known. The cell walls are thickened, and heavily impregnated with materials like cutin and suberin. Even where it is not particularly hard or thick the coating is usually very resistant to decay or to the action of chemical reagents. In many cases also it is highly impervious to water. As the embryo has usually to absorb external water if the seed is to germinate, the coating cannot remain watertight indefinitely, but there are many cases where a seed can absorb water only through a small part of its surface, or only after the resistance of the coating has been broken down by slow processes of softening and decay.

The inner tissues of a resting seed are almost wholly parenchymatous, though the embryo has an immature vascular system. These tissues are usually hard and horny owing to their low water content. In the first stages of germination there is an absorption of water and a pronounced softening of the tissues; the dissection of most of the seeds described in the later part of this chapter is much easier after the specimens have been soaked in water for a day. This absorption of water is often very rapid, so that the weight of the seed may be doubled in a few hours, and it causes an expansion of the tissues which is sufficiently powerful to overcome considerable mechanical resistance. The swelling commonly bursts the testa or pericarp, and can be caused experimentally to burst strong containers (*e.g.* a glass bottle, packed with dry peas and plunged in water). The seeds of cultivated plants which are ordinarily grown from seed will swell and germinate almost at once if they are given the minimum conditions for growth (*i.e.* water, air, and a reasonable temperature), and the process of germination can be conveniently observed by placing seeds in moist sand or sawdust. Such studies are apt to give a misleading impression of the behaviour of seeds in general. In many plants the seed is **dormant**, which means that instead of germinating as soon as the conditions are appropriate for growth it waits until it has been, as it were, unlocked or triggered-off by some particular treatment. The treatment required to break the dormancy of a seed varies in different cases: some need exposure to light, some need a period of frost, and so on. Once dormancy is broken, the seed will germinate in conditions exactly similar to those which failed to make it germinate before (see p. 303).

Longevity

In conditions which do not permit germination a seed will remain **viable** (that is, capable of germination) for some time, though dormancy effects often become harder to overcome as time passes. Eventually, however, even a resting seed will die, almost always without any detectable change in its appearance. Ordinarily the only way to find out whether a seed is viable or not is to give it the appropriate conditions for germination and see what happens. Even then a negative result is not conclusive; failure to germinate may indicate a dead seed, or it may be due to dormancy which the experimental procedure failed to break.

In uncontrolled or "natural" conditions of storage many seeds soon lose their viability. With seeds which have fairly permeable coats and which germinate readily when moistened, the period of survival ranges from a few days (willows and poplars) to about twenty-five or thirty years (some grasses and legumes). The longer periods and the very short ones are relatively uncommon; with most species in this category (which, of course, includes all the common crops) death at two to five years may be regarded as the normal thing. In any one seed sample the death rate is low at first, then rises to a peak which brings the death of most of the seeds, and falls again until the death of the last survivor. With wheat, for instance, a very few seeds may survive twenty years or even a little longer, but most are dead at twelve, and some are dead at five. Where the expectation of life is short (not more than a year or two) it is often possible to maintain viability far beyond the normal term by controlling the conditions of storage. This usually involves keeping the seed in dry air at a temperature only slightly above freezing. In the laboratory poplar seeds can be kept viable for at least twenty times their normal span. Seeds which naturally live longer do not react in this way; so far as can be seen at present no amount of tinkering will make much difference to life-spans of ten years and over.

An old collection of seeds, especially if it can be accurately dated, is likely to arouse the record-breaking instinct in a botanist who comes across it. What is the very oldest seed that can be made to grow? All the really noteworthy figures come from hard-coated seeds, those which are impermeable to water and often take many years to start off, even in continuously wet conditions. (For experimental purposes one nicks the coating with a file, or softens it with sulphuric acid.) Among the hard-coated seeds, which occur in a large number of species, survival to eighty years is certainly quite common, and there are several reliable records (all for rather large seeds) in the range 150-200 years. Beyond this it is difficult to go, because a dated collection of seeds more than 200 years old is a very uncommon thing. It will not, however, be very surprising if the figures ultimately have to be raised a little. Very much longer periods of survival, running into thousands of years, have sometimes been claimed, but are not generally accepted.

The Nature of the Reserves

In many seeds, of which rice is the outstanding commercial example, there is a very high proportion of starch among the reserve materials, so much in fact that the energy expended by the growing seedling in the period before it begins to photosynthesise must be almost wholly derived from this starch supply. Every seed contains also a reserve of proteins, sufficient in all cases for the growth which occurs before the plant becomes self-supporting.

Perhaps the most characteristic seed reserve material, however, is fat, normally in a liquid form. This is biologically intelligible, because fats, having a low oxygen content, have a higher calorific value than carbohydrates (p. 224). Oxygen is not a fuel, and can in any case always be obtained from the atmosphere. Considered as a fuel, starch is merely diluted by the oxygen which it contains. More calories can be packed into a given bulk and weight by storing fat. It is significant that many plants which accumulate starch in their vegetative storage organs nevertheless produce oily seeds, and interesting also that oily seeds usually contain only tiny quantities of starch.

It must not be forgotten that *all* the requirements for the early growth of the seedling must be met from the supplies in the seed, with the single exception of water. Until the root system is established there will be no reliable external source of minerals, nor is a very young seedling in a favourable position for the production of substances like vitamins, which, though required only in minute quantities, are essential for growth. In fact, a seed ordinarily contains a rather concentrated supply of mineral elements, with, sometimes, a noticeably generous stock of the rarer ones. There is also a complete set of vitamins and hormones, or of closely related substances, which can readily be converted into the active forms.

The Parts of the Embryo

There are some seeds, notably those of orchids, in which the embryo in the ripe seed is still at such an early stage of development that distinct organs cannot be recognised. Ordinarily, however, the embryo at the time when the seed is shed has a well-developed root tip or **radicle**, which is continuous with a stem-like organ known as the **hypocotyl**, and one or more **cotyledons**, which are fleshy lobes connected to the upper end of the hypocotyl, that is to the end furthest from the radicle.

It was formerly the custom to regard the cotyledons as leaves. This idea began as a flight of fancy by Goethe, the German poet; its adoption leads to no useful result. It is true that some cotyledons show leaf-like tendencies in their behaviour. They may for instance possess axillary buds. There is, however, quite as much to be said against this view, and in practice it is always necessary to make a clear distinction between a leaf and a cotyledon.

The number of cotyledons is variable. The flowering plants consist of two great series, the **monocotyledons** and the **dicotyledons**, and it is, of course, a general rule, as the form of these names would suggest, that a monocotyledon has one cotyledon while a dicotyledon has two. Exceptions occur, however, in significant numbers. In a very high proportion of dicotyledonous species, seedlings are occasionally seen with more than two cotyledons. Examples can often be found where large numbers of seedlings are being grown. Similarly, though only very rarely, a monocotyledonous species may produce a small proportion of individuals with two cotyledons. There are also some dicotyledonous species (e.g. *Ranunculus ficaria*) in which the seedling has quite regularly only a single cotyledon. In many conifers there are several cotyledons, up to a dozen or so, standing in a whorl upon the hypocotyl.

The condition of the stem apex or **plumule** at the time of germination varies greatly. In some of the larger seeds with substantial reserves the plumule is well developed, with several of its leaves clearly visible. It is, however, more usual for the growth of the plumule to be delayed, so that the shoot at the time of germination consists only of an undifferentiated apical meristem. When there are two or more cotyledons the plumule occupies a central position between them, and its growth from the first continues in the direct line of the hypocotyl. In monocotyledons there is a strong tendency for the cotyledon to lie in line with the hypocotyl, so that the

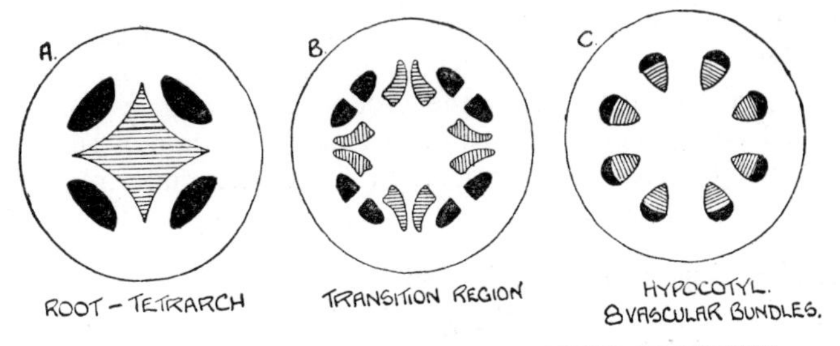

Fig. 68. TRANSITION FROM ROOT TO HYPOCOTYL IN SEEDLING OF *Ricinus*.

plumule grows out of a notch or slit in the side of the seedling. These differences are not important, but they can lead to some puzzling differences in the appearance of seedlings.

The radicle has the typical anatomy of a root, and differs from the other roots of the species principally in having a constant number of protoxylem groups. (Most species of flowering plants have four, but there are a good many with only two. Other numbers are much less common.) The hypocotyl has in all essentials the anatomy of a stem, though there are some differences in the detailed arrangement of the vascular bundles. It follows that between the hypocotyl and the radicle there must be a region in which substantial rearrangement of the vascular tissues is accomplished. The protoxylem must pass from the external position in the radicle to an internal one in the hypocotyl, and so on. Fig. 68 will sufficiently indicate the kind of re-arrangement which is found.

In the great majority of cases the radicle is the first part of the embryo to start into active growth, and it behaves in a typically root-like manner as soon as it emerges from the seed. The cotyledons are much more variable in their functions. In most non-endospermic seeds the main reserves are in the cotyledons, which are then usually very thick. (There are some exceptional cases in which storage is mainly in the hypocotyl.) In endospermic seeds the digestion and absorption of the endosperm reserve is ordinarily carried out by the cotyledons. Besides these functions of storage and absorption, however, the cotyledons often act as photosynthetic organs. Although there is a very large minority of species in which the cotyledons never escape from the seed coats at all, it is more usual for the cotyledons to be raised into the air and spread out as green leafy structures. This is the basis of the important distinction between **epigeal** forms of germination, in which the cotyledons emerge and photosynthesise, and **hypogeal** forms, in which the cotyledons remain within the coats and make at best a trivial contribution to the photosynthetic activity of the seedling. "Hypogeal" means "below the ground", which is a conception drawn from gardening practice. In nature, although seeds may be buried by accident, germination must often take place upon the surface of the soil.

Biological Aspects of Germination

Many peculiarities in the germination of seeds can be related directly to simple biological needs. The prompt development of the radicle is itself a reflection of the seedling's need for water, and the fact that a wild seed is often not effectively buried no doubt increases the urgency of this need. A seed may, however, be covered, if not with soil at least with leaf-litter. The first photosynthetic organ has therefore to be raised into the air in a manner which will allow it to overcome without damage to itself the resistance of any obstacle which may lie in its way. To push a shoot with lateral appendages, whether leaves or cotyledons, directly through soil or litter, point first, would be liable to sheer off the lateral organs, or at least to bruise or tear them. In fact the majority of seedlings form a definite **hook**, the stem axis being bent sharply back upon itself so that the lateral organs are drawn through any obstruction backwards. In epigeal cases the hook is formed by the hypocotyl and it is the cotyledons which are shielded from harm, while in hypogeal germination the hook is formed by the plumule and the lateral organs are leaves. The principle, however, is the same in both cases, and it is worth noticing that leaves and shoots arising from rhizomes sometimes show a similar effect. Generally these hooks are sensitive to light, and straighten out as soon as they are illuminated; if seedlings are grown in total darkness their hooks often persist indefinitely. The occurrence of hooks is not universal. In particular some monocotyledons have plumules in which all the parts are rolled together to make a spear-like mass which, because of its smooth tapering shape, can be driven straight up through the soil without harm.

In an epigeal seedling the spreading of the cotyledons at once provides a photosynthetic surface which is sufficient to maintain continuous growth of the radicle. There may then be no great urgency about the development of the leaves, and in fact many epigeal seedlings start in life with only the most rudimentary plumule. The parsnip is a typical case of this interrupted type of development, the seedling having a rather prolonged period of independent life before its first leaf reaches a size at which its photosynthetic output can compare with that of the cotyledons. In hypogeal seedlings the position is quite different. Here survival depends upon the establishment of foliage before the reserves are used up. Accordingly the plumule in hypogeal plants is often well developed in the dry seed, with several leaves already formed and ready to expand.

There are some other significant differences in plumular behaviour. In most epigeal seedlings the first few internodes of the plumule are of almost negligible length. The need here is to get leaves out, rather than up. They are up already, because of the growth of the hypocotyl. The first leaves of an epigeal plumule may be of small size and simplified shape, but their status as foliage leaves, effective organs of photosynthesis, is never in doubt. In hypogeal cases, on the other hand, the first task of the plumule is elongation. Not only are its first internodes usually of considerable length, but its first few leaves are often mere cataphylls, so that the plumule may be several internodes high before irreplaceable reserves are committed to the production of a normal lamina.

These biological relationships are undoubtedly very important. The conditions of survival for a seedling are much more critical than those for an established plant of the same species. The special needs of the seedling are often the decisive factor in determining whether or not a particular species can grow in a particular place.

Some features of seedling behaviour are related to the mechanical necessities of the situation rather than to biological requirements. When, for instance, a seed has a very large supply of reserve materials, then the cotyledons will either be very bulky or they will be for a long time fully occupied with the digestion and absorption of a massive endosperm. It is therefore hardly surprising that really big seeds are predominantly hypogeal.

The Seedlings of Leguminosae

The seedlings of the Leguminosae (p. 414) are particularly suitable subjects for a student's first practical exercises, because of their large size, the diversity of their behaviour, and the very definite arrangement of their parts. These plants are dicotyledons, all those commonly seen in Europe being non-endospermic.

Broad bean (*Vicia faba*, Fig. 69). Upon the testa of the intact seed is a dark elongated marking known as the **hilum.** This is the place where the seed was attached to a stalk springing from the wall of the pod. At one end of the hilum is a small opening known as the **micropyle**, the position of which is readily revealed by wiping a soaked seed and then squeezing it gently so that a little water is driven out through the pore. (Although many other seeds have an open micropyle like that of the broad bean it must not be supposed that this situation is universal. Every seed possesses a micropyle, but in many cases it is completely closed by the time the seed is ripe, so that water passes through it no more easily than through any other part of the testa.)

Inside the testa is a massive embryo, with the two cotyledons filling by far the greater part of the volume. The radicle, though stout, is quite short, and points towards the micropyle. This arrangement, which is found in all seeds, is a consequence of the way in which the embryo develops, and there is no reason to believe that the micropyle is ever of any special significance in providing a way of escape for the radicle. The plumule of the broad bean is in a relatively advanced state of preparation, with several leaves clearly visible. The reserves, which are almost wholly in the cotyledons, consist mainly of starch and protein.

Germination is hypogeal, the emergence of the radicle being followed very soon by that of the plumule. There is a conspicuous plumular hook, which straightens when it comes into the light. The reserves in the broad bean are greatly in excess of the minimum required to support the early growth of the radicle and plumule. Up to half of each cotyledon can be cut off before sowing, and the plant will still grow almost normally if the mutilated seed is placed in the surface layer of soil. At least half of the reserves, therefore, may be available as an insurance against unfavourable conditions such as germination at an excessive depth.

The plumule grows into a four-angled stem with leaves in a distichous arrangement (p. 55), and with the first leaf on the side away from the two cotyledons. The first two leaves are cataphylls, very similar to the stipules and petiole bases of the foliage leaves which follow. The third leaf (which is the first foliage leaf) has two leaflets, its rachis ending in a little point between them.

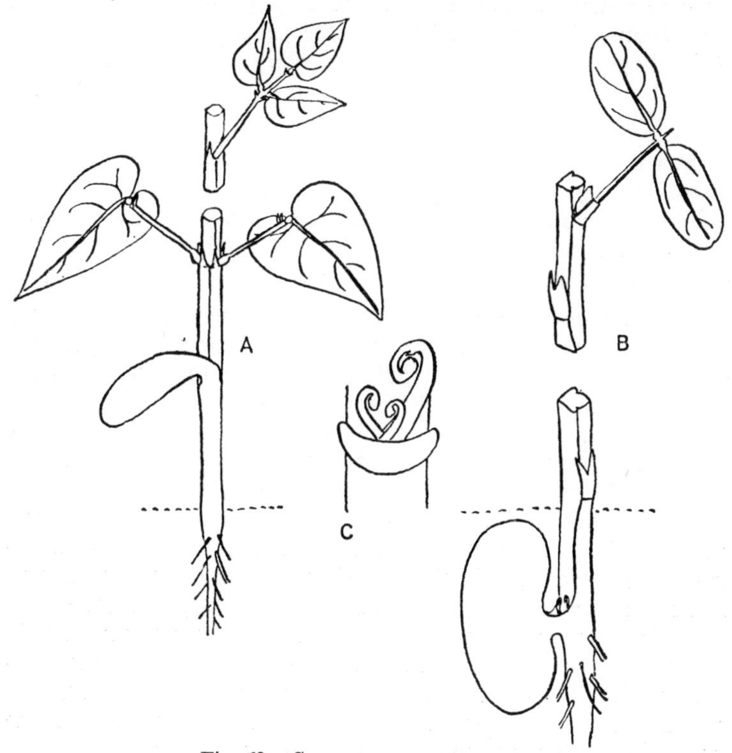

Fig. 69. STRUCTURE OF SEEDLINGS.
A, French bean; B, broad bean; C, front view of a node of broad bean, showing three axillary buds.

A few other leaves of similar construction follow, but the upper leaves (usually the eighth or ninth onwards), have more than two leaflets each. In the axil of each cotyledon, and of each of the lower leaves, is a series of axillary buds (Fig. 69, C). By the time the plant has unfolded a few foliage leaves there are usually three or four clearly visible buds at each node. The great excess of reserves in the cotyledons makes it possible by cutting the plant to cause exaggerated development of any bud as required. If, for instance, at an early stage the plumule is cut off below its first cataphyll the principal axillary bud of each cotyledon will grow out. If now these two shoots are cut off below their own first leaves, the subordinate axillary buds of the cotyledons will be induced to grow, and so on. By this kind of manipulation as many as six or seven shoots can often be produced from one axil before the plant is exhausted. In many bean varieties some of the upper leaves of the plumule (usually about the fifth to the eighth) have no axillary buds at all, though at a higher level still the production of axillary buds is resumed with the onset of flowering.

Pea (*Pisum sativum*). The pea is very closely related to the broad bean and the seedling is similar in plan, but all the parts are smaller. There are some differences in the details of behaviour; examine, for instance, the arrangement of the buds in the cotyledonary axils of a sample of each species.

French bean (*Phaseolus vulgaris*). Although a member of the same family, this plant is not very closely related to the previous examples, and differs considerably from them in the structure of the seedling. The testa and embryo are very similar to those of other Leguminosae, but upon germination the hypocotyl forms a hook and withdraws the cotyledons from the soil. These cotyledons, however, do not really open out as one might expect. They are epigeal in position, but, although they become green, their general behaviour is not otherwise very different from that seen in the hypogeal types. Not only do they remain curved to one side as though still imprisoned in the seed, but instead of growing, as most epigeal cotyledons do, into broad photosynthetic structures, they merely shrivel as the reserves are withdrawn from them. Above the cotyledons (Fig. 69, A) the plumule produces two leaves which are opposite, followed by other leaves in a spiral succession. All the leaves are compound, the leaflets having pulvini and stipels, but whereas the later leaves have three leaflets each the two leaves of the first pair have only one leaflet each.

This pattern of development is a most interesting one, with many points which call for comparison with other plants. The fact that the first plumular leaves are simpler in form than those which follow is merely an instance of an almost universal principle; in plants with compound leaves (*e.g.* ash, laburnum, elder) or with lobed leaves (*e.g.* thistles, *Delphinium*, carrots) the seedling is likely to attain the full complexity of leaf only by stages. The fact that the two first plumular leaves are opposite, though the later ones are alternate, can also be regarded as a rather extreme case of a very widespread phenomenon (p. 82).

One thing which stands out, however, is the presence in this epigeal seedling of features which are more usually associated with hypogeal development. Quite apart from the behaviour of the cotyledons themselves one cannot overlook the remarkable precocity of the first two leaves, or the enormous length (by epigeal standards) of the first plumular internode. In fact there is every reason to suspect that this plant has had hypogeal ancestors in the not very distant past. Our next example adds further weight to this theory.

Scarlet runner bean (*Phaseolus multiflorus*). The relationship between this species and the French bean is extremely close, and in

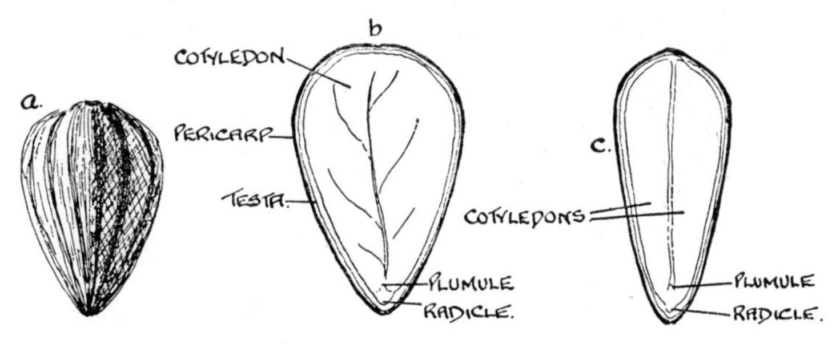

Fig. 70. SUNFLOWER SEED.
A, external; B, embryo; C, section at right angles to cotyledons.

many respects the seedlings are almost indistinguishable. The runner bean, however, is hypogeal, with a plumular hook.

Seedlings of other Dicotyledons

Sunflower (*Helianthus annuus*). In this case the commercial "seed" is in fact a one-seeded fruit, and the effective coating (Fig. 70) is the pericarp, in which, of course, it is useless to look for a micropyle. Inside the hard shell the embryo normally lies quite loosely, but with two or three delicate membranes adhering closely to it. Not all this papery material is part of the testa. Some of it is inner pericarp, and in most specimens the complete exposure of the testa would call for much patient and skilful dissection. The testa has a vascular system, a single vascular strand running up one side of the seed and dividing into three or more branches, which run over the top and down the far side. These veins are probably important in the development of the seed, but their activity is at an end when the seed is ripe.

Germination follows a typical epigeal pattern, with no endosperm. The plumule is, at the time of germination, a mere cone of undifferentiated meristem. The cotyledons are photosynthetic for some time and grow considerably beyond their original size. The first plumular leaves appear late, and the internodes associated with

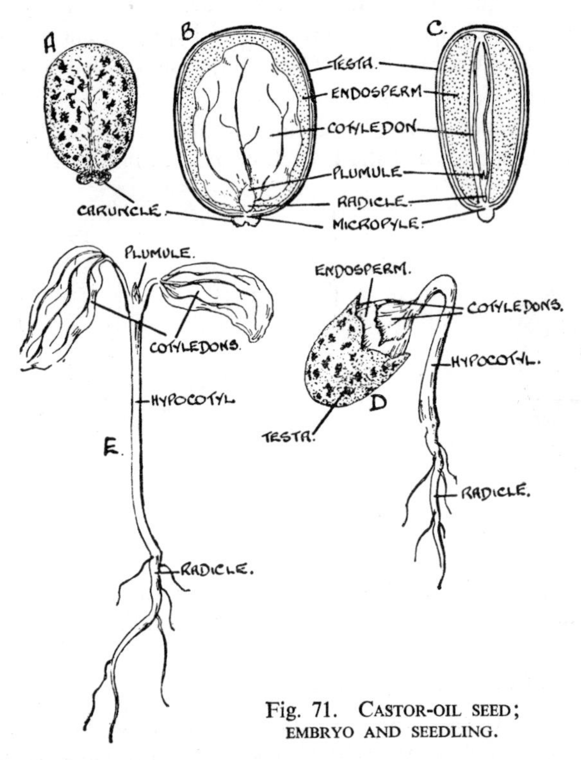

Fig. 71. CASTOR-OIL SEED; EMBRYO AND SEEDLING.

them are very short. The reserves in this species consist predominantly of oil, though there are substantial amounts of protein as well.

Castor-oil (*Ricinus communis*). This is an endospermic seed. At one end (Fig. 71) is a fleshy two-lobed **caruncle**, an outgrowth of the testa which overlaps the micropyle. The micropyle in this instance is not an open pore. In the outer coating of this seed three layers can be distinguished. The outer part of the testa softens upon soaking and can be easily scraped away. Inside this is a hard shelly layer. Removal of this exposes a flimsy membrane containing a system of veins similar in function to those of the sunflower seed, although they are very different in arrangement. The veins here form a complex pattern radiating from a common centre (usually visible as a dark spot) at the end furthest from the micropyle. Removal of the membrane to display this vascular system is a nice exercise in dissection. It is easier to stain the veins by treating the whole kernel with phloroglucin and hydrochloric acid. Within this last membrane lies the endosperm, a mass of parenchyma loaded with reserves of oil and protein. Embedded in the endosperm is the embryo with two large but thin cotyledons, a short radicle, and a very rudimentary plumule. The embryo as a whole

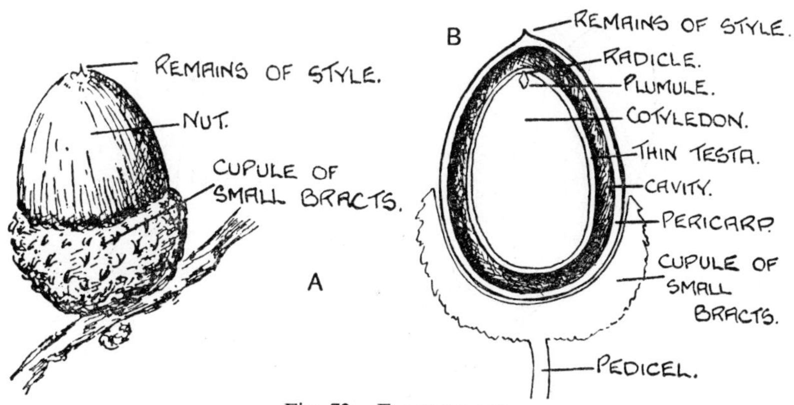

Fig. 72. FRUIT OF OAK.
A, external features; B, L.S. in plane of cotyledons.

is flattened in the plane of the cotyledons, and almost divides the endosperm into two, so that it splits easily along the edge.

Germination is very similar to that of the sunflower with a hypocotylar hook, but with the cotyledons lingering for some time in the endosperm while they drain it of reserve materials. The castor-oil and sunflower illustrate very well the principle, which can be widely applied, that the presence or absence of endosperm in the seed does not in itself make much difference to the general course of germination.

The seed of *Ricinus* is the source of the famous oil, but it should be noted that the seed also contains very poisonous substances from which the medicinal oil has been freed.

Oak (*Quercus*). The acorn (Fig. 72) is a fruit, usually one-seeded, though specimens with several seeds (almost always one much bigger than the others) are not rare. The stony shell is entirely derived from the pericarp, the testa being a thin membrane. The seed is non-endospermic, with massive cotyledons, and germination is hypogeal, with a typical succession of plumular cataphylls.

Sycamore (*Acer pseudoplatanus*). The fruit breaks into two or occasionally three one-seeded portions, each of which has a large wing which is an enlargement of the pericarp, and a chamber containing a single seed (Fig. 73). The seed is non-endospermic, with the embryo folded backwards and forwards in a characteristic way. Germination follows a straightforward epigeal pattern with a pair of foliage leaves at the first plumular node. This species tends to be variable in the number of cotyledons, and where large numbers of

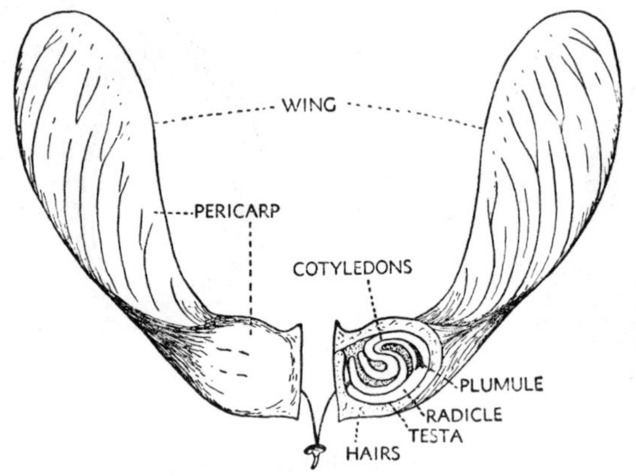

Fig. 73. FRUIT OF SYCAMORE.
Wall of fruit cut away on the right side to show seed with embryo.

seedlings are available it is almost always possible to find a few with three or even four cotyledons. The embryo is outstandingly advanced in its development, with the cotyledons deeply green even in the unopened seed.

Ash (*Fraxinus excelsior*). This is another plant with a winged fruit (Fig. 74), but its seedling makes a rather sharp contrast with that of the sycamore. The seed here is endospermic, with a relatively immature embryo. The reserve is largely in the form of hemicellulose (p. 173) which makes the endosperm rather hard and horny. In the development of the fruit there is an abortion of some of the parts, and as a result the seed is left with a rather complex stalk structure, actually of a compound character, the parts of which are separately labelled in the figure. Germination is epigeal, showing usually a very clear succession of leaf-forms leading up to the pinnate leaves of the established plant.

NOTE.—Besides the examples which have been described, it is desirable for a student to look at a wider selection of the common smaller dicotyledonous vegetable and flower seeds in the early stages of their growth (lettuce, radish, carrot, cabbage, poppy, *Nigella*, etc.). These plants are all epigeal, some of them endospermic, some non-endospermic. Their small size, and the comparative uniformity of their development, will put the peculiarities of the larger types into a truer perspective. They will be of interest also in showing the various ways in which cotyledons may be lobed and folded, and in illustrating the progression of leaf-forms upon the plumule.

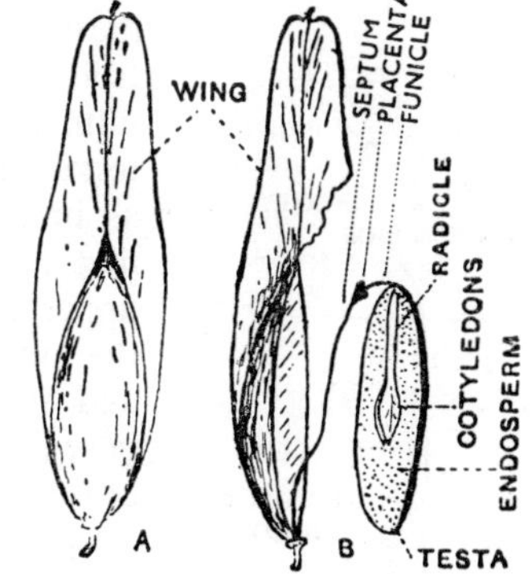

Fig. 74. FRUIT AND SEED OF ASH. A, entire; B, seed exposed and cut so as to show the embryo.

Seedlings of Monocotyledons

It so happens that all the monocotyledonous seeds which are ordinarily employed in elementary teaching are endospermic. Non-endospermic monocotyledons exist, but they are plants which are not convenient for demonstration purposes (orchids, many water plants). Almost all monocotyledons show a strong tendency to develop the main root system from adventitious roots sprouting from the base of the stem, with the radicle and any lateral roots arising from it playing only a minor and essentially temporary part in the life of the plant. There are many monocotyledons in which the radicle never branches at all, and quite a few in which it does not develop far enough to make any significant contribution to the establishment of the plant. In dicotyledons, on the other hand, the radicle almost always grows vigorously and produces many branches. This is true even of species of rhizomatous perennials which will be entirely dependent on adventitious roots in later life.

Onion (*Allium cepa*). The seeds are irregular in shape, and slightly pointed at the micropylar end. Inside is a slender rod-like embryo embedded in endosperm. Upon germination the radicle emerges first. Then, as is common in monocotyledons, there is very active elongation of the lower part of the cotyledon. The whole middle part of the seedling, with the hypocotyl, plumule, and cotyledon base, is pushed out of the testa by this cotyledonary growth, and if the seed is germinating below the soil the cotyledon stalk becomes sharply doubled up as shown in Fig. 75. The tip of the cotyledon remains within the testa and absorbs the endospermic reserves.

This is a very common pattern of monocotyledonous development, and it has important consequences in the later life of the plant. Because there is practically no elongation of the hypocotyl, and because the active growth of the cotyledon tends to drive the whole lower part of the seedling bodily downwards into the soil, the plumule starts its growth from a point which is below the soil surface. This is often the case even when the seed germinates upon the surface, and even in plants which are technically epigeal, with the cotyledon ultimately freeing itself entirely from the testa. In many monocotyledons, therefore, as in the onion, the seedling has from the first an underground stem, with only the upper parts of its leaves projecting above the soil. The plumular internodes are short, and the plumule in the early stages of its growth is hidden within the sheathing base of the cotyledon.

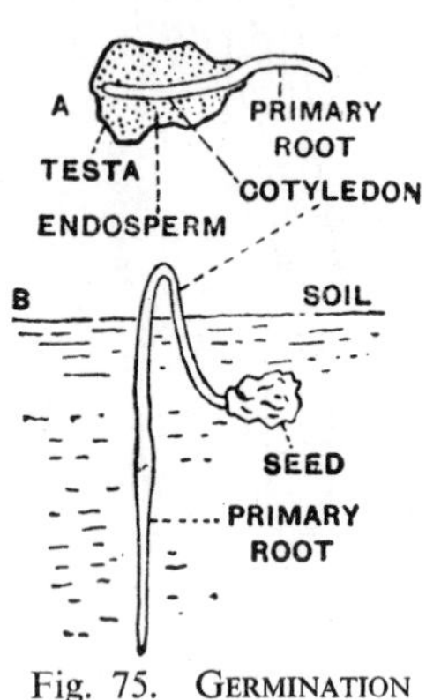

Fig. 75. GERMINATION OF ONION.

Date (*Phoenix dactylifera*). The date stone (Fig. 76) is the seed of a one-seeded berry. The greater part of its bulk consists of endosperm, which is extremely hard owing to the thickening of the walls of the cells by hemicellulose, which is here the main reserve substance (p. 23). The seed has a deep groove in one side; the position of the little embryo is indicated by a bulge half-way down on the side opposite the groove. Germination is relatively slow and requires high temperatures but is otherwise quite easy to bring about, and the plant is a very good example of the behaviour of monocotyledonous seedlings.

The upper part of the cotyledon is purely absorptive, and never escapes from the endosperm. The cotyledon stalk and sheath elongate considerably, thrusting the hypocotyl, which elongates hardly at all, deeply into the soil. The plumule, in the typical monocotyledonous manner, begins with a succession of internodes of almost negligible length, and the plant has in fact a considerable number of leaves before the stem comes above ground at all. The radicle is more active than in many other monocotyledons, and branches extensively, but it forms no part of the permanent root system of the tree.

Maize (*Zea mais*). The embryo of the grasses has several special organs which are not to be seen in the monocotyledons generally. The structure, and the general course of germination, are basically the same in all the common grasses, including the cereal grains, but for reasons of size it is customary to use for demonstration the seeds of maize, and especially of the "Horsetooth" varieties (Fig. 77).

The "seed" of grasses is in reality a one-seeded fruit, with the testa and the pericarp inseparably fused together to make a compound coating (fruit a **caryopsis,** see p. 429). The greater part of the volume is occupied by endosperm, but the embryo is larger, and very much more advanced in its development, than are those of many endospermic seeds. The embryo lies in a basal position, and its outline is marked by a distinctive patch upon one side of the grain. The endospermic reserve is mainly in the form of starch, though the outermost region, just under the testa, is particularly rich in protein; this is called the **aleurone layer**. Lying against the endosperm is a thick plate known as the **scutellum**. This is a digestive organ, and it is certainly part of the cotyledon, though perhaps not the whole of the cotyledon. The remainder of the embryo is attached to the central part of the scutellum, with its radicle pointing towards the base of the fruit and its plumule facing the other way. The radicle and the plumule are not in any way abnormal in themselves, but each of them is enclosed in an outer sheath which has no counterpart in the seedlings

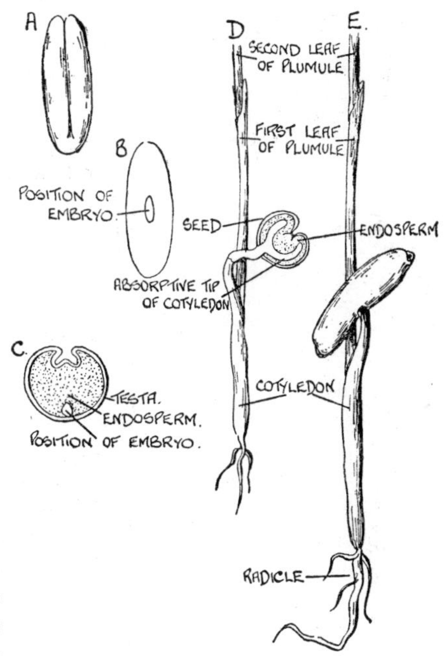

Fig. 76. Date seed.
A, external; B, T.S. through embryo; C, seedling.

of other families of monocotyledons. The sheath surrounding the radicle is called the **coleorhiza**; it has only very limited capacities for growth, and at an early stage the radicle bursts out through it. The sheath surrounding the plumule is called the **coleoptile**; it is a tube which is actually open at the end, where there is a small pore. The coleoptile has some vascular tissue, and grows very actively in the early stages of germination. Ultimately it is outpaced by the leaves of the plumule. In many grass seedlings there is yet another special organ known as an **epiblast**, which is a little scale on the side of the embryo opposite the scutellum. It has no known function.

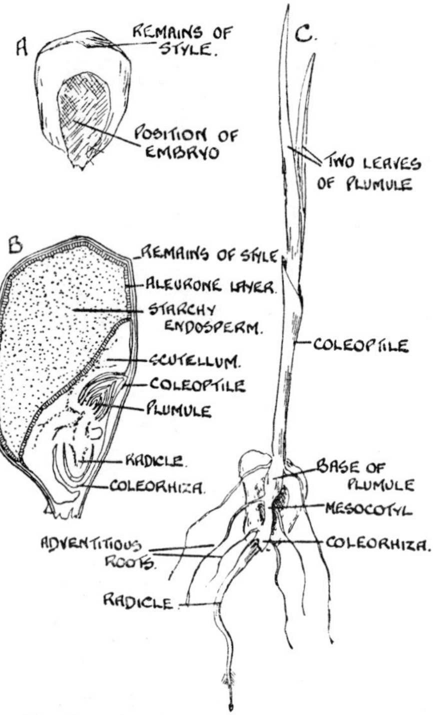

Fig. 77. Maize grain and seedling.
A, external; B, L.S. through embryo; C, seedling.

The unusual form of the grass embryo has provoked a great deal of argument. There is some suspicion, though certainly no proof, that the epiblast, the coleorhiza, and the coleoptile, like the scutellum, are to be regarded as parts of the cotyledon. The coleoptile (especially that of *Avena*, the oat) has played an important role as a subject for physiological experiments (see p. 288). In the germination of maize there is appreciable elongation of the part of the embryo which lies above the attachment of the scutellum but below the base of the coleoptile. This region must, at least provisionally, be regarded as part of the cotyledonary node, and is known as the **mesocotyl**.

The grasses are quite exceptional among endospermic seeds in having an important part of their reserves in the embryo itself, instead of carrying almost everything in the endosperm. The endosperm has nearly all the starch, and some of the protein, but the embryo has a great deal of additional protein, a considerable amount of oil, and almost the whole supply of some of the most important vitamins and minerals. In making white flour from wheat, most of the embryo is discarded in the bran. In European conditions this is offset because people receive in other components of their diet an equivalent for the substances removed from the flour. In communities where other sources of vitamins are lacking, removal of the embryo immediately leads to deficiency diseases in the human population. This danger is particularly acute with rice, the endosperm of which has little to offer but starch.

7 THE STRUCTURE OF LEAVES

Every leaf owes its origin to a localised increase in the activity of the apical meristem of a stem. Why a particular part of the meristem should suddenly increase its rate of cell division is not clear, but mathematical analysis and the results of many experiments point strongly to the conclusion that each existing leaf primordium tends to prevent the appearance of any new primordium in its vicinity, and that the next leaf always arises where the sum of the inhibitions due to all the existing leaves is a minimum (Fig. 78). In the later stages of growth the distribution of meristematic activity in leaves follows no constant law. Sometimes, as in the leaves of ferns, there is definite apical growth, but this is unusual. The general pattern is one of diffuse all-over cell division and enlargement, with some intensification at the margin of the lamina (Fig. 149). There are, however, many monocotyledonous leaves in which there is a persistent intercalary meristem at the base. The blind ends which occur in the vascular system of most reticulately veined leaves (Fig. 29) apparently always arise by breakage, the veins failing to keep pace with the growth of the surrounding tissue. See also reference to leaves of chimaeras (p. 85).

Petiole, Rachis, and Midrib

In such leaf-structures as present a stalk-like external appearance (and this will include any very large and prominent ribs of the lamina) the anatomy is always closely related to that of the stem of the same plant. There is the same basic pattern of xylem, cambium, and phloem, with a cortex composed of parenchyma and collenchyma. Even in deciduous leaves the activity of the cambium is often far from negligible, though the production of secondary vascular tissue usually does not continue after the leaf has reached maturity.

In some plants the petiole in transverse section presents a completely radial disposition of tissues, and may then be structurally almost indistinguishable from a young stem. Much more commonly, however, the petiole is dorsiventral, often distinctly gutter-shaped, with a concave upper surface. Petioles differ greatly in the degree to which this external dorsiventrality affects the vascular system. There may be a complete vascular "cylinder" with a central pith, more or less distorted to fit the gutter-shaped outline, or the vascular system itself may be an open trough. Especially in large petioles the vascular system may be rather complicated (see Figs. 79, B, D).

The Lamina

In the lamina there is no massive vascular system but only wandering strands of various sizes, mostly very small, and all of them,

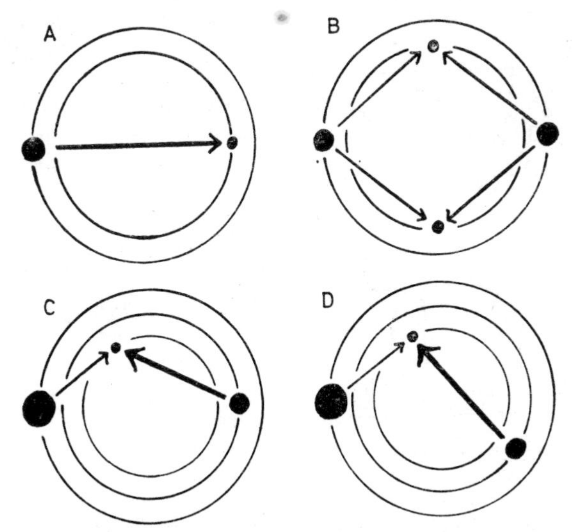

Fig. 78. INHIBITORY FIELD THEORY OF PHYLLOTAXY.

Each diagram is a plan of a shoot apex. Nodes are shown as circles, leaf-primordia as black spots which grow larger. An existing primordium exerts an influence, strong at first but afterwards diminishing, which tends to prevent the appearance of any new primordium in its vicinity. These inhibitory forces are shown by arrows, the new primordium arising at the point of its nodal circle which is most remote from the sources of inhibition. A, only one primordium is inhibiting at a time, resulting in distichous phyllotaxy (often slightly distorted by gravitational and other influences, see p. 82 and Fig. 26). B, two primordia formed at a time, of equal age and therefore equal inhibiting power, resulting in decussate phyllotaxy. C, the origin of a phyllotactic spiral, two primordia of unequal age, even though diametrically opposite, giving an unbalanced distribution of forces. D, a stable spiral system, reduced to its two main inhibitory forces, though complete explanation requires the inhibitions due to still older leaves to be taken into account.

in ordinary cases, with their phloem towards the lower surface of the leaf and their xylem towards the upper surface. Except for the vascular strands the inner tissue of the lamina in most leaves is wholly parenchymatous, and may be called the **mesophyll**. In typical dicotyledonous leaves all the cells of the mesophyll are

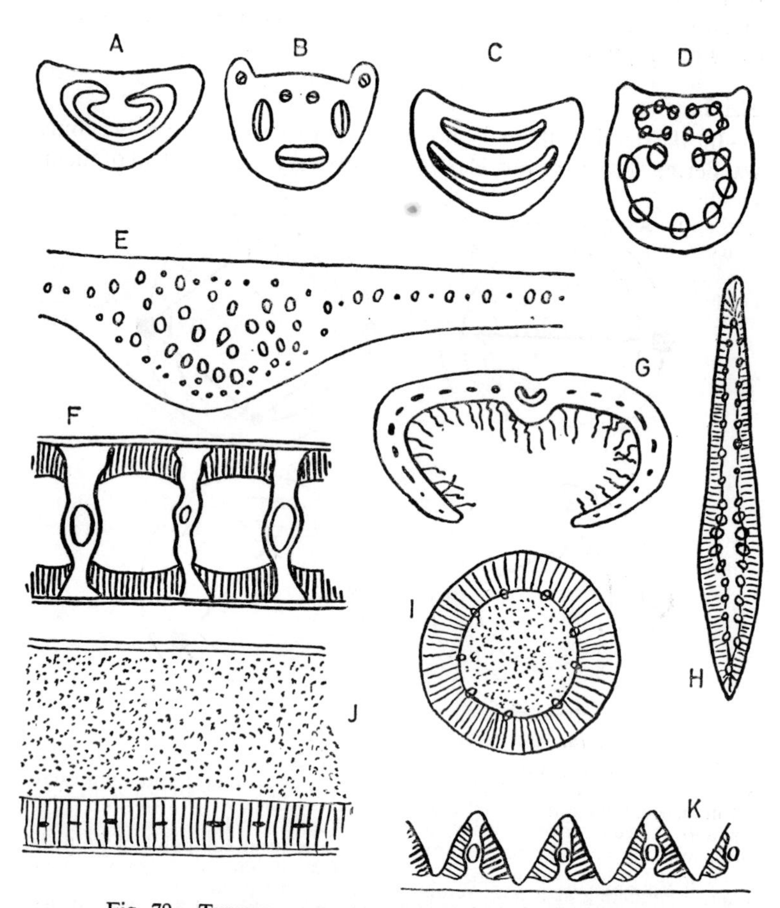

Fig. 79. TYPES OF LEAF-STRUCTURE IN TRANSVERSE SECTION.

A-D, various forms of petiole. E, common situation in large soft-leaved monocotyledons, also found in such dicotyledons as *Nymphaea*: midrib with numerous bundles. F, type of monocotyledon with sclerotic ribs running from face to face, vascular strands embedded in the ribs, photosynthetic tissue (striped) between them. G, type of leaf found in *Erica*, lavender, etc., with edges rolled downwards in varying degrees, sometimes almost meeting, usually with hairs on lower surface (see p. 32). H, vertically flattened phyllode type as in *Acacia*, *Iris*, etc. I, succulent leaf as in *Sedum* or *Mesembryanthemum*, with central water-storage tissue (dotted). J, leaf with thick layer of water-storage tissue lying above the photosynthetic part of the lamina, as found in various tropical plants. K, a common type of grass leaf, ribbed on the upper surface, with the photosynthetic tissue on the sides of the ridges, the lower surface being sclerotic.

photosynthetic, and a rather sharp distinction can be drawn between the **palisade** tissue and the **spongy** tissue (shown in Fig. 7). These tissues are highly ventilated. The amount of intercellular space in the palisade is often under-estimated because a transverse section of the lamina has to be very thin indeed before it becomes obvious that one palisade cell is not in close contact with its neighbours. In fact it is common for as much as a third of the total volume of a lamina to consist of intercellular space. The internal atmosphere of the mesophyll communicates with the external air by way of numerous stomata.

Variability of the Lamina

Of all the vegetative parts of the higher plants, the leaf lamina is that which exhibits the greatest structural diversity. The principal types of variation which occur may be classified as follows:

1. Variation Related to External Conditions. Much that is observed in the structure of leaves can be related to three external factors acting singly or jointly, the light intensity, the humidity, and the angle of the leaf to the vertical. Some plant species display marked rigidity of organisation, their leaves being almost the same whatever the environmental conditions. Other species are highly adaptable, and can be caused, by varying the conditions, to produce leaves of very different construction. No species is completely inflexible, and none, of course, is infinitely plastic.

The development of a typical palisade requires a high light intensity. In shade-dwelling species, and in the shade leaves of adaptable species, the difference between palisade and spongy tissue is greatly reduced. Light intensity also has a direct influence upon the thickness of the lamina, and upon the distinctness of the epidermis. In shade leaves the lamina is thinner and all the epidermal cells possess chloroplasts, which in sun leaves are found only in the guard cells of the stomata.

In general the distribution of stomata upon a leaf is such that the number of stomata is greater where the light intensity is less and the humidity is higher. A horizontal leaf usually has most of its stomata, often all of them, upon the lower surface, but a vertical leaf like that of *Iris* will have roughly equal numbers on the two sides (and very likely palisade on both sides as well). The distribution of stomata is rather sensitive to external factors; in leaves which fold up at night there are more stomata per unit area upon the parts which are covered by the folding, and in some plants the number of stomata is measurably influenced by the point of the compass which the epidermis happens to be facing.

The relationship between plant structure and the general humidity of the environment is discussed in Chapter 21. It is enough here to say that high humidity is usually associated with large cells, a thin cuticle and a general lack of thick cell walls, low humidity with small cells, thick cuticle, and the production of sclereids and fibres, or, alternatively, with the development of water-storage tissues.

Although every species preserves a certain range of adaptability, many of the differences between species represent a genetic fixation of the features appropriate to particular environments. When we see the holly leaf, with its very thick cuticle, or the stonecrop leaf with its inner mass of water-storage parenchyma, we are looking at the consequences of adaptive evolution under a warmer and sunnier climate than that of Britain.

2. Taxonomic Variation. Every plant, in the structure of its leaf, and perhaps most especially in the epidermis of its leaf, shows features characteristic of the family and genus to which it belongs. One family has simple hairs, another has branched ones, others produce distinctive sclereids in the mesophyll, and so on. Small fragments of leaf tissue can usually be identified with considerable accuracy, and this possibility is of some practical importance. With only the rarest exceptions, however, we have at present no reason to suppose that these differences of structure are important functionally. In some groups of plants each stoma is surrounded by two epidermal cells, in other groups it is surrounded by three; this probably has no more bearing upon the plant's prospects in life than the exact form of a man's finger-print has upon his financial circumstances.

3. Variation Related to the Age of the Plant. A seedling usually cannot produce immediately the leaf-structure found in mature plants of the same species. The young plant produces a succession of leaves which only gradually attain the adult form (Fig. 153). In many species a similar though shorter sequence is seen on each lateral shoot, the axillary bud starting life with a noticeably juvenile form of leaf.

4. Consequences of Phyllode Construction. There are some dicotyledons (*Acacia*, p. 78 and Fig. 41) in which the leaf is a **phyllode**, a flattened petiolar structure which has taken over the photosynthetic function normally performed by the lamina, the lamina itself having been eliminated. This condition is of great interest because many lines of evidence point to the conclusion that most parallel-veined monocotyledonous leaves have been evolved by the development of phyllodes in plants which no longer produce a true lamina.

If we imagine a stem-like petiole to undergo compression, it will be evident that in the flattened blade which results two similar sets of vascular tissue will face each other, xylem to xylem. This situation exists in *Acacia* phyllodes and in such leaves as those of *Iris* (Fig. 79, H). In most monocotyledonous leaves such "upside-down" bundles as may be present are smaller and less numerous than those in the normal position with their xylem towards the upper surface. In many monocotyledons the lignified tissues (fibres or parenchyma) associated with the vascular strands form strong ribs running right through the leaf from face to face (Fig. 79, F). Some of these leaves are of great thickness, and only the part of the mesophyll near the surface is then photosynthetic.

Stomata

Although stomata are widely distributed upon the aerial parts of the higher plants it is upon the leaf that they normally reach their greatest importance as channels of gaseous exchange.

Each stoma develops from a single initial cell. In the simplest case this initial divides at once into the two guard cells, but in many examples the stomatal initial cuts off a few subsidiary cells before the final division into guard cells. Some families of plants are especially distinguished by the number and arrangement of their subsidiary cells. Even when there are no subsidiary cells in the strict sense the epidermal cells adjoining the stoma often show a certain constancy in number. The two guard cells, which are invariably sister cells, separate slightly, and a pore is formed between them.

The wall of the guard cell is so thickened that an increase in the hydrostatic pressure within the cell will cause the stomatal pore to open, while a loss of pressure allows the pore to close. There are two alternative mechanisms which will accomplish the required movement. In most plants the guard cells are roughly of the form shown in Fig. 80, A. The wall here consists of four parts. The part facing the outside air, and the part facing the inside of the leaf, are thick, and will neither bend nor stretch appreciably. Between the guard cell and the adjoining cell of the general epidermal layer are thin walls which, upon any increase in the pressure within the guard cell, will stretch considerably. Next to the pore is a thin part, not long enough to stretch significantly, but perfectly capable of bending, and so acting as a hinge. The effect of increasing pressure is shown by the dotted outline: the depth of the cell increases, the thick parts of the wall are forced apart, and the hinge portion is drawn back from the pore. The inner and outer edges or lips of the pore which are shown in the figure are quite inessential; some plants have the outer lip but not the inner one.

In the grasses and a few other plants the stomata operate upon a fundamentally different plan (Fig. 80, B). Here each guard cell has a thick-walled central section, lying beside the pore, and two terminal thin-walled bulbs. When the internal pressure increases the bulbs swell, and the thick-walled central parts of the guard cells (which, of course, do not swell to anything like the same extent) are driven apart, so opening the pore.

Although stomata occur in very large numbers their pores are so small that even a highly ventilated leaf with all its stomata open has only a very small percentage of its surface actually occupied by

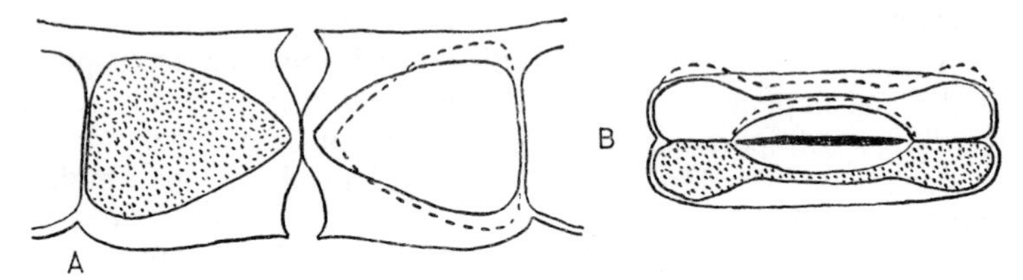

Fig. 80. STOMATAL MOVEMENT.
In each stoma the cavity of one guard cell is stippled, and the other is shown with a double outline, the continuous line showing the cavity in closed position, the broken line the open position. A, a normal stoma in transverse section. B, a grass stoma in surface view. Further explanation in the text.

stomatal pore. It might therefore appear that the diffusion of gases in and out of leaves would be rather severely restricted by the small size of the openings. In reality it is quite clear from mathematical studies and from experiments that the resistance offered by very small pores to the diffusion of gases through them is much less than one might expect. Area for area, a pore of stomatal dimensions is from seven to ten times as effective in passing gases as a very large hole would be. This can be most easily understood as an edge-effect. A gas molecule passing through the central part of a large opening must move straight ahead among the jostling of its fellows. One which passes near the edge of the opening can go "round the corner" and so find a clearer passage. But a small pore has no central area to speak of; it is all edge. Of course the epidermis of a leaf, considered as a perforated diaphragm, is restrictive of gas movement; even with the stomata open gas movement is less free than it would be with the epidermis removed. But the restriction is much less severe than a simple calculation of stomatal areas would lead one to suppose.

Leaf-fall

The dropping of leaves is only one example of the controlled separation of plant organs from the main body. Flowers, fruits, petals, and other structures are commonly shed in a similar way.

The actual separation is due in all these cases to the production of an **abscission layer**, a plate of parenchyma in which the middle lamella becomes mucilaginous, so that the cells separate. A leaf just upon the point of falling is held in position only by the cuticle and the xylem. Although wind and gravity may account for the final break, the preparations depend upon the metabolic activity of the abscission layer cells. The leaves upon a dead branch will wither, but they do not fall.

Underneath an abscission layer there is always a protective layer of some kind. In many cases this is an ordinary periderm formed well in advance. In other examples, however, the formation of a periderm is delayed, and a temporary sealing layer arises by suberisation of ordinary parenchyma, in a manner similar to that often seen in the outer cortex of a young root at the death of the epidermis. A sealing layer of this kind is replaced by a periderm at a later stage.

In most plants a leaf separates at a surface which is more or less flush with the outside of the stem. There are, however, many cases where part of the leaf-base, possibly including stipules or a sheath, is left behind. Sometimes the shedding of leaves is a two-stage process, as in compound leaves where the leaflets drop before the rachis. Some plants, such as ferns and many monocotyledons, have no true leaf-fall. They have sealing layers but no abscission tissue, and their stems are enveloped in dead leaf-bases. Leaf abscission is by no means confined to woody plants, though it tends to be overlooked in herbs.

It is very easy, by withholding water or exposing a plant to poisonous gases, to provoke leaf-fall much earlier than it would otherwise occur. We do not know, however, the factors that regulate the normal course of abscission. Although one tends in the first instance to think of leaves falling in autumn it must be remembered that the first steps, the laying out of the abscission tissue and sealing layer, take place much earlier in the year. In any case, the timing is very different in evergreen species, many of which have their main period of leaf-drop in spring or summer.

8 CYTOLOGY

Cytology is the study of cells. It is particularly concerned with details of cell structure and with the interpretation of this structure in terms of function. This subject has already been introduced in Chapter 2, and much of what has been written in other chapters is also of relevance to cytology or even validly included within it. For example, in considering plant structure it is impossible to differentiate clearly between cytology and anatomy; and in matters of function the boundary between cytology and physiology is very ill-defined. The aim of this chapter is to treat in greater detail some of the topics mentioned briefly in Chapter 2 and not developed elsewhere in the book.

There is a widespread but mistaken impression that cytology deals predominantly or even exclusively with the cell nucleus. This impression is largely due to the fact that the nucleus undergoes a spectacular sequence of changes each time the cell divides, and these changes can usually be observed and interpreted with an optical microscope. Other parts of the cell are much less accessible to study with this instrument because of their smaller size or because their existence is less obviously eventful. Throughout the early years of the twentieth century cytologists were dependent upon the optical microscope as their main research tool, and therefore their interests were dominated by nuclear phenomena. As a result, the principal features of nuclear behaviour during cell division and their genetical implications have been understood for many years, whereas only recently has there been any approach to an understanding of certain other aspects of cytology such as the growth of cell walls or the structure of chloroplasts. These recent developments owe a great deal to the use of new instruments and new techniques. Some of these are improvements or refinements in microscopy; others represent more radical departures from traditional methods. A few of the techniques of modern cytology are briefly described below:

(*a*) **Phase Contrast Microscopy.** The usual method for examining, say, the chromosomes in dividing cells requires that the cells are first killed and fixed, that is preserved without distortion of their structure. The cells may then be sectioned or squashed, followed by selective staining to give contrast between the chromosomes and the rest of the cell. If the cells are not stained in this way, the chromosomes are transparent and almost impossible to see with a conventional optical microscope. However, the succession of chemical and mechanical treatments may cause alteration in structure so that the finished product does not resemble the natural state. The production of these effects of treatment, known as artefacts, has been a serious source of error in some cytological work, though the most refined modern techniques avoid them almost completely. One method by which one can confirm the absence of artefacts in fixed and stained preparations is to observe similar cells in the living state with a phase contrast microscope. This instrument uses a normal light source but has an optical system which produces an image in which objects with different refractive indices appear different in brightness. In this way chromosomes may, without staining, be made to appear dark and in sharp contrast to the brighter cytoplasm. The method has not only confirmed the accuracy of pictures of cell structure obtained after fixing and staining, but has made possible direct studies of the changes in cell structure with time. Whereas formerly the sequence of events in cell division had to be pieced together from fixed cells at various stages, the whole process may now be observed in a single living cell.

(*b*) **Ultra-violet Microscopy.** The power of a microscope to reveal details of structure, known as its resolving power, is limited by the wavelength of the radiation used: the shorter the wavelength, the greater the resolving power. The optical microscope uses visible light with a mean wavelength of about 5,500 Å. With the best lens system available, this will allow two objects as close together as about 2,400 Å to be seen as two separate objects. If they are closer together they will not be separable. This therefore sets the limit of resolution of the microscope. Other microscopes have been constructed which use ultra-violet (u.v.) radiation instead of visible light, with a consequent increase in resolving power. Thus u.v. radiation with a wavelength of 2,600 Å can be used to resolve objects only 1,100 Å apart. There are considerable technical problems in building and using a u.v. microscope. For example, the lenses must be made of fused quartz because glass is opaque to u.v. radiation, and the image cannot be viewed directly since not only is the u.v. radiation beyond the range of visibility but it is also damaging to the eye. However, the usefulness of the instrument makes these difficulties tolerable. U.v. microscopy not only allows greater resolution of detail, but also permits the recognition and measurement of certain constituents of the cell, such as nucleoprotein, because of their absorption of particular u.v. wavelengths.

(*c*) **Electron Microscopy.** The principle of increasing resolving power by using radiation of shorter wavelength is applied to a much greater degree in the electron microscope. This uses a beam of electrons instead of a beam of light, the wavelength of which may be as small as 0·05 Å. Although in theory this could resolve objects which were even smaller, such high resolution has not been achieved in practice. Even so, good resolution of objects only 10 Å apart, which is within the capabilities of modern electron microscopes, is a vast improvement on what is possible with microscopes using visible or u.v. light. Since the 1940's when widespread study of biological material by electron microscopy began, knowledge of cell structure has undergone a rapid expansion. The electron microscope has not only helped to explain the structure and function of objects already recognised, but has revealed features of cellular construction whose existence was previously unsuspected. Again, there are technical problems involved, such as the fact that electrons are easily absorbed or deflected even by air. The inside of the microscope must therefore be evacuated during use and the specimen must be dry and sufficiently thin to allow part of the electron beam to pass through it. A section intended to show details of cytoplasmic structure, for instance, needs to be not more than about 0·06 μ in thickness, compared with 12 μ which is a common thickness for sections to be examined with the light microscope. Also, as with the u.v. microsope, the image cannot be viewed directly; it must be projected on to a fluorescent screen or recorded photographically.

(*d*) **Crystallographic Techniques.** Advantage has been taken of the fact that some constituents of the cell are crystalline—perhaps not with the regular molecular pattern of, say, common salt, but at least with sufficient orderliness among the molecules to enable them to be studied by crystallographic techniques. These techniques include **polarisation microscopy**. When crystals of some types are struck by a beam of polarised light (p. 213), the light will be transmitted unchanged only if the plane of polarisation bears a particular relationship to the molecular orientation within the crystals. Thus examination with a polarising microscope is a useful technique in the analysis of crystal structure. Cellulose, the principal component of plant cell walls, consists of long chain molecules which are sometimes organised into a crystalline arrangement (see p. 173). Polarisation microscopy has therefore been applied in determining the orientation of cellulose molecules in cell walls, knowledge of which helps in understanding the growth and properties of the walls.

Another technique borrowed from crystallography is **X-ray diffraction analysis**. The principle here is that when a parallel beam of X-rays passes through matter some of the radiation is scattered. If the material causing the scattering consists of atoms or molecules arranged at random, the scattered radiation is sent out uniformly in all directions. But if there is a regular crystalline structure the radiation emitted forms a diffraction pattern, with strong radiation in some directions and practically none in others, which can be recorded on X-ray-sensitive film. The form of this pattern depends on the spacings between atoms in the structure, and the technique can therefore be used to investigate the arrangement of atoms in crystalline compounds. One notable success has been its use in calculating the structure of the nucleic acids (see p. 168), which has led to a clearer understanding of their function. In addition, if the inter-atomic spacings in a compound are already known, X-ray diffraction methods may be useful for recognising the presence of that substance particularly when chemical analysis is not possible. This technique has been used in studying the chemical composition of plant cell walls.

Armed with such a variety of techniques, the cytologist is nowadays able to study cells much more thoroughly than before, and though the investigation of the nucleus is still an important field of research, it is now accompanied by equally intensive study of other parts of the cell.

Nuclear Division

Since every cell originates from division of a pre-existing cell, the process of division is of fundamental importance. As has already been stated, some features of the process can be clearly seen with an optical microscope, and these will be considered first.

Most living cells appear to retain the ability to divide, though in differentiated tissues cell division may be very rare, and only when stimulated by some unusual occurrence such as wounding do the cells resume meristematic activity. The normally meristematic tissues of the plant make the most suitable material for a study of the sequence of events during cell division, and actively growing root tips have frequently been used for this purpose. Roots are somatic tissues, that is they are part of the plant body which cannot contribute directly to the next generation. The type of cell division which occurs in root tips is typical of somatic tissues, and the process of nuclear division associated with it is called **mitosis**.

Some of the stages through which the nucleus passes during mitosis are shown in Plate 8. This sequence of photomicrographs has been made from fixed and stained cells of *Vicia faba* (broad bean). It should be noted that the staining procedure used shows up the chromosomes very clearly but does not stain other structures such as the cell wall, nucleolus, or spindle (see below). The presence of these other structures can be demonstrated by alternative techniques.

Before mitosis begins, the nucleus is said to be in **interphase** (Plate 8, *1*): the term "resting nucleus" is not recommended

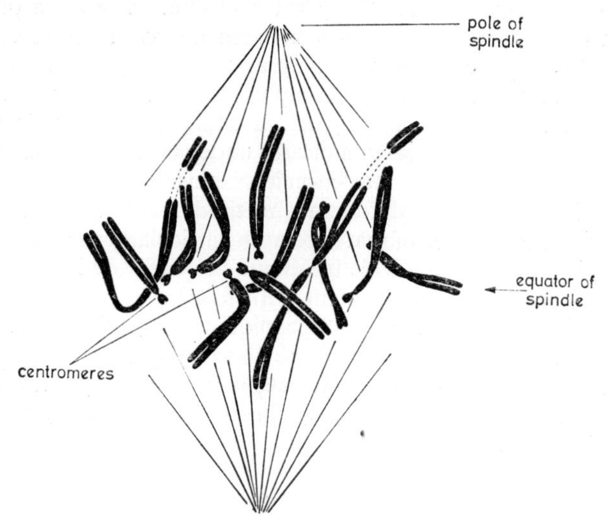

Fig. 81. *Vicia faba:* METAPHASE OF MITOSIS.
Enlargement of chromosomes shown in Plate 8, *6*.

since the nucleus is metabolically active even though it shows no visible sign of activity. The interphase nucleus in a root tip occupies a large part of the cell volume (Fig. 3) but it is enclosed in a nuclear membrane which gives it a definite spherical or ovoid shape. Little or no structure can be recognised within the nucleus, though a spherical nucleolus may be visible, embedded in an apparently granular matrix. The first sign that the cell is about to divide is that this matrix changes and appears to consist of a mass of contorted threads (Plate 8, *2*). This is the beginning of the period known as **prophase**. At this early stage it is impossible to see whether there is a single very long thread or a number of separate ones, but as prophase advances it becomes clear that there are several threads which, by growing shorter and fatter, gradually become visibly distinct from one another (Plate 8, *3* and *4*). These threads are the chromosomes, and there is evidence that they retain their separate identities throughout the life of the cell. Towards the end of prophase, when the chromosomes are approaching maximum contraction, the nucleolus, which has been diminishing in size, finally disappears. The nuclear membrane ruptures at about the same time, allowing the chromosomes to become more dispersed (Plate 8, *4* and *5*), though they still appear haphazardly arranged. It can now be seen that each chromosome is a double structure, made up of two parallel threads (**chromatids**) held together at some point along their length by a **centromere**, which is clearly visible in some chromosomes in Plate 8, *6*, as an unstained constriction (see also Fig. 81 which shows the chromosomes of Plate 8, *6*, on a larger scale).

The next period of mitosis is known as **metaphase** during which the chromosomes become arranged in an orderly fashion. This is associated with the appearance of the **spindle**, a semi-solid body shaped like two cones joined by their bases, which occupies a large part of the cell volume. The spindle has a fibrous structure, with the fibres running from the ends or **poles** towards the region of maximum diameter, known as the **equator**. When, as in *Vicia faba*, most of the chromosomes have their centromeres near one end, the orderliness of chromosome arrangement may not be very obvious (Plate 8, *6*); but when it is realised that the centromeres are lying all in the same plane, the orderliness is more apparent. It is impossible to define precisely the moment when prophase ends and metaphase begins: in fact the period when the chromosomes have almost reached maximum contraction but before they are organised on the spindle is sometimes called prometaphase (Plate 8, *5*). There is no such doubt about the end of metaphase. The next period, **anaphase**, begins with the division of each centromere into two, and the movement of the two halves towards opposite poles of the spindle (Fig. 82). Each half-centromere is attached to one of the two chromatids, so that during anaphase each chromatid is separated from its partner. When separation is complete (Plate 8, *7*) each former chromatid can be regarded as a fully fledged chromosome. Thus two identical groups of chromosomes assemble at opposite poles (Plate 8, *8*). The arrival of these two groups at the poles marks the end of anaphase and the beginning of **telophase** which in many ways is a reversal of prophase and leads to the formation of two interphase nuclei. The chromosomes lengthen, become more slender, and entangle with one another. The nucleolus reappears in each nucleus, and the nuclear membrane is reconstituted (Plate 8, *9*, *10*, and *11*). This completes the nuclear division but cell division also requires the formation of a new wall separating the two nuclei. This process will be described later in this chapter (p. 171).

Reference has been made in Chapter 2 to the important part played by the nucleus in governing the activities of the cell and of the organism as a whole. More precisely, it is the chromosomes which carry the set of instructions which determine the nature and properties of the cell. It is therefore highly significant that mitosis is a mechanism which ensures that the two daughter nuclei each receive a set of chromosomes identical with those formerly present

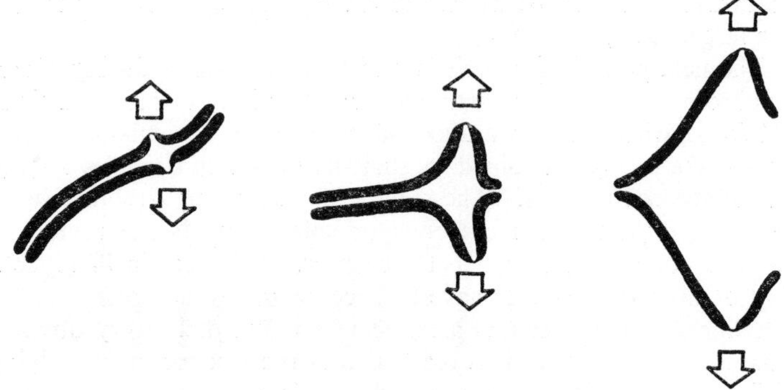

Fig. 82. SUCCESSIVE STAGES IN THE DIVISION OF ONE CHROMOSOME DURING ANAPHASE OF MITOSIS.

in the parent nucleus. Hence during the development of a multicellular plant, in which all nuclear divisions up to the time of reproduction are mitotic, the set of instructions originally assembled in the zygote is faithfully reproduced throughout the individual.

Because of their importance, chromosomes have been the subject of very detailed investigation. Some of this investigation has been concerned with molecular structure and biochemical activity, and the results are helping to provide an understanding of how the chromosomes govern the cell. But even the relatively crude study possible with the optical microscope can supply useful information about chromosomes in addition to the facts about their behaviour during mitosis which have already been described. At metaphase of mitosis it is generally possible to count the number of chromosomes in each cell (see Plate 8, *6*), to measure their relative lengths and to record the positions of the centromeres. All these features can be represented in a diagram (Fig. 83) with the chromosomes arranged in order of length and each one straightened out to make comparison easier. It can be seen in the diagram that the set of twelve chromosomes from the root tip of *Vicia* consists of six pairs, with the two members of a pair exactly similar to each other. This type of arrangement is extremely common: the total number of chromosomes varies from species to species between very wide limits, but it is generally an even number with the total complement divisible into corresponding sets. The two chromosomes in each pair are described as **homologous chromosomes**, or simply **homologues**.

It will also be seen in Fig. 83 that each of the longest pair of

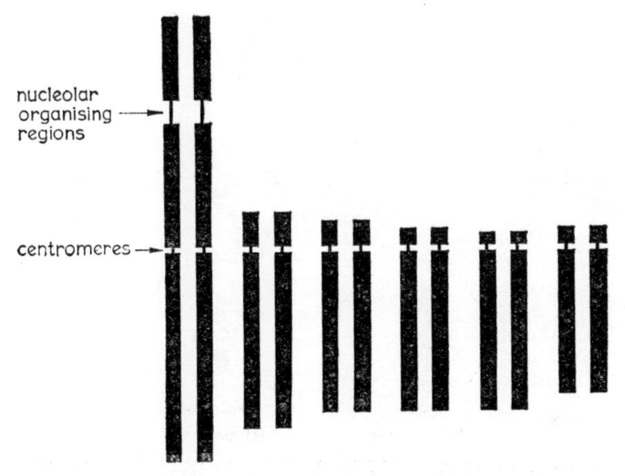

Fig. 83. THE CHROMOSOMES OF *Vicia faba* SHOWN DIAGRAMMATICALLY.

chromosomes has a prominent constriction in addition to the centromere. These are the **nucleolar organising regions**, and as the name implies, it is in association with these regions that the nucleolus redevelops during telophase. Similar nucleolar organising regions can be found in the chromosomes of other species, though they are not necessarily located on the longest pair.

The significance of chromosomes occurring in homologous pairs in somatic cells becomes clear when we consider the alternative type of nuclear division known as **meiosis** which occurs at one point in the life-cycle of every organism which reproduces sexually. In flowering plants it occurs in the anthers and ovules shortly before the formation of male and female gametes. In some general features, mitosis and meiosis are rather similar: in both processes the chromosomes pass through the same cycle of contraction (prophase), orientation (metaphase), separation (anaphase), and consolidation (telophase). But in their effects the processes are very different. Mitosis reproduces with precision a given type of nucleus and maintains a constant chromosome number: meiosis, on the other hand, produces genetic diversity and reduces the chromosome number by half. The reduction is the result of *two* divisions of the nucleus during which each chromosome divides only *once*. This halving of the chromosome number almost inevitably means that the products of meiosis are not genetically uniform, since in most organisms the set of instructions cannot be divided into two identical halves. The genetical consequences of meiosis are considered further in

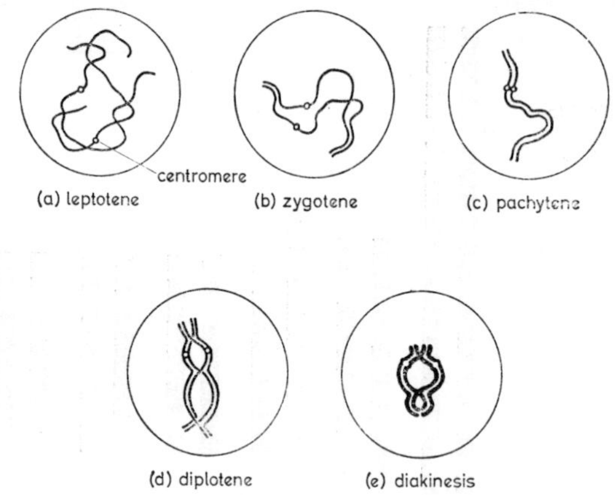

Fig. 84. BEHAVIOUR OF A SINGLE PAIR OF HOMOLOGOUS CHROMOSOMES DURING PROPHASE OF MEIOSIS.

Chapter 22. We are here primarily concerned with the features of chromosome behaviour which distinguish meiosis from mitosis. Foremost among these are the following:

(*a*) At an early stage, the homologous chromosomes become closely paired with each other and remain associated throughout much of the first nuclear division. This is in striking contrast to the complete lack of association between homologues during all the mitotic divisions which precede meiosis. There is at present no satisfactory explanation of why two chromosomes which show no mutual attraction during vegetative development should suddenly associate together shortly before gamete formation, but the change has important effects on the whole course of nuclear division, as the commentary given below will show.

(*b*) At anaphase of the first nuclear division there is no division of centromeres. Again, we have no explanation of this failure to divide, but its consequences are clear. Just as division of the centromeres at mitosis is an essential factor in maintaining the original chromosome number, so failure to divide results in the halving of the chromosome number.

The following description of meiosis pays special attention to those features which represent departures from the standard pattern of mitotic division. It should be read in conjunction with a study of Plate 9 and Fig. 84. The two nuclear divisions which constitute meiosis are known as divisions I and II, and each phase is distinguished accordingly.

Prophase I. During this phase the chromosomes pass through a succession of stages which are referred to by different names. The earliest of these stages is **leptotene** ("thin threads") when the interphase chromosomes resolve themselves by contraction into visible strands which are long, slender, and greatly entangled with one another (Fig. 84, A). This resembles the earliest stage of mitotic prophase, but the resemblance does not persist. While the chromosomes are still very long and thin, each one makes contact with its homologue, often at the ends to start with, and side-by-side pairing gradually extends along the whole length. The stage during which pairing develops is called **zygotene** ("paired threads") (Fig. 84, B), and when pairing is complete **pachytene** ("thick threads") has been reached (Fig. 84, C). This stage is shown in Plate 9, *1*, though here the pairing is so close that the doubleness of each strand is not apparent. Each double strand constitutes a **bivalent**, that is an association of two homologous chromosomes. Although contraction of chromosome length continues through zygotene, it is by no means finished when pairing is complete, and the bivalents continue to shorten throughout the remainder of prophase I. This further shortening is accompanied by some relaxation of the pairing between homologues, so that the double nature of the bivalents becomes obvious (Plate 9, *2*, Fig. 84, D). This stage is **diplotene** ("double threads"). Each bivalent at diplotene has the shape of a cross or a number of loops, with the homologues clearly separated for most of their length, but held together at one or more points known as **chiasmata** (singular: chiasma). In favourable material, examination of diplotene bivalents at high magnification shows that each chromosome consists of two chromatids, and that a chiasma is a point where two of the four chromatids cross each other (Fig. 84, D). The genetical significance of this crossing-over between chromatids is discussed on p. 648.

The final stage of prophase I is **diakinesis** ("moving apart") during which there is a continuation of the trends seen at diplotene (Fig. 84, E). Separation of the pairs of chromatids in a bivalent becomes more pronounced, and the contraction of bivalents reaches its greatest extent. Associated with these changes is a movement of chiasmata towards the ends of the bivalents. Some chiasmata may slip off the ends of the bivalents completely, so it is common for a bivalent at the end of diakinesis to have fewer chiasmata than at diplotene. Finally the nuclear membrane ruptures, allowing greater dispersal of the fully contracted bivalents.

Metaphase I. The random arrangement of bivalents during prophase is followed by their becoming orientated on a spindle similar to that formed during mitosis. Unlike mitotic metaphase, however, the centromeres do not lie in the plane of the equator, but the two members of each pair of homologous centromeres lie

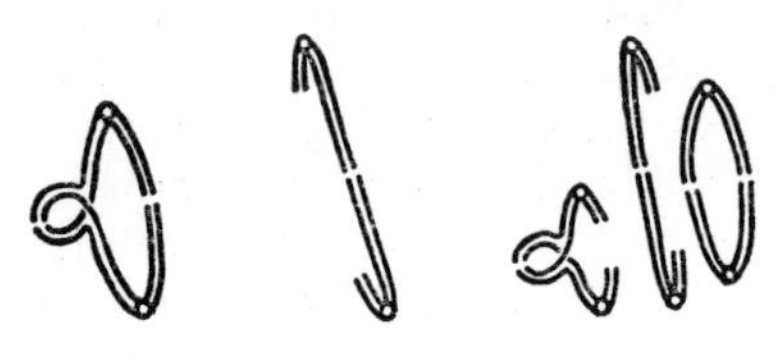

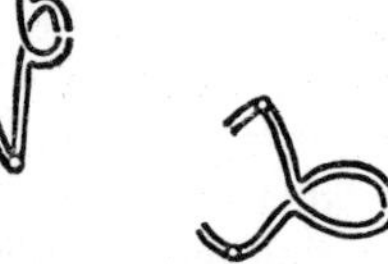

Fig. 85. *Narcissus:* METAPHASE OF MEIOSIS.
Enlargement of bivalents shown in Plate 9, *4*, represented diagrammatically to indicate positions of centromeres and chiasmata. The bivalent on the extreme left could have been derived from the bivalent shown in Fig. 84.

on either side of it. Those parts of the chromatids which are adjacent to the centromeres often show signs of stretching at this stage, indicating that homologous centromeres are strongly attracted towards opposite poles. They are prevented from moving far apart, however, by the chiasmata which stubbornly hold the bivalents together (Fig. 85). Just as metaphase of mitosis is the most favourable stage for counting the chromosome number in somatic cells, so metaphase I of meiosis has the bivalents most distinct and easy to count. Plate 9, *4*, for example, shows clearly that the *Narcissus* variety from which the photograph was made has seven bivalents corresponding to its somatic chromosome number of fourteen.

Anaphase I. As in mitosis, anaphase is a period of movement towards the poles of the spindle, but in this case it is not initiated by any division of centromeres. The pairs of homologous centromeres which have been straining apart throughout metaphase, finally overcome the resistance offered by chiasmata and separate each bivalent into two parts. Each part consists of two chromatids joined together by an undivided centromere which leads the way to the pole (Plate 9, *5*, *6*, and *7*).

Telophase I (Plate 9, *8*). The spindle now disperses, the cell contains two distinct groups of half-bivalents, and the first division of meiosis is almost complete. The length of telophase I is very variable from species to species depending on how quickly the second division follows the first. In *Narcissus* there is a pause between the two divisions sufficient to allow the formation of interphase nuclei with their customary lack of apparent structure (Plate 9, *9*). In other species the second division begins sooner and telophase I is therefore very abbreviated with only partial lengthening of the chromatids.

Division II is closely similar to normal mitotic division except that here there are two nuclei dividing synchronously side by side. **Prophase II** is related in duration to telophase I, since the one is the reverse of the other. If telophase I has been prolonged so is prophase II, and *vice versa*. The half-bivalents, with their centromeres still undivided, become shorter and fatter (Plate 9, *10*), and when maximum contraction has been reached they orientate themselves on two newly-formed spindles, one for each group. This stage is **metaphase II** (Plate 9, *11*). Then follows the first and only division of centromeres during the whole of meiosis. This heralds the beginning of **anaphase II**, and the associated chromatids, which have been visibly separate since diplotene of prophase I, finally part company (Plate 9, *12*, *13*). Although this process is superficially similar to anaphase of mitosis, there is an important difference. The chromatids which separate at mitotic anaphase are exact replicas of each other since they have been formed by duplication of a single structure. The same is usually not true of anaphase II in meiosis because of crossing-over, which can result in two unlike chromatids being attached to the same centromere at the end of division I. **Telophase II** completes the sequence of events. There are now four groups of chromosomes, each of which takes on the appearance of an interphase nucleus in the usual way (Plate 9, *14*, *15*).

The four nuclei produced after meiosis generally become the nuclei of four separate cells which are jointly referred to as a **tetrad**. Sometimes all four cells of a tetrad persist, as in the anthers of a flowering plant where each tetrad becomes four pollen grains. In the ovules, however, three cells out of the four degenerate leaving one which becomes the embryo sac. There is a remarkable parallel here with the corresponding situation in higher animals. The four products of meiosis in primary spermatocytes all develop into sperm cells, but of the four products from primary oocytes only one survives as an egg cell.

Since meiosis is an essential event in every sexual life-cycle, it follows that each life-cycle includes two phases which differ in the number of chromosomes per nucleus. Before meiosis there is the double or **diploid** number; after meiosis, the halved or **haploid** number. Meiosis, then, brings to an end the diploid phase and begins the haploid. At another stage in the life-cycle is the event of fertilisation at which two haploid gametes unite. This restores the diploid chromosome number and explains why the diploid complement consists of two similar sets of chromosomes: one set has been contributed by each of the gametes. The importance and relative lengths of the two phases in the sexual life-cycle will be discussed in Chapter 14.

Chemistry of the Nucleus

The visible behaviour of chromosomes during mitosis and meiosis shows how they are regularly distributed each time a cell divides and each time gametes are produced. This is clearly of importance in the study of inheritance, since the resemblance between parents and offspring depends upon transmission of the correct set of instructions from one generation to the next. However, visible events give no indication of the way in which the set of instructions carried by the chromosomes is put into practice. Any complete explanation of how the chromosomes control the cell must be to a large extent in chemical terms since all the activities of the cell are fundamentally chemical processes. There has therefore been intense interest in analysing the chemical structure of chromosomes. Recent advances in knowledge of this subject have been rapid and spectacular, but space does not allow more than a very brief account in this book.

Chemical analysis of nuclei is made difficult by their small size and chemical complexity, but it is certain that the major constituents are proteins and nucleic acids. Nucleic acid molecules are made up from three sorts of chemical unit: phosphate, nitrogenous bases, and sugars. Most nuclei contain two sorts of nucleic acid differing in the sugar present. If this is ribose, the acid is **ribonucleic acid** (RNA), and if the sugar is deoxyribose, **deoxyribonucleic acid** (DNA). Chromosomes consist largely of DNA, and there is convincing evidence from various sources that this is the constituent which carries the set of instructions. It is tempting to think of these instructions as being written in some form of "words", and although the analogy must not be taken too far there is in fact variation within DNA molecules which is known to correspond to the various letters and words of a more conventional message.

Fig. 86, A shows diagrammatically the association of phosphate, sugar, and nitrogenous base, known as a **nucleotide**, which is the basis of DNA structure. Nucleotides become linked together by

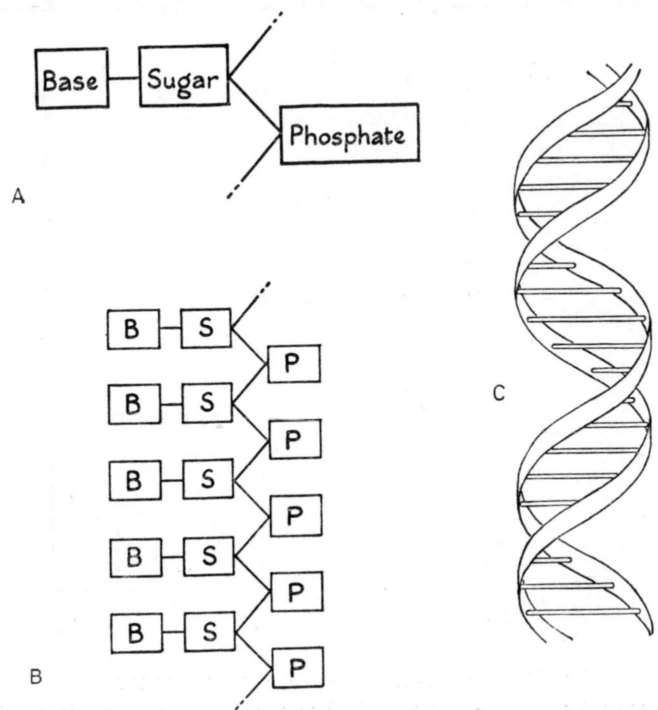

Fig. 86. THE STRUCTURE OF DNA.
A, a nucleotide; B, part of a polynucleotide chain; C, the double helix. Each helical ribbon represents a polynucleotide chain. The horizontal bars represent hydrogen bonds between opposite bases.

their phosphate units into long **polynucleotide** chains (Fig. 86, B) which occur in pairs. The two members of a pair are wound round each other to form a double helix, and are attached together not only by the winding itself but also by hydrogen bonds between the nitrogenous bases of opposite nucleotides (Fig. 86, C). The diagram so far gives no indication of variation along the length of the double helix which could represent the words of a message.

In fact the phosphate and sugar residues are similar in every nucleotide, but the bases are not. DNA from most organisms contains four bases. Two of these are purines, namely **adenine** and **guanine**, and two are pyrimidines, **cytosine** and **thymine**. Because of differences in the size of these molecules, and because of limitations on the pairs of bases between which hydrogen bonding readily occurs, the base belonging to one nucleotide is always matched with one other particular base on the opposite nucleotide.

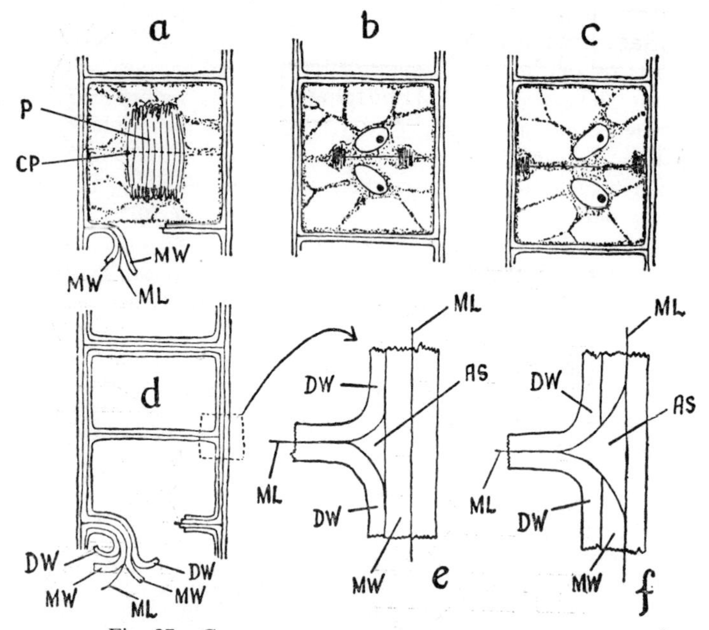

Fig. 87. CELL WALL FORMATION AND CELL DIVISION.
P, phragmoplast; CP, cell plate; MW, mother cell wall; ML, middle lamella; DW, daughter cell wall; AS, air space. In (*a*) and (*d*) the wall is shown broken and bent back in order to make clear the different layers.

Thus adenine is always paired with thymine and guanine with cytosine. It therefore follows that the sequence of bases present in one nucleotide chain determines the sequence of bases in its partner. Apart from this restriction, there may be any base sequence along the DNA molecule, and with four bases to choose from the possible variation is considerable.

It is convenient to regard a pair of opposite nucleotides as one letter of the code in which the instructions are written. If one treats each pairing and its inversion (*e.g* adenine—thymine and thymine—adenine) as two distinct types of nucleotide pair, then the code is made up of four letters. This may seem very few when one is accustomed to an alphabet of twenty-six letters, but it appears to be sufficient for the purpose.

We now return to the problem of how the code message present in the DNA is used by the cell as a set of instructions. We must continue to consider the cell and its characteristics in chemical terms. Each cell is capable of a great variety of chemical activities, most of which are dependent on the ability to produce particular enzymes. Each enzyme is partly or wholly a protein, and therefore consists of amino acids assembled in a particular linear order (see p. 250). There are only about twenty different amino acids found in proteins, but since a single enzyme molecule may include several hundred assorted amino acid residues, the number of possible arrangements, and therefore the variety of possible enzymes, is almost limitless. Recent discoveries have indicated that each amino acid corresponds to a certain sequence of three nucleotide pairs in the chromosomal DNA. The pattern of nucleotide pairs in the DNA can therefore be translated into chains of amino acids, and thus into proteins with specific enzyme activity. This translation is an essential part of the synthesis of enzymes, and so it comes about that a certain set of chromosomes dictates which enzymes can be produced and thereby controls the potentialities of the cell.

Formation and Composition of Cell Walls

Some of the events which take place in cell division have already been described (p. 159). The formation of two daughter nuclei at the end of mitosis is generally followed directly by the separation of the protoplast into two parts, one associated with each nucleus. In plant cells this requires a new wall dividing the mother cell into two, formation of which frequently begins during telophase. We will again consider the process seen in the meristematic cells of a root apex, though the principal features to be described are common to dividing cells in other parts of the plant. When the two groups of chromosomes reach opposite poles of the cell, the space between them contains a barrel-shaped fibrous structure reminiscent of the spindle and possibly derived from it called the **phragmoplast** (Fig. 87, *a*). The new cell wall makes its first appearance as a thin sheet, the **cell plate**, across the equator of the phragmoplast, beginning at the centre and spreading outwards to meet the mother cell wall. This centrifugal spreading is associated with a change in the appearance of the phragmoplast which also spreads outwards and becomes much more restricted to the equator of the cell (Fig. 87, *b* and *c*). The cell plate is destined to become the middle lamella of the wall which will separate the two daughter cells. Cellulose is deposited upon it on both sides, and at the same time a new layer of cellulose is deposited on the inner surface of the mother cell wall. At this stage therefore (Fig. 87, *d*), there is an intact mother cell wall enclosing two daughter cells each with its own complete wall. It is uncertain how the daughter cells finally free themselves from this parental embrace, which they undoubtedly do, but the enlargement of cells following division is probably responsible, at least in part. Some workers believe that during enlargement the daughter cell walls stretch without rupturing, whereas the mother cell wall breaks along the line of union between the daughter cells. Fig. 87, *e* and *f*, illustrates this hypothesis, which is a plausible explanation of how daughter cells eventually come to have completely individual walls.

The variety of changes which can subsequently occur to the cell wall may be gauged from the features of the different tissues described in Chapter 2. In addition to variation within a single plant, there are also differences in structure between similar tissues in different species. It is difficult, therefore, to make any concise generalisations about cell wall structure, except in relation to the classes of chemical compounds which are of widespread occurrence in cell walls. A knowledge of the properties of these compounds is helpful in understanding the ways in which cell walls fulfil their functions.

(*a*) **Pectic substances** (see p. 205) are the principal constituents of the middle lamella, and occur to a lesser extent in the primary wall also. The word pectic implies that these substances can undergo reversible changes between liquid or semi-liquid and solid states. Thus in growing tissues the middle lamella contains acidic pectic substances such as pectins (methylated pectic acids) which are water-soluble and have a soft, jelly-like consistency. This gives some adhesion between cells, but also allows them to slide in relation to one another during cell elongation. In mature tissues, however, the pectic substances form salts such as calcium and magnesium pectates which are insoluble and provide a firm cement between adjacent cells. The reverse changes occur during the ripening of fruit and contribute to the characteristic softening of the tissues. The quantity of pectin present is an important factor if the fruit is to be used for jam-making, since the setting of jam is due to the gelatinising properties of pectin. Damsons and crab-apples have a high pectin content and make jam or jelly which sets readily.

Strawberries, however, are low in pectin and require prolonged boiling to extract sufficient pectin for setting.

(*b*) **Cellulose** (see p. 205) is invariably present in the cell walls of higher plants, though the proportion of cellulose varies between wide limits. The length of cellulose molecules is also variable, with the longest chains consisting of as many as 3,000 glucose residues. These molecular chains are arranged in bundles called **microfibrils**, each of which contains up to about 2,000 molecules and has a diameter of 100-250 Å. This small size means that microfibrils cannot be distinguished with an optical microscope, though they are well within the resolution of an electron microscope. However, in some parts of cell walls, particularly the secondary wall, the microfibrils are themselves grouped into bundles of several hundred known as **macrofibrils** with diameters of 0·5 μ or more, which are large enough to be seen with an optical microscope. They are visible as striations on the walls of summerwood tracheids in longitudinal sections of some coniferous timbers.

Within a single microfibril there are places where the cellulose molecules are arranged with the extreme regularity of a true crystal: these regions are called **micelles**. Elsewhere in the microfibril the molecules are less regularly arranged. The degree of crystallinity is sufficient for crystallographic methods to be of use in investigating the orientation of cellulose microfibrils in cell walls. These methods, together with electron microscopy, have been widely used in the study of cell wall structure.

It will be recalled that when formation of a cellulose wall begins in a newly formed cell, the cell is undergoing substantial enlargement. The wall must therefore be capable of expansion. In fact, the first-formed wall consists of a loose meshwork of microfibrils which show little or no tendency to be orientated in a particular direction. As the cell elongates, the meshwork becomes drawn out in the direction of elongation while further deposition of microfibrils maintains the thickness of the wall. Only when the cell has reached its final size and shape does the wall begin to have a more rigid and permanent structure. The microfibrils are now deposited with regular orientation and may be massed together into macrofibrils. Each new layer of cellulose has the fibrils lying parallel to one another, but the direction of orientation may alter in successive layers.

(*c*) **Hemicelluloses** (see p. 205). This name is given to a group of long chain polymers which occur in association with cellulose. Some hemicelluloses appear to be of structural importance. Thus xylan (polymerised xylose) is a frequent component in the cell walls of secondary xylem where it is intimately associated with cellulose and probably contributes to the strength of the tissue. Other hemicelluloses act as reserve materials. The seeds of *Phoenix dactilifera* (date palm) contain mannan (polymerised mannose), and some seeds in the Leguminosae contain galactan (polymerised galactose), which though deposited in the cell walls are part of the reserves and are used up as the seed germinates.

(*d*) **Lignin.** Although customarily used in the singular, this name refers to another group of polymers with certain properties in common. They show two important differences from the cell wall polymers discussed already. Firstly, although the chemistry of lignins is imperfectly known, it is clear that they are not built up from sugars or sugar derivatives. There is some agreement that the fundamental unit of structure is *p*-hydroxy phenyl propane, molecules of which can be substituted and linked up in various ways, thus providing a number of different lignins. Secondly, polymerisation is not into long, unbranched chains capable of regular orientation within the wall, but into an irregular three-dimensional arrangement of branched chains.

The lignified walls of secondary xylem have a structure comparable with that of reinforced concrete. The orderly framework of cellulose (and hemicellulose) fibrils corresponds to the steel rods, while the amorphous lignin filling the spaces between resembles the concrete. Lignin, like concrete, makes a useful contribution to the strength of this composite structure, but is too brittle to be a satisfactory building material without reinforcement. This is demonstrated by the effects of certain wood-rotting fungi such as *Merulius lacrymans* (the cause of dry rot) which consume cellulose but not lignin. The timber which remains after a serious attack of dry rot therefore consists largely of lignin without any reinforcement, and its strength is negligible.

(*e*) **Cutin and Suberin.** These terms refer to a group of fatty acid polymers which, unlike most of the other cell wall polymers, are water-repellent. They are common in the cell walls of the outermost tissues of higher plants where their waterproofing qualities are of importance in water conservation. It is customary to describe the waterproofing of the epidermis as consisting of cutin, and that of the bark of trees as suberin, but the substances present give almost identical staining reactions. More sophisticated chemical methods might show a reliable difference between them.

The Structure of Cytoplasm and its Inclusions

The brief account of the cytoplasm and its inclusions which is given in Chapter 2 is written almost entirely in terms of what can be seen with an optical microscope, and which the student can verify by his own observations. Reference was also made, however, to recent discoveries made by electron microscopy. The additional information which has come to light in this way has given considerable help towards bridging the gap between the anatomical and the physiological study of cells. Biochemists have already revealed many of the reactions which happen inside cells; we are now approaching a fuller understanding of where each reaction occurs and how the structure of cells enables all the reactions to be integrated with one another. Before reviewing some of the features of structure which appear in electron micrographs, it should be emphasised once more that the observations have been made on specimens which have been killed and usually sectioned, and are in a high vacuum. Each of these necessary parts of the technique may give rise to artefacts, and there is as yet no means of confirming that details of structure seen in electron micrographs are present in living cells. However, the similarity of appearance shown by specimens prepared in different ways strongly suggests that the pictures of the fine structure of cells produced by careful electron microscopists are a reliable guide to the situation in living cells.

One of the most striking revelations of electron microscopy has been the importance of fine membranes in the structure, and presumably in the functioning of cells. The outer boundary of the protoplast, known as the plasma membrane, and the membrane surrounding the nucleus have long been recognised from observations with the light microscope. It is now clear that these are part of a much more extensive system of membranes in the cytoplasm. The plasma membrane, for example, is not a continuous, smooth surface to the protoplast but is invaginated here and there (Fig. 88) to form the lining of tubes or vesicles within the cytoplasm. These membrane-enclosed compartments are called **cisternae**. In electron micrographs of many types of cell similar cisternae can be seen, most of which do not appear connected with the plasma membrane. The outlines of cisternae seen in sections may be circular, oval, or sausage-like, suggesting that the cisternae are all shapes between circular tubes and flattened tubes. The flattened tube type of cisterna, with two membranes lying face to face with a rather constant spacing between them, is particularly common. It is difficult to determine the length and extent of individual cisternae since one is faced with the problem of relating a two-dimensional image of a thin section to the three-dimensional object of which it forms a part. But it is considered likely that the apparently separate cisternae seen in one section are all part of a single system of branched canals (the endoplasmic reticulum) ramifying through the cytoplasm and having outlets through the plasma membrane. Although the endoplasmic reticulum can be seen in almost all types of cell which have been examined, it is not equally well developed in all of them. Meristematic cells in particular show very few cisternae. It appears that during differentiation the system grows

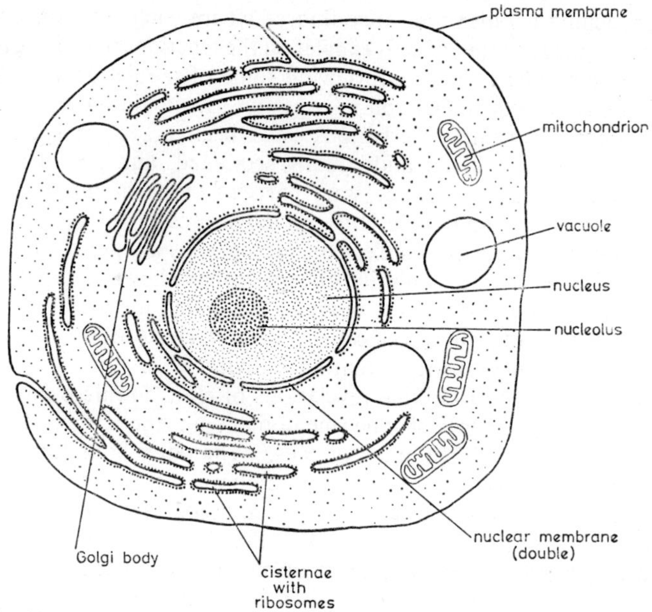

Fig. 88. DIAGRAM OF A THIN SECTION THROUGH A GENERALISED CELL.

in extent and complexity, and in mature cells it is a most conspicuous feature of the cytoplasm.

The nuclear envelope is also part of the system. Although generally referred to as the nuclear membrane, the envelope is now known to consist of two membranes which enclose what has been described as a "moat" around the nucleus. The outer membrane is continuous with the membranes of the endoplasmic reticulum, so that the nuclear "moat" is itself an extension of the system of cytoplasmic canals. At intervals, the nuclear envelope is perforated by pores which pass through both membranes and appear to give continuity between the nuclear sap and the cytoplasmic matrix.

The full significance of the endoplasmic reticulum can only be guessed at present, but there is some evidence which indicates what its functions include. Over a large part of the reticulum the outer surface of the membranes is associated with small particles, each about 100 Å across, which have a high content of ribonucleic acid and are called **ribosomes**. These are known to play an important part in protein synthesis, receiving information from the nucleus and translating it into specific amino acid sequences (see p. 171). The regularity with which ribosomes are situated on the membrane

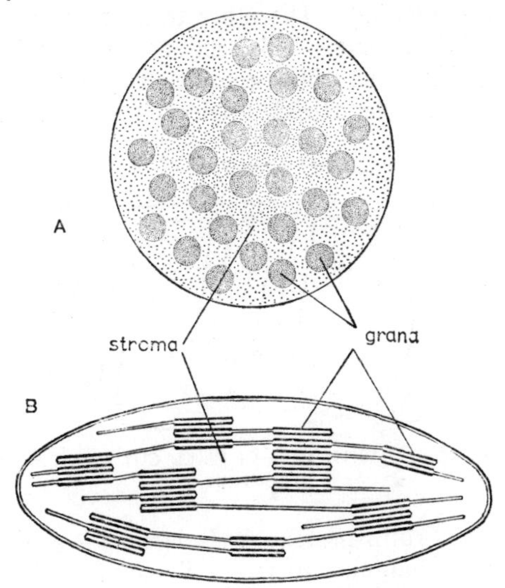

Fig. 89. CHLOROPLAST STRUCTURE.
A, chloroplast in face view; B, thin section through chloroplast.

surfaces strongly suggests a functional connection. The reticulum may also act as a system of communication and transport within the cell, or as a means of partitioning the cytoplasm so that separate reactions can proceed on either side of the membranes without interfering with each other.

One specialised part of the reticulum which has been seen in plant and animal cells of many types constitutes the **Golgi body**, named after the Italian cytologist who first recorded its presence in nerve cells of animals. It frequently consists of a number of flattened cisternae lying close to and parallel with one another, and is never associated with ribosomes. Its function has been a subject of controversy over many years and is still obscure, though there is some evidence that it may be the region where new membranes are produced during development of the endoplasmic reticulum.

Electron microscopy has also revealed important structural features of chloroplasts and mitochondria, the sites of photosynthesis and respiration respectively, and again an elaborate arrangement of membranes has been demonstrated in both of them. If the swollen disc-shaped **chloroplasts** of higher plants are examined in face view at magnifications which are low for the electron microscope (say 5,000 ×) it can be clearly seen that within each chloroplast is a number of dense circular bodies about 0·5 μ across which are called **grana** (Fig. 89). The more transparent matrix in which these lie is called the **stroma.** Thin sections of chloroplasts examined at higher magnifications show that each granum is a stack of disc-shaped lamellae piled at right angles to the surface of the chloro-

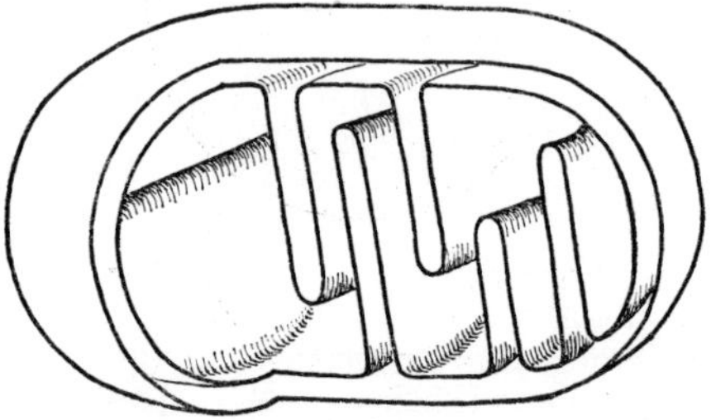

Fig. 90. MITOCHONDRION WITH PART OF WALL CUT AWAY TO SHOW INTERNAL STRUCTURE.

plast (Fig. 89 and Frontispiece). Each lamella is made up of a pair of flat membranes lying face to face. Some of the lamellae extend outwards from the grana into the stroma. It is believed that chlorophyll is concentrated in the grana between the pair of membranes in each lamella, and that the light reactions of photosynthesis occur here, while the dark reactions occur in the stroma.

Mitochondria vary greatly in size and shape (see p. 26), and their internal structure is consequently variable also, but there are certain features which appear very commonly. Each mitochondrion is bounded by a pair of membranes, the outer one smooth and the inner one folded or invaginated. The inner membrane thus makes a number of shelves, ridges, or finger-like projections into the interior of the mitochondrion, which are called **cristae** (Fig. 90). It will be seen that both in the outer wall and in the cristae there is a double structure with a more or less constant spacing between the two membranes which face each other. The shape of the mitochondria and the extent to which cristae are developed varies between related individuals grown under different conditions, and with time during development of a single individual, the variation possibly being related to the respiratory activity of the tissues.

In conclusion, attention is drawn to the repeated occurrence of pairs of parallel membranes in those parts of the cell known to be connected with fundamental metabolic activities. A comparable arrangement has been described for much of the endoplasmic reticulum, for the lamellae in the chloroplasts, and for the general structure of the mitochondria. Insufficient is known of the precise conditions under which protein synthesis, photosynthesis, and respiration occur in the living cell, but it is significant that in all these cases the process is associated with a similar type of structure.

9 THE PLANT IN RELATION TO WATER

Living plants are relatively wet structures, containing a high proportion of water. The nucleus, the cytoplasm, and the vacuole are all aqueous systems with more or less solid matter suspended in them. Although the tracheids and vessels of the xylem lose their cytoplasmic and vacuolar contents when they are mature, they do not normally dry out but remain filled with an aqueous fluid, the xylem sap.

A plant's requirement for water, and indeed the amount of water that it contains, changes as it grows and develops. In many seeds the cells of the embryo (and of the endosperm if one is present) are air-dry, having lost water by evaporation to the air through the hilum or through the testa if it is porous. Such dry seeds retain for extended periods of time the ability to germinate if once they are given access to water and air at a suitable temperature. The so-called dry seed is not completely dry—there will be a small loss of water if it is heated to 100° C.—but it is sufficiently desiccated to slow down biochemical activity; enzyme-controlled reactions (p. 207) proceed only with extreme slowness and metabolic activity (p. 206) is therefore negligible. If such a seed now takes up water it swells and metabolic activity becomes evident. The respiration rate of bean seeds for instance increases very rapidly as the seeds take up water (Fig. 107). As the seed develops into a seedling and so to a mature, rooted plant, it requires increasing amounts of water. The source of water is the soil. One of the characteristics of a fertile soil is its ability to hold a good proportion of the water that falls upon it as rain and so to act as a reservoir of water for plant growth. The water taken up by the roots supplies the shoot system as well as the roots themselves. Since the roots are spread out in a damp medium there will be little or no evaporation of water from them, but the shoot system is exposed to the air which has a very great drying power unless it already has a relative humidity close to 100 per cent. Despite its covering of cuticle the shoot loses water by evaporation (even when the stomata are closed) but it does not in fact dry out because it is continually replenished with fresh supplies of water from the soil—provided the soil can supply water fast enough. If the soil itself is dry or incapable of supplying water rapidly then the leaf will lose water faster than it is replenished. The leaf will dry out, and if it is not heavily lignified it will droop and wilt, losing its normal posture. Evidently the water content of a leaf contributes materially to its rigidity. To understand the connection between water content and mechanical strength we must consider first the water economy of individual cells.

WATER RELATIONS OF INDIVIDUAL CELLS

The majority of living cells in the mature tissues of plants are characterised by the presence of a large central vacuole and differ in this respect from most meristematic cells and from the cells of animal tissues. The vacuole confers upon the cell some important properties by reason of the osmotic pressure exerted by the contents of the vacuole. This will become clear after a short digression on the nature of osmosis.

Osmosis

If a solution is separated from pure water by a fully permeable membrane, molecules of solute and molecules of water will diffuse through the membrane so that eventually the two chambers have identical contents, each holding dilute solution. Osmosis is a process which occurs when a solution is separated from water (or from another solution) by a semi-permeable membrane—one that is permeable to molecules of water but not to molecules of solute. Such membranes can be made and studied in the laboratory. Copper ferrocyanide membranes, for instance, behave in this way. A membrane with considerable mechanical strength can be made by causing copper ferrocyanide to precipitate into the fine passages of a porous clay pot. If such a pot containing sucrose solution is immersed in pure water, the molecules of sucrose will be retained inside the pot, but the molecules of water can pass freely in either direction through the pot. However, the rate of movement from water to solution will be faster than the reverse movement, the net result being an overall passage of water into the solution, which will continue (in theory at least) until the solution has reached infinite dilution; this passage of water into a solution from which it is separated by a semi-permeable membrane is termed osmosis. If the vessel containing solution is equipped with a stopper pierced by a long tube the solution will be forced up the tube and will then exert a hydrostatic pressure (Fig. 91). A point will be reached when this hydrostatic pressure just balances the force of osmosis (the net tendency for water to enter the solution) and the solution will rise no further in the tube. The pressure exerted by the column of solution is then said to equal the osmotic pressure exerted by the solution in question. If the solution had been subjected to a hydrostatic pressure equal to the osmotic pressure this would have completely prevented the entry of water molecules into it. Experiments with systems like this show that the osmotic pressure is proportional to the concentration of solute, so long as we are dealing with relatively weak solutions. The osmotic pressure of substances which dissociate in solution is related to the concentration of ions in the solution. So far, we have considered the apparatus set up with solution inside it and water outside, but the same principles apply when it is immersed in a solution. For instance, if the pot contains 0·3 M. sucrose and it is placed in 0·1 M. sucrose there will be an osmotic movement of water molecules from the weaker solution (which has the lower osmotic pressure) to the stronger one. Water will flow into the vessel containing the stronger solution. If the vessel is closed, water will still tend to enter it with a pressure equal to the osmotic pressure. If the walls of the vessel are weak they will be stretched or even burst; if they are strong, they will resist the osmotic pressure opposing it with an equal and opposite hydrostatic pressure.

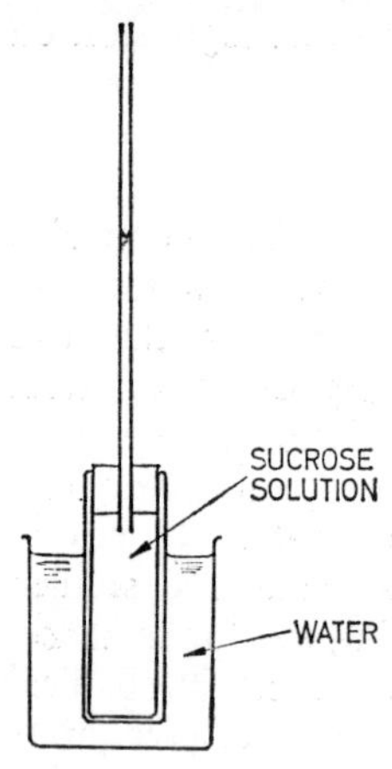

Fig. 91. SIMPLE OSMOMETER WITH MEMBRANE DEPOSITED IN POROUS POT.

Osmotic Phenomena in Plant Cells

How do the principles of osmosis outlined above apply to living plant cells? In considering their water relations we may think of their structure in a simplified way. There are three components of importance. First, the outer wall composed largely of cellulose and pectic substances which are laid down in a relatively loose framework so that the wall offers no appreciable resistance to the passage of water or of solutes: it can be regarded as fully permeable. Next comes a rather thin layer of cytoplasm bounded to the inside and the outside by membranes. The cytoplasm with its boundary layers acts as a semi-permeable membrane—that is, to repeat, one which allows free passage of water molecules but is impervious to solutes. (We shall see later that this statement needs amplification—the cytoplasm is not completely impervious.) In the centre of the cell is the vacuole occupying most of the volume of the cell. Within the vacuole is a solution of inorganic salts, sugars, and possibly other substances like tannins and pigments as well. We have here the components of an osmotic system. If a cell is immersed in water the vacuolar solution is separated from the water by a semi-permeable membrane (the cytoplasm) and water therefore tends to enter the vacuole, enlarging it and therefore expanding the cytoplasm, which in turn pushes up against the cell wall, causing it to enlarge. Some cells have such weak walls that when the cell is placed in water it expands to the point where the wall bursts. An example is the germinating pollen-grain. (The usual environment for a pollen-tube is the stigma where it will grow in a sugary medium which will expose the cell to a smaller net osmotic pressure than does immersion in water.) Most cells have walls strong enough to resist the osmotic pressure. The wall simply becomes distended when the cells have free access to water, just as a bicycle tyre distends as air is forced into the inner tube. Like the tyre, the cell now becomes stronger. It is distended with water and the osmotic force which tends to drive yet more water into the vacuole is now opposed by an equal hydrostatic pressure exerted by the wall. Such a cell is said to be turgid. The cells in the leaf of a plant which is plentifully supplied with water are not quite fully turgid, but they are probably not far from this condition. A tissue composed of such turgid cells has a natural strength of its own. It is this turgor which maintains the architecture of soft herbaceous plants causing the stem to stand erect and the leaves to spread out as thin flat sheets of tissue.

Now consider what happens if a cell is placed not in pure water, but in a weak solution such as 0·3 M. sucrose. Such a solution has an osmotic pressure which will oppose the osmotic pressure in the vacuole. The net osmotic pressure causing water to enter the vacuole is therefore less than when the cell was in water, the force exerted on the layer of cytoplasm and wall is less, and the wall by its natural elasticity will contract a little—just as the bicycle tyre shrinks as air leaks out of the tube. Being less distended the cell (and the tyre) are now less rigid; they have lost their turgor and become flaccid. Another way in which a turgid cell may lose its rigidity is by evaporation of water into the atmosphere. This is the situation in a herbaceous plant deprived of water. The leaf cells lose water by evaporation faster than the root system can replace it. If the leaf has few lignified cells to give it strength, it will droop and wilt.

Suction Pressure

As we have seen, a cell placed in water soon becomes fully turgid. The osmotic pressure due to the vacuolar contents is then balanced by an equal and opposite pressure exerted by the wall (the wall pressure). Thus, in a turgid cell:

Osmotic pressure = Wall pressure.

In a cell that is not turgid, the wall is not so distended and therefore exerts a somewhat lower wall pressure. The osmotic pressure being due simply to the concentration of solutes in the vacuole is now opposed by a smaller wall pressure and there remains a net tendency for water to enter the cell. The cell is said to have a suction pressure equal to the difference between osmotic pressure and wall pressure.

Suction pressure = Osmotic pressure − Wall pressure.

This equation is a perfectly general one. The case we considered first, that of the fully turgid cell is one in which the suction pressure is zero; the cell was immersed in water and it took up sufficient water to dilate the cell fully, so raising wall pressure until it just balanced osmotic pressure.

Plasmolysis

If the cell whose fortunes we have been following is now transferred from the 0·3 M. sucrose solution to one that is three or four times as strong, a new and dramatic event is likely to occur, for the osmotic pressure of this new solution will probably exceed that of the vacuolar solution. In consequence, water will move from the vacuole out into the surrounding sucrose solution. The vacuole and layer of cytoplasm around it will consequently shrink, allowing the wall to contract at the same time. As the vacuole contracts in volume so its contents become more concentrated and exert a higher osmotic pressure. Contraction will continue until the osmotic pressure of the vacuole has risen to equal that of the solution in which the cell is immersed. With a molar sucrose solution this is likely to require contraction of the vacuole to less than one-half its original volume. The surrounding layer of cytoplasm contracts likewise, but the cellulose wall is a somewhat rigid structure, incapable of much movement. Consequently the cytoplasm and vacuole contract away from the wall and come to lie inside it and separate from it (Fig. 92). The cell is then said to be plasmolysed. It is easy to plasmolyse cells and the results are striking and readily observed. However, it must be recognised that this is not an event that occurs naturally in the life of any cell and it is one that damages the cell by breaking the plasmodesmata. Nevertheless, observations of plasmolysis still have some value. First they enable us to determine for the cells of any particular tissue the osmotic pressure of the vacuolar sap. If some cells of a tissue are immersed in water and others in each of a series of sucrose solutions of steadily increasing concentrations, the strongest solutions will plasmolyse the cells because the osmotic pressure of the sucrose exceeds that of the vacuole. Lower concentrations cause less and less severe plasmolysis. The concentration which just fails to cause any detectable plasmolysis is the one that has an osmotic pressure equal to the osmotic pressure of the vacuolar contents. In this way many measurements of osmotic pressure have been made; typically, plant cells have osmotic pressures of around ten atmos-

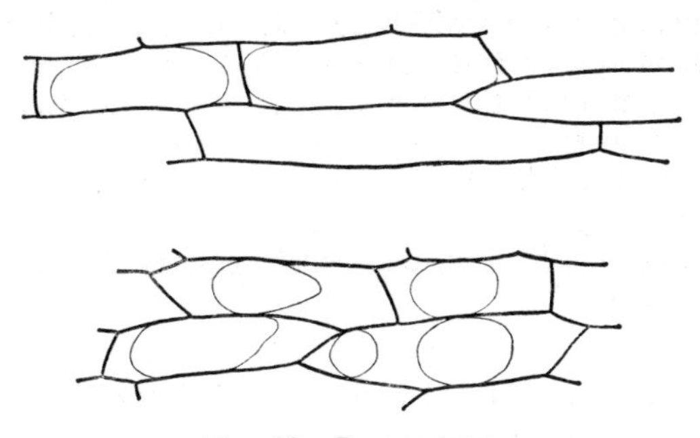

Fig. 92. PLASMOLYSIS

Above: Plasmolysis of a group of cells from the inner epidermis of onion bulb scales after immersion in 0·5 M. sucrose for twenty minutes. The cells have not all behaved alike; they differ in physiological properties just as they do in size and shape. The cell at top left has undergone a fair degree of plasmolysis, the one on the right only shows evidence of plasmolysis at the ends of the cell, while the one below has not plasmolysed at all. In a weaker solution, a lower proportion of the cells (or none of them) would have become plasmolysed. In a stronger solution more of the cells would be plasmolysed and plasmolysis would be more complete. The lower drawing shows cells after immersion in M. sucrose for one hour. The protoplasts have contracted right away from the cell walls; in one cell it has become constricted into two portions.

pheres which is about the osmotic pressure exerted by a 0·4 M. solution of sucrose.

A second value of plasmolysis experiments is the insight they give us into the permeability of cytoplasm and its boundary membranes. A cell immersed in a strong solution of sucrose or sodium chloride becomes plasmolysed in a few minutes and stays in this condition for a long time. But a cell immersed in a strong solution of glycerol slowly recovers after an initial rapid plasmolysis: the vacuole and cytoplasm first contract away from the wall and then expand out again more slowly until the cytoplasm comes to lie against the wall once more. This reversal of plasmolysis is known as **deplasmolysis**, and it is the result of a passage of solute molecules across the cytoplasm into the vacuole. As the concentration of glycerol in the vacuole rises, so it exerts a greater osmotic pressure in opposition to that exerted by the bathing medium. When the osmotic pressure in the vacuole becomes equal to that in the plasmolysing solution the cell will have recovered from plasmolysis. It is evident that the cytoplasm and its membranes, while being fully permeable to water and being impermeable to sucrose and sodium chloride (being, in short, semi-permeable) are, nevertheless, penetrated slowly by molecules of glycerol. From experiments of this sort it is possible to judge which molecules penetrate through cytoplasmic membranes and which do not. In general, it can be said that large molecules and those which are ionised are unable to diffuse freely through the membranes. This is not to say they are quite unable to enter cells—for plant cells do, of course, contain inorganic salts which are taken up from the soil. These salts do not *diffuse* through the cytoplasm into the vacuole: they enter by a quite different mechanism, one which requires the expenditure of energy (p. 262).

Loss of Semi-permeability in Senescent and Dying Tissues

It should now be clear that living tissues consist of individual cells with watery contents permeated by an air space system running between the cells. Why does the water remain within the cells and not invade the air spaces? The key factor is the cytoplasmic membranes which maintain the integrity of the cytoplasm itself and set up the osmotic system which tends to cause water to enter the vacuole rather than to leave it.

When an organ comes near the end of its life it is said to reach the stage of senescence; at this time green tissues commonly turn yellow. Another event characteristic of senescence is that the cytoplasmic membranes become disorganised so that the vacuolar fluid, no longer subject to osmotic forces, oozes out into the intercellular spaces. Bulky tissues then become soft, waterlogged, and sponge-like; water can be squeezed out of them with pressure from the fingers. This is the behaviour of over-ripe fruit and of other fleshy organs like the spadix of *Arum* at senescence; it is also what happens when vegetables are cooked, for the high temperature coagulates the protein component of the membranes. In less bulky tissues like leaves, the water is rapidly lost by evaporation into the air and the leaf quickly withers and dries out because there can be no transpiration stream in the absence of cell membranes (see pp. 188-9).

TRANSPIRATION

The transpiration stream is a current of water passing from the soil through the roots, up to the shoot system, and finally replacing water that evaporates into the air from the leaves. This loss of water from the leaves of a growing plant can be demonstrated very simply as shown in Fig. 93. By covering the plant pot with rubber sheeting or aluminium foil it is an easy matter to ensure that no water can be lost from the root system, the soil surface, or from the pot itself. A measure of the rate of water loss can be obtained by weighing such a plant at intervals. More sophisticated apparatus is needed to determine the rate of transpiration of a crop plant or of a tree growing in soil, one method being to pass a stream of air over the shoot system or a part of the shoot system and then find by how much the water content of the air has increased. It is important to agriculturalists and foresters to know how much water their field crops need, but measurement on the field scale poses severe problems. In one investigation crops were grown in very large concrete containers (25 yd square) and the loss of water by transpiration (and evaporation from the soil surface) assessed by subtracting from the observed rainfall over a period of time the amount of water percolating to the bottom of the tank. The loss of water by evaporation from the soil surface was determined in a further tank filled with the same type of soil as the others, but maintained free of vegetation.

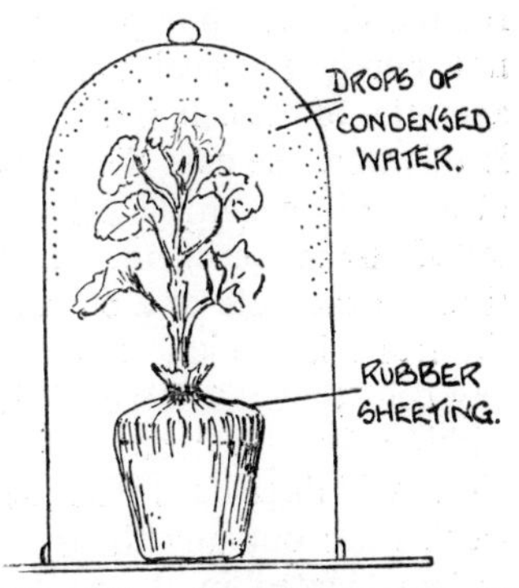

Fig. 93. DEMONSTRATION OF TRANSPIRATION BY A GROWING PLANT.

The following figures will give some idea of the magnitude of transpiration. A mature maize plant contains about 2 litres of water—this is the amount of water which will be lost if the whole plant is put in an oven at 100° C. for a couple of days. However, during its growth from the seedling stage a maize plant transpires around 200 litres of water. The amount of water which passes through a plant in the transpiration stream is evidently *much* larger than the amount present in the plant at any moment. The amount of water that a plant transpires depends, among other factors, on its leaf area. A 30 ft tree may transpire 200 litres of water (*i.e.* about 44 gal.) in the course of a single day in the summer.

Mechanism of the Ascent of Sap

Many trees grow to considerable heights (*Sequoia* may reach 300 ft) and plant physiologists have long wondered how water reaches their crown. The crux of the problem is this. In physical systems composed of pumps and pipes it is found that water cannot be sucked up to heights greater than about 34 ft in a single lift. If a pump is set at the top of a pipe 60 ft high with its lower, open end in water, the pump may raise the water to 34 ft but above this will appear a vacuum. This is the height of water which atmospheric pressure will support, and the system is comparable to a water barometer. It seems, therefore, that we must envisage some force exerted from below that is pushing the water up the tree—or perhaps there are pumping stations situated at regular intervals up the bole of the tree? Such theories generally require that the pump is operated by the living tree itself; they are not purely physical systems but are powered by the metabolic activities of the cell, making use of the energy released in respiration. If this were the case then water should be unable to rise up the bole of a tree in which the cells were dead. This is an idea that can be tested by experiment. In the early 1890's Strasburger sawed through the bole of a 60 ft oak tree and then placed the cut end of the trunk in a picric acid solution. Although the acid would kill any cells that it contacted, it was carried up to the top of the tree within a few days; so also was fuchsin, a dye that was added to the picric acid three days after the start of the experiment. Strasburger's work rules out any theory which relies exclusively on a pumping system located in the roots (since the solution was raised in the complete absence of roots) and it implies also that the ascent of sap does not require the expenditure of metabolic energy since it continues even in the presence of a poison. The theory most generally accepted to-day is the cohesion theory proposed by Dixon and Joly, working in Dublin in 1894. Their views will first be stated in modern terms and then the implications of their theory and experimental tests of it will be discussed. Dixon and Joly suggested that the motive power for the ascent of sap was generated in the leaves as water evaporated from the moist surfaces of leaf cells and passed into the intercellular air spaces of the leaf. This water vapour diffused out through the stomata into the atmosphere. As a leaf cell loses water by evaporation so it becomes less turgid and its suction pressure rises. In consequence it draws water from neighbouring cells with lower suction pressure and these in turn draw water from their neighbours, and so on. The immediate source of supply is the water in the liquid-filled xylem vessels and tracheids, and so water is pulled up the plant through the xylem. As water ascends the xylem so further supplies are pulled out of the soil and through the root system. In short, one may think of a continuous column of water from leaf cell down to soil; as water evaporates from the leaf cells so it is drawn out of the soil and up through the plant. The motive power comes from above, being generated by the evaporation of water from the leaf cells. The sun's heat is the source of energy that causes the evaporation of water by imparting sufficient energy to water molecules to enable them to escape from the liquid to the vapour phase. The surface of a raindrop is gently convex and evaporation can proceed freely from it. Conditions at the interface between water and air in leaf cells may be quite different, however. The outer layers of the cell are in effect a meshwork of fine fibrils. In a fully turgid leaf this meshwork will be completely filled with water so that the interface is a plane surface, but in a less turgid leaf the interface will retreat into the spaces between the fibrils so forming numerous minute concavities. The drier a leaf becomes, the deeper the concavities. Now water molecules are less able to escape into the vapour phase from such a concave surface than from a plane one. It follows that more energy (from sunlight) is needed to cause evaporation from the concavities of leaf cells than from a free water surface, and it is this extra energy that pulls the water column up from the soil.

According to the theory, there should be continuous columns of water through the xylem from root to leaf. If this is the case, then cutting through the bole of a tree with a saw to beyond the half-way mark and then making a second cut a few inches higher from the opposite side should sever all intact columns of water and stop transpiration. When this experiment was tried there was no evidence to suggest that transpiration had stopped for the leaves continued to transpire; evidently the columns of water do not run vertically straight up a tree—or sufficient water can be passed horizontally through the xylem cell walls to allow the continuance of transpiration.

A second consequence of the theory is that if the motive power comes from above, pulling up columns of water, this water should be in a state of tension. This can be investigated by experiments involving puncture of the xylem channels. If the stem of a herbaceous plant is immersed in a solution of a dye such as fuchsin and then severed and held under the dye for a few seconds, the movement of the dye can be traced by subsequently sectioning the stem. If the plant was transpiring rapidly, the dye will be found to have penetrated for some distance in the xylem both above and below the cut, showing that the xylem contents were in a state of tension when the cut was made. A simple demonstration that a transpiring shoot can create a tension is shown in Fig. 94.

Another requirement of Dixon and Joly's theory is that columns of water as high as trees should cohere; they should not rupture producing gas bubbles. They should not, in fact, break in the way that long columns of water do in physical models with pumps and pipes. Further experiments with such physical systems have shown that water does not cavitate readily if it is confined within *narrow* tubes the walls of which are perfectly wetted (and if the water is absolutely clean and free from particles that might act as nuclei for gas bubbles). These conditions presumably apply in the plant where water is conducted through xylem tracheids (20-80 μ diam.) or vessels (up to 500 μ across). If a gas phase should suddenly appear in a vessel or in a tracheid it will be confined to that vessel or tracheid and will not spread to neighbouring xylem elements because the cell walls are permeable to liquids but not to gases. The xylem thus consists of elements which are self-sealing as regards bubbles of gas. There remain, however, problems as to what happens to the transpiration stream in a severe winter. Deciduous trees, to be sure, will have shed their leaves, and transpiration may be slow even in evergreens, but the problem envisaged here has to do with the fact that gases are practically insoluble in ice: when tap water is set to freeze in a refrigerator, gases are expelled from the water. If the water in the xylem elements of a tree freezes in the winter one would imagine that the conducting elements would be blocked with gas bubbles. How then is the stream resumed next spring? It seems that in oak, ash, and elm which have vessels of large diameter, the only functional vessels are those of the current year (which will be liquid-filled as the cells differentiate from cambial

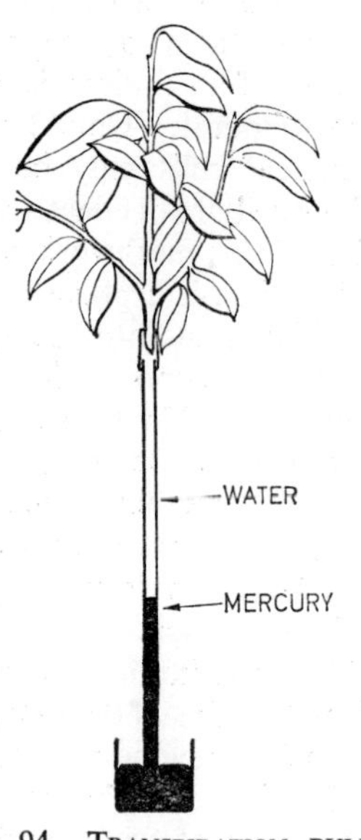

Fig. 94. TRANSPIRATION PULL. As the shoot transpires, water and mercury are raised up the glass tube. Under favourable conditions the mercury will rise above thirty inches but the experiment usually terminates before this as air leaks into the glass tube through the intercellular air spaces of the shoot.

initials)—but there is evidence to suggest that in other trees the gas redissolves in the xylem sap as the weather warms.

Root Pressure and Guttation

The importance of Strasburger's experiment (p. 188) is that it showed that the aerial parts of a tree can raise water from the cut end of the bole to the foliage; and that this does not depend on the activity of living cells. The experiment tells us nothing, however, about the activity of the root in this regard. Does the root system have any role in the upward movement of water? This question can be explored by decapitating a plant and attaching to the cut stump a length of tubing (Fig. 95). If the plant was in vigorous growth and the rooting medium was well watered, then liquid will exude from the cut stump and begin to rise in the tubing. The exudation is due to root pressure. By means of a manometer it is possible to measure the pressure with which liquid is exuded. Generally this is quite small, of the order of one atmosphere or less, although higher values have been recorded occasionally. A root pressure of one atmosphere would support a column of water about 30 ft high and so would be insufficient to account for active transpiration in a tall tree. For this reason, and because the rate at which liquid exudes from a cut stump is considerably slower than the observed rate of transpiration in the intact plant, it is generally considered that root pressure is not an important force in transpiration. There is, however, one situation where root pressure does have a role. When the atmosphere is humid there is little evaporation of water from the leaf surfaces, and transpiration is very slow: root pressure may then account for the ascent of sap in a small plant. If the flow of liquid due to root pressure exceeds the rate of evaporative loss from the leaves, then drops of liquid may appear at the leaf tips at hydathodes (p. 50). This phenomenon, known as guttation, may be demonstrated by placing a cover over the plants to raise the humidity (Fig. 96). Much of the "dew" seen on blades of grass early in the morning after a warm, humid night consists of water guttated from the leaves.

The Path of Water Movement

That water passes up the shoot in the tracheids and vessels of the xylem is indicated by several lines of evidence. First Strasburger's experiment shows that living cells are not involved; then experiments in which a stem is ringed by removing a complete ring of bark and phloem from a short length of the stem indicate that these outer tissues are not essential for the continuance of transpiration.

When a cut shoot is placed with its lower end in an eosin solution, subsequent sectioning of the stem shows that the dye has travelled up the stem as the solution was absorbed and has stained the walls of the xylem vessels and tracheids.

There is no need to emphasise the idea that the vessels and tracheids of the shoot are well suited by their structure to the function of water transport. What of the root system? In the upper reaches of the root water will of course be conducted through the xylem, but at the tip of the root water must be conducted across

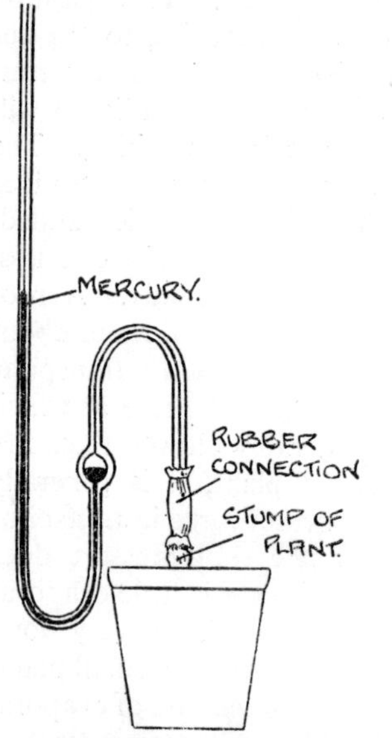

Fig. 95. DETERMINATION OF ROOT PRESSURE BY ATTACHING AN OPEN-ENDED MANOMETER TO THE STUMP OF A VIGOROUSLY GROWING WELL-WATERED PLANT.

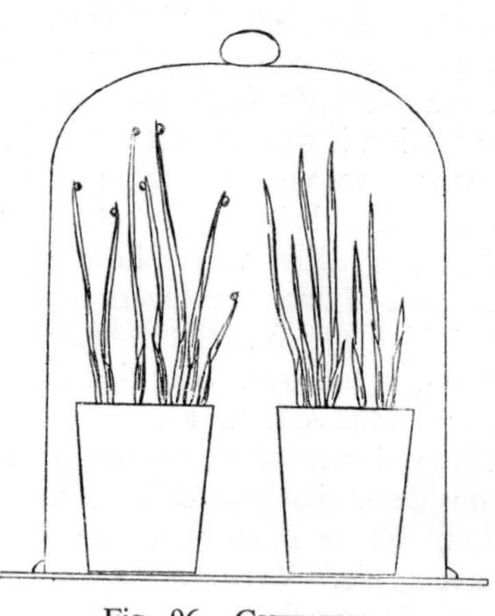

Fig. 96. GUTTATION.

Left: Guttation by seedlings of *Avena* placed in a humid atmosphere. On the right are comparable seedlings which have been watered with 10 per cent. sodium chloride. By its high osmotic pressure this solution prevents the development of root pressure and in consequence no guttation is observed.

the root from the soil to the xylem. The root hair system greatly enlarges the surface area of the roots and so the area across which water can pass from soil to plant. From the root hairs water passes across the cortex and so to the stele. The exact route that the water follows in its journey across the root is not certain; it may pass into the living contents of each cell or perhaps it is confined all the way to the wet cell walls. In either case we would expect its passage across the root to prove more difficult than its subsequent ascent in the hollow vessels and tracheids of the xylem. Experiment bears

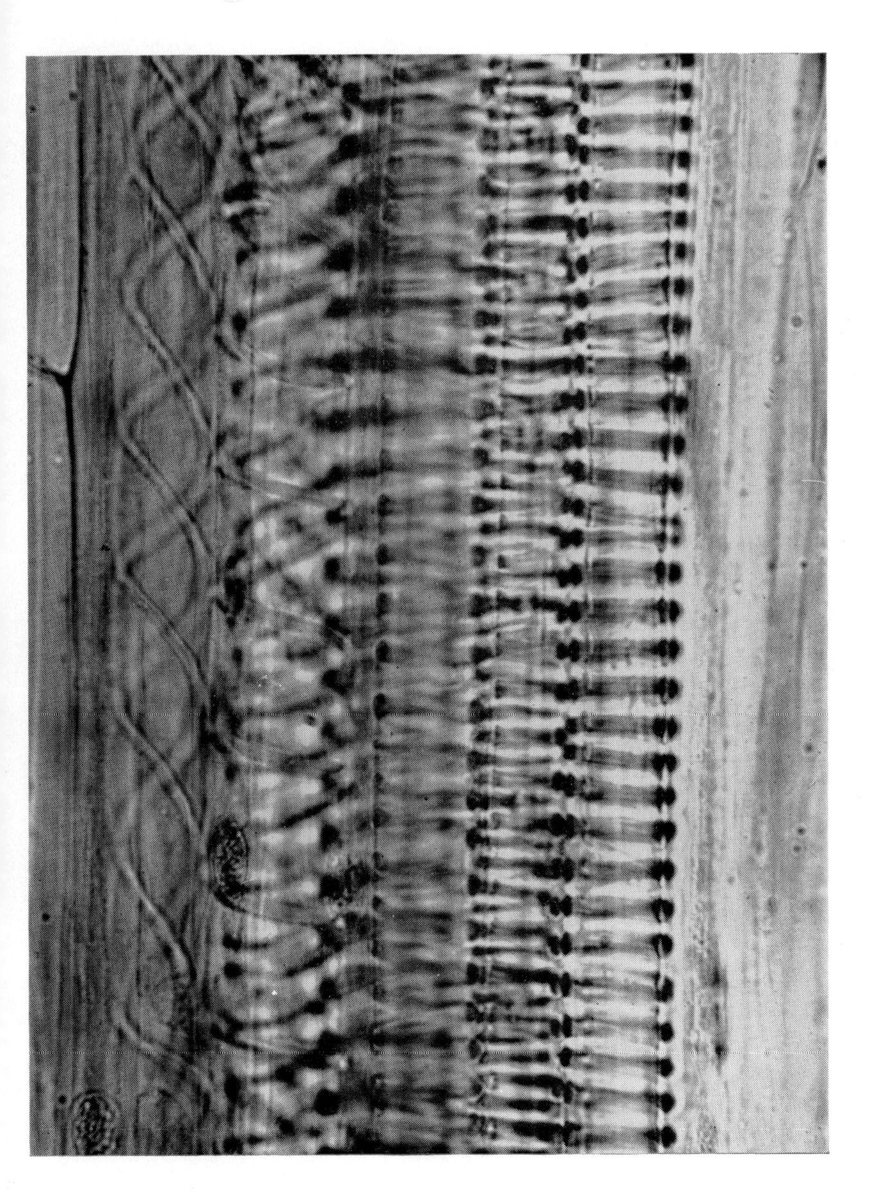

PLATE 5

SPIRALLY-THICKENED XYLEM ELEMENTS IN A LONGITUDINAL SECTION OF TULIP STEM. The first cells to be formed were those on the left, and elongation of the stem has pulled out the spiral coils. As we move towards the right, the spirals show a progressive reduction in spacing, because the cells were formed later and have consequently undergone a smaller amount of stretching. (× 600.)

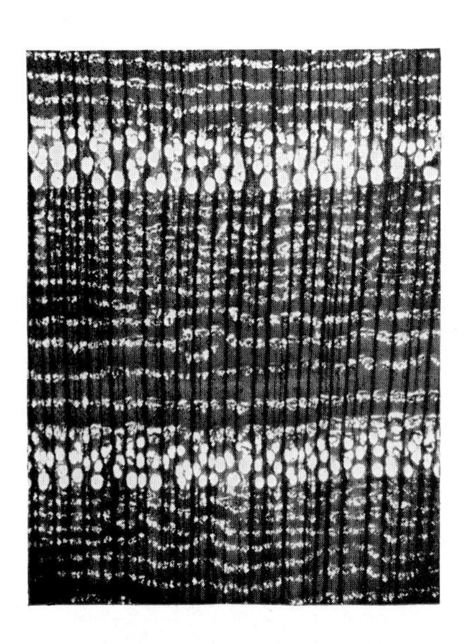

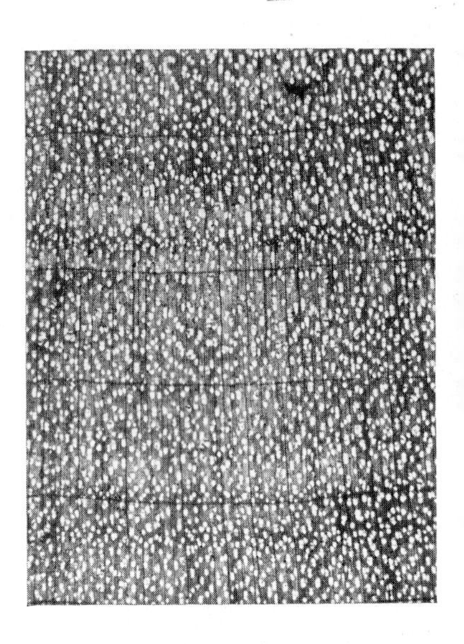

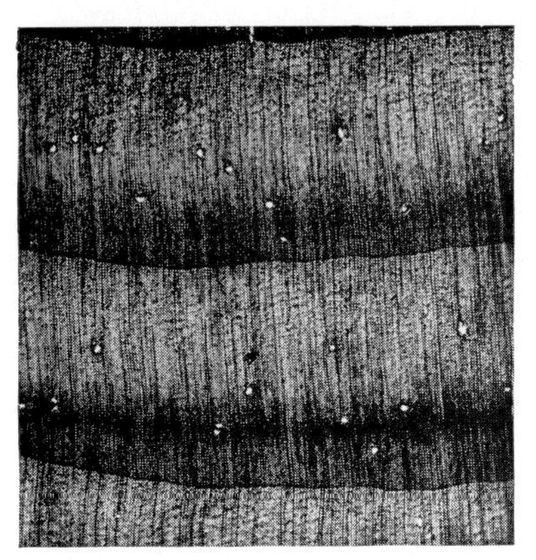

PLATE 6

Above left: ELM, T.S. WOOD × 10. Ring porous.

Above right: BIRCH, T.S. WOOD × 10. Diffuse porous.

Below left: PINE, T.S. WOOD × 10. Tracheids and resin ducts.

Below right: YEW, T.S. WOOD × 10. Tracheids, no resin ducts.

out this expectation: the immediate effect of cutting off the root system of a sunflower plant under water is to double the rate of transpiration. Evidently the roots offer a notable resistance to the passage of water.

Control of Transpiration Rate

The transpiration stream is a current of water passing up the shoot sytem evaporating into the internal air space of the leaf and then diffusing out through the stomata into the atmosphere. The

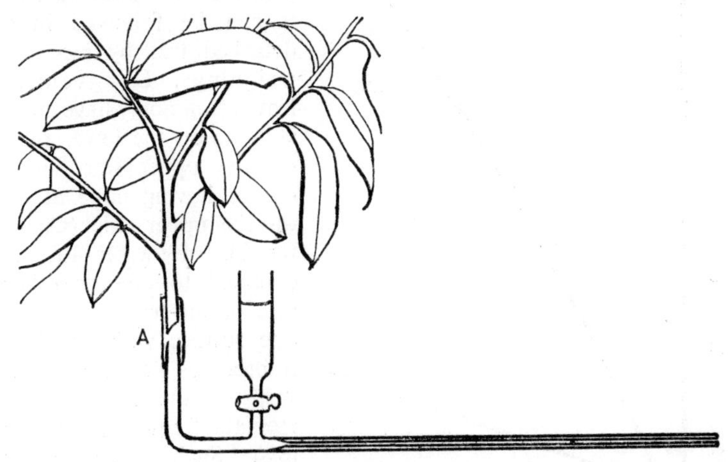

Fig. 97. POTOMETER DESIGNED TO MEASURE THE RATE OF UPTAKE OF WATER BY AN EXCISED SHOOT.

The rate of water flow in the capillary tube is determined by following the movement of the water meniscus. At the end of its traverse the bubble can be returned to the open end of the capillary by opening the tap to admit more water. The rate of water uptake by a small plant complete with its roots can be measured with a modified type of potometer in which the chamber A is enlarged to take the root system.

rate at which this current moves is controlled by that step in the process which is slowest. In considering transpiration rate we have therefore to examine soil water supply, the factors that govern water loss from the leaves and the evaporative power of the air.

Some of the atmospheric factors involved can be studied in simple experiments with a **potometer** (Fig. 97). When a shoot is placed under a bell jar so that it is in an atmosphere of high relative humidity, the rate of transpiration falls. On the other hand, a stream of air passing over the leaf surface will increase the rate of transpiration by preventing the build-up of a layer of relatively humid air close to the leaf surface. Some plants have much sunken stomata or rolled leaf blades, modifications which are likely to slow down transpiration by maintaining a humid atmosphere about the leaves (see p. 623 for more details of these plants).

That water loss from the shoot system is largely confined to the stomata is suggested by observations on the anatomy of the epidermis and is confirmed by experiment. Water loss by the leaves of a shoot can be measured in a potometer or it can be followed in a detached leaf by repeated weighings. Dorsiventral leaves commonly have more stomata on the lower than on the upper side, some indeed having none at all on the upper side (Chapter 7). If water loss is confined to one or other side of the leaf by coating one surface with vaseline, it becomes possible to investigate the influence of stomatal frequency on water loss. Such studies show that most of the water is lost through the stomata, but that an appreciable amount evaporates directly from epidermal cells, passing through the cuticle. Cuticular transpiration is often about one-tenth as fast as stomatal transpiration (with the stomata open), but it may account for as much as half the total water loss in young leaves with incompletely developed cuticle or in leaves developing in the shade. When the stomata are shut transpiration continues at a reduced rate through the cuticle. As they open, stomatal transpiration comes into play, its rate depending, among other factors, on the width of the aperture —and on whether there is any wind (Fig. 98). In perfectly still air

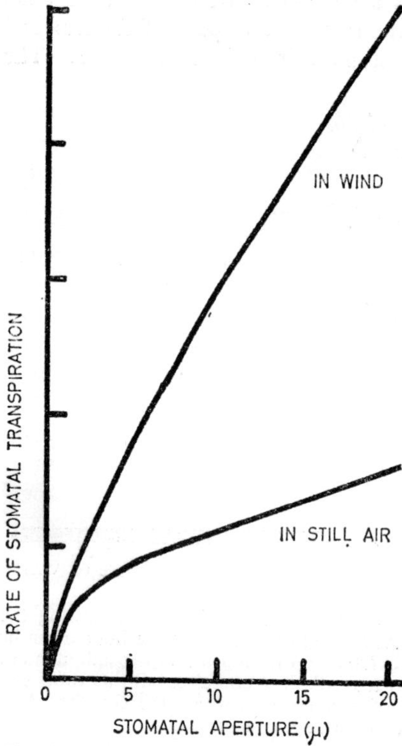

Fig. 98. THE EFFECT OF STOMATAL APERTURE ON STOMATAL TRANSPIRATION IN STILL AIR AND IN WIND.
Data from an experiment on *Zebrina pendula* leaves by Bange, 1953.

reduction of the stomatal aperture from 20 μ to 10 μ has little effect on transpiration rate: only when the stomata are almost completely shut do they exert much control over transpiration. The reason for this behaviour is that as water molecules diffuse out of the leaf a layer of air immediately outside the stomata becomes saturated with water vapour. This layer acts as a considerable barrier or resistance, preventing the diffusion of further water molecules out of the leaf; in fact it limits the rate of transpiration. Only when the stomata are so far shut that they offer a resistance of comparable magnitude do they have much influence on the rate of transpiration. This is, however, rather a theoretical situation for a breeze of no more than one mile per hour is sufficient to blow away the layer of saturated air. Once the external resistance is removed, stomatal aperture exerts a considerable degree of control over transpiration rate. To see how this control works we need to know on the one hand when the stomata open and when they close, and on the other, what mechanism controls their opening and closing.

Generally, stomata are open by day and closed by night, but they may also close more or less completely for a period around midday, and they tend to close under conditions of water stress or drought. The structure of the stomata was discussed on p. 153, where it was seen that stomatal aperture is governed by the guard cells. Although the structure of the guard cells is not the same in all plants, their movements are always the result of turgor changes. When the guard cells become more turgid they move apart, enlarging the stomatal aperture. Simple experiments in which pieces of epidermis are stripped from a leaf and immersed in solutions of various osmotic pressure show that we are dealing with osmotic changes in the vacuolar sap of the guard cells. The majority of the cells of the epidermis possess neither chloroplast nor starch, but the guard cells have both. An early theory of stomatal operation (due to von Mohl, 1856) proposed that the chloroplasts of the guard cells produced sugars by photosynthesis in the light and so raised the osmotic pressure of the guard cell vacuoles, causing the stoma to open. However, recent measurements show that guard cell photosynthesis does not produce sugar fast enough to account for the observed rate of stomatal opening. In 1908 Lloyd observed that when stomata opened in the morning there was an accompanying fall in the starch content of the guard cells; conversely, in the evening the stomata closed and guard cell starch rose. Lloyd proposed that these events were correlated in a causal fashion, the opening of the stomata being governed by hydrolysis of starch to sugar; he further suggested that the equilibrium position (p. 208) of the starch $\rightleftharpoons$ sugar reaction was influenced by light, being pushed in the direction of hydrolysis in the light. Thus starch was hydrolysed to sugar in the light so increasing the number of osmotically active particles in the sap, raising the guard cell osmotic pressure and causing the stomata to open. The weakest link in this otherwise attractive hypothesis concerns the influence of light on starch hydrolysis. The reaction starch $\rightleftharpoons$ sugar is a complex one governed by several enzymes (see p. 209 and p. 227). *In vitro* at least, these enzymes are not light-sensitive. Many enzymes are, however, pH-sensitive and Lloyd's views were elaborated by Sayre (1926) who found that in the light when the stomata opened and guard cell starch diminished in amount, the contents of the guard cells became less acid. At night the reverse changes occurred, the guard cells becoming more acid as starch reappeared and the stomata closed. Sayre supposed that light *caused* the guard cells to become less acid either by some direct effect or by photosynthetic removal of carbon dioxide from the leaf. The more alkaline conditions were supposed to favour hydrolysis of starch to sugar and this in turn caused the stomata to open. However, we have no evidence that light by itself exerts a major influence on guard cell pH, nor is it clear that under field conditions photosynthesis could effectively reduce the carbon dioxide concentration of the air around the guard cells. Nevertheless, we now have direct evidence from laboratory experiments that the carbon dioxide content of the air inside the leaf *can* control stomatal aperture. Heath observed in 1950 that the stomata of *Pelargonium* and wheat opened markedly when the carbon dioxide concentration was reduced below the normal 0·03 per cent., whether in the light or the dark. At the same time there was a decrease in the starch content of the guard cells; this is presumably the immediate cause of stomatal opening, but the mechanism by which a low carbon dioxide concentration can influence starch content remains an open question, one that is still the subject of active research.

THE SOIL AND SOIL WATER

Soils are complex mixtures of mineral and organic materials. The mineral component owes its origin to the disintegration of the parent rock, which is initially due to physical forces such as temperature fluctuation and sand-blasting, and to chemical decomposition through the action of water containing carbon dioxide in solution. The sizes of the mineral particles depend on many factors, such as the type of parent material, mode, and degree of weathering, and on whether the soils have been formed *in situ* or transported either by wind or water from the place of weathering and deposited elsewhere. The particles range in size from stones and gravel, through sand (2·0-0·02 mm. diam.) and silt (0·02-0·002 mm. diam.) to clay (less than 0·002 mm. diam.). The particles of clay are of colloidal dimensions.

However, the soil does not consist entirely of mineral particles. Organic matter of both plant and animal origin, and in varying stages of decomposition, is also present. Plant and animal remains decomposed to such an extent as to have lost their cell structure form the **humus** of the soil. The colloidal humus, together with the inorganic clay of the soil cements the mineral particles into larger aggregates which in a fertile soil are soft and porous, and called **soil crumbs**. The soil crumbs imbibe water readily and hold inorganic ions, especially bases, which are thereby prevented from being washed out of the soil. The humus serves as substrate for the growth of a vast flora consisting of fungi, bacteria, and algae. In addition, there is a fauna ranging in size from Protozoa up to earthworms, insects, and the like. To say that the humus is the substrate for the growth of these organisms means that it supplies materials that they require for growth. When dead plant material falls on a soil it will contain soluble sugars and nitrogen compounds which are immediately available to the micro-organisms; when these substances are exhausted further growth is only possible if the insoluble materials of the plant are decomposed. This means especially the breakdown of cellulose and lignin, which are formed in higher plants. Some micro-organisms possess enzymes (p. 207) enabling them to break down cellulose and lignin, and it is this attack by micro-organisms which converts plant remains into humus.

The pores of the soil, the regions between the particles, comprise from one-third to one-half the volume of the soil. They are occupied partly by soil water and partly by the soil atmosphere. The air in the soil is not identical with ordinary air, usually having a higher carbon dioxide content due chiefly to the respiration of the soil flora and fauna.

Since the soil particles are small in size they have a large total surface area. A cube of material with sides 1 cm. long has a total surface area of 6 sq. cm. If this cube is now bisected, two fresh surfaces are created and the area rises to 8 sq. cm. Cutting these two pieces in half brings the surface up to 10 sq. cm. and, in fact, each further subdivision will result in the creation of fresh surfaces. The amount of surface is thus an indication of the fineness of the material. A loam soil has a very large surface area: about 50,000 sq. cm. per gram of soil; this means that a cubic centimetre of soil has an internal surface area of roughly 5 sq. yd. Adsorbed on to this extensive surface, held in the many angles between the soil particles and occupying some of the soil pores, is the soil water. This water is derived ultimately from rain.

Soil Water

In agricultural and forestry practice it is desirable, to say the least, that the water falling upon a soil as rain should enter the soil, rather than run off the soil where there is any slope in the ground. Such surface run-off, if it is severe enough, will lead ultimately to soil erosion. A good cover of vegetation over a soil and good soil structure help to prevent run-off and encourage penetration of water into the soil.

The movement of water within a soil is slow. The means by which it moves depends on the quantity of water that is present. For a start we require the concept of **field capacity**. If a soil is saturated with water and then allowed to drain freely under gravity, it will only lose some of its water. What remains constitutes the field capacity of the soil. A heavy rain may deposit water on the soil faster than it can penetrate. Such free-standing water on the soil surface moves into the soil, slowly bringing each successive layer of soil up to the field capacity before it moves down to the next layer. In one experiment, standing water brought the top 6 in. of a soil to field capacity in one hour; after six hours it had moved down 24 in.

After a heavy rainfall, then, the soil remains saturated to its field capacity. What happens next? The surface layers of the soil lose water by evaporation, and in addition, water is removed by the plant roots. The soil then has less water than at field capacity. Water disappears from the larger pores of the soil as they become air-filled, while the films of water around the soil particles and in the angles between the particles become thinner. The movement of water in the soil is now much slower, as the water films are thinner. In a classic experiment, Veihmeyer and Hendrickson set up a soil sandwich. A 2-ft layer of soil wetted to its field capacity (containing 22 per cent. water) was layered in a container between two 2-ft layers of the same soil in a dry condition (14·5 per cent. water). The container remained closed for 139 days. When it was opened samples of soil at various levels were removed to determine their water contents. It turned out that water had moved no more than 8 in. from the damp soil into the dry soil on each side. Evidently the movement of water from soil at field capacity into dry soil is very slow indeed when there is no adjacent supply of free water.

It follows that in such a soil, plant roots are very dependent on the water in their immediate vicinity. We must think therefore of plant roots growing to regions of the soil where water is available rather than of water moving in the soil to the roots. Compare the rate of movement of water in a dry soil (8 in. in 139 days) with the growth of roots in a good soil; wheat roots grow about $\frac{1}{2}$ in. per day and maize roots up to 2 in. per day.

These considerations draw attention to root growth as a factor governing the ability of a plant to obtain water from a soil. In the first place it should be made clear that roots do not take up water equally all along their length. Although there is some evidence to suggest that the older, suberised roots of trees can absorb water through lenticels and cracks in the bark, the young growing roots are probably the main organs of water absorption. Experiments in which short lengths of a root, near the tip, were enclosed in small potometers indicate that the most rapid water absorption is in the region of the root in which the xylem is becoming differentiated, but in which the outer layers of the root have not yet become heavily suberised and impermeable. This is in fact the region in which root hairs develop. It has been estimated that under soil conditions the proliferation of root hairs increases several-fold the surface area of the root and so the area available for the entry of water. This may be of relatively little consequence when ample soil water is available but under conditions of water shortage the area of surface in contact with soil particles may become critical.

The number of root apices and their disposition within the soil are therefore important factors in determining the volume of soil and so the amount of water to which the plant has access. Because the root system cannot be seen without laborious excavation its extent is often under-estimated. Where soil conditions are good, root systems may penetrate to depths of several yards. The extent of branching can be judged from one experiment in which the soil was carefully washed away from the root system of a field-grown grass (*Agropyron cristatum*). After two years' growth the roots totalled no less than 315 miles in aggregate length. The plant must have produced miles of fresh root each week during the growing season.

When plants are grown close together their root systems are, of course, less extensive than when they are grown on their own. Thus it has been reported that the root systems of barley and wheat are nearly one hundred times smaller when the plants are sown in rows 6 in. apart than when they are grown without such competition. This is by no means the only factor to influence the growth of a plant's root system. Thus the fact that the growth of tomatoes is more influenced by dryness of the soil than is the growth of lettuce has been traced to differences in root growth. Tomatoes fruit early in life and root growth then decreases so that the roots can only tap the water in a limited volume of soil. On the other hand, lettuce which continues vegetative growth through the season makes vigorous root growth and so can draw on the water contained in a relatively large volume of soil. In general, root growth is hastened by vigorous leaf growth and retarded by the development of fruits.

This raises the question of the water-holding capacity of a soil. How much water can a plant draw from a soil? To answer this question we must first consider in more detail the contribution made to the properties of a soil by two of its constituents, namely sand and clay.

Soils in which particles of sand predominate are referred to as light, because they are easily worked. In these soils the particles pack loosely, and do not aggregate to form larger compound particles. These soils drain readily and have relatively little capacity to absorb and retain water (or mineral substances). In clay soils, on the other hand, fine clay particles predominate. If the calcium content of the soil is sufficient, and if there is plenty of humus, such soils have a good crumb structure, and as the soil crumbs are relatively large and loosely packed, the soil is well aerated and drains satisfactorily. It retains water, and inorganic salts are not readily lost by drainage. However, such a soil, if mismanaged, may form when wet a pasty, intractable mass which dries out to form hard clods. The crumb structure is destroyed and waterlogging and poor aeration result from the impeded drainage. This condition will arise if the soil is compacted while it is wet, or if it is flooded with sea-water which has the effect of converting the calcium clay to a sodium clay which does not readily form soil crumbs.

Since a clay soil has finer particles than a sandy soil it has a larger surface area and so holds more water in the films around the particles. A clay soil at field capacity therefore has a higher water content than a sandy one at its field capacity. The water in a clay soil at field capacity may weigh 50 per cent. as much as the dry weight of the soil: in a sandy soil the figure would be only about 20 per cent. As a soil dries out the water (or, more strictly, the soil solution) that remains in it is held more firmly by forces of adsorption and in addition its osmotic pressure is raised as it becomes a more concentrated solution. In consequence the water becomes less readily available to plant roots. There comes a point, as the soil dries out further and further, when the water is held so firmly that it is no longer available to plants. The soil is not dry; it still contains water but this water is retained by forces that are greater than the transpiration pull can produce in the roots. At this point the plant may continue to lose water by transpiration, but it will be unable to replace it from the soil. The water content of the soil at this point is termed the **permanent wilting percentage.**

The water that is useful to a plant is that which lies between the permanent wilting percentage and the field capacity of the soil. Water in the soil drier than the permanent wilting percentage is not available to the plant, while if the soil is wetter than the field capacity this again is of little use to the plant for the soil will be poorly aerated or even waterlogged, and the roots of most plants

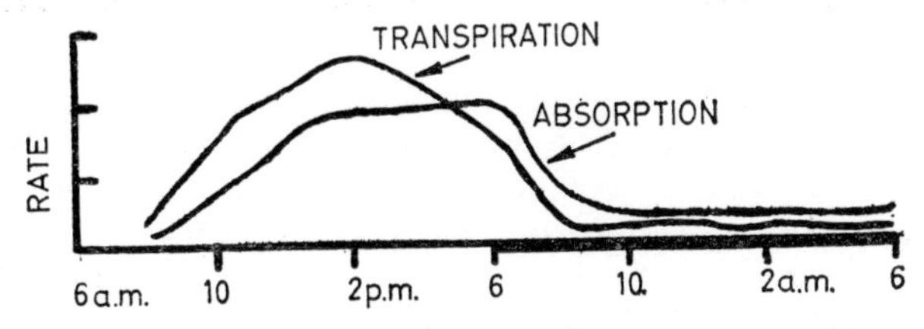

Fig. 99. RATES OF TRANSPIRATION AND ABSORPTION OF WATER FROM THE SOIL BY SUNFLOWER PLANTS ON A BRIGHT, HOT SUMMER DAY. Data of Kramer, 1937.

cannot survive for long under such conditions; they require an aerated soil for normal growth. Within this useful range of water content, between field capacity and permanent wilting percentage, a clay soil holds more water than a sandy soil.

The control of transpiration rate by stomatal aperture and the diurnal changes in stomatal aperture have already been discussed. Generally the stomata open in the morning and transpiration then begins, becoming faster as the day warms up. The supply of water from the soil may lag behind water loss—because the soil is poorly supplied with water or perhaps simply because of the resistance of the roots to water flow (p. 192). In consequence the water content of the plant falls. Later in the day transpiration slows down and from then on the plant regains its lost water, absorption of water from the soil now becoming faster than water loss. Some time during the night the plant regains its original water status (Fig. 99). Now if this cycle of events is somewhat exaggerated the plant may wilt by day, but recover on its own overnight. This temporary wilting may be a fairly common event and is probably of no great consequence. However, if the plant cannot recover unless the soil is watered, it is said to be permanently wilted. Prolonged periods of permanent wilting result in reduced photosynthesis (because the stomata are shut and the supply of carbon dioxide therefore curtailed) and so to reduced and stunted growth. There is no doubt when soft-stemmed plants wilt; their leaves and shoot apices droop. But tough evergreen leaves such as those of heather or *Rhododendron* may suffer equally from drought, although they do not show it by drooping.

A hot summer's day is not the only time to be on the look-out for wilting. It is often observed in Britain on cold days at the end of the year, especially in plants that are natives of warmer climates. The resistance of the root system to the passage of water is heightened at low temperatures and the water content of the plant therefore falls.

10 METABOLISM

The study of plant metabolism is concerned with the biochemical changes going on in living cells. These changes result in the synthesis of the chemical components of the adult plant from simple inorganic materials obtained from the soil or the air. To appreciate the nature and magnitude of this biochemical traffic we must first survey the variety of substances found in plants and then consider what are the raw materials from which they have been synthesised.

Chemical Composition of Plants

The greater part of the mass of a plant consists of water. The proportion of water in a tissue is found by drying a weighed quantity in an oven until there is no further change in weight. The resulting weight is known as the **dry weight**. In many fruits the dry weight is only 10 per cent. or even less of the fresh weight, while in leaves and other non-woody tissues the dry weight is around 20 per cent. of the fresh weight. Dormant seeds contain far less water and here the dry weight may be 85 or 90 per cent. of the fresh weight.

The material that is left when a tissue is dried is largely organic in nature. Chemical analysis shows that while carbon, hydrogen, oxygen, and nitrogen must rank as the principal elements in the dry matter, many others are present as well. Table 2 (p. 255) presents such an analysis for the dry matter of maize plants. It will be seen that fourteen elements account for 99 per cent. of the dry weight. However, several elements are regularly present in plants in only trace quantities and there can be little doubt that the remaining "undetermined" fraction included small amounts of boron, copper, molybdenum, sodium, zinc, and perhaps some other elements as well.

This sort of chemical analysis has its value in showing what elements are present in a plant and demonstrating the great variety of mineral salts that plants absorb from the soil, but it tells us nothing of the nature of the compounds in which they occur in plants or of the way in which these compounds are synthesised or broken down. To list all the classes of compound found in plants would be pointless. Some, such as alkaloids, tannins, and rubber are not found in all green plants. The synthesis of these compounds is evidently not an essential part of the life of all green plants and for this reason we will not consider their nature and metabolism in any detail. There are, however, four classes which demand our attention because they are ubiquitous and because they have important roles in metabolism. These are the fats, the carbohydrates, the proteins, and the nucleic acids.

The **fats** are esters of glycerol with fatty acids. Many plant fats are in fact oils, being liquid at the temperatures at which plants grow. (The so-called essential oils such as clove oil or oil of eucalyptus are quite different in nature; they are scented and are probably the end-products of minor pathways of metabolism.) Several different fatty acids are found in plant fats and commonly each individual fat molecule is an ester of glycerol with one molecule each of three different fatty acids;

$$\begin{matrix} CH_2OH \\ | \\ CHOH \\ | \\ CH_2OH \end{matrix} + R_1.COOH + R_2.COOH + R_3.COOH \rightleftharpoons \begin{matrix} CH_2O.CO.R_1 \\ | \\ CHO.CO.R_2 \\ | \\ CH_2O.CO.R_3 \end{matrix} + 3\ H_2O$$

The seeds of most angiosperms contain a store of fat which is formed in the seeds as they mature and consumed in the early stages of germination (p. 224). Fats and allied substances are important constituents of the many membrane systems found in cells such as the endoplasmic reticulum, the tonoplast, and the membranes of mitochondria and chloroplasts.

The **carbohydrates** are typified by the sugars such as glucose and fructose. These are hexose sugars with the formula $C_6H_{12}O_6$. They are commonly present in low concentration in plant cells. Larger amounts may be found in fruits or swollen roots like the carrot. Glucose and fructose are termed monosaccharides in distinction to the disaccharides in which two hexose sugars are condensed together. Maltose is formed from two molecules of glucose, while sucrose or cane-sugar is formed from one molecule of glucose and one of fructose. Sucrose is widely distributed in plants being particularly abundant in the roots of sugar-beet and the stem of sugar-cane; these form the commercial sources of household sugar.

The monosaccharides form several important polysaccharides. These are polymers, in which the monosaccharide groups are united end to end, with the elimination of molecules of water, to form long chains. Starch (p. 46) is a high molecular weight polymer of glucose found in plants in the form of insoluble grains. The seeds of many angiosperms including all Gramineae and Leguminosae contain much starch and so do many underground organs such as the tubers of potato and the corm of *Ranunculus bulbosus*. Starch can be regarded as a storage product in plant cells since it can be hydrolysed to sugars which are then available for growth and respiration. This change takes place when a seed germinates or a potato sprouts. In the green cells of leaves starch tends to accumulate by day as a result of photosynthesis, and to disappear at night as it is hydrolysed and then translocated away to the rest of the plant. A number of polysaccharides are found in plant cell walls. Cellulose is a polymer of glucose, the molecules being united in a manner that is different from that in starch. The other polysaccharides are more complex. The pectic substances (found typically in the middle lamella) are polymers of acid derivatives of hexose sugars, while there is a group of cell wall constituents including polymers of some pentose ($C_5H_{10}O_5$) and hexose sugars (sometimes containing acid derivatives of sugars as well) which are referred to as hemicelluloses. Some seeds such as *Phoenix* (date) have stores of hemicellulose which are mobilised on germination, but with this exception these polysaccharide wall constituents do not act as reserve materials; once synthesised they undergo little further metabolic change. Lignin, another constituent of the cell wall, is not a carbohydrate, although like them it is composed of carbon, hydrogen, and oxygen.

The remaining two types of plant constituent, the **proteins** and the **nucleic acids**, can be said to resemble starch in being large polymers, the proteins formed from the amino acids and the nucleic acids from nucleotides. However, there is an important difference between starch and these molecules for starch is a polymer of glucose residues alone, and although the starch from one plant may not be identical in all respects with the starch in another, the differences are comparatively trivial. On the other hand, there are twenty different amino acids in proteins which permits a tremendous diversity of protein structure. There may be several hundred different types of protein within a single cell, each with its own distinctive properties. In like manner the nucleic acid molecules are made up from four distinct nucleotides, and again many different nucleic acids are possible. The proteins and nucleic acids are discussed in more detail elsewhere (p. 250 and p. 168 respectively).

Sources of Plant Constituents

Two sources of raw material for metabolism are available to a land plant, the atmosphere, and the soil. From the air it obtains oxygen for respiration, carbon dioxide for photosynthesis, and the nitrogen that is fixed (converted to organic form) by a few plants. The soil supplies the water that passes through the plant in the transpiration stream and is lost from the leaves, and also the water that resides in the vacuole and cytoplasm of each living cell. The water in plant cells functions in the first place as a solvent. Thus the water of the vacuole may contain acids, sugars, pigments, and other substances in solution and it is the osmotic pressure exerted by the vacuolar fluid that maintains parenchyma cells turgid and so contributes to the mechanical strength of unlignified stems and leaves (p. 183). In addition, a small proportion of the water in plants plays a direct role in metabolism acting as a reagent in processes such as photosynthesis and the hydrolysis of starch and sucrose. Water is, of course, only one of many substances taken up by plants from the soil, for the soil constitutes a great reservoir of inorganic nutrients. The majority of these are subject to metabolic change once they are absorbed by plants. Nitrogen, for instance, is taken up as nitrate or ammonium ions but most of the nitrogen in plants is converted to amino acids, proteins, or nucleic acids. Again, sulphur is taken up as sulphate but is reduced to the sulphydryl (—SH) level in amino acids, while magnesium is absorbed as the ion but some of it becomes incorporated into the molecule of chlorophyll in non-ionic form. Potassium, on the other hand, appears in plant cells as free cation.

Pathways of Metabolism

We are now in a position to sketch out some of the chief pathways of metabolism in an angiosperm. The energy of sunlight is utilised in the production of carbohydrate from carbon dioxide and water (photosynthesis), and from the sugars so formed other carbohydrates are derived. Some of the sugar is broken down to simpler compounds which are the starting points for a wide range of syntheses. A few of the substances synthesised are, like the sugars, compounds of carbon, hydrogen, and oxygen alone; fatty acids and carotenoid pigments (p. 25) are examples. But most of the syntheses involve the mineral nutrients as well. Thus the synthesis of nucleic acids involves nitrogen and phosphorus, the synthesis of proteins nitrogen and sulphur, while chlorophyll contains nitrogen and magnesium as well as carbon, hydrogen, and oxygen.

It is obvious that all these synthetic processes must be in a state of high activity when tissues are growing by cell division. Each time a new cell is formed a fresh quota of cell constituents has been synthesised—new cell wall, new chromosomes, new tonoplast, and so on. Not one of these constituents is made in a single synthesis. A chromosome contains protein, nucleic acid, and fatty substances, while the primary wall contains cellulose, pectic substances, and sometimes other polysaccharides and proteins as well. What is not so obvious is that even mature cells have an active metabolism. Experiments with isotopes have shown that proteins, for instance, are in a state of flux, being continually broken down (perhaps to the level of amino acids, though this is not certain) and then reassembled. A recent investigation disclosed that 1 per cent. of the proteins of bean leaf chloroplasts are subject to such a turnover every hour.

All the synthetic processes require a supply of energy. The process of respiration, in which sugars are oxidised to carbon dioxide and water, generates a supply of energy in a form that can be geared to the work of synthesis.

It should now be clear that the living cell is the seat of a great many biochemical changes, diverse in their nature, yet interdependent and interlocking. The synthesis of protein, for instance, requires the reduction of nitrate absorbed from the soil, its union with carbon compounds derived ultimately from photosynthesis to form amino acids which are condensed together, the whole depending on a supply of energy from respiration. To maintain such a diversity of biochemical operations within the confines of a single cell implies a high degree of organisation. We have already seen that the electron microscope reveals a marvellous degree of spatial organisation within the cell. Another aspect of the organisation of molecular traffic within the cell comes from the study of enzymes. All the reactions we have been considering are catalysed by enzymes and we shall see later (p. 217) that some of the enzymes are themselves arranged in such a way as to define the order of the reactions which they catalyse. If the organisation should break down then we could well expect disordered activity with enzymes catalysing reactions in an indiscriminate and haphazard manner. This is precisely what happens in the last stages of senescence that lead to cell death. The cell is said to be in a state of **autolysis**; rather than perform syntheses, the cell destroys itself.

It is worthwhile at this point to distinguish between the two main directions of metabolism. **Anabolism** is the name given to all the synthetic processes, while **catabolism** is the term used for processes in which complex molecules are degraded to simpler. One catabolic process, respiration, is continually operating in living cells but usually it is accompanied by anabolic activity: only in senescence and death does catabolism predominate.

ENZYMES

Enzymes catalyse reactions, the rate of reaction being faster in the presence of an enzyme than in its absence. This is simple enough, but most of the reactions that concern us in living cells are reversible, proceeding in both forward and reverse directions. If A can form B, then B can also form A.

$$A \rightleftharpoons B.$$

In a situation like this we have to enquire whether forward and reverse reactions proceed with equal ease or whether one of them will predominate over the other. Thus the reaction

$$\text{Starch} + n \text{ Water} \rightleftharpoons n \text{ Glucose}$$

is reversible. We know that starch can be readily hydrolysed on boiling with acid—but can starch be synthesised by the reverse reaction, and just how would the presence of the enzyme amylase influence the reaction? Can amylase, in fact, catalyse the synthesis of starch as well as its hydrolysis?

To answer these questions we must consider more closely the nature of reversible reactions, such as that between A and B. If we start with pure A it will begin to form B, but as the concentration of B builds up so the back reaction comes into play and the net conversion of A to B slows down. Eventually a position of equilibrium is reached when the two reactions proceed at equal speed. The rate of the forward reaction, v_1, is given by the velocity constant K_1 multiplied by the concentration of A,

$$v_1 = K_1 [A],$$

and likewise for the reverse reaction

$$v_2 = K_2 [B].$$

At equilibrium the two rates are equal

$$K_1 [A] = K_2 [B].$$

Now if the conversion of A to B involves no energy change, then K_1 and K_2 will be equal, and when the reaction has gone to equilibrium equal amounts of A and B will be found in the solution. But if, on the other hand, the conversion of A to B results in a liberation of energy then $A \rightarrow B$ will have a higher velocity constant than the reverse change $B \rightarrow A$. It follows from the equation above that when equilibrium is reached A will be present in smaller amount than B. The position of equilibrium is thus determined by the energetics of the reaction, lying in the direction in which energy is released.

These considerations are quite independent of the presence or absence of an enzyme. Enzymes do not influence the position of equilibrium; but they may hasten the attainment of equilibrium. Many reactions are so slow at room temperature that we cannot observe any appreciable change. A sterile solution of sucrose, for instance, remains a solution of sucrose for as long as we care to watch it. However, when it is acidified and warmed sucrose is hydrolysed quite quickly. The enzyme invertase will catalyse the hydrolysis of sucrose at room temperature, the rate of the hydrolysis depending on the amount of invertase present (Fig. 100).

The reaction catalysed by invertase is a reversible one,

$$\text{Sucrose} + \text{Water} \rightleftharpoons \text{Glucose} + \text{Fructose.}$$

The position of equilibrium can be judged from Fig. 100. At least 99·9 per cent. of the sucrose is hydrolysed by the time equilibrium is attained. It follows that the hydrolysis must be accompanied by a substantial release of energy (and that the reverse process, the synthesis of sucrose, will demand a supply of energy). Invertase

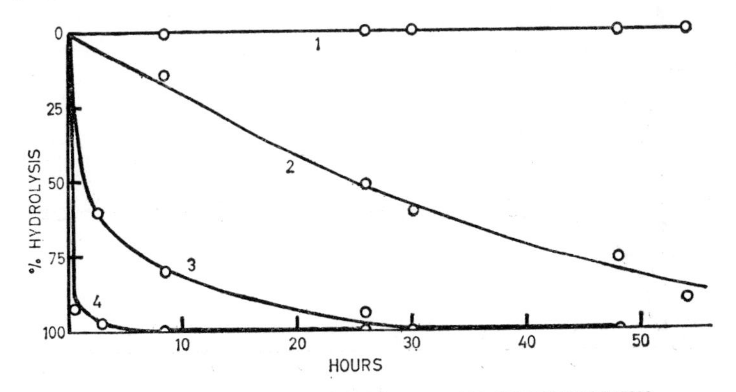

Fig. 100. THE ACTION OF YEAST INVERTASE ON THE REACTION SUCROSE + WATER ⇌ GLUCOSE + FRUCTOSE.

In the absence of invertase (curve 1), sucrose is not hydrolysed at a measurable rate, but when invertase is added hydrolysis proceeds virtually to completion. In curve 2 one unit of invertase was present, for curve 3 ten units, and for curve 4 one hundred units.

can be dubbed a hydrolytic enzyme since the reaction it catalyses is overwhelmingly hydrolytic. It *does* catalyse sucrose synthesis as well, but it is a hopelessly inefficient synthesis with a yield of less than 0·1 per cent. How then *do* plants synthesise sucrose? Not, surely, with the help of invertase. Our dilemma is resolved by recent research which has disclosed a quite distinct set of enzymes that bring about the synthesis of sucrose, making use of energy released in respiration to promote the synthesis (p. 227).

A similar situation obtains in the case of starch. Amylase catalyses the hydrolysis of starch, while the synthesis is a more complex, energy-requiring process catalysed by a different group of enzymes. And likewise the proteases are hydrolytic enzymes, the synthesis of proteins being catalysed by a whole array of enzymes, some of them located in the ribosomes (p. 177).

On the other hand, the action of lipase differs from that of invertase in that the reaction it catalyses,

$$\text{Fat} + \text{Water} \rightleftharpoons \text{Fatty acid} + \text{Glycerol},$$

proceeds with no more than a trivial energy change. The position of equilibrium is therefore quite evenly balanced with 62 per cent. of the fatty acid free and 38 per cent. combined as fat (Fig. 101). Lipase *can* therefore catalyse both the hydrolysis and synthesis

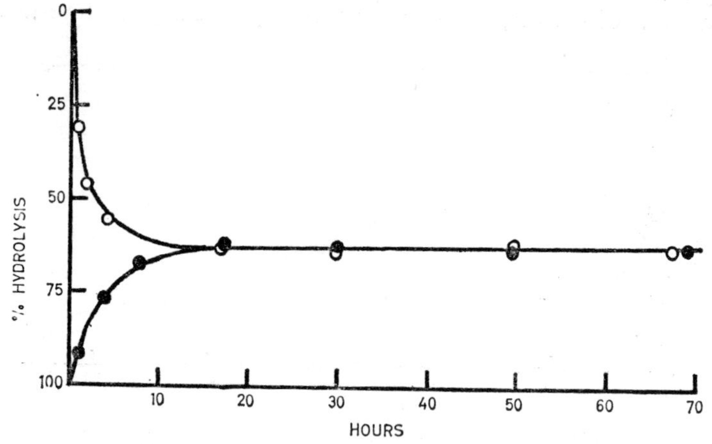

Fig. 101. THE ACTION OF *Ricinus* LIPASE ON THE REACTION OLIVE OIL + WATER ⇌ GLYCEROL AND FATTY ACIDS.

Lipase catalyses the hydrolysis of olive oil (open circles), and also the synthesis of olive oil from fatty acids and glycerol (closed circles). In each case equilibrium is attained after about twenty hours with rather more than 60 per cent. of the fatty acid in the free state. Data of Armstrong and Gosney, 1914.

of fats and it is thus reasonable to suppose that this may be the reaction by which fats are synthesised in developing seeds as well as being the reaction by which they are hydrolysed in germination.

Some enzymes then, like amylase, catalyse hydrolytic processes while others promote syntheses. Most of the enzymes chosen for study and experiment by beginners are in fact hydrolytic ones. Historically, they were among the first to be discovered, their substrates and products being well-recognised chemical entities for which simple tests were available. The recognition and assay of some other enzymes such as cytochrome oxidase or the sequence of enzymes responsible for the synthesis of sucrose demand sophisticated techniques and expensive apparatus. The choice of hydrolytic enzymes for study should not be taken to imply that these enzymes are of central importance in metabolism; that position would be reserved for enzymes concerned in the major routes of synthesis and the well-established pathways of respiration. To be sure, amylase plays a part in the germination of starchy seeds, but the precise role of invertase in plant metabolism remains obscure to this day.

The sections that follow deal with the extraction and assay of enzymes, their properties and their location and organisation within the cell. A few enzymes are finally selected for individual discussion.

Extraction of Enzymes

Extraction and purification of an enzyme are necessary preliminaries to the investigation of its properties. Since most enzymes are intracellular, being located within the cytoplasm of the cell, extraction involves breaking the cells to release the enzymes. This is usually done by grinding the tissue in a pestle and mortar with the addition of a solution buffered around pH 7. The buffer prevents inactivation of the enzymes by the acid contents of the cell vacuoles as the cytoplasm and vacuole intermingle under pressure from the pestle (see also p. 214). The cell walls are strained off by passing the mixture through muslin. The resulting liquid is known as a **homogenate**. It contains the various cytoplasmic enzymes, but is far from being a pure enzyme preparation; it is a two-phase system—a solution of substances such as sugars, amino acids, and proteins, and a suspension of the various particles found in plant cells (nuclei, starch grains, chloroplasts, and mitochondria). Some plant enzymes such as amylase are soluble and if such an enzyme is under study the homogenate can be cleared of unwanted particulate matter by centrifuging it. A centrifuge is a machine which can rotate tubes of liquid at high speed, subjecting the tube contents to powerful centrifugal forces. A centrifugal field equivalent to 20,000 times that of gravity (20,000 $\times$ g.) will remove most of the particles from a homogenate. Further purification of a soluble enzyme involves the precipitation of unwanted proteins from solution. This is achieved by adding ammonium sulphate which lowers the solubility of proteins. The first addition of ammonium sulphate is so adjusted as to bring relatively insoluble proteins out of solution but to leave the desired enzyme unchanged. The insoluble protein is removed by filtration and a second quantity of ammonium sulphate added to the solution, sufficient to precipitate the enzyme which is then filtered off and dissolved in water. The solution is next freed of ammonium sulphate by dialysis, the solution being placed inside a length of cellophane tubing and suspended in a large volume of water. The salts will slowly diffuse out, but the molecules of enzyme being larger are retained within the membrane. Finally, it may be possible to crystallise the enzyme.

It has not proved possible to prepare some enzymes in soluble form. An example is cytochrome oxidase. Investigation has shown that such enzymes are located in one or other of the particulate components of the cytoplasm. Cytochrome oxidase itself is located in the mitochondria and other enzymes are located in the chloroplasts. Such enzymes may be prepared for study by centrifuging a homogenate at moderate speed so as to sediment particles larger than those it is wished to study. This will leave the desired particles in suspension. By pouring the suspension into a fresh tube and centrifuging more rapidly the particles can now be isolated. About 1,000 × g. for ten minutes is required to bring down chloroplasts and 10,000 × g. for twenty minutes to sediment mitochondria.

A few enzymes are secreted by cells and appear outside them (extracellular enzymes). One example is the secretion by some pathogenic fungi of enzymes which hydrolyse the pectic substances of plant cell walls; another is the secretion of digestive enzymes by carnivorous plants. Such enzymes can be collected in extracellular fluids. The fungal enzymes, for instance, will appear in the medium in which the fungi are set to grow in culture, while the liquid inside a pitcher of *Nepenthes* (pitcher plant) is a source of protein-digesting enzymes.

Some enzymes are very stable and once prepared they can be kept for months or years without deterioration. Such enzymes are now articles of commerce. Amylase and invertase, for instance, can be purchased without difficulty. On the other hand, many enzymes (cytochrome oxidase is one example) are labile and have to be prepared freshly whenever they are required for experiment. There may indeed be some breakdown even during the time that it takes to prepare the enzyme. For this reason enzyme preparations are performed quickly and the work is done in a cold room at 2-4° C. to slow down enzyme inactivation.

Enzyme Assay

Once an enzyme has been prepared its activity must be determined. Indeed, if the enzyme is one for which no reliable methods of extraction are recorded in the literature it will be necessary to make repeated assays of activity to ensure that the enzyme is in fact being purified by the procedures adopted and is not inadvertently thrown down the sink at some stage.

Enzymes are assayed by incubating them with their **substrate** (the substance they act upon) under specified conditions and then measuring the amount of substrate that has undergone change. Thus the activity of an invertase solution might be determined by incubating 1 ml. of it for thirty minutes at 25° C. with 1 ml. of 0·2 M. sucrose buffered at pH 7. At the end of the thirty-minute period the extent of sucrose hydrolysis would be measured either by determining the amount of reducing sugar that has been produced (glucose and fructose reducing Fehling's solution, while sucrose does not) or by taking advantage of the different behaviour exhibited towards plane polarised light by these sugars. A beam of ordinary light has wave-motions in all directions perpendicular to the direction of travel, but if a beam passes through a Nicol prism or a sheet of "Polaroid" its wave-motions become restricted to a single plane. When such polarised light is passed through a sugar solution the plane of polarisation is changed. A mixture of glucose and fructose rotates the plane of polarisation in the opposite direction from sucrose. With the aid of a polarimeter, therefore, the degree of hydrolysis of sucrose could be determined. Invertase activity would then be expressed as so many milligrams of sucrose hydrolysed or so many degrees change in the plane of polarisation under the specified conditions.

Enzyme Properties

Enzymes catalyse biochemical reactions, speeding up the attainment of equilibrium. A small amount of enzyme will catalyse the reaction of a relatively large quantity of substrate. Each molecule of enzyme can catalyse the reaction of some tens or hundreds of thousands of molecules of substrate in a minute and can continue to work at such a rate for long periods. It is, nevertheless, true that if only a small amount of enzyme is present a reaction will proceed relatively slowly. Biochemists sometimes have the experience of postulating a sequence of enzyme-catalysed steps by which a pigment, say, could be synthesised, only to find that there is not enough of a particular enzyme present in the tissue to enable the sequence to proceed at the rate at which the pigment is synthesised in the plant.

Many enzymes are quite specific as to the substrates whose reaction they will catalyse. Succinic dehydrogenase, for example, will only catalyse the oxidation of succinate and amylase will only hydrolyse starch. Invertase is not completely specific as it will hydrolyse some allied sugars as well as sucrose, while lipase at the other extreme has a very low specificity, acting upon a variety of fats.

All the enzymes that have been studied so far are proteins, although the molecule may also contain a non-protein portion. The structure of proteins is considered later (p. 250) and it is sufficient to point out here that they are very large polymers made up from twenty different kinds of amino acid joined end to end. The properties of a protein depend on the number of amino acids in the chain, the order in which they are arranged, and the way in which the resulting chain is folded. A great variety of structures is evidently possible. From recent work on protein structure and on the nature of enzymes it appears that the specificity of enzymes towards

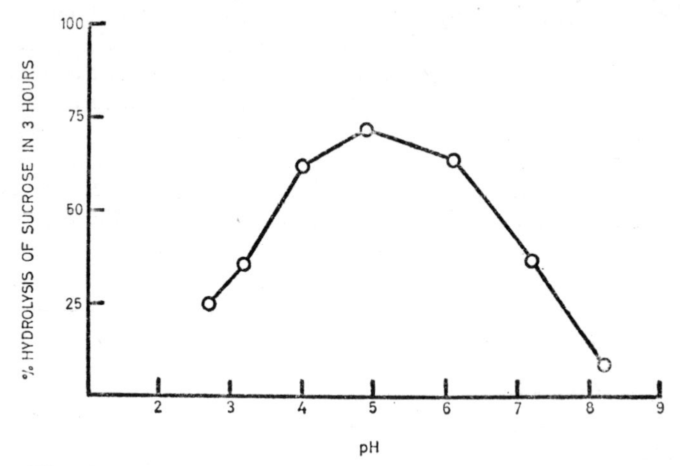

Fig. 102. THE EFFECT OF pH ON THE ACTIVITY OF YEAST INVERTASE.

substrates is governed in part by the structure of the enzyme protein. The composition and shape of the enzyme protein corresponds in some way to the nature and shape of a particular substrate or group of allied substrates. The non-protein portion of an enzyme may also play some part in determining specificity.

Like other proteins, enzymes are sensitive to changes of acidity in the medium in which they operate. Acidity is measured by hydrogen—ion concentration and expressed on the scale of pH, a neutral solution having a pH of 7, an acid one a lower pH, and an alkaline one a pH above 7. Each enzyme has an optimum pH at which its activity is greatest; as the pH is shifted away from the optimum its activity declines more or less sharply (Fig. 102). For this reason the pH of the solution must be carefully controlled in all experiments with enzymes and prevented from changing during the reaction even if there is a production or consumption of acid—as in fat hydrolysis. Stability of pH is achieved by adding a buffer to the mixture of enzyme and substrate. Buffers are mixtures of weak acids or weak bases with their salts. Phosphate mixtures are often used as buffers around pH 7. One of the difficulties that arises when one wishes to assess the activity of an enzyme in the living cell is uncertainty as to the pH prevailing in the region of the cell in which the enzyme is situated. The vacuoles of plant cells are buffered at an acid pH, usually around 5, but lower values are recorded for some plants, *e.g.* green cooking apple pH 3·2, lemon fruit pH 2·4, *Begonia* leaves pH 2·2. It is doubtful whether the pH in the cytoplasm ever falls so low, but there may well be differences in pH in the different regions of the cytoplasm.

Chemical reactions can be hastened by raising the temperature, the rate being roughly doubled by a rise of 10° C. This is expressed by saying that Q_{10} for the reaction is about 2. The same relationship holds for enzyme-catalysed reactions, although an additional factor comes into operation at the higher temperatures, for enzymes then become inactivated and the reaction will slow down. When this point is reached a comparatively small rise in temperature is sufficient to destroy the enzyme completely and bring the reaction to a standstill. The temperature curve of an enzyme-catalysed reaction is therefore an asymmetric one with a peak rate at a temperature around 50° C., although with some enzymes it may be higher (Fig. 103). The inactivation of enzymes is a progressive phenomenon, the degree of inactivation becoming more severe the longer the enzyme is exposed to the high temperature. Prolonged exposure to a temperature as low as 40° C. may cause some inactivation, but at 100° C. a few minutes is sufficient to cause complete inactivation. This may be used as a test for an enzyme; if a preparation no longer catalyses a reaction after five minutes boiling, then it can be taken that the catalyst is an enzyme.

Like other proteins, enzymes can be precipitated from solution by the salts of heavy metals such as lead, copper, or mercury, and once precipitated they lose their powers as catalysts. In addition, some enzymes can be inhibited by certain poisons. Thus malonic acid inhibits the enzyme succinic dehydrogenase and cyanide inhibits cytochrome oxidase. If such an inhibitor is specific in its action, inhibiting just one enzyme, it can be used to test for the activity of that enzyme. Thus one can attempt to determine whether succinic dehydrogenase is involved in the respiration of a tissue by comparing the respiration of tissue in the presence of malonate with the respiration of a control. If the respiration is inhibited then it is likely that succinic dehydrogenase is involved in the respiration. Unfortunately few inhibitors are quite specific, most of them affecting several enzymes, a fact that detracts from their usefulness in metabolic studies.

Many enzymes are not fully active unless an activator or coenzyme is present. Enzyme activators are metal ions such as magnesium or manganese. **Coenzymes** are organic substances with relatively small molecules when compared to enzymes. An enzyme,

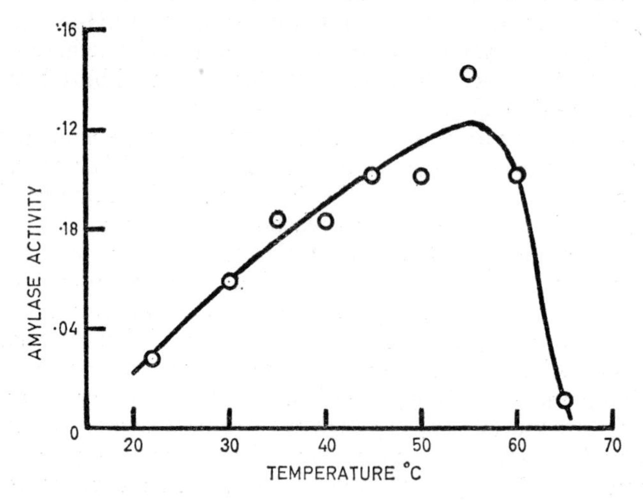

Fig. 103. THE EFFECT OF TEMPERATURE ON THE ACTIVITY OF BEAN AMYLASE. Data from a class experiment. Twenty cotyledons of 7-day old *Phaseolus vulgaris* seedlings were ground up in 30 ml. water and the homogenate filtered through muslin. 0·25 ml. portions of filtrate were added to 5 ml. 0·1 per cent. starch at the required temperature and drops of the mixture taken for test with iodine to determine when all the starch had been hydrolysed. Enzyme activity is measured by the reciprocal of the time for hydrolysis in minutes.

being a protein, has a very large molecule. Papain, for instance, has a M.W. of about 20,700 and succinic dehydrogenase one of around 200,000. A coenzyme, on the other hand, has a M.W. of less than 1,000. Some coenzymes are simple derivatives of substances that we need in small amounts in our diet (since we cannot synthesise them for ourselves). These substances are vitamins. Thus thiamine pyrophosphate is a coenzyme for the enzyme carboxylase; thiamine itself is Vitamin B_1. A number of coenzymes act as carriers transferring the product of one reaction to a second enzyme which will transform it further. The coenzyme ADP, for instance (p. 227), carries high-energy phosphate.

The Organisation of Enzymes in Cells

Some metabolic processes are catalysed by single enzymes; the breakdown of hydrogen peroxide, for instance, is catalysed by the one enzyme catalase. But the great majority of enzyme catalysed processes are more complex than this, proceeding in many steps. Thus the respiration of sugars involves the action of some three or four dozen enzymes. In such a multi-enzyme system, the product of one enzyme is the substrate of the next. In this way the enzymes act in sequential order, "in teams". The order need not necessarily be a linear one—it may branch if the product of one enzyme action can be substrate for either of two further enzymes. For example, succinate, one of the intermediates in the respiration of sugar, may be oxidised or it may suffer a quite different fate involving reaction with the amino acid glycine and yielding eventually substances such as chlorophyll or cytochrome oxidase. One must therefore visualise a series of pathways of metabolism in cells, the paths sometimes being interconnected where substances can act as substrate for more than one enzyme.

A considerable number of enzymes has now been recognised. Over 800 enzymes were listed in 1964 and more are being discovered each year. Not all of these enzymes are present in any one cell, some, for instance, being known only in bacteria or animals, but there can be no doubt that plant cells must each contain hundreds of enzymes which are so organised as to catalyse reactions that lead ultimately to the production of all the many substances that go to form new cell materials. How this organisation is brought about we cannot yet say in detail, but we have some clues. The fact that many enzymes are specific for a single substrate will itself ensure that they act in a particular order. One enzyme cannot operate until the substrate it requires has been produced by a previous enzyme. The organisation of cytoplasm with its many membrane systems dividing the cell into discrete regions also affords a mechanism for the organisation of enzymes. Groups of soluble enzymes may be held in association within a structure such as the chloroplast, or an enzyme may be held apart from a potential substrate. Thus the enzyme polyphenol oxidase catalyses the oxidation of certain phenolic compounds by oxygen. The enzyme is present in the cytoplasm of apples and potatoes, while there are some phenolics present in the tissue probably in the cell vacuoles. So long as the cells remain intact, enzyme and substrate are held apart and there is no colour change. But if the apple is bitten or the potato peeled the substrate comes in contact with the enzyme in the damaged cells and the tissue browns as the phenolics are oxidised. Another aspect of enzyme organisation is the association of groups of insoluble enzymes in particulate structures. Thus the enzymes involved in cell oxidations and the generation of high-energy phosphate (p. 227) are located in the walls of the mitochondria.

The enzyme complement of a cell may change as the cell develops. Thus the cells of bean cotyledons and the cells of barley endosperm have little amylase activity in the first day or two of germination but thereafter the enzyme appears rapidly.

Enzyme Activities

Enzymes are usually given names in which the suffix -ase is added to a root indicating the nature of the substrate or the reaction. Thus amylase hydrolyses starch (Latin—amylum), and maltase hydrolyses maltose. Invertase also catalyses a hydrolysis, that of sucrose; the hydrolysis is accompanied by an inversion of the direction in which the solution rotates the plane of polarisation of light. A more detailed treatment of a few enzymes is given in the paragraphs that follow. Some further enzymes are discussed elsewhere, *e.g.* transaminase (p. 250) and proteolytic enzymes (p. 252).

Amylase (formerly known as diastase). The hydrolysis of starch is a complex process in which the large molecule of starch is first broken down to smaller molecules (the dextrins) and these are degraded to maltose which in turn is finally hydrolysed to glucose. Starch is coloured blue-black by a solution of iodine in potassium iodide but dextrins colour iodine purple or brown according to their size, while the ultimate product, sugar, is not coloured at all. This change in colour reaction can be used to follow the progress of starch hydrolysis by amylase. If a starch solution is incubated with amylase and drops of the mixture taken from time to time for test with iodine, then the time taken for the blue-black colour to fade to some standard tint, or to disappear altogether is an inverse measure of the activity of the enzyme; the shorter the time the more active the preparation.

The endosperm of cereals contains abundant reserves of starch in the form of grains ranging in size up to 100 μ diameter. These grains are far too large to be translocated out of cells as such and the starch can only be assimilated by the embryo in germination when it has been hydrolysed to sugar. The production of amylase on germination can readily be examined by placing cut seeds on the surface of agar containing 0·1 per cent. starch. If iodine is poured on to the agar a few days later the area from which the starch has been digested will show up as a white circle on a dark blue ground.

The amylase activity of germinating barley is employed in the brewing industry to convert the starch into sugars which can be fermented by yeast. Barley grains are soaked and allowed to germinate for some days so that amylase activity develops and the starch is hydrolysed. If germination were allowed to proceed unchecked the sugars would be consumed in the growth and respiration of the embryo. However, this is just what the maltster strives to avoid as it is, for him, a waste of sugar. Germination is therefore arrested when the yield of sugars is maximal, by drying off the grains. The product is known as malt. The sugars are extracted from the malt with warm water and then fermented by yeast.

Zymase is a mixture of enzymes responsible for the fermentation of sugars. It was first extracted from yeast but comparable extracts able to ferment sugars to carbon dioxide and ethanol can be obtained from angiosperms.

Carboxylase is one of the enzymes present in zymase. It decarboxylates pyruvic acid, yielding carbon dioxide and acetaldehyde

$$CH_3.CO.COOH \rightarrow CO_2 + CH_3.CHO.$$

This is one of the reactions involved in fermentation and is followed by reduction of the acetaldehyde to ethanol.

Catalase catalyses the breakdown of hydrogen peroxide in solution into water and oxygen. This breakdown occurs slowly at room temperature in the absence of enzyme, but more rapidly in the presence of catalase.

Dehydrogenase and oxidase enzymes. The oxidations that take place in plant cells do not involve simply the addition of oxygen to a molecule. Rather they proceed in the first place by the removal of hydrogen from a molecule on to a coenzyme which is thereby reduced. The reduced coenzyme is then passed to an oxidase enzyme by which it is re-oxidised with concomitant reduction of atmospheric oxygen to water. The sequence of events is considered in more detail in the next section (p. 231).

RESPIRATION

Respiration is essentially a process in which a substrate—usually a hexose sugar—is converted to simpler substances with the liberation of energy. Some of this energy appears as heat but some is released in a form in which it can be used to promote synthetic processes within the cell. When respiration occurs in air (aerobic respiration) the sugar is completely oxidised to carbon dioxide and water, but in the absence of oxygen (anaerobic conditions) the final products are carbon dioxide and ethanol. Respiration is a characteristic of all living cells.

Demonstration and Measurement of Gas Exchanges

A simple apparatus for demonstrating the production of carbon dioxide by respiring tissues is shown in Fig. 104. The apparatus as it stands will show whether or not carbon dioxide is being produced by a tissue, but some modification is needed if accurate quantitative information is required since the baryta in *A* will absorb only a

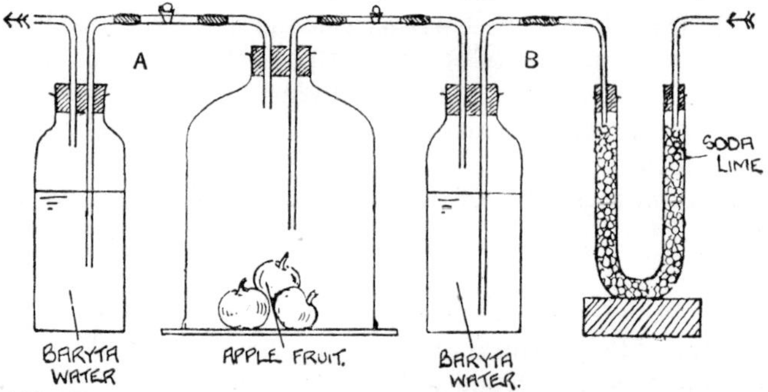

Fig. 104. DEMONSTRATION OF CARBON DIOXIDE PRODUCTION IN RESPIRATION. A stream of air is forced through soda-lime to remove its carbon dioxide and bubbles next through a bottle of baryta water B which serves as a check on the effectiveness of the soda-lime tube; if the air is quite free of carbon dioxide the baryta water will remain clear as the experiment progresses. The carbon dioxide-free air passes through a jar containing plant material and then through a second baryta water tube A. If carbon dioxide is produced in respiration the liquid in A will soon become cloudy as baryta is converted to barium carbonate.

fraction of the carbon dioxide contained in the bubbles passing through it. To ensure complete absorption the inlet tube should be constructed so that the bubbles are small and each bubble should be made to travel slowly up a long column of baryta water held in an inclined tube (Pettenkoffer tube). If the liquid in the tube is titrated with acid at the end of the experiment, then, knowing the original strength of the baryta water it is possible to calculate precisely how much carbon dioxide it has absorbed.

Oxygen is necessary for aerobic respiration and the relative proportions of oxygen taken up and carbon dioxide evolved can be assessed roughly with the simple retorts of Fig. 105. For accurate measurements of the gas volumes the Warburg apparatus is used

(Fig. 106). Here the tapering end of the retort is replaced by a manometer, the flasks are held in a water bath, and correction is made for any fluctuations of temperature or atmospheric pressure. This apparatus is capable of determinations at the micro level, a change in gas volume of only a few microlitres (1 μl. = 10^{-6} litre) being readily measured.

The rate at which a tissue respires can be determined from measurements made over a period of time. It will be seen from Fig. 107 that dormant seeds respire very slowly indeed. Enzymes are relatively inactive in the dormant seed but regain their activity as the cells become hydrated in early germination. Over the first

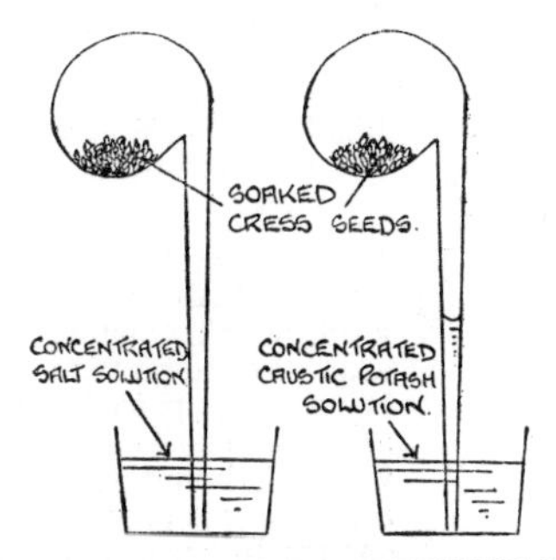

Fig. 105. DEMONSTRATION OF GAS EXCHANGES IN RESPIRATION.

Germinating cress seeds are held in retorts, the open ends of which dip into liquid. The seeds absorb oxygen from the atmosphere and evolve carbon dioxide. The end of the right-hand retort dips into strong alkali which absorbs carbon dioxide as fast as it is produced in respiration. The rise of liquid up the stem of this retort demonstrates the absorption of oxygen from the air enclosed in the retort. The end of the left-hand retort dips into strong salt solution (in which carbon dioxide is even less soluble than in water); in this case there is little or no change in the level of the liquid. The volume of carbon dioxide evolved is therefore equal (within the rather crude limits of accuracy of the experiment) to the volume of oxygen taken up.

fifteen hours (in *Phaseolus vulgaris* seeds) the rise in respiration rate follows closely the uptake of water. As germination proceeds further the seedling tissues begin to grow by cell division and then the respiration rate of the seedling rises simply because there are more respiring cells. If we wish to know how the respiration rate of one part of a plant (say a tomato fruit) compares with another (tomato root) some account must obviously be taken of their difference in size. This is most easily done by expressing respiration rate in terms of tissue weight, that is to say as millilitres of oxygen taken up per hour per gram of tissue, although even this procedure leaves something to be desired for the fruit contains far more water than the root. The most satisfactory measure therefore is millilitres of oxygen absorbed per hour per gram dry weight of tissue. We have already seen how respiration rate rises suddenly at the onset of germination. As the young seedling grows, the respiration rate reaches a peak level and then begins to decline steadily. Mature plant tissues such as leaves, stems, and storage organs respire

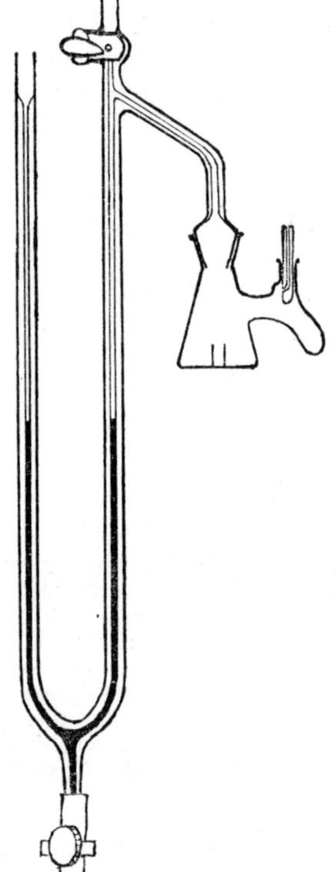

Fig. 106. THE WARBURG APPARATUS PROVIDES A MICRO-METHOD FOR MEASURING GAS EXCHANGE.

It consists essentially of a small (25 ml.) conical flask attached to a manometer. The flask has a centre well, a main compartment, and a side-arm. For respiration measurements the tissue or extract is placed in the main compartment and alkali-soaked filter paper in the centre well. Carbon dioxide is absorbed in the alkali as fast as it is produced and the manometer responds to oxygen uptake. From successive readings of the pressure of the gas in the flask the rate of oxygen uptake can be calculated. If alkali is omitted from a second flask the manometer will indicate any difference between carbon dioxide evolution and oxygen uptake. Substrates or inhibitors can be added from the side-arm and there is provision for gassing the flask with a gas phase other than air. The flasks are held in a constant temperature water bath and shaken from side to side. A flask containing water alone is set up alongside the experimental ones; its fluctuations enable corrections to be made for variation in barometric pressure or in the temperature of the water bath.

more slowly, weight for weight, than young seedlings. The respiration of tissues in the last phase of development—senescence—has not received much attention apart from studies on fruits and detached leaves (see p. 319), but here there is evidence for a rise in respiration rate when fruits ripen or leaves yellow; this is the climacteric rise which is in turn followed by a fall in respiration rate as the tissue ultimately dies.

The Q_{10} for respiration is around 2, but as the temperature is raised above about 40° C. respiration rates become slower. Temperature changes affect respiration rate, therefore, much as they influence enzyme activity (p. 215).

Respiratory Quotient

The most obvious manifestations of respiration are the gas exchanges. The evolution of carbon dioxide and the uptake of

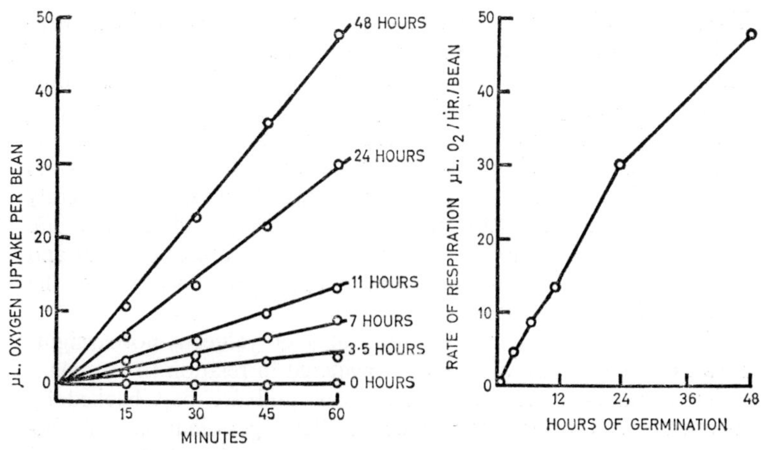

Fig. 107. OXYGEN UPTAKE BY GERMINATING SEEDS MEASURED IN THE WARBURG APPARATUS.

The respiration rate of dry seeds of *Phaseolus aureus* (mung bean) was compared with that of seeds and young seedlings sampled after various periods of germination at 25° C. The graph on the left shows the amount of oxygen taken up at quarter-hourly intervals by seeds after 0, 3·5, 7, 11, 24, and 48 hours. In each case, respiration proceeds at a steady rate. In the graph on the right the rates of respiration (μl oxygen taken up per hour per bean) are plotted against the time of germination. The dry seeds (0 hours) respire at a negligible rate but once germination starts the rate of respiration rises rapidly, initially as a result of hydration of the cells already present in the seed, and later as a consequence of growth and the production of new cells.

oxygen can be measured without great difficulty and for many years such measurements provided the main body of information available on plant respiration. Some insight into the underlying biochemical events can be gained from the ratio of these quantities, the **respiratory quotient** (R.Q.). The R.Q. is defined as the ratio of the volume of carbon dioxide evolved to the volume of oxygen absorbed at the same time.

If sugar is respired according to the overall equation

$$6\,O_2 + C_6H_{12}O_6 \rightarrow 6\,CO_2 + 6\,H_2O$$

the ratio will be 1·0 and it is true that for many plant tissues R.Q. is very close to unity. However, several other metabolic processes besides the aerobic respiration of sugars involve oxygen or carbon dioxide and will, therefore, modify the R.Q. For instance, if tissues are held under nitrogen, sugars undergo alcoholic fermentation according to the equation

$$C_6\,H_{12}O_6 \rightarrow 2\,CO_2 + 2\,C_2H_5OH.$$

The R.Q. here is infinity. If aerobic respiration and alcoholic fermentation proceed at the same time (as they will in low concentrations of oxygen) then the R.Q. will be between one and infinity. In some tissues, especially in succulent plants, carbon dioxide fixation occurs. This is a process in which carbon dioxide is taken up in the dark with the formation of sufficient malic acid to render the tissues acid. Such a carbon dioxide consuming process will evidently lower R.Q. values. Other reactions which might affect R.Q. are the oxidation of phenolic compounds (which requires oxygen) and the reduction of nitrate to ammonia in roots (which will reduce the consumption of external oxygen).

It follows that the interpretation of R.Q. values is not straightforward. They must always be considered in relation to the metabolic events likely to occur in a tissue and are best backed by independent biochemical evidence. The germination of fat-containing seeds can be taken as an example of such a concerted attack based on R.Q. measurements, analytical data, and biochemical studies.

In the early stages of germination the R.Q. of seeds commonly falls below unity. During the germination of *Zea* (maize), for instance, a minimum value of 0·73 has been recorded, for *Helianthus* (sunflower) 0·55, and for *Ricinus* (castor bean) 0·30-0·35. These low values are only temporary, for mature growing tissues generally have an R.Q. around 1·0. In the cereals the low R.Q. values last for only a few days. In one experiment with *Triticum* (wheat), R.Q. was 1 on the first day, fell to 0·7 on the second day, but had risen to 1 again by six days. Seeds which store large quantities of fat, on the other hand, are characterised by a prolonged period of low R.Q. In *Linum* (flax) seeds, R.Q. fell to 0·4 at the fourth day and had only risen as far as 0·6 by the seventeenth day. What can be the cause of this pronounced phase of low R.Q. in fatty seeds?

It is clear for a start that carbohydrate respiration will give an R.Q. of unity. Fats like carbohydrates are compounds of carbon,

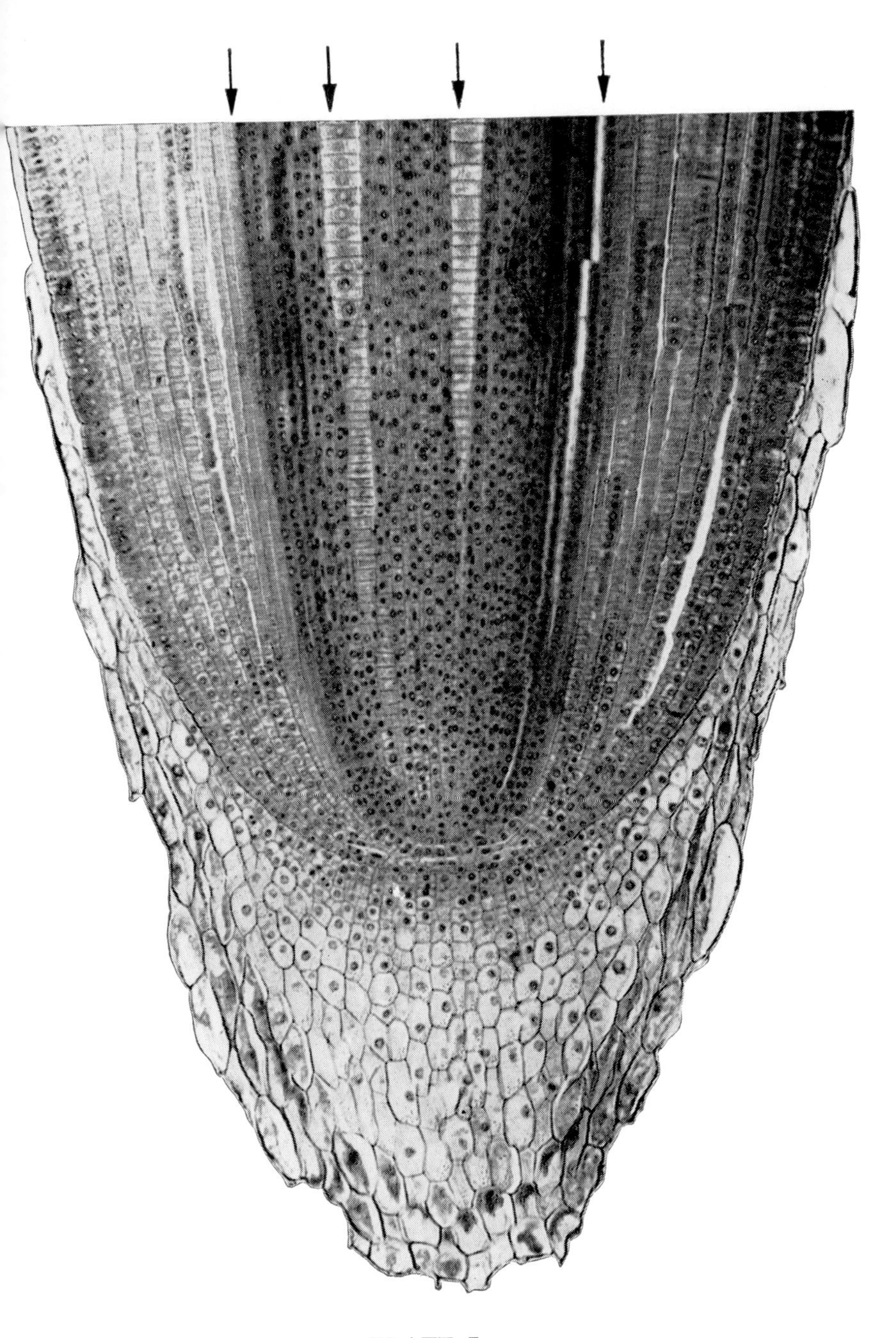

PLATE 7

LONGITUDINAL SECTION THROUGH A ROOT APEX OF *Zea* (MAIZE). The outer arrows mark the outer limits of the stele, the inner ones point to cell-rows which are differentiating as vessels. The cracks in the cortex have arisen during the preparation of the specimen; as is common in root tips the union between different cell-rows is weaker than that between cells in a row. Notice how meristematic activity in the cap is concentrated in the inner central part of the cap.

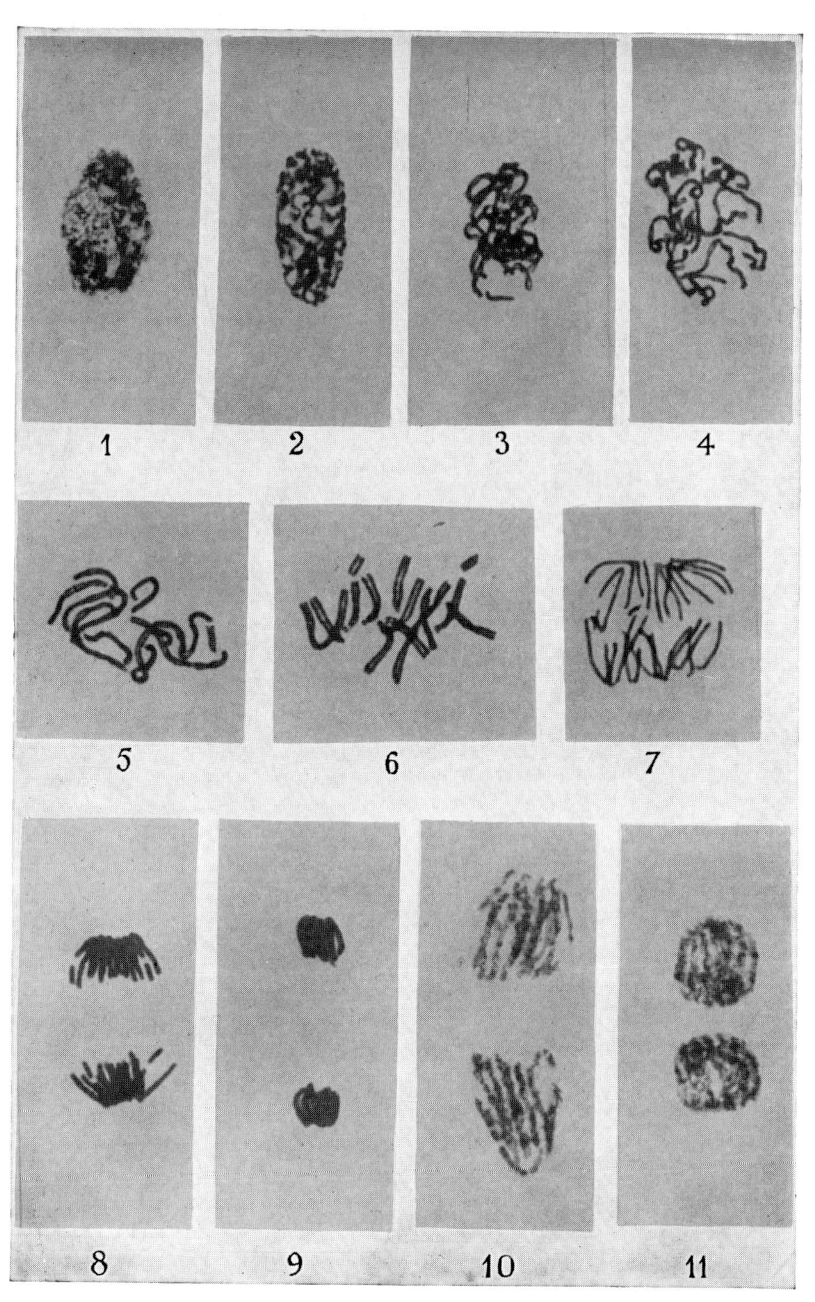

PLATE 8

STAGES OF MITOSIS IN THE ROOT TIP OF BROAD BEAN (*Vicia faba*), see pp. 160-2.

hydrogen, and oxygen, and could in theory be oxidised completely to carbon dioxide and water. Fats are esters of glycerol and fatty acids, but it will simplify the arithmetic and make no substantial difference if we consider the fatty acid alone. Taking palmitic acid, $C_{16}H_{32}O_2$ as an example, we can calculate the R.Q. that would result from fatty acid oxidation:

$$C_{16}H_{32}O_2 + 23\ O_2 \rightarrow 16\ CO_2 + 16\ H_2O.$$

The R.Q. is therefore $\frac{16}{23} = 0{\cdot}7$, a value which again is considerably higher than that observed in *Ricinus* (0·30-0·35). The seed of *Ricinus* consists of a testa enclosing a massive, fat-storing endosperm which in turn surrounds the small embryo with filmy cotyledons.

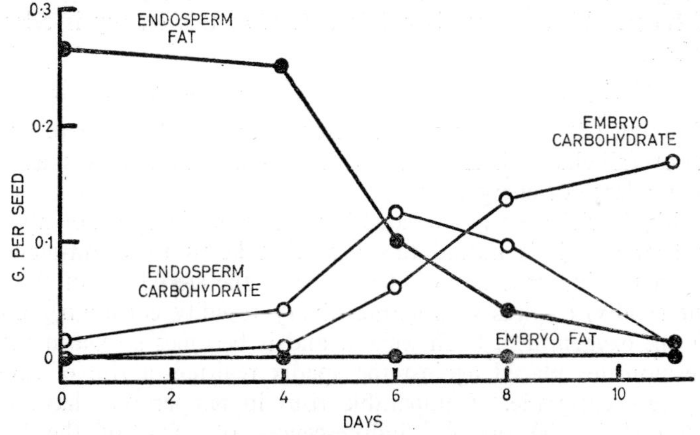

Fig. 108. CHANGES IN FAT AND CARBOHYDRATE CONTENT OF ENDOSPERM AND EMBRYO OF GERMINATING *Ricinus* SEEDS.

Fat stored in the endosperm is converted to carbohydrate and then translocated as such to the embryo. Data of Desveaux and Kogane-Charles, 1952.

Chemical analyses of these seeds have been made at various stages of germination (Fig. 108). It will be seen that the endosperm of the dry seed contains fat but this has all disappeared after twelve days. The embryo which is almost devoid of carbohydrate at the start acquires 0·17 g. carbohydrate by twelve days. Far from being oxidised to carbon dioxide and water, it is now clear that most of the fat has been converted to carbohydrate. Since carbohydrate accumulates for a while in the endosperm, although there is no build-up of fat in the embryo, it follows that the conversion of fat to carbohydrate must take place in the endosperm, the carbohydrate then being translocated to the embryo. The chemical analyses thus focus attention on the metabolism of the endosperm.

Detailed biochemical studies of the manner in which the fatty acids are broken down and the fragments then reassembled as sugar molecules indicate that the conversion proceeds according to this overall equation:

$$C_{16}H_{32}O_2 + 11\ O_2 \rightarrow C_{12}H_{22}O_{11} + 4\ CO_2 + 5\ H_2O.$$

The R.Q. of this equation $= \frac{4}{11} = 0{\cdot}35$ which accords in a most satisfactory manner with the observed R.Q.

The Energetics of Respiration

When sugar is burned or oxidised to carbon dioxide and water, energy is released, about 690,000 calories for every gram-molecule of sugar. If the sugar is oxidised *in vitro* this energy is released as heat,

$$C_6H_{12}O_6 + 6\ O_2 \rightarrow 6\ CO_2 + 6\ H_2O + 690{,}000 \text{ calories.}$$

Although respiration is very different from the burning of sugar, the overall change is the same, with the same end-products, and the same release of energy.

Much of the energy liberated in the course of respiration appears as heat and it is indeed this heat that keeps us warm-blooded. When the inflorescence of *Arum* opens, the sterile tip of the axis (the spadix) respires with extraordinary rapidity consuming up to 20 ml. oxygen/hr/g. fresh weight, and it becomes so warm that a thermometer placed against the spadix registers a rise of several degrees centigrade. Comparable rises in temperature have been recorded in the opening inflorescences of some of the larger Compositae. These are instances where a bulky tissue has a very rapid respiration. However, most plant tissues respire more slowly, having an oxygen uptake of around 0·1-0·5 ml./hr/g. fresh weight, and, moreover, since they are diffuse in structure they will readily lose heat to the atmosphere. To detect any rise in temperature that can be reliably attributed to respiration it is usually necessary to insulate the material from its surroundings, as for instance by placing it in a vacuum flask.

Respiration in plants is accompanied, then, by the liberation of heat energy. However, it must be emphasised that this heat energy is wasted energy so far as the plant is concerned. To be sure, steam engines are kept running with a supply of heat and the organic chemist has frequent recourse to the Bunsen burner to speed up his reactions. The plant has an equal need for energy for its organic syntheses; but the synthetic processes in plants are all accomplished at air temperature (or soil temperature in the case of roots) and are catalysed by enzymes. The energy they require is supplied in a form other than heat.

The elucidation of the mechanism of energy transfer in living cells has been one of the outstanding achievements of biochemistry. The principles involved apply equally to plants, animals, and micro-organisms. Energy is stored, transported, and transferred in the form of potential energy in chemical bonds, in particular, in certain organic phosphorus compounds which are said to contain **high-energy phosphate**. A compound containing high-energy phosphate releases on hydrolysis more energy than a simple ester of phosphate. If the compound *is* in fact hydrolysed the energy of its high-energy phosphate may be dissipated as heat. However, enzymes are available within cells which catalyse reactions in which the hydrolysis is coupled to an energy-requiring process. In this way some of the energy available in the high-energy phosphate is consumed in the synthesis, only the remainder appearing as heat. High-energy phosphate is stored in plant cells as a pyrophosphate, **adenosine triphosphate** (abbreviated **ATP**). This is a compound of the base adenine, the sugar ribose, and an array of three phosphates, the last of them being a high-energy phosphate. When ATP is hydrolysed it yields inorganic phosphate (P_i) and adenosine diphosphate (ADP) with a release of energy

$$\text{ATP} + H_2O \rightleftharpoons \text{ADP} + P_i + \text{Energy}.$$

ATP therefore can be regarded as a substance which stores high-energy phosphate. With a molecular weight of 507, ATP is a relatively small molecule—at least compared to proteins—and it is therefore mobile within cells and can transport high-energy phosphate from one part of a cell to another.

The high-energy phosphate of ATP can be consumed in energy-requiring processes such as the synthesis of starch or sucrose. The synthesis of starch can be expressed thus:

$$\begin{array}{ccc} n\,\text{ATP} & \searrow\!\swarrow & n\,\text{Glucose} \\ n\,\text{ADP} + n\,P_i & \swarrow\!\searrow & \text{Starch.} \end{array}$$

Many examples could be given of such coupled reactions in which ATP is used to promote a synthesis. Indeed they are involved in all the major pathways of synthesis starting from the mineral nutrients absorbed from the soil and the carbohydrate formed in photosynthesis and yielding ultimately proteins, nucleic acids, pigments, and so on. In addition, the chemical energy of ATP may be converted to mechanical energy as in the movement of flagella and cilia and the streaming of cytoplasm in cells. Another transformation is from chemical energy to light energy. Some bacteria and fungi are luminescent; they are sources of light and they glow in the dark. This light is generated once again at the expense of ATP.

ATP can be regarded therefore as the currency for energy transformations in living cells, the energy being available to drive synthetic processes, to do mechanical work, or to generate light. The hydrolysis of ATP was shown above as a reversible reaction. The synthesis of ATP will require energy and in the living cell the generation of ATP is coupled to the process of respiration in which energy is released.

$$\begin{array}{ll} C_6H_{12}O_6 + 6\,O_2 & n\,ADP + n\,P_i \\ 6\,CO_2 + 6\,H_2O & n\,ATP. \end{array}$$

It was shown on p. 226 that in the oxidation of sugar, considered as a chemical process, 690,000 cals. are released per gram molecule of sugar. In the course of respiration, as shown above, some energy is retained in the form of potential energy in the molecules of ATP. It should be emphasised here that the law of the conservation of energy applies as much in plant metabolism as it does in other systems. The coupling between respiration and ATP production is less than 100 per cent. efficient. The respiration of a gram molecule of sugar therefore yields some ATP together with correspondingly less than 690,000 cals. of heat energy.

Sugars and other respirable materials can therefore be regarded as stores of potentially useful energy. The ultimate and original source of this energy is sunshine, for it is the sun that provides the energy for photosynthesis, the process in which sugars are synthesised in green tissues.

The Biochemistry of Respiration

While it is true to say that sugars are oxidised to carbon dioxide and water in respiration, this statement does no more than name the initial substrates and the final products. It gives no indication of the mechanism by which the oxidation is brought about. Two major routes or pathways of respiration, each involving many enzyme-catalysed reactions, have now been recognised in plant tissues—but only the better understood and more common of them will be described here. This pathway involves three successive stages—glycolysis in which the sugar molecules are split, the Krebs cycle in which the split products are consumed, and the final oxidation steps.

Glucose is a hexose sugar with the formula $C_6H_{12}O_6$. In the initial steps of **glycolysis** (Fig. 109) the hexose is twice esterified with phosphate yielding a hexose diphosphate which cleaves to give two molecules of phosphoglyceraldehyde, the phosphate ester of a triose sugar with the formula $C_3H_6O_3$. This aldehyde is oxidised to the corresponding acid (phosphoglyceric acid) which in turn suffers a series of changes involving loss of its phosphate. The final product is pyruvic acid, $CH_3.CO.COOH$.

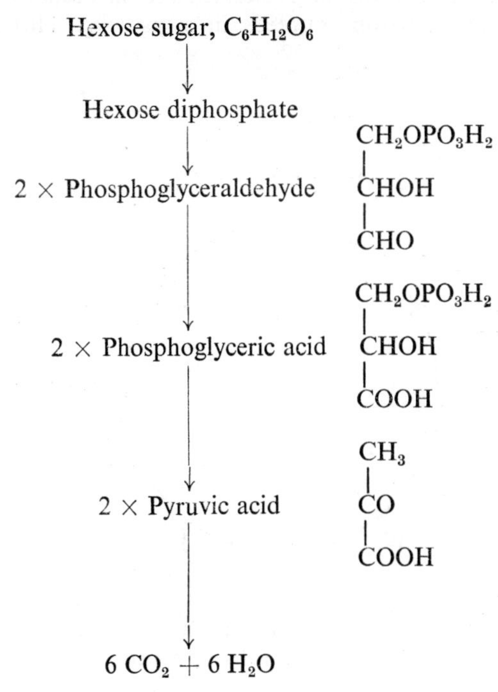

Fig. 109. OUTLINE OF THE DISSIMILATION OF GLUCOSE IN AIR.

The final oxidation of pyruvic acid involves the Krebs cycle (Fig. 110). High-energy phosphate is consumed in the initial conversion of hexose to hexose diphosphate; it is generated in the oxidation of phosphoglyceraldehyde to phosphoglyceric acid and again in a step that lies between this compound and pyruvic acid.

The glycolytic conversion of glucose to pyruvate takes place in the soluble phase of the cytoplasm but the enzymes involved in the subsequent stages of respiration are all located in the mitochondria. Pyruvic acid first suffers an oxidative decarboxylation. In chemical terms this could be described as a process yielding acetic acid and carbon dioxide.

$$CH_3.CO.COOH + \tfrac{1}{2}\,O_2 \rightarrow CH_3.COOH + CO_2.$$

However, the biological system is more complex than this and yields instead of acetic acid the acetyl derivative of a coenzyme, namely coenzyme A. Coenzyme A (abbreviated as CoA) is a rather complex derivative of ADP whose precise structure need not concern us here. The acetyl CoA is oxidised through the **Krebs cycle**—or more accurately, coenzyme A is liberated and the acetate completely oxidised. The oxidation proceeds in steps (Fig. 110) involving

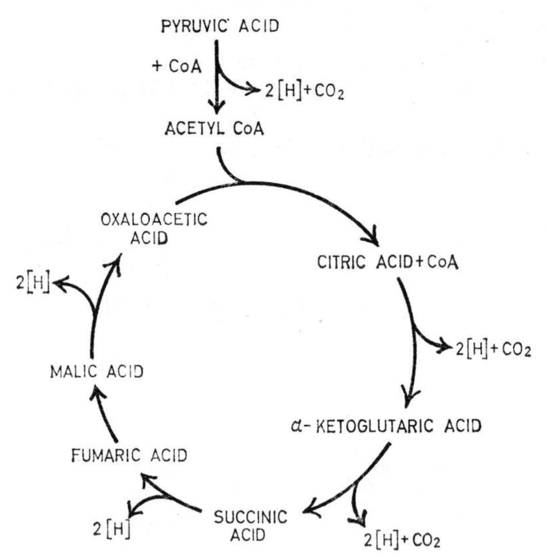

Fig. 110. OUTLINE OF THE CONVERSION OF PYRUVIC ACID TO ACETYL CoA AND ITS OXIDATION IN THE KREBS CYCLE.
[H] represents reducing power.

two decarboxylations in which carbon dioxide is formed and four oxidation steps.

$$CH_3.COOH + 2\,O_2 \rightarrow 2\,CO_2 + 2\,H_2O.$$

The sequence of events starts with the condensation of acetyl CoA with oxaloacetic acid, a 4-carbon compound, to yield free CoA and a 6-carbon compound, citric acid. Then follows an oxidative decarboxylation yielding α-ketoglutarate (a 5-carbon compound) and another oxidative decarboxylation which gives succinic acid (4-carbon). Two molecules of carbon dioxide have now been released. The remaining stages of the cycle involve two further oxidations and they end in the regeneration of oxaloacetic acid. Thus the complete cycle involves the production of 2 molecules of carbon dioxide and the consumption of 4 atoms of oxygen (since the oxidation of 2 atoms of hydrogen takes one atom of oxygen)—as required by the equation set out above. Each molecule of acetate entering the cycle as acetyl CoA is therefore completely oxidised as it passes from one enzyme to the next in the sequence. The process as a whole is cyclic in that it is initiated by the condensation of a molecule of oxaloacetic acid with a molecule of acetyl CoA and it ends in the regeneration of a molecule of oxaloacetate available to condense with another molecule of acetyl CoA.

The Krebs cycle involves several oxidations. These oxidations are initiated by the transfer of hydrogen from the substrate on to a coenzyme, and from the coenzyme to an oxidase enzyme which has the power to catalyse its final union with atmospheric oxygen. To take a specific instance, the oxidation of succinate to fumarate involves the removal of hydrogen from the succinate, and its transfer to a coenzyme named cytochrome. This is an iron-containing protein, red in colour, which can suffer alternate oxidation and reduction. It is first reduced by succinate (under the influence of the enzyme succinic dehydrogenase) and then oxidised by atmospheric oxygen (a reaction catalysed by the enzyme cytochrome oxidase).

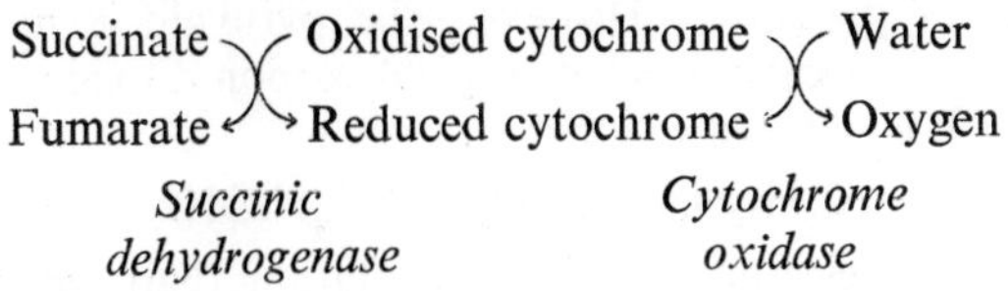

Succinate ⤫ Oxidised cytochrome ⤫ Water
Fumarate ↙ ↘ Reduced cytochrome ↙ ↘ Oxygen

Succinic dehydrogenase *Cytochrome oxidase*

In reality the situation is more complex than this as the hydrogen is passed in sequence to several different cytochromes on its way to oxygen, and in many oxidations the chain includes another coenzyme as well. However, the oxidations of the Krebs cycle all result finally in the transfer of hydrogen to cytochrome oxidase. The coenzymes ensure that the various dehydrogenases (succinic dehydrogenase for succinate oxidation, malic dehydrogenase for malate oxidation, and so on) are all linked to the same final oxidation step. The Krebs cycle enzymes are located in the mitochondria, and the same is true of the associated cytochromes. The mitochondria are equipped therefore with an enzyme system able to catalyse the complete oxidation of pyruvate to carbon dioxide and water.

It was emphasised earlier that some of the energy released in respiration is trapped as high-energy phosphate. If we go back to the start of glycolysis we find that the whole process actually begins with a *consumption* of ATP. Two molecules of ATP react with one of hexose to yield hexose diphosphate.

$$\text{Hexose} + 2\ \text{ATP} \rightleftharpoons \text{Hexosediphosphate} + 2\ \text{ADP} + 2\ \text{P}_i.$$

High-energy phosphate is therefore required to initiate the respiratory sequence, but in the later stages of glycolysis and in the final oxidations ATP is generated in quantities that are more than sufficient to compensate for this initial consumption. Most of the high-energy phosphate generated in respiration is in fact produced in the terminal oxidations involving cytochromes and cytochrome oxidase. These oxidations are located in the mitochondria. It is for this reason that the mitochondria have been named the "power houses" of the cell; their role in respiration is comparable to the role of chloroplasts in photosynthesis.

Aerobic and Anaerobic Conditions

Many micro-organisms such as yeast can survive under aerobic *or* anaerobic conditions. They are said to be facultative anaerobes. Others such as the bacterium *Clostridium* are obligate anaerobes only living in the absence of air. Under such conditions there is of course no possibility of aerobic respiration and sugars are dissimilated by a fermentation of some sort. In yeast the fermentation of sugar proceeds by the glycolytic pathway (Fig. 109) as far as the production of pyruvate. However, the pyruvate is not oxidised as in air, but is decarboxylated to yield carbon dioxide and acetaldehyde which is reduced to ethanol.

$$C_6H_{12}O_6 \rightarrow 2\ CO_2 + 2\ C_2H_5OH.$$

Less energy is released in this fermentation than when sugar is completely oxidised in air, the difference being accounted for by the heat of combustion of ethanol. Some ATP is generated but the yield of ATP per mole of glucose is less than in aerobic respiration.

When angiosperm tissues are placed under nitrogen, sugars are broken down as in yeast, yielding carbon dioxide and ethanol. Such anaerobiosis is probably not a natural condition for plant tissues, and they cannot survive it for long periods.

PHOTOSYNTHESIS

The organic substances around us are constantly being consumed as they are burnt, respired in living tissues, or broken down by the action of micro-organisms. Photosynthesis is the one process by which carbon dioxide is returned to the organic state. It is the primary source of all our foodstuffs: without it life on earth would soon stop. As the population of the world increases year by year the problem of growing sufficient food for everyone becomes more and more pressing. It is important, therefore, in considering photosynthesis to pay particular attention to the factors which limit its rate and to ask whether the world's crops could be made to yield more food.

The essential requirements for photosynthesis are green cells, a supply of carbon dioxide, and light. Elementary demonstrations of these requirements are readily made by means of starch prints.

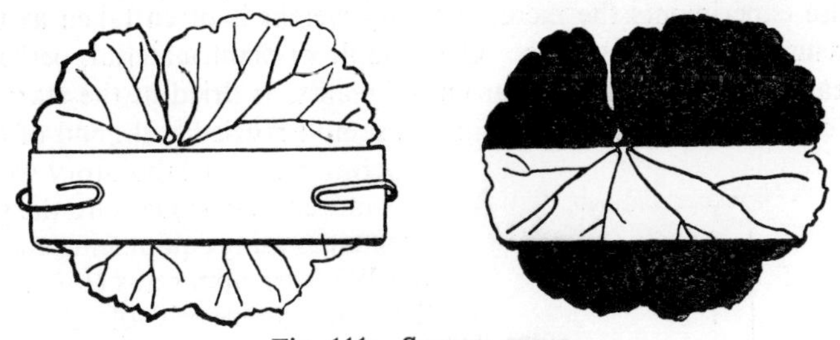

Fig. 111. STARCH PRINT.
A stencil prevents photosynthetic formation of starch in the areas of the leaf that it covers.

If a plant such as *Pelargonium* is held in the dark for a few days the starch in its leaves is hydrolysed to soluble sugars which are translocated out of the leaf. When such a plant is brought back into the light starch will appear as a product of photosynthesis. The leaf may be tested for starch by immersing it first in boiling water and then in warm alcohol until it is bleached. If it is now immersed in an iodine solution any starch present will stain blue-black. By

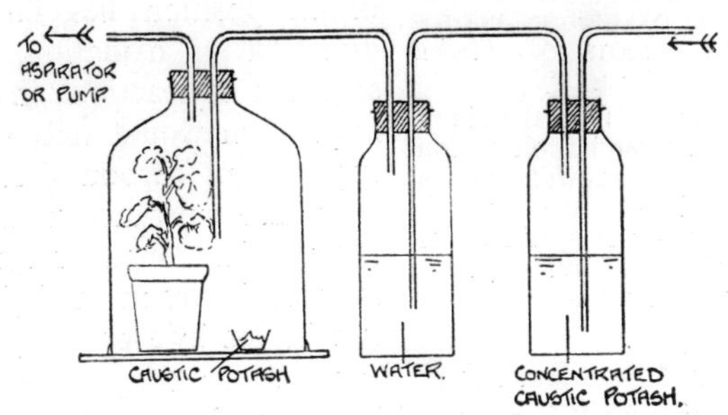

Fig. 112. APPARATUS FOR MAINTAINING A PLANT IN A STREAM OF CARBON DIOXIDE-FREE AIR.
No photosynthesis is possible under these conditions.

such means the necessity for light is readily shown (Fig. 111). The need for chlorophyll can be demonstrated, using a variegated leaf or some non-green part of a plant. If a plant is held under a bell jar from which carbon dioxide has been removed with soda-lime—or if carbon dioxide-free air is passed over a plant (Fig. 112) then there will be no photosynthetic starch production. When shoots of the water plant *Elodea* are illuminated, bubbles of a gas rich in oxygen can be collected (Fig. 113).

The experimental investigation of photosynthesis demands accurate methods of measurement. In long-term field and greenhouse experiments the increase in dry weight is often taken as the measure of photosynthesis. One sample of plant material, perhaps a leaf or a whole plant or group of plants, is dried at the start of the experiment and a second, similar, sample is dried at the end of the experiment. For laboratory work it is more usual to measure the gas exchanges using equipment such as the Warburg apparatus (Fig. 106). The photosynthesis of *Chlorella* cells, for instance, can be measured by immersing them in a buffered bicarbonate solution, which serves as a source of carbon dioxide, and then following the evolution of oxygen.

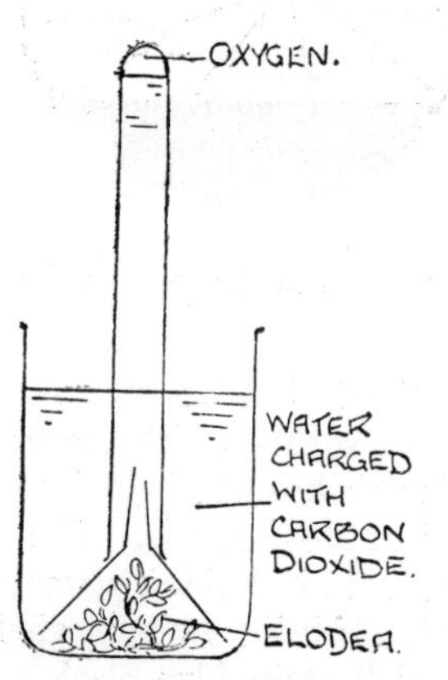

Fig. 113. Demonstration of the evolution of oxygen in photosynthesis by shoots of *Elodea canadensis*.

Bubbles of gas issue from the illuminated shoots and can be collected in the test-tube. The gas will kindle a glowing splint showing that it is rich in oxygen; the gas is a mixture of oxygen with the gases present in the air spaces of the shoots.

The respiratory oxidation of sugar is accompanied, as we have seen, by a considerable release of energy. For this reason the equilibrium position lies far in the direction of oxidation, and the sequence of reactions involved in respiration would only synthesise sugar from carbon dioxide and water in a most inefficient manner. Nevertheless, sugar *is* synthesised in green leaves in the light. This is achieved by a pathway of metabolism which differs from that in respiration; the pathway is called photosynthesis and it is powered by energy from sunlight. Respiration and photosynthesis differ therefore in their energy relationships and in the metabolic routes by which they proceed. It remains true, however, that the net outcome of photosynthesis is the opposite of that of respiration. The overall chemical equations for the two processes show this clearly:

Photosynthesis: $6\,CO_2 + 6\,H_2O \rightarrow C_6H_{12}O_6 + 6\,O_2$

Respiration: $C_6H_{12}O_6 + 6\,O_2 \rightarrow 6\,CO_2 + 6\,H_2O$.

Now, if respiration and photosynthesis are *both* occurring in a leaf the increase in dry weight or evolution of oxygen will not measure photosynthesis itself, but photosynthesis minus respiration. How can we tell if the two proceed simultaneously? Not, it will be evident from the equations above, by simply measuring dry weights or changes in gas volumes. Such measurements could not show whether respiration were at work in the light as well as photosynthesis. This problem has been tackled in experiments using isotopically-labelled oxygen. Isotopes are varieties of an element which differ in physical properties such as mass (their atoms having nuclei of somewhat different composition), but which have identical chemical properties. The various isotopes of an element will therefore be metabolised in the same way, but they can be distinguished by their physical properties. In the present case it was possible to distinguish between the consumption in respiration of oxygen rich in the heavy isotope with atomic weight 18 and the production of ordinary oxygen (atomic weight 16) in photosynthesis. The outcome of the experiments was the discovery that (in *Chlorella*, at least) respiration accompanies photosynthesis in the light, being as fast in the light as it is in the dark. To determine the true rate of photosynthesis it therefore becomes necessary to know the rate of respiration. This can be found quite simply by making a second set of measurements in the dark when photosynthesis will be eliminated. The true rate of photosynthesis is then given by the difference between the measurements made in the light and those in the dark.

Chloroplasts and Chlorophyll

The green pigment chlorophyll, an indispensible requirement for photosynthesis, is located within the chloroplasts. In higher plants these are disc-shaped bodies, about 5 μ across. They are very numerous in the mesophyll cells of leaves which may contain as many as 50 to 100 per cell, but less abundant in guard cells and the outer cells of aerial stems; many cells, of course, as in the root, lack chlorophyll altogether. Some algae such as *Chlorella* have one large chloroplast per cell. The pigment is not uniformly distributed within the chloroplast but confined to regions known as grana of which there are from 10 to 100 in each angiosperm chloroplast. Under the electron microscope the grana are seen to be piles of flattened sacs, some of the sacs being very large and stretching from one granum to the next (see Frontispiece and Chapter 8). The blue-green algae and photosynthetic bacteria have no chloroplasts; instead the pigments are organised into small, spherical particles less than 1 μ in diameter.

Chloroplasts contain two types of pigment, the chlorophylls which are green and associated with them several yellow carotenoids. (Some leaves such as those of the copper beech contain in addition anthocyanins, but these are not chloroplast pigments; they are soluble in water and located in the vacuole.) The chloroplast pigments are all somewhat hydrophobic in nature (not water-soluble) and may be extracted from fresh leaves or powdered dried leaves with 90 per cent. acetone. The resulting solution is a mixture of

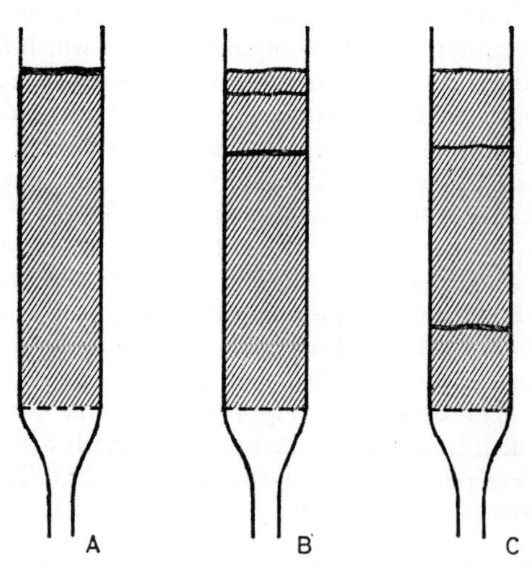

Fig. 114. COLUMN CHROMATOGRAPHY OF CHLOROPLAST PIGMENTS.

The column is prepared by pouring a slurry of dry sucrose in petrol ether into the glass tube and allowing the sucrose to settle. A dry solution of chloroplast pigments is poured on to the top of the column (A) and as it percolates down the pigments separate (B). The carotenes are hydrocarbons and therefore strongly hydrophobic; they are not absorbed on the column and pass freely down with petrol ether. The chlorophylls are less strongly hydrophobic and are absorbed to some extent by the column so that they move less quickly. A greater degree of separation can be obtained by pouring more petrol ether on to the column to develop it (C).

the chloroplast pigments. The individual components of this mixture may be separated out by taking advantage of their different solubilities in various solvents, but a more elegant procedure is that of chromatography which was introduced by Tswett in the early years of this century. The pigments are transferred to petrol ether (by shaking the acetone solution with petrol ether), the petrol ether is then freed of water, and the pigments separated out on a column of powdered sugar or chalk (Fig. 114).

Two chlorophylls are found in leaves, chlorophyll *a* and chlorophyll *b*. They are organic substances with very similar complex ring structures containing at the centre an atom of magnesium. In the chloroplast the chlorophyll molecules are thought to be closely associated with protein. Weak solutions of chlorophyll *a* are green-blue in colour; solutions of chlorophyll *b*, a more yellowish green. These colours result from the absorption of light at the blue and red ends of the spectrum—as can be seen if a chlorophyll solution is held in front of a spectroscope. With a spectrophotometer the precise amount of light absorbed at each

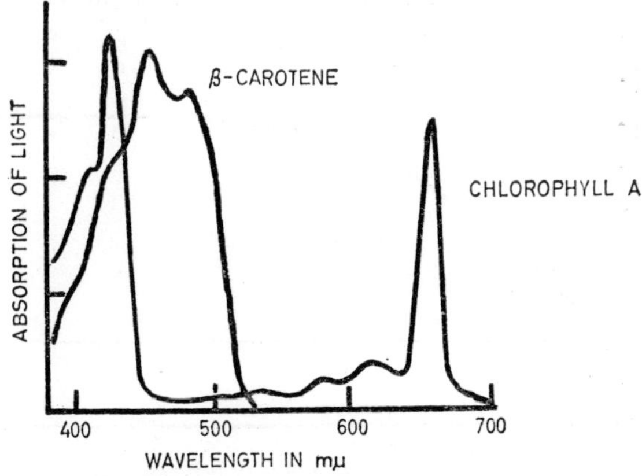

Fig. 115. ABSORPTION SPECTRA OF CHLOROPHYLL *a* AND β-CAROTENE. Light of wavelength 400 mμ appears violet to the eye; 700 mμ is in the red.

wavelength can be determined, so providing the data for an absorption curve (Fig. 115).

The carotenoids are yellow pigments, absorbing light mainly at the violet end of the spectrum. They are present in chloroplasts and also in the plastids of some non-chlorophyllous cells such as the perianth of *Cheiranthus* (wallflower), the root of *Daucus* (carrot), and fruit of *Lycopersicum* (tomato).

Photosynthesis and Light

In complete darkness plants do not grow normally; they become etiolated (p. 312). However, etiolation is suppressed by very weak exposures to light—by intensities, in fact, which are too low for photosynthesis. If a plant is held at such a low light intensity its sugars and starch will be lost in respiration and never replaced by photosynthesis, a situation to which the plant must soon succumb.

As a minimum, to maintain itself as it is without gain or loss of carbohydrate the plant must receive sufficient light to enable photosynthesis to compensate for respiration. As the light intensity is increased above this compensation point photosynthesis proceeds more rapidly until a plateau is reached when the plant is saturated with light. Full summer sunshine is more than sufficient to saturate the photosynthesis of most leaves, but in winter the light intensity often falls so low as to limit the rate of photosynthesis (Fig. 116).

In ample sunlight the rate of photosynthesis may be 5-10 times the rate of respiration but as the light intensity falls at dusk, photosynthesis will become slower and slower until at night the gas

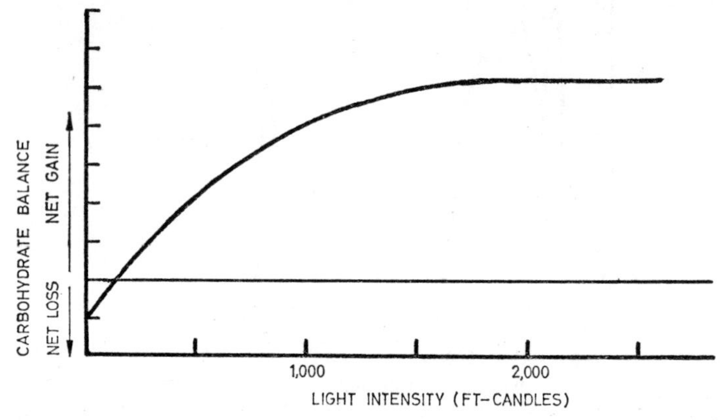

Fig. 116. PHOTOSYNTHESIS RATES IN LIGHT OF DIFFERENT INTENSITIES (diagrammatic).

In total darkness carbohydrate is lost by respiration. The compensation point is the light intensity at which the carbohydrate loss due to respiration is balanced by the gain from photosynthesis. The rate reaches a peak at about 2,000 ft-candles. In mid-summer on a cloudless day the light intensity may reach 10,000 ft-candles; in winter in Britain it may fall to a few hundred ft-candles.

exchanges of respiration alone will be evident. It follows that by day carbon dioxide will diffuse into the leaf and oxygen out of it (photosynthesis faster than respiration), but at night the reverse is true for oxygen will enter the leaf as it is used in respiration, and carbon dioxide will diffuse out.

When light falls on a leaf about 80-90 per cent. of it is absorbed, the remainder being reflected from the leaf or transmitted through it. If the light intensity is high enough, sufficient light may be transmitted to allow photosynthesis in a second layer of leaves below the first and perhaps in a tier below this as well. The aim of the agronomist is to achieve good crop yields which demands the maximal utilisation of sunlight at all times. He must endeavour therefore to have his fields covered with leafy plants for as long a period of the year as possible and to ensure that the spread and density of the leaves is such as to absorb a high proportion of the sunlight falling on the field. In practice this means encouraging abundant leaf growth, especially in mid-summer when light intensity is at its highest, but aiming at the same time to have a good cover of leaves in the spring and autumn. Efficient use of spring sunshine is not easy to achieve in temperate climates because most crop plants have only a small leaf area at this time (Fig. 117).

The role of chlorophyll in photosynthesis is to absorb light energy and make it available for the energy-requiring synthesis of carbohydrate. Since chlorophyll does not absorb green light very

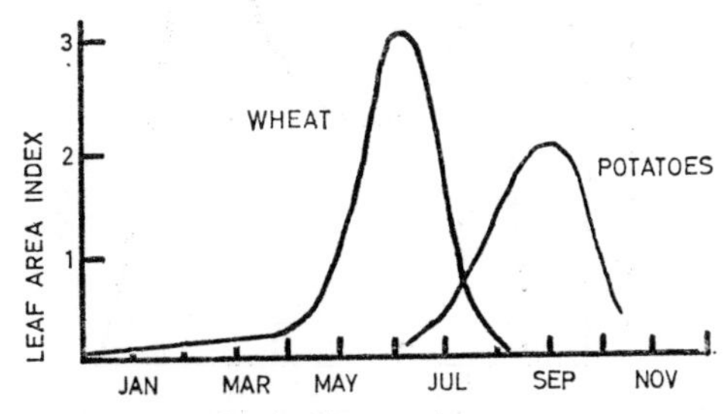

Fig. 117. LEAFINESS OF CROP PLANTS AT DIFFERENT SEASONS OF THE YEAR. Leafiness is expressed as leaf area index which is leaf area per unit area of land. An index of one is equivalent to a single continuous canopy of leaf over the land; an index of two means a double canopy of leaf, one above the other. Data of Watson, 1947.

strongly, it might be expected that green light would be rather ineffective in photosynthesis. However, experiment (Fig. 118) shows that, on the contrary, photosynthesis in wheat leaves under green light (490-570 mμ) is at least half as rapid as under red light (650-700 mμ). In experiments with *Chlorella* the dip in photosynthesis rate in this part of the spectrum is even less pronounced. Some green light is absorbed by the carotenoid pigments and recent work suggests that its energy is then passed on to neighbouring molecules of chlorophyll where the light reaction of photosynthesis actually takes place.

Of the solar energy that is absorbed by leaves only a very small proportion, of the order of 2 per cent., is actually utilised in photosynthesis under field conditions. Several factors contribute to this disappointingly low figure. On the one hand some wavelengths are not used at all in photosynthesis (the infra-red radiation) or used only with some loss of efficiency (green light); while on the other hand, the rate of photosynthesis may be limited as we shall see below by the low carbon dioxide content of the air or by low temperatures.

The Supply of Water and Carbon Dioxide

Water is one of the reactants in photosynthesis, but when it is recalled that roughly 80 per cent. of the fresh weight of a plant is water it will be evident that plants are unlikely to be short of water for photosynthesis. Not only is a plant composed primarily of water, but water passes in a continual stream (the transpiration

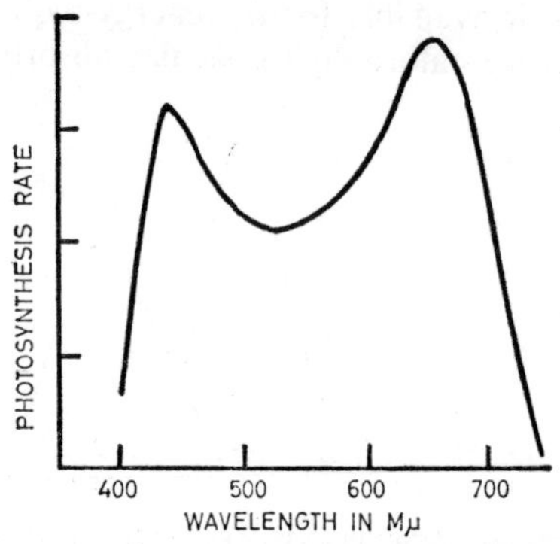

Fig. 118. THE ACTION SPECTRUM OF PHOTOSYNTHESIS IN WHEAT LEAVES. The graph shows the relative rates of photosynthesis when the leaves are illuminated with light of different wavelengths. At each wavelength the same amount of light energy was supplied. After Bonner and Galston, 1952.

stream) up the xylem of land plants, from the root system to the leaf cells from which it evaporates. In terms of traffic, far more water molecules pass through the stomata than either carbon dioxide or oxygen. This is illustrated by some measurements on the comparative rates of transpiration, photosynthesis, and respiration in trees (Table 1).

TABLE 1

RATES OF TRANSPIRATION, RESPIRATION, AND PHOTOSYNTHESIS IN SOME TREES
Data of Polster, 1950.

	TRANSPIRATION mg. water transpired/g. fresh wt of leaf	RESPIRATION mg. CO_2 produced per g. fresh wt of leaf	PHOTOSYNTHESIS mg CO_2 utilised per g. fresh wt of leaf
Betula	9,500	23	67
Quercus	6,020	18	43
Pinus	1,880	8	17

Plants obtain the carbon dioxide they require for photosynthesis from the atmosphere. The concentration of carbon dioxide in the air is rather small, only about 0·03 per cent. by volume as compared with 21 per cent. of oxygen. As carbon dioxide is consumed in photosynthesis further supplies diffuse from the air through the stomata and so to the air-space system of the leaf. Carbon dioxide is moderately soluble in water and will therefore dissolve in the liquid wetting the walls of the leaf cells. It then diffuses through the cytoplasm to the chloroplasts (or is carried to them by cytoplasmic streaming) where the biochemical reactions of photosynthesis take place. Submerged plants utilise the carbon dioxide dissolved in the water. Thus the journey of carbon dioxide molecules to the chloroplasts is accomplished by simple diffusion from the air or the water around the plant. Diffusion in the aqueous phase is very much slower than diffusion of carbon dioxide as a gas.

If the concentration of carbon dioxide in the atmosphere around a plant is lowered, then photosynthesis is retarded. The same may happen under natural conditions when the stomata of a leaf shut—for instance, when there is a shortage of water in the soil. Although most leaves have large intercellular air spaces occupying $\frac{1}{4}$-$\frac{1}{2}$ of the volume of the leaf, the carbon dioxide in this volume of air will soon be exhausted. If the carbon dioxide concentration in the atmosphere is raised within certain limits, then photosynthesis will become faster. It is worth noting that by their respiration at night plants automatically cause some carbon dioxide enrichment of the air near ground level if there is no wind. In a maize field carbon dioxide concentrations varying between 0·055 per cent. and 0·080 per cent. were recorded 100 cm. above ground level at 6 a.m.; by 10 a.m. the concentration had fallen to its mean daily value of 0·025 per cent.

Temperature and Photosynthesis

At high temperatures photosynthesis is inhibited. This is not unexpected since enzymes themselves are inactivated at high temperature. The effect of more moderate temperatures cannot be stated quite so simply since it depends on another factor—the intensity of the light. At low light intensities, temperature does not influence photosynthesis rate, that is to say Q_{10} is about unity (Fig. 119). With a stronger light, a rise in temperature will increase the rate of photosynthesis, Q_{10} now being about 2. The interpretation of such experiments is important for the insight it gives into the mechanism of photosynthesis. A Q_{10} of 1 is characteristic of physical processes such as diffusion, or the decomposition of hydrogen peroxide in light which like other photochemical changes is basically physical in nature. Chemical and biochemical processes have a Q_{10} of 2. We can understand the experimental observations noted above if we suppose that there are two consecutive steps in photosynthesis—the photochemical one with $Q_{10} = 1$ followed by a biochemical one with $Q_{10} = 2$. When there is little light, photosynthesis is necessarily slow, the light reaction with $Q_{10} = 1$ limiting the rate. But at high light intensities the photochemical process

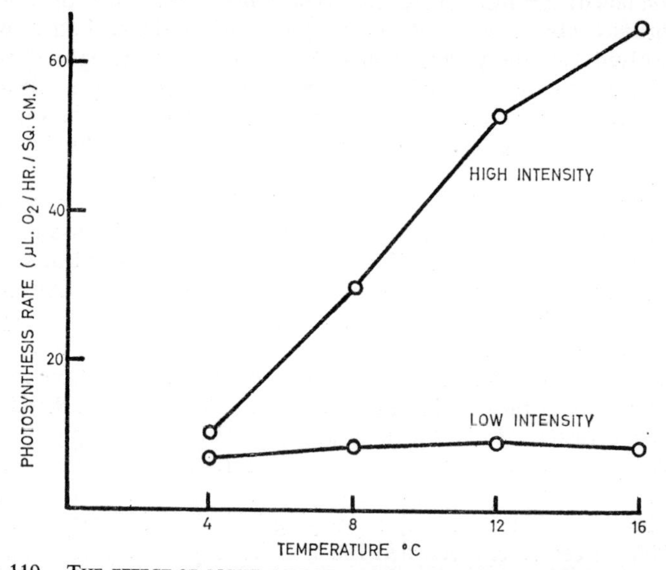

Fig. 119. THE EFFECT OF LIGHT INTENSITY ON THE RESPONSE OF PHOTOSYNTHESIS IN THE ALGA *Gigartina* TO CHANGE OF TEMPERATURE.

For the low light intensity a filter transmitting 10 per cent. of the light was placed in front of the light source. Data of Emerson and Arnold, 1934.

is thought to proceed so fast that its products (which are the substrates for the biochemical process) accumulate more rapidly than the biochemical process can accept them. At high light intensity photosynthesis is limited by the biochemical process with $Q_{10} = 2$.

Biochemistry of Photosynthesis—The Hill Reaction

The experiments on photosynthesis described so far have concerned its rate and the way in which this is affected by change of light intensity, carbon dioxide concentration, or temperature.

Intact leaves or whole plants were used in all these investigations. This is the approach of the physiologist. It has yielded information of practical value as well as the concept that photosynthesis involves two separate reactions: the light reaction (photochemical) and the dark reaction (biochemical).

The biochemist's approach to photosynthesis soon leads him to study systems less intact than whole leaves. Since chlorophyll is located in the chloroplasts and, moreover, since starch appears within the chloroplasts of green leaves in the light, the biochemist soon reaches for his pestle and mortar to grind up leaf cells and single out the chloroplasts for study *in vitro*. The procedure for isolating chloroplasts is outlined on p. 212.

This approach was used by Hill in Cambridge in 1940. He extracted chloroplasts from leaves of *Stellaria media* and *Lamium album* and found that they produced oxygen on illumination—provided that a suitable hydrogen acceptor was added to the preparation. This is the Hill reaction (or chloroplast reaction). It is most easily studied if a dye such as 2, 6-dichlorophenol indophenol is used as hydrogen acceptor since the dye becomes colourless when reduced. Quantitative studies show that four equivalents of hydrogen appear for every mole of oxygen liberated. The reaction is thus in effect a splitting of water yielding oxygen and reducing power [H]:

$$2\,H_2O \xrightarrow[\text{light}]{\text{chlorophyll}} 4\,[H] + O_2$$

$$[H] + \underset{\textit{blue}}{\text{Oxidised dye}} \rightarrow \underset{\textit{colourless}}{\text{Reduced dye}}$$

Oxygen can be produced in this reaction as rapidly as in photosynthesis, and indeed there are many parallels between the Hill reaction and photosynthesis. They are influenced alike by changes of light intensity or temperature and by the presence of certain specific poisons. Again, when the water used in the experiments is labelled with isotopic oxygen, the oxygen liberated in each case is likewise labelled. These lines of evidence all suggest that the Hill reaction is part of the photosynthetic process—that part, namely, which requires light and results in the evolution of molecular oxygen. The Hill reaction proceeds in the absence of carbon dioxide and it follows from this and from the isotope experiment just described that the oxygen liberated in photosynthesis is evolved from the water and not from the carbon dioxide. It is worth stressing this point since the equation generally written to describe photosynthesis carries a different implication. If the equation

$$6\,CO_2 + 6\,H_2O \rightarrow C_6H_{12}O_6 + 6\,O_2$$

were correct it would follow that no more than half the oxygen (*i.e.* six atoms) could come from the water, the rest being derived from the carbon dioxide. However, experiment shows that the oxygen actually comes from the water and we should therefore amend the equation by adding six molecules of water to each side so that now all twelve atoms of oxygen can originate from the water

$$6\,CO_2 + 12\,H_2O \rightarrow C_6H_{12}O_6 + 6\,H_2O + 6\,O_2.$$

Photosynthesis is an energy-consuming process just as respiration is an energy-yielding one. The energy required for photosynthesis is derived from sunlight. The chloroplast acts as a transformer converting the light energy into chemical energy. Recent work has extended our understanding of this light reaction.

The essence of the Hill reaction is the liberation of oxygen from water and the generation of reducing power by illuminated chloroplasts. Hill was unable to achieve any carbon dioxide fixation in his preparations, that is to say the formation of organic substances from carbon dioxide. However, Arnon working in California with somewhat different chloroplast preparations reported in 1954 that he was able to realise the conversion of carbon dioxide into carbohydrate alongside the evolution of oxygen. In addition, his chloroplast preparations formed ATP in the light. It is now recognised that the light reaction in photosynthesis consists in the liberation of oxygen and the generation of reducing power and ATP. How these two, reducing power and ATP are involved in the fixation of carbon dioxide will become clear in the next section.

Biochemistry of Photosynthesis—the Path of Carbon

We have now considered the capture of light energy by the chloroplast and its transformation to chemical energy. There remains the problem of the conversion of carbon dioxide to carbohydrate. Since enzymes catalyse relatively simple reactions such as a hydrolysis, an oxidation, a reduction, or a transfer we may surmise that a process as complex as the synthesis of carbohydrate must involve many steps. The problem is simply to identify the steps. This means that we must allow a period of photosynthesis and then by analysis of the plant seek to identify any intermediates between carbon dioxide and sugar that may have appeared. This will be no mean task for the intermediates may not accumulate in any quantity, being metabolised rapidly to carbohydrate instead. Indeed, when sunflower plants were analysed at the start and end of a one hour period of photosynthesis the carbon of the carbon dioxide fixed was found to be distributed thus:

Monosaccharide	10 per cent.
Sucrose	52 ,, ,,
Unidentified sugar	3 ,, ,,
Unidentified polysaccharide	1 ,, ,,
Starch	25 ,, ,,
Residue	7 ,, ,,
Recovery	98 ,, ,,

It is clear that in the period of one hour at least 91 per cent. of the carbon dioxide taken up has been metabolised to carbohydrate: no large amount of intermediates can be present.

In the decade 1945-55 the path of carbon in photosynthesis was investigated in a brilliant series of experiments by Calvin in California. He argued that if intermediates were formed in small amounts and rapidly metabolised it would only be possible to distinguish them with certainty from other products of photosynthesis present in small quantity, in experiments of very short duration. If the time were reduced sufficiently then it should be possible to detect the product into which carbon dioxide was *first* converted on its way to carbohydrate. Calvin was able by progressively reducing the time of photosynthesis to demonstrate the formation of intermediates, to separate and identify them and to show that their number was reduced until in the very shortest periods the first step in the path of carbon stood revealed. Calvin's achievement was made possible by his imaginative use of techniques that first became available at that time. The path of carbon was traced by supplying carbon dioxide in which some of the carbon was radioactive so that the products of photosynthesis would be labelled. Calvin was one of the first to use the long-lived isotope of carbon of mass 14 (^{14}C) which had been discovered in 1940. Suspensions of *Chlorella* cells in an illuminated glass vessel were supplied with radioactive bicarbonate for a few seconds and then ejected into boiling aqueous methanol which killed them and extracted soluble materials from the cells including the products of photosynthesis.

The alcoholic solution was evaporated to small volume, spotted on to the corner of a sheet of filter-paper, and its constituents then separated by two-dimensional paper chromatography (Fig. 120). The products of photosynthesis together with other cell constituents were then spaced out on the paper—but they were invisible. Autoradiography was used to discover their position. A sheet of photographic film was placed firmly in contact with the chromatogram and left in the dark. Radiation from the ^{14}C-containing spots on the paper "exposed" the adjacent area of film so that when the film was developed darkened spots appeared. The positions of the labelled products of photosynthesis were thus located. The areas of the chromatogram corresponding to the darkened spots on the film were cut out, the ^{14}C-containing substance washed off each

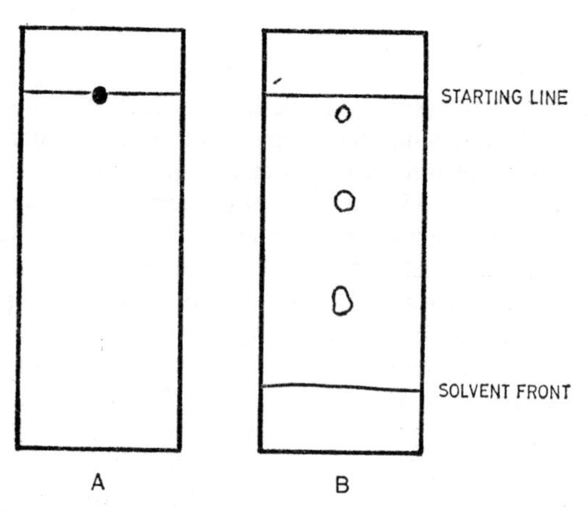

Fig. 120. PAPER CHROMATOGRAPHY IS A MEANS OF SEPARATING AND IDENTIFYING THE COMPONENTS OF A MIXTURE.

A drop of the mixture is placed on the paper near one end (A). The upper end of the paper is bent over into a trough containing solvent such as aqueous, acidified butanol. As the solvent flows down the paper it separates the substances according to their relative solubility in the solvent and in water which is absorbed on to the cellulose fibres of the paper (B). Water soluble substances are held relatively strongly by the paper and move only a short distance from the starting line. A hydrophobic substance will move nearer the solvent front. The distance that a spot moves relative to the solvent front is a characteristic of that particular substance in that solvent and can be used as a means of identification. The resolution between the spots can be improved by running the paper with one solvent and then after drying the paper turning it through 90° and running with a second solvent; this is two-dimensional chromatography. The substances to be separated may be coloured and therefore visible. If they have no colour, the paper is sprayed with a reagent that will give a coloured product: thus acids can be made visible by spraying with a pH indicator.

piece of paper and then subjected to chemical analysis. The value of the radioactive tracer in these experiments was that it enabled Calvin to separate out the products of the experimental period of photosynthesis from other soluble compounds already present in the *Chlorella* cells. In the short periods of photosynthesis that Calvin used it would have been very difficult by any other means to detect the minute quantities of photosynthate that were formed.

The chief outcome of Calvin's work was the discovery that when the period of photosynthesis was reduced to a few seconds the carbon dioxide was converted to phosphoglyceric acid. This, then, is the first product of carbon dioxide metabolism. It is readily converted to sugars by a reversal of the early steps of glycolysis (Fig. 109). Where the path of glycolysis involves an oxidation (phosphoglyceraldehyde to phosphoglyceric acid) accompanied by the generation of ATP, the reverse is true of photosynthesis. The conversion of phosphoglyceric acid to sugar requires reducing power and a supply of ATP—and these it will be recalled are precisely the products that appear when chloroplasts are illuminated.

When Calvin allowed longer periods for photosynthesis other products appeared besides phosphoglyceric acid, among them 5, 6, and 7 carbon sugars, amino acids, organic acids, and lipids. From studies of their radioactivity Calvin came to the conclusion that phosphoglyceric acid was formed in a reaction between carbon dioxide and ribulose diphosphate. Ribulose is a pentose (5-carbon sugar) and its diphosphate reacts with carbon dioxide to yield two molecules of phosphoglyceric acid.

$$CO_2 + \text{ribulose diphosphate} \rightarrow 2 \text{ phosphoglyceric acid.}$$

The ribulose diphosphate is furnished by the photosynthetic process itself since it rapidly becomes labelled in experiments with $^{14}CO_2$: the precise pathways involved are still under investigation, but we can now summarise the mechanism of photosynthesis as in Fig. 121.

Fate of the Products of Photosynthesis

It is usual to regard a sugar as the end-product of photosynthesis but glucose does not usually accumulate in quantity in plant cells. To be sure, some glucose may be consumed in respiration as soon as it is formed, but as was pointed out earlier (p. 238) in bright sunlight photosynthesis is several times faster than respiration, and although a portion of the sugar may be consumed in the synthesis of other cell products such as cellulose, it is usual to find some stock-piling of the products of photosynthesis. In dicotyledons this usually takes the form of starch which accumulates in the leaves by day, but is translocated away at night, in the form of soluble sugars, to other parts of the plant. Such leaves show a diurnal variation in starch content. The leaves of many monocotyledons (e.g. *Allium*, *Scilla*) are substantially free of starch, but are rich in sugars, principally sucrose.

Glucose is the starting point for the synthesis of cellulose and other substances found in cell walls. In those parts of a plant which lack chlorophyll, glucose also provides the carbon skeletons of some amino acids. Glutamic acid, for instance, is synthesised from α-ketoglutarate and ammonia (p. 249). The α-ketoglutarate required for this synthesis is derived from glucose by the reactions of glycolysis followed by the first few steps of the Krebs cycle. In like manner glucose is the ultimate source of the carbons in fatty acids. However, in green tissues fats and amino acids may be formed more directly from phosphoglyceric acid without the intervention of a sugar. The fats and amino acids are therefore to be regarded like sugar as primary products of photosynthesis, although they appear in smaller

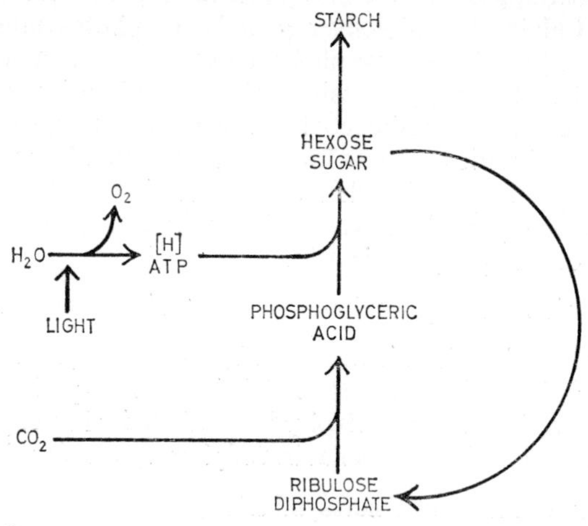

Fig. 121. OUTLINE OF THE BIOCHEMICAL STEPS INVOLVED IN PHOTOSYNTHESIS. To the left is the photochemical process. This results in the formation of ATP and reducing power which are required to drive the cyclic system on the right so causing the fixation of carbon dioxide. [H] represents reducing power.

amount than the sugar. In some algae such as *Vaucheria* the main product of photosynthesis is not sugar but fat.

NITROGEN METABOLISM

Plants contain a great many nitrogen compounds. The proteins, nucleic acids, and chlorophyll are among the most important as judged by their central roles in metabolism. Chlorophyll has already been discussed, the nucleic acids are considered in Chapter 8, and we have here to deal with the proteins. Before considering the nature and metabolism of proteins it is well to be clear about the amino acids of which they are composed.

Amino Acids

The amino acids found in plants are relatively small organic molecules which have a terminal acidic (—COOH) group and a subterminal or α-amino ($—NH_2$) group. A generalised formula is $R.CH\,NH_2.COOH$ where R can stand for any one of a variety of aliphatic or aromatic groups. About seventy-five different amino acids have now been recognised in plants and the number is still rising as chromatographic methods are applied to more and more plants, but fortunately we need only concern ourselves here with the twenty which are components of proteins. A few examples must suffice to show the range of structures encountered. The simplest of the amino acids is glycine and there are several with an aliphatic chain, such as leucine. The chain may bear a reactive group as in serine or cysteine.

Glycine	$H.CHNH_2.COOH$
Leucine	$\begin{matrix} CH_3 \\ CH_3 \end{matrix} \rangle CH.CH_2.CHNH_2.COOH$
Serine	$HOCH_2.CHNH_2.COOH$
Cysteine	$HSCH_2.CHNH_2.COOH$
Glutamic acid	$COOH.CH_2.CH_2.CHNH_2.COOH.$

Most of these α-amino acids have simply the one carboxylic acid group and the amino group adjacent to it, but there is an important group of amino acids which bear an extra acidic group; glutamic acid is one of these, and its amide, glutamine is also found in proteins.

Nitrogen enters plant metabolism in the form of nitrate or more rarely ammonium ions, which are absorbed by the roots. Nitrates are reduced to ammonium ions and from them amino acids are synthesised. If the reduction of nitrate takes place in the roots by reducing power generated in respiration (Fig. 110), there will then be little free nitrate in the shoot tissues. In some plants, nitrate is translocated to the leaves and is there reduced in the light by reducing power generated from water (Fig. 121).

The main point of entry of nitrogen into the amino acids seems to be the process in which α-ketoglutaric acid is reduced and aminated to yield glutamic acid

$$\underset{\alpha\text{-ketoglutaric acid}}{\begin{matrix} COOH \\ | \\ CO \\ | \\ CH_2 \\ | \\ CH_2 \\ | \\ COOH \end{matrix}} + NH_3 + \underset{\text{coenzyme}}{\text{Reduced}} \rightarrow \underset{\text{glutamic acid}}{\begin{matrix} COOH \\ | \\ CHNH_2 \\ | \\ CH_2 \\ | \\ CH_2 \\ | \\ COOH \end{matrix}} + H_2O + \underset{\text{coenzyme}}{\text{Oxidised}}$$

The reduction is operated by a coenzyme which itself became reduced in the course of respiration. The amino group in glutamic acid may then be transferred to a variety of α-keto acids in a reaction termed transamination, which is catalysed by a transaminase enzyme. Here, for example, is the action of glutamic-pyruvic transaminase:

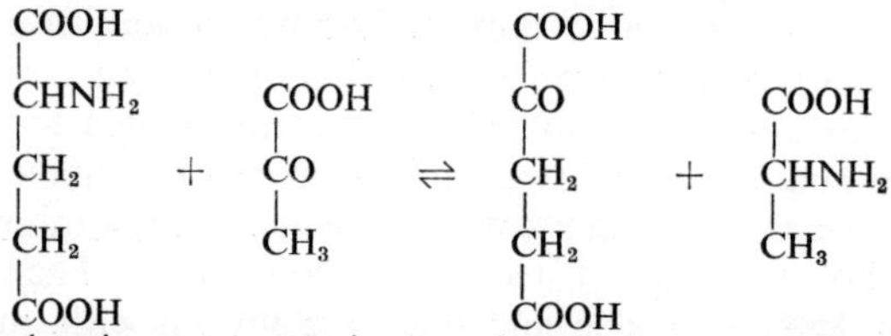

$$\begin{array}{ccccccc}
\begin{array}{l} COOH \\ | \\ CHNH_2 \\ | \\ CH_2 \\ | \\ CH_2 \\ | \\ COOH \end{array} & + & \begin{array}{l} COOH \\ | \\ CO \\ | \\ CH_3 \end{array} & \rightleftharpoons & \begin{array}{l} COOH \\ | \\ CO \\ | \\ CH_2 \\ | \\ CH_2 \\ | \\ COOH \end{array} & + & \begin{array}{l} COOH \\ | \\ CHNH_2 \\ | \\ CH_3 \end{array} \\
\text{glutamic acid} & & \text{pyruvic acid} & & \alpha\text{-ketoglutaric acid} & & \text{alanine}
\end{array}$$

The reaction results in the synthesis of the amino acid alanine at the expense of the amino group in the glutamic acid. Amino acids can condense with one another to form peptides: this is the linkage by which they are united in proteins. The condensation involves elimination of water and the resulting peptide is a linear chain. Thus:

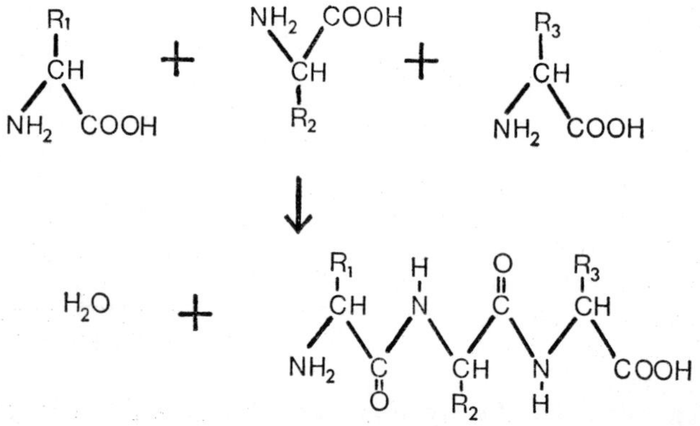

$$\begin{array}{ccccc}
\begin{array}{c} R_1 \\ | \\ CH \\ / \quad \backslash \\ NH_2 \quad COOH \end{array} & + & \begin{array}{c} NH_2 \quad COOH \\ \backslash \quad / \\ CH \\ | \\ R_2 \end{array} & + & \begin{array}{c} R_3 \\ | \\ CH \\ / \quad \backslash \\ NH_2 \quad COOH \end{array}
\end{array}$$

$$\downarrow$$

$$H_2O \quad + \quad NH_2{-}\underset{\displaystyle R_1}{CH}{-}\underset{\displaystyle O}{\overset{}{C}}{-}\underset{\displaystyle H}{N}{-}\underset{\displaystyle R_2}{CH}{-}\overset{\displaystyle O}{C}{-}\underset{\displaystyle H}{N}{-}\underset{\displaystyle R_3}{CH}{-}COOH$$

Proteins are very large molecules which yield amino acids when hydrolysed by acids or under the influence of a protease enzyme. The molecular weight of an amino acid is of the order of 100, while the molecular weight of a protein may be somewhere between 15,000 and 1,000,000. This means that each molecule of protein will contain from 150-1,000 amino acid residues. Analysis of the amino acid content of proteins reveals that proteins differ from one another in the relative proportions of the different amino acids that they contain; one protein may contain a high proportion of alanine, while another has comparatively little. Now since the amino acids are joined to form a continuous peptide chain it follows that proteins can also differ from each other in the order in which the amino acids are arranged in the chain. If a molecule of alanine lies between a serine and a cysteine in one protein (an arrangement which may be coded as S-A-C), a second protein might have a different arrangement, perhaps serine-alanine-leucine (or S-A-L). There are clearly many ways of building up a protein containing 500 amino acids selected from among the twenty different sorts—just as 500 letters of the alphabet can be arranged in many different ways.

A protein then, is a linear chain of amino acids arranged in a particular order. Thanks to the work of Sanger in Cambridge in 1955 we have a means of determining this order and the complete amino acid sequences of some of the simpler proteins have now been published. A linear chain of 500 amino acids would be quite long. From the valency bond angles and inter-atomic distances it can be calculated that each amino acid residue occupies a linear distance of 0·36 mμ. (1 mμ $= 10^{-9}$ metres.) Five hundred of these residues will therefore extend to 180 mμ. Calculations of this sort can be checked against observations of the actual size of protein molecules as seen under the electron microscope. The outcome of such observations is that the molecules are quite short and it follows that the peptide chain must be folded back and forth so that the space it occupies is very much less than its extended length would suggest. Perutz and Kendrew, in Cambridge, have succeeded in elucidating the tortuous foldings of two proteins.

In summary it can be said that protein molecules are complex because they are large and composed of twenty different units (the amino acids). They are specific, one protein differing from another, in part because they differ in amino acid composition and arrangement, and in part because the amino acid chains are differently folded. Many proteins are enzymes and their specificity as enzymes is determined in part by their particular structure (p. 213). If the structure of a protein is altered or destroyed then its activity as an enzyme may be affected. The change is termed **denaturation** and often results in the protein becoming insoluble. Boiling or treatment at somewhat lower temperatures will denature proteins; so will the actions of acids, the salts of heavy metals, detergents, ultra-violet radiation, and violent mechanical actions like stirring, shaking, or causing a foam to appear on a protein solution. Care must always be taken in experiments with enzymes to avoid anything that might cause denaturation.

The mechanism of protein synthesis and its relation to the nucleic acids is discussed later but we may consider here the situations in which protein synthesis is to be found. Growth by cell division obviously requires protein synthesis for proteins are present in the soluble phase of the cytoplasm and also in nucleus, mitochondria, chloroplasts, and several of the other particulate components. The amount of protein per cell continues to increase even in the sub-apical regions where the cells extend in length by vacuolation and the cytoplasm becomes narrowed down to a thin layer between vacuole and wall. This phase of protein metabolism—the rapid synthesis of protein in growing tissues—has been studied mainly in seedlings. Protein is synthesised at the expense of protein reserves in cotyledons or endosperm. The endosperm reserves in barley have an amino acid composition different from that of the proteins of germinating seedlings so that the reserve proteins must be hydrolysed (by protease enzymes) to their constituent amino acids which are translocated to the growing embryo where they, together with some freshly-synthesised amino acids, are reassembled to form the proteins of the growing cells. In mature plant tissues there may be no overall protein synthesis but isotope experiments show that some proteins at least are subject to turnover, being broken down to soluble constituents and then resynthesised. Whether this process applies equally to all the proteins in the cell, and what is its precise significance, are not yet clear. When a leaf reaches the phase of senescence the breakdown process predominates and the protein level falls, a change usually associated with loss of chlorophyll. These changes can be somewhat delayed by applying a synthetic hormone (Chapter 11) to the leaf surface.

NITROGEN FIXATION

All plants require a source of nitrogen from which proteins, nucleic acids, and other organic nitrogenous substances can be synthesised. For the great majority of plants the source is nitrate or ammonia, absorbed from the rooting medium. We are concerned here, however, with a group of organisms that have the power of fixing atmospheric nitrogen, converting it into organic form. A number of micro-organisms have this ability—many blue-green algae and certain bacteria among them (see Chapters 18 and 19), but nitrogen fixation is also a characteristic of some angiosperms, notably the Leguminosae. The legumes bear on their roots numerous swellings or nodules which contain bacteria of the genus *Rhizobium*. Neither legume nor bacterium alone has the power to fix nitrogen—only the bacteria in the environment of the legume nodule can do this.

The bacteria can exist on their own in the soil or in association with a legume in the **nodule**. When a legume is grown in a fertile soil a small proportion of its root hairs become infected by the bacteria which pass in through the root hair and on through adjacent cells, eventually causing some cortical cells to begin dividing. The growing mass of cortical cells forces its way out of the root and becomes organised as a nodule (Fig. 122) with meristematic cells at its apex and a central core of infected tissue consisting of large cells in which the bacteria are situated. The nodule has a limited life, surviving generally for a few weeks or months. The final degeneration of the nodule is signalled by the multiplication of the bacteria which spread to the intercellular spaces. The nodule tissue collapses and the bacteria are released to the soil. Young nodules are white in colour. When they start fixing nitrogen they become red due to the presence of haemoglobin, and on senescence this is converted to a green substance. The biochemical significance of the haemoglobin is not yet clear.

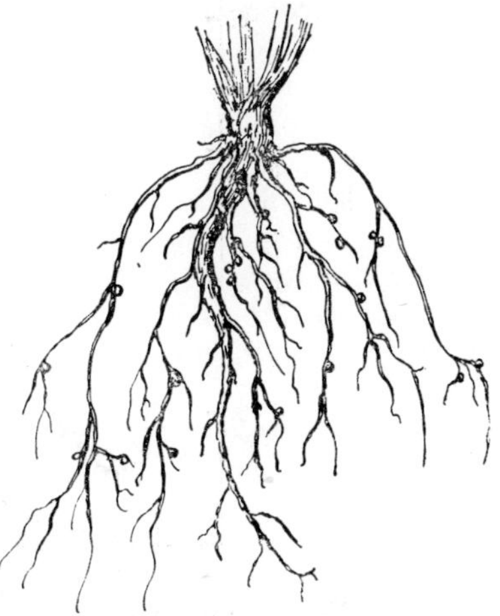

Fig. 122. Diagrammatic view of the root system of a leguminous plant showing root nodules.

The nitrogen content of the nodules increases in the early stages of their growth (Fig. 123). It is likely that during infection and nodulation the bacteria commandeer nitrogen from the host plant, but later in development the nodules do not gain much in nitrogen, most of what is fixed being passed on to the host plant. Experiments with isotopically labelled nitrogen indicate that the first product of nitrogen fixation in nodules is ammonia which is rapidly incorporated into amino acids. The fate of these amino acids can be investigated by collecting some of the xylem sap that exudes from the stump of a pea plant from which the shoot has been severed. The sap of nodulated plants has a higher amino acid content than the sap of control plants which lacked nodules because they were grown in a soil free of *Rhizobium*. Amino acids formed in the nodule are evidently passed to the xylem and so distributed through the host plant.

The relationship between *Rhizobium* and host is a reciprocal one—a symbiosis in which each partner benefits from the activity of the other. The host obviously gains fixed nitrogen from the bacteria in the nodule, while the bacteria rely on the host for carbohydrate. The closeness of this reliance can be judged from the

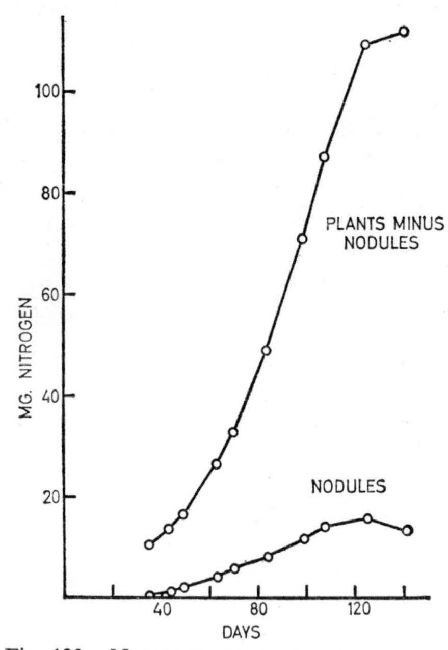

Fig. 123. NITROGEN FIXATION IN SOYA BEANS.

Seeds were dipped in a suspension of *Rhizobium* and then grown, eight to a pot, in nitrogen-free sand. Plants were sampled at various intervals. The nodules were excised and the nitrogen content of nodules and of plants minus nodules was determined. The results are shown above. The original seeds contained 11·3 mg. nitrogen per seed.

No nitrogen was fixed in the first thirty-five days as the plants then contained 11·4 mg. nitrogen, but the total nitrogen content was higher at each subsequent analysis. Nitrogen fixation takes place in the nodules but they retain relatively little, most of the nitrogen being passed on to the remainder of the plant. By contrast, there was no increase in the nitrogen content of control plants which were not inoculated with bacteria and therefore formed no nodules; after 112 days they still only contained 10·6 mg. nitrogen per plant. Data of Bond, 1936.

fact that the decay of nodules is accelerated if their supply of carbohydrate from the host is reduced as may happen if the leaves are shaded or reduced in size by mowing or grazing.

The economic importance of nitrogen fixation by legumes lies in the fact that there is a constant drain on the nitrogen of agricultural land, every crop taken from the soil removing in its protein some nitrogen from the field. In addition, nitrate is easily leached from soils by rain. The nitrogen that is removed can be replaced by spreading manures or fertilisers over the land—or by growing a leguminous crop. The combined nitrogen of the nodules is released into the soil at the time when the nodules decay. If cattle are grazed on the crop they will hasten nodule decay and also spread some of the fixed nitrogen in their faeces.

MINERAL NUTRITION

Seeds can be grown in distilled water, but even if the resulting seedlings are given adequate illumination they will not grow to maturity, for they need a supply of mineral nutrients in the rooting medium, and although the seed must contain some salts the supply is not sufficient for long-continued growth. It has already been pointed out that chemical analysis of a plant reveals the presence of many chemical elements (Table 2), but it does not make clear whether

TABLE 2

WEIGHTS OF THE ELEMENTS PRESENT IN MATURE MAIZE PLANTS

All figures are averages for five plants. Average dry weight of a plant was 835·9 g. Data of Miller, 1938.

ELEMENT	WEIGHT grams	PER CENT. OF TOTAL DRY WEIGHT
Oxygen	371·4	44·43
Carbon	364·2	43·57
Hydrogen	52·2	6·24
Nitrogen	12·2	1·46
Phosphorus	1·7	0·20
Potassium	7·7	0·92
Calcium	1·9	0·23
Magnesium	1·5	0·18
Sulphur	1·4	0·17
Iron	0·7	0·08
Silicon	9·8	1·17
Aluminium	0·9	0·11
Chlorine	1·2	0·14
Manganese	0·3	0·04
Undetermined	7·8	0·93

they are all truly *required* by the plant or whether they have entered the plant simply because they were present in the soil. We can determine which elements are strictly necessary by growing plants in nutrient cultures, that is to say, in solutions of known composition. Simple experiments can be devised in which young seedlings (cereals or *Helianthus*) or alternatively *Tradescantia* cuttings are held in the corks of culture bottles so that their roots dip into culture solutions. The region of the stem passing through the cork must be kept dry to prevent the growth of moulds, and the bottles should be wrapped in dark paper to stop algal growth. The solutions will need to be aerated from time to time and should be renewed every four or five weeks. Plants grown under these conditions and placed in the light will make satisfactory progress as judged by colour, growth in length, and dry weight, if the culture medium contains certain elements, notably nitrogen, phosphorus, potassium, calcium, magnesium, and sulphur. These elements are essential for without them a plant cannot complete its life-cycle, that is to say it will not grow into a healthy adult plant that flowers and sets seed. Moreover, these are **macronutrients** which means that they are required in relatively large amounts. The need for a further group of essential elements, the **micronutrients** is only revealed if highly purified chemicals are used and great care is taken in setting up the experiments. The list of micronutrients is a fairly long one and includes boron, copper, iron, manganese, molybdenum, and zinc. These substances are only required by plants in very small amounts, and indeed high concentrations may prove toxic. Sprays of 5 per cent. copper sulphate solution, for instance, are lethal to dicotyledonous weeds, and have, in fact, been used as herbicides. Nutrient culture experiments reveal also that some of the elements that appear in plants are not really necessary for their growth. This is true of silicon which is present in fair quantity in the leaves of grasses (Table 2) and stem of *Equisetum*, and of sodium which is not required by land plants, although it may promote growth in cases of potassium shortage.

Plants grown in a medium containing one salt alone, say potassium sulphate, succumb sooner than those grown in distilled water. Potassium sulphate, however, is not toxic when it is present as one constituent of a complete culture solution, and indeed experiment shows that the addition of a second salt, especially the salt of a divalent metal such as magnesium, will counteract the toxicity of the potassium salt. Evidently the various nutrients must be present in balanced proportions; the solution is then said to be physiologically balanced.

Functions of the Mineral Elements in Plants

Our knowledge of the roles that mineral elements play in plant life is derived from two sources. On the one hand, as soon as we find that magnesium, for example, is a constituent of chlorophyll, it becomes clear that magnesium is involved in the synthesis of chlorophyll, and that it is also involved in photosynthesis in so far as without magnesium there can be no photosynthesis. We have knowledge of this sort for phosphorus also, since it is involved in processes of energy transfer (p. 227) and the mere fact that inorganic phosphates appear as intermediates in photosynthesis and respiration denotes a function in these pathways of metabolism. Likewise we can say that calcium is involved in cell wall metabolism since it appears in the form of calcium pectate in the middle lamella, and that sulphur, like nitrogen, is involved in protein metabolism since it appears in proteins. A number of elements are constituents of enzymes or enzyme activators: in this group fall iron, manganese, magnesium, molybdenum, and zinc.

The metabolic approach to function, however, fails us when we come to potassium which is one of the most abundant elements in plant ash (Table 2). So far as is known all the potassium of plant cells is present as the free inorganic ion so that we cannot say it is involved in any particular aspect of metabolism. True, there is some evidence of a function for potassium as an enzyme activator but its concentration in plants seems far higher than would be required for such a function. The problem is somewhat deepened by the fact that potassium seems to have some special significance for plants since they contain some ten times as much potassium as sodium, while in animals the two elements appear in roughly equal amounts. Some insight into the role of potassium may be gained by a second type of approach—the study of plants growing in media that are potassium deficient. What symptoms do such plants show and how could these symptoms be caused? In potassium deficiency the water content of leaves is reduced and ultimately the apices and margins of the older leaves wither. It seems possible that potassium makes an important contribution to vacuolar osmotic pressure so that disturbed water relations result when potassium is deficient. Another function that has been suggested for potassium is the maintenance of ionic balance in the cytoplasm. The study of deficiency symptoms may also enlarge knowledge gained from strictly metabolic studies. Thus chlorophyll contains magnesium and in magnesium deficiency plants become chlorotic; they are typically pale green in colour or even yellow. However, chlorosis also develops when there is a deficiency of iron or manganese: from which it can be deduced that these elements or their compounds must somehow be concerned with the synthesis of chlorophyll.

Deficiency symptoms are therefore important because they may give a lead on the metabolism of mineral nutrients, but they also have a practical value because they may be clear enough to enable one to diagnose deficiencies in the field. The symptoms of a particular deficiency may vary somewhat from one plant species to another but standard descriptions and photographs are available for many of the major crop plants suffering from a variety of deficiencies and these may help in diagnosis. The task is, of course, made harder by the fact that a particular symptom such as chlorosis may have several possible causes. If more than one element is deficient then again correct interpretation of the symptoms observed may be very difficult.

The Soil as a Source of Inorganic Nutrients

The soil is not only important to plants as a source of water, it also serves as a reservoir of nitrogen and mineral substances. Chemical analysis of a soil reveals the presence of nitrogen and other plant nutrients greatly in excess of the requirements of crop plants, and yet these frequently show a response to nitrogen and mineral fertilisers. Manifestly, therefore, the soil is unable to supply their needs.

So far as the supply of nitrogen is concerned, we should note first that nitrogen is not strictly a "mineral" element—only in a few parts of the world, *e.g.* Chile, can nitrates be mined from the soil. Most of the nitrogen of the soil is present in the bodies of bacteria and fungi, in Protozoa and larger animals, and in partially decomposed plant and animal remains. Only a small amount is present in the forms that plant roots can absorb—nitrate and ammonia. The supply of soluble nitrogen compounds in the soil is continually replenished through the activities of soil microorganisms (Chapter 19).

The ultimate source of the other plant nutrients is the mineral skeleton of the soil. The fact that soils containing plenty of plant nutrient might yet be unable to supply the needs of plants led to the idea that the nutrients in the soil could be divided into those which were available and those in the rock fragments that were unavailable. As the available nutrients were absorbed they were replaced more or less rapidly by the chemical breakdown of mineral particles. This concept may be illustrated by an experiment in which plants were grown under greenhouse conditions in pots of soil. Each pot contained 400 μg. (1 μg. $= 10^{-6}$ gram) available phosphorus in the soil solution. The plants were analysed after forty days and it was then found that each contained 200,000 μg. phosphorus. Assuming a steady rate of uptake this means that the plants each absorbed 5,000 μg. phosphorus per day from the soil. But the soil only had 400 μg. available phosphorus—so that the supply of available phosphorus must have been consumed and replenished from the unavailable phosphorus on average twelve times a day. The rate at which unavailable nutrients become available is one factor determining the nutrient-supplying power of the soil. Of the two main types of mineral particle in the soil, sand and clay, the former consists of almost pure silica and can therefore yield only a negligible amount of nutrients. It is otherwise with clay. Clay particles are not only chemically complex but very reactive both chemically and physically. Associated with the clay particles are ions of the important bases, potassium, magnesium, and calcium, and these form a source from which the available nutrients in the soil can be replenished. Soils with a high proportion of clay are therefore generally richer than sandy soils in plant nutrients. Of the bases associated with clay, calcium in amount generally exceeds the sum of all the others.

Under conditions of heavy rainfall some of the bases associated with the clay go into solution and are carried away in the drainage water. This loss is chiefly of calcium. If the soil, as frequently happens, contains a reserve of calcium carbonate, the calcium ion lost by the clay will be replaced by calcium from this reserve and the soil will remain unaltered in character. If no reserve of this type is present, the lost calcium ions will be replaced by hydrogen ions and the soil will become acid. A high degree of acidity develops more rapidly in sandy than in clay soils and is most likely when the parent rock material from which the soil has been derived has a low content of calcium. Different plants differ in their tolerance of soil acidity. Thus oats and potatoes will grow in soils too acid for wheat, barley, or clover, but most plants can grow in a moderately acid soil. If the acidity becomes very pronounced it may affect the plants noticeably and in a variety of ways.

Acidity may have a direct effect on plant growth, but its indirect effects are probably more important. Thus acidity increases the solubility of the aluminium and manganese compounds in the soil, and so the plant may suffer from an excessive supply of these substances, which, except in low concentrations, are toxic. Extreme acidity, particularly on sandy soils, to the extent that it reflects a severe loss of bases (especially calcium) from the soil, may be accompanied by a calcium deficiency, an inability of the soil to supply the plant with sufficient calcium. This, however, is unusual. Finally, acid soils are often infertile largely because they form an unfavourable medium for the activity of beneficial nitrifying and nitrogen fixing bacteria (Chapter 19).

Under natural conditions the nitrogen and minerals absorbed from the soil are returned to it in the form of dead plant and animal remains, and excreta (although some nitrogen may be lost as ammonia). Hence the soil is not depleted of these substances except by drainage losses. Nitrates are readily washed out of the soil but losses of the other inorganic nutrients are not very large because they are held by the colloidal humus and clay in the soil.

When crops are taken from a soil there is a removal of the minerals and nitrogen that the plants had absorbed. These losses can be made good by manuring or fertilising the soil. **Manures** supply plant and animal matter to the soil as well as mineral nutrients and so contribute ultimately to its humus content. **Fertilisers** are relatively concentrated sources of mineral nutrient. They may be of natural origin like hoof and horn, a nitrogenous fertiliser which is slowly decomposed by soil micro-organisms supplying soluble nitrogen over a long period; or synthetic products such as ammonium sulphate (a by-product of the coal industry) to which plants respond very quickly. The nutrients that most commonly become deficient under field conditions are nitrogen, phosphorus, and potassium. The bulk of the fertiliser industry is concerned with the supply of these nutrients. Occasionally a soil is encountered with a serious deficiency of some micro-nutrient. Large areas in Australia were unproductive until it was discovered that they were molybdenum deficient. The application of as little as one ounce of molybdenum sulphate per acre is sufficient to overcome the deficiency.

The response of a crop to manures and fertilisers depends on the amount supplied (Fig. 124). Above a certain level saturation is reached, further applications then showing no increased return in crop yield. Too large a dose of one nutrient (in the form of a fertiliser) may indeed create fresh problems, for a nutrient that was formerly present in adequate supply may now become deficient: the various nutrients must be present in balanced amounts.

Different plants are found to vary in the readiness with which they absorb various elements. This is one of the reasons for the adoption in agriculture of the practice known as "rotation of crops". By this we mean that a variety of crops are grown in a rotation extending over some years on any particular plot of land instead of the same crop being grown year after year.

A typical four-course rotation would be wheat, roots, barley, clover, in this order. It should be noted that the farmer includes as "roots" not only mangels, swedes, and sugar-beet, but also other crops not grown for their roots such as potatoes, cabbage, kale, etc.

The clover is generally red clover (*Trifolium pratense*) and is grown in admixture with rye-grass (*Lolium* sp.). It will occupy the ground usually for one year only after the barley. However, the "clover" crop may include white clover (*Trifolium repens*) and also a number of species of grasses, and remain in possession of the land for several years before being ploughed up in preparation for the succeeding wheat crop. In some districts lucerne (*Medicago sativa*) may be grown instead of clover. A rotation of this sort must not be thought of as something rigid. In practice it is adjusted to suit the prevailing conditions. Thus wheat or oats may replace barley, two or three cereal crops may be grown in succession, or an additional

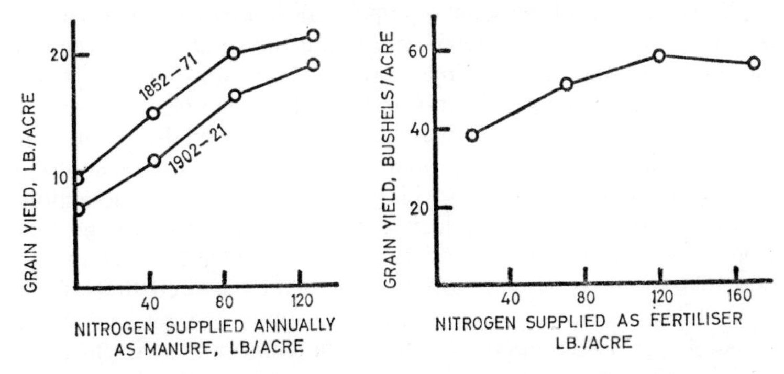

Fig. 124. RESPONSE TO INCREASED DOSES OF MANURE OR FERTILISER. *Left*, the effect of manure on wheat crops grown on Broadbalk Field at Rothamsted Experimental Station, over two twenty-year periods. This field had received no nitrogen since 1839. *Right*, response of maize plants to a nitrogen fertiliser. From Russell, 1952.

crop (peas, carrots, or other vegetable) may be interpolated in the succession of crops.

The leguminous crop of clover or lucerne not only provides fodder for animals but adds to the store of nitrogen and humus in the soil, and so benefits the following wheat crop. This beneficial effect of clover was known to the Romans but the reasons for it were not understood until much later (p. 252). Further, the mixed crop of clover and grasses is found to improve the soil structure, encouraging crumb formation. Any available animal manure is generally applied to the root crop, the other crops utilising any residual manurial effect of this and receiving applications of fertiliser. Thus the rotation results in an economical and efficient use of manure. Economy of manure is not, however, the only reason for this practice. Because different types of crop require cultivation at different seasons of the year, a rotation of crops gives the maximum opportunity for weed eradication. By depriving pests and disease-causing organisms of their suitable hosts, it reduces the losses of crop due to these causes. If several types of root crop are grown, it is possible to arrange that no plot carries the same root crop oftener than once in eight or even twelve years, and this helps to keep in check diseases like club-root (due to the fungus *Plasmodiophora brassicae*) which confines its attacks to members of the Cruciferae, and pests such as potato eelworm.

The Mechanism of Salt Uptake

Soils consist of various organic and inorganic materials, an aqueous phase surrounding or immersing the solid particles and a gas phase at least in the upper layers of the soil. The aqueous phase contains mineral salts in solution. It is the immediate source of the water—and also of the minerals—absorbed by plants. It might be thought that the plant would simply take up the solution around its roots thereby absorbing water and salts in one action. There is, however, much evidence against this view. In the first place, if the salts entered passively with soil water then we should find that the mineral composition of a plant mirrored that of the soil. If the soil had a high potassium content, then the plants would also. Table 3 presents some data from an experiment from

TABLE 3

THE UPTAKE OF CATIONS BY DIFFERENT PLANTS FROM THE SAME CULTURE SOLUTION

Plants were grown from seed in a nutrient solution containing equal amounts of sodium, potassium, magnesium, and calcium ions. After two months the plants were analysed and the proportions of each cation present determined. Data of Collander, 1941.

	PER CENT. OF CATION PRESENT			
	SODIUM	POTASSIUM	MAGNESIUM	CALCIUM
Original culture solution	25	25	25	25
Helianthus (sunflower)	2·3	54	17	27
Pisum (pea)	6·0	62	12	20
Zea (maize)	2·9	70	16	11
Plantago maritima	28·5	39	11	21

which it is clear that plants are selective as regards which salts they will absorb, and moreover, all plants do not make the same selection. It is interesting to find that a maritime plant (the last on the list) shows a strong preference for sodium. A second point concerns the relative concentration of salts within a plant and in the solution outside it. If salts entered cells passively along with the water, we should expect that the final concentration inside the cells and outside would be the same, as this is a characteristic feature of movement by diffusion. What is the evidence? The clearest and neatest experiments have been done, not with intact plants, or even whole roots, but with slices or discs of storage tissue such as beetroot or carrot. It is worth noting that such discs of tissue will take up salts from the external solution even though there is no concomitant water uptake comparable to the transpiration stream in an intact plant. In one experiment a gram of carrot tissue was sliced and placed in 17 ml. of 0·005 M. potassium chloride solution. At the end of two days most of the salt had been taken up from the solution and now resided within the tissue; the concentration of potassium chloride within the tissue had risen until it was approximately 1,000 times that in the external solution. Diffusive movement of salt could never end in such inequality. Finally a theoretical point. When salts are absorbed by tissue discs they enter the vacuoles of the cells. This means that they must pass in turn across plasmalemma, the main body of the cytoplasm and then the tonoplast; and this constitutes as we have seen (p. 182) a semi-permeable membrane. Water can diffuse through such a membrane and indeed does so when a flaccid cell is placed in water; but the very name "semi-permeable" denotes that solutes are unable to diffuse through the cytoplasm with its boundary membranes (some exceptions are noted on p. 186).

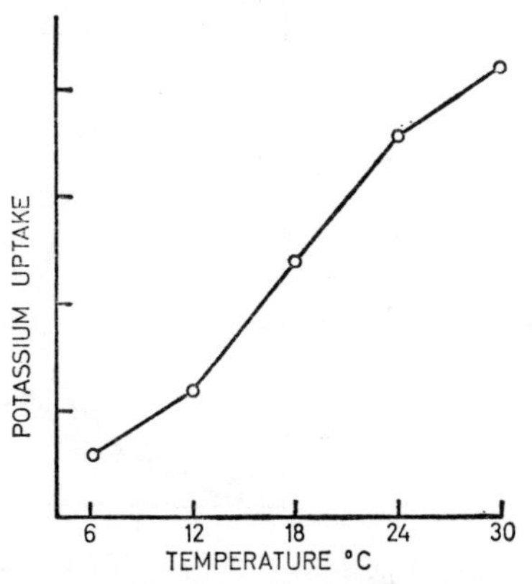

Fig. 125. THE EFFECT OF TEMPERATURE ON THE UPTAKE OF POTASSIUM BY EXCISED BARLEY ROOTS.
Data of Hoagland, 1944.

It follows, if diffusion cannot account for the uptake of salts, that there must be some active force driving salts *into* the vacuoles. Once they are inside they will remain there simply because the barrier prevents their egress. The barrier pumps salts into the vacuole, even against a concentration gradient. To do this the barrier must expend energy and we could well anticipate that a supply of high-energy phosphate (p. 227) would be necessary. Experiment shows that, as expected, salt uptake stops if the tissue is deprived of oxygen. Further, the uptake of salts is influenced by temperature with a Q_{10} of about 2 (Fig. 125). The evidence all combines to imply that there is a pump situated at the barrier, operated by some biochemical mechanism and powered with respiratory energy. Beyond this, we cannot yet go with certainty, but current research may soon reveal the precise nature of the pump.

What has been said so far centres around the uptake of salts by individual cells and we should next place it in the context of the entire plant rooted in soil. Salts pass across the root towards the stele, some being absorbed and passed into the vacuoles of cortical cells. The remainder penetrate the stele and are transferred to the xylem vessels and tracheids in which they are carried up to the shoot (p. 187). The details of this transverse passage of salts across the

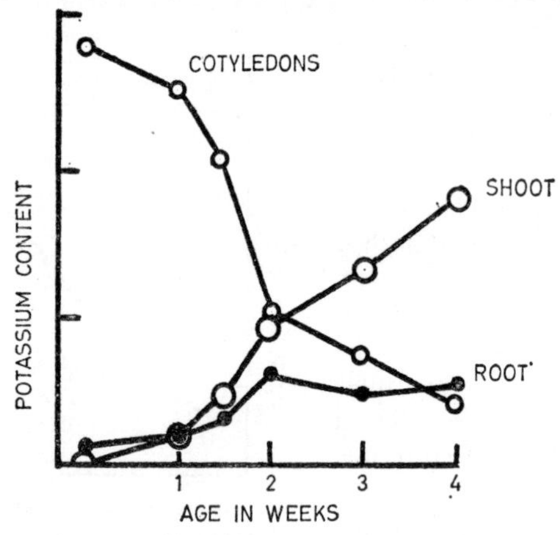

Fig. 126. MOVEMENTS OF POTASSIUM IN GERMINATING PEAS GROWN FOR FOUR WEEKS AT 20° C. IN THE DARK IN THE ABSENCE OF SUPPLIED POTASSIUM. POTASSIUM STORED IN THE COTYLEDONS IS TRANSFERRED TO THE ROOT AND SHOOT SYSTEMS AS GERMINATION PROGRESSES.

Data of Sutcliffe, 1962.

root are still obscure. It is not clear whether the salts pass through the cortex simply in the wet cell walls of cortical cells or whether they move in the cytoplasm passing from one cell to the next through the plasmodesmata. The mechanism of transfer from living cells into tracheids and vessels is not completely understood; nor is the role of the thickened cells and passage cells in the endodermis. Once in the xylem, mineral salts are distributed throughout the shoot system of the plant.

During the course of development there is often a redistribution of some mineral salts in the plant. In particular, as leaves senesce they commonly lose some salts, presumably by phloem transport out of the leaf. In a few instances the fate of this salt has been studied in detail. When the inflorescence and grain develop in oat plants they draw phosphate not from the soil, but from the senescing leaves. Under conditions of mineral shortage this sort of redistribution can be very marked. It is the old leaves of a plant that first show symptoms of potassium deficiency because their potassium is translocated to supply the apex. Likewise, potassium is readily translocated out of the cotyledons of a germinating pea (Fig. 126). Potassium and also phosphate are relatively mobile ions. On the other hand, iron and calcium are less mobile and a deficiency of these elements first declares itself in the young leaves at the apex.

HETEROTROPHIC NUTRITION

The pathways of metabolism that have been described so far (apart from nitrogen fixation) are found alike in angiosperms and other green plants. Some aspects of photosynthesis, for instance, have now been studied in a wide variety of green plants and there is good evidence, for one thing, that phosphoglyceric acid is the first product of photosynthesis in each of them. As regards respiration, the majority of investigations have been made with angiosperm material, often seedlings or fruits or storage organs, this choice being dictated by ease of supply and economic importance: however, it is again broadly true that the same pathways of metabolism are found when respiration is studied in different tissues or in different organisms. Furthermore, although our knowledge of processes like protein synthesis or lignin synthesis is far from complete (rather few tissues have been investigated in any detail) the results to date do encourage the view that they always proceed by the same pathways. It is findings such as these that justify attempts to chart the pathways of metabolism in living cells. A much simplified chart for plant cells is shown in Fig. 127. Sugars are used on the one hand for syntheses (some of them involving mineral nutrients) and on the other for respiration to supply energy. As it stands this pattern of events applies to many organisms. What the diagram does not show is the origin of the sugar and this is the issue that we must next take up.

In green plants sugar is produced by photosynthesis, but there are two other means by which it can be obtained. One, known as chemosynthesis, is found only in certain bacteria and discussion of it is postponed to Chapter 19. The second source of sugar is the external environment. We have here the essential difference between the nutrition of plants and animals. Green plants are said to be

autotrophic because they synthesise their own carbohydrate and are to this extent self-sufficient. Animals, on the other hand, are **heterotrophic** requiring carbohydrate in their food. They may use soluble sugars present in their environment or, like man, eat plant foods which contain sugar and starch, the latter being hydrolysed to sugar in the alimentary canal. It must not be supposed that this typically animal type of nutrition is confined to animals for it is also the mode of nutrition of all the fungi. They obtain carbohydrates from the environment, store some within the hyphae, utilising the

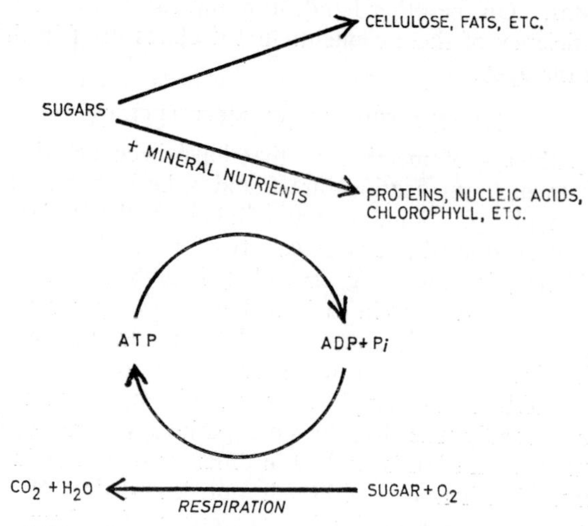

Fig. 127. DIAGRAM TO SUMMARISE THE MAIN PATHWAYS OF METABOLISM IN PLANT CELLS.

The sugars are the starting points for syntheses of substances which like the sugars contain only carbon, hydrogen, and oxygen and for syntheses in which various of the mineral elements are also involved. All the syntheses are promoted by catalysts (the enzymes) and by a supply of energy in the form of high-energy phosphate which is generated in the respiratory oxidation of sugars.

remainder in synthetic processes or in respiration or fermentation to provide energy. Most of the bacteria are likewise heterotrophic, although a number are capable of photosynthetic processes; these differ somewhat from thc photosynthesis of green plants and are discussed in Chapter 19.

Heterotrophy is the most usual mode of nutrition in organisms that lack chlorophyll, while green plants are autotrophic. In a single-celled organism like *Chlorella* or an algal filament (*Spirogyra*) every cell is green, capable of photosynthesis, and so autotrophic. However, in angiosperms the situation is more complex. As a whole, the typical angiosperm is undoubtedly autotrophic, producing sugars in photosynthesis and absorbing none from the environment. But if we look closer we must realise that many individual angiosperm cells lack chlorophyll. The cells of the leaf epidermis (apart from the guard cells of the stomata) and the cells of the root system below ground are incapable of photosynthesis and so must rely on a supply of sugar synthesised in the light by green cells. We can say that an angiosperm is a mosaic of autotrophic and heterotrophic parts, the former supplying the latter so as to make the organism as a whole autotrophic. Sometimes, when seeds are sown, seedlings appear which are yellow in colour because they lack chlorophyll altogether. Such albino plants are genetic mutants. If left to themselves, even in the light they would eventually die when the carbohydrate reserves of the seed had been exhausted. Their life can, however, be spared if they are fed with sugar so making them heterotrophs. In one experiment albino maize plants were raised to maturity in the dark by immersing the ends of the leaves in tubes of sterile sucrose solution. In like manner, it is now possible to culture the roots of some plants on their own, detached from the shoot. The root is excised under sterile conditions and placed in a petri dish filled with a nutrient medium containing a sugar as well as various inorganic salts, certain vitamins and other growth factors. The whole procedure for culturing roots is very similar to the procedure for culturing a fungus like *Mucor* on a sugar and salts medium. Both detached root and *Mucor* mycelium are heterotrophs and must be supplied with sugars.

Another aspect of heterotrophy in angiosperms should be mentioned here, namely that they obtain at least most of the amino acids they require from their food (the remainder being synthesised by processes like transamination). By contrast, the autotrophs characteristically synthesise their own amino acids from inorganic nitrogen salts.

It was emphasised above that the angiosperms are autotrophic; and so they are, most of them. The sections that follow will describe some biological curiosities—angiosperms which are heterotrophic because they assimilate either carbohydrates or organic nitrogen compounds.

Heterotrophic Angiosperms Lacking Chlorophyll

A few angiosperms have little or no chlorophyll and are therefore practically incapable of photosynthesis. They are classed as parasites which are organisms that obtain their nutriment from other living organisms.

Cuscuta (dodder) is a member of the family Convolvulaceae. The commonest British species are parasites of clover, nettles, hops, gorse, and heather. The seeds contain a thread-like embryo embedded in endosperm. On germination they send a little root into the ground, while the shoot elongates rapidly and at the same time nutates in ever-widening circles (p. 286). If it meets a suitable host plant, the dodder stem twines around the host and develops suckers or haustoria which penetrate into the tissues of the host (Fig. 128). The xylem and phloem of these organs make contact with the xylem and phloem of the host (Fig. 129) and thus the parasite obtains organic substances as well as water and salts. Meanwhile the root of the parasite dies. The thin reddish stem branches copiously and produces small scaly leaves and numerous small clusters of flowers. If the dodder seedling does not reach a suitable host plant it soon dies. However, once they are established, some species of *Cuscuta* grow so vigorously that they may annihilate a crop partly by exhausting the host plants of organic metabolites and partly by shading them from the light.

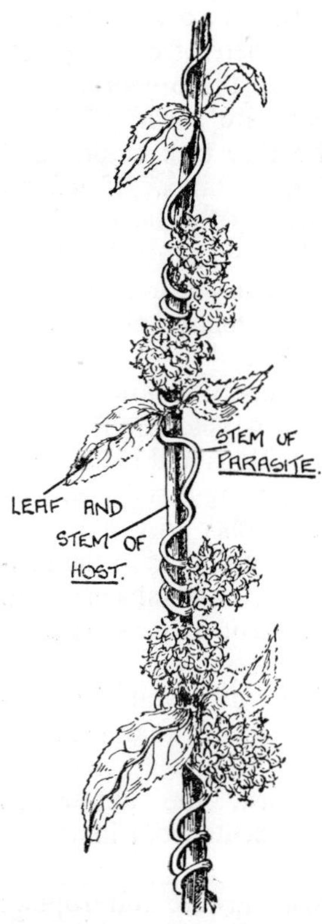

Fig. 128. *Cuscuta* IN FLOWER PARASITISING A STEM OF NETTLE.

Orobanche (broom-rape) and *Lathraea* (tooth-wort) belong to the family Orobanchaceae and are both root parasites. *Lathraea* is a parasite on the roots of hazel, while the British species of *Orobanche* chiefly parasitise the roots of composites and legumes. The seeds of *Orobanche* are very small and will only germinate if close to the roots of a suitable host (apparently because the host roots secrete some germination-promoting substance). The seed puts out a small root which penetrates the roots of the host and forms a sucker that passes through to the stele. The shoot then enlarges, developing into a tuber. In due course the tuber forms erect, scaly, aerial shoots which bear flowers, but are devoid of chlorophyll.

Neottia (bird's-nest orchid) is found growing in the humus of woods. The lower part of the stem is covered with a mass of short, thick roots (hence the name bird's-nest) and the upper part of the stem, ending in a raceme of flowers, bears small yellowish brown scales (Fig. 130). *Neottia* is heterotrophic for it has little or no chlorophyll but unlike *Cuscuta* and *Orobanche* it does not parasitise another angiosperm. The roots of *Neottia* are mycorrhizal (p. 570) and the plant can be said to parasitise the fungus, for the fungus

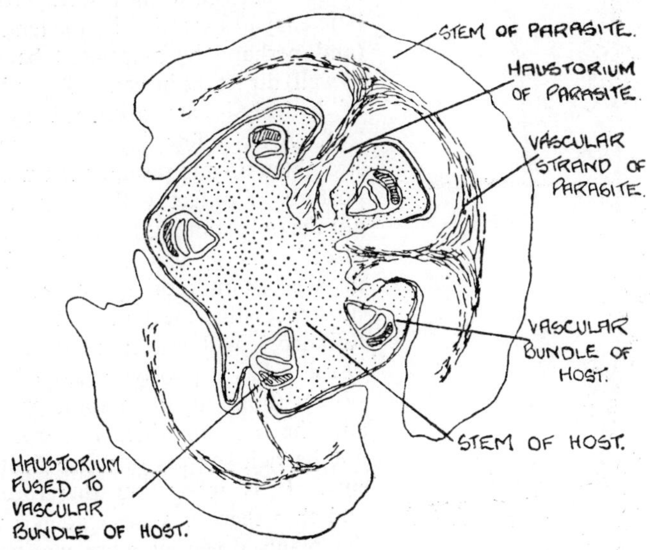

Fig. 129. TRANSVERSE SECTION OF STEM OF A HOST PLANT SHOWING TWINING STEM OF *Cuscuta* AND HAUSTORIA PENETRATING INTO THE HOST TISSUES.

alone has the enzyme equipment needed to make use of the organic substances present in the humus.

Carnivorous Plants

This is a group of plants which capture insects and some other small animals and digest their proteins, absorbing the soluble nitrogen compounds so formed. A few typical genera will be described to illustrate the types of mechanism by which insects are caught.

Drosera grows in bogs, and owes its popular name of sundew to the drops of sticky fluid, secreted by the tentacles, which glisten in the sun like dew (Plate 10). The tentacles stand out from the surface of the leaf and are of two kinds, longer marginal ones, and shorter inner ones. Insects are attracted to the secretion (probably by its appearance and fungus-like odour) and then become stuck to it. The tentacles soon begin to move, the stimulus being transmitted (by means unknown) from one to the next. The curvature of the long marginal tentacles is a nastic one (its direction not being governed by the direction of the stimulus). The tentacles bend over inwards so as to bring the insect towards the shorter tentacles in the course of about an hour. The shorter tentacles exhibit a slow tropic movement towards the insect. Proteolytic enzymes secreted by the tentacles (and perhaps by associated bacteria as well) digest the insect. The products of hydrolysis are absorbed by the leaf. After a few days the tentacles straighten up and resume their normal posture. Contact with an insect is not the only stimulus to cause a curvature; it may also be induced by physical stimuli or by contact with substances like meat or white of egg. Raindrops will not cause curvature. *Drosera* has a poorly developed root system (none at all in some species) and the bogs in which it grows will not be rich sources of mineral nutrients. It is interesting therefore to find that there is some evidence that the plants do grow more vigorously if fed with insects. In some classic experiments made nearly one hundred years ago, a group of plants fed with insects produced four times as much seed in terms of weight as unfed control plants. The dry weight of the winter buds was twice that of the controls.

Fig. 130. *Neottia.*

Dionaea (Venus' fly-trap, Fig. 131) is a native of Carolina, where it grows in peat bogs; it is often cultivated in hothouses. The leaves are two-lobed, and the midrib functions as a hinge. Each lobe bears marginal teeth, and on its upper surface three long sensitive hairs jointed at their bases. When one of these is touched by an insect, the two lobes of the leaf snap together, the marginal teeth cross one another and trap the insect. Digestive glands on the leaf surface secrete enzyme only when stimulated by an insect or a small piece of meat. The leaves are only slightly sensitive to chemical stimuli, but if the closing of the lobes has been caused by an insect they press tightly against each other and hold the insect fast, whereas the closing remains incomplete, leaving a wide space between the lobes, if the hairs have been touched by, say, a pencil. In the latter case the leaf opens again, but if an insect has been caught the leaf remains closed until the digested products have been absorbed.

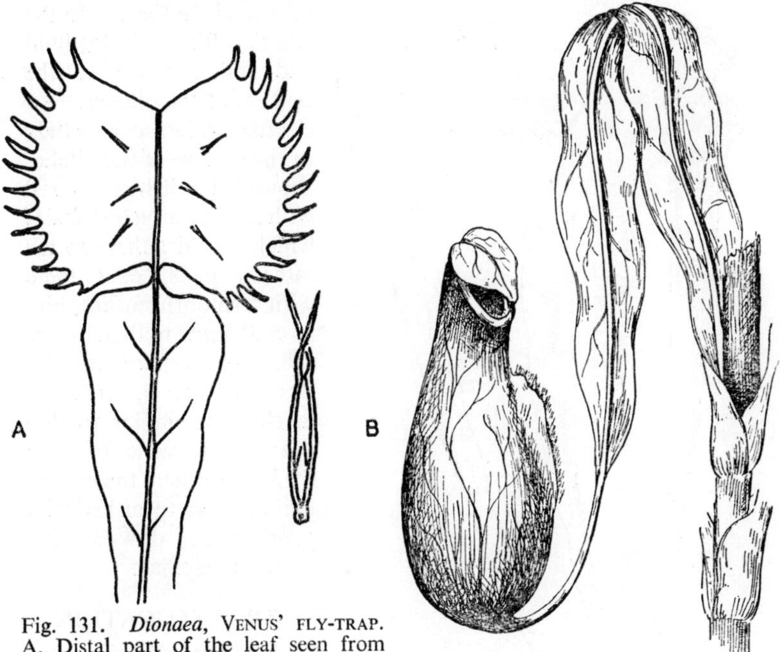

Fig. 131. *Dionaea*, VENUS' FLY-TRAP. A, Distal part of the leaf seen from above with the lobes opened. B, Section of a closed leaf.

Fig. 132. PITCHER OF *Nepenthes*.

Nepenthes (pitcher plant) is a tropical plant with a creeping rhizome from which coarse climbing stems arise. It has long leaves, the midribs of which are extended to form insect-trapping pitchers that may be up to 30 cm. in height (Fig. 132). The tip of the pitcher is closed with a lid in early development. When the lid opens insects can gain entry but the hollow pitcher remains to some extent protected from rain. Insects are attracted to the pitcher by its brilliant colour and by the secretion of nectar. If they once enter the pitcher they are unable to leave but tumble instead into the liquid that fills the lower third where they are drowned and then digested. The liquid contains digestive enzymes (proteases) secreted by cells of the pitcher wall; a flourishing microfauna develops in addition, once the pitcher opens. The collar of the pitcher is armed with sharp barbs that would prevent large insects from escaping. Smaller insects attempting to climb the wall of the pitcher obviously find difficulty in doing so for they wipe their footpads against their mouthparts and abdomen as if to clean them. In the end they lose their foothold and slither down to the bottom of the pitcher. An electron microscope study of the surface of the pitcher showed that it was covered with loosely attached scales which would adhere to the insect's pads, coat them with a smooth surface, and so contribute to their downfall. *Sarracenia* (Fig. 133) has an insect trapping mechanism similar to that of the inflorescence of *Arum* (p. 366), for here the epidermal cells are furnished with prominent downwardly-pointing papillae.

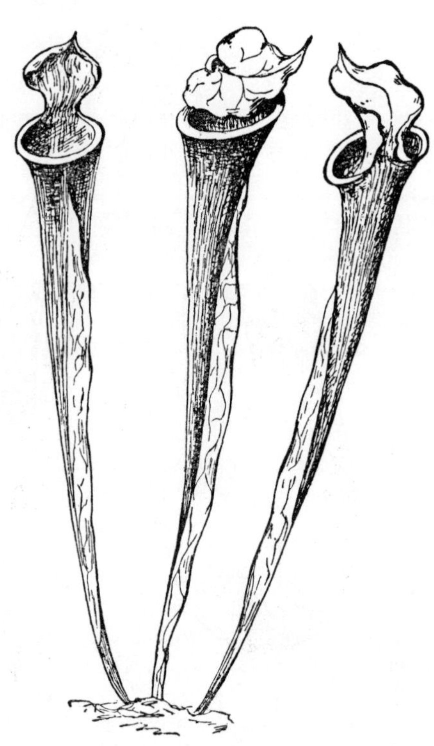

Fig. 133. *Sarracenia*.

TRANSLOCATION

We have so far considered the various aspects of plant metabolism as more or less isolated events, but in the plant their activity is so regulated and co-ordinated as to result in the growth and development that we observe. One aspect of this co-ordination is the movement of substances from place to place within the plant. Water is taken up from the soil by the root system and transported through the xylem to the aerial parts of the plant. Inorganic salts are also absorbed by the roots and supply the whole plant; photosynthesis can only occur in green tissues so that carbohydrates must be transported from these tissues to those which lack chlorophyll.

In addition, there must obviously be a flow towards seeds and fruits which build up reserves of carbohydrate, protein, and fat in varying proportions, and also to underground storage organs. Conversely, when a seed germinates and when a bud bursts, as the shoot within it begins to elongate, there must be a flow of metabolites into the new growth. This movement is termed translocation. We have to consider now what are the channels of transport, what substances are moved in them, and what causes the movement.

Transport in the Xylem

The transpiration stream is a flow of liquid from roots to shoot through the tracheids and vessels of the xylem. Analyses of the xylem sap obtained by centrifuging lengths of stem or by collecting the exudate from decapitated shoots shows that it always contains inorganic salts and may, in addition, bear some sugars and nitrogen compounds. Since inorganic salts and water are both taken up from the soil—although by different mechanisms (compare p. 188 and p. 262)—and since both are moved to the shoot system, the presence of salts in the xylem sap suggests that this is the channel by which they are translocated in the plant. An elegant test of this hypothesis was made by Stout and Hoagland in 1939. A willow cutting was grown in culture solution and allowed to develop three branches. At the start of the experiment a 9-in. slit was made in the bark of two of the shoots and the bark pulled gently away from the wood. A length of waxed paper was inserted between bark and wood in one branch, and the stripped area then wrapped in paper; the second shoot was wrapped up in the same way but with bark and wood in contact with one another, while the third was left as untreated control. A small amount of potassium nitrate containing radioactive potassium was then added to the culture solution and the plants left in the light for five hours. The shoots were then analysed to determine in which tissues the potassium was to be found. Where the bark and wood remained in contact there was no difficulty in detecting radioactivity in the wood—but the bark had an equal radioactivity. However, when the wood and bark were effectively isolated from each other with waxed paper then only the wood became radioactive. It was concluded that potassium had been translocated up from the root system through the xylem and then moved laterally into the cambium and outer tissues. Only when the outer tissues were isolated from the cambium was this lateral transport stopped. It is evident that all the living cells of the shoot must have their complement of inorganic substances. Cells that are formed at the apices of the shoots or in the enlarging leaves lie at the termini of the xylem transport system, but this lateral transfer provides for living cells lower down the shoot.

Transport in the Phloem

Harvey's discovery of the circulation of the blood in 1628 stimulated interest in the mechanism of translocation in plants. The earliest experiments were made by ringing or girdling stems, the outer tissues being completely removed from a short length of stem. The aim in such experiments is to remove just the phloem by cutting away the bark, but in practice it is difficult to avoid damaging the young (outer) xylem cells and in consequence, water movement may be somewhat obstructed. In the course of a few weeks the stem above a ring may grow and swell with an accumulation of sugars. This suggests that sugars produced in the leaves are normally translocated down in the bark, but are forced instead to accumulate if the bark is interrupted by ringing. A more complete picture emerges from measurements made over a short period immediately after the stem has been ringed. In one experiment the stems of a batch of cotton plants were ringed in the morning and plants taken at various intervals over the next twenty hours to determine the sugar content of bark and wood. Above the ring sugars accumulated in both bark and wood, but the level of sugars below the ring declined. The simplest interpretation of these results is that sugars produced in photosynthesis were translocated in the phloem down to the ring and there accumulated in the phloem and adjoining xylem. The decline in sugar level below the ring can be attributed to the normal continuation of downward translocation.

Analyses of the bark of a leafy shoot at various times of day can provide information on the type of sugar that is translocated from the leaves. Since the bark may contain static reserves of sugar, comparison must be made between the sugars present by day and those found at night when photosynthesis will have stopped and translocation of carbohydrate from the leaf will have slowed down. A neater way of separating the translocated sugars from those already present is to expose one leaf of a plant to radioactive carbon dioxide and then determine what labelled carbohydrates appear subsequently in the various parts of the plant. In one experiment a vine leaf was exposed to radioactive carbon dioxide in the light and samples of bark along the stem subsequently harvested for analysis: the major part of the radioactive carbon was found in sucrose with smaller amounts in glucose and fructose. We may therefore conclude that sucrose is the main form in which carbohydrates are translocated in the bark. To ascertain whether the sucrose passes equally through all tissues of the bark or not, we need information about the localisation of sucrose in the bark.

If a shallow, horizontal incision is made into the bark of certain trees (such as *Fraxinus* and *Acer* species) drops of sap will exude. As much as 0·1 ml. can be collected from a cut several centimetres long. The sap has a high sucrose content (up to about 20 g./100 ml.) which suggests that it originates from the translocation stream. The volume of exudate that appears is larger than the volume of the cells that were cut and the mind grasps at the idea that it comes from the sieve tube system—and that this is indeed the channel of translocation. Fortunately, we now have further evidence from recent experiments that make use of the remarkable skill of aphids. The course of the stylets of aphids feeding on plant tissues can be followed by sectioning the tissue. It is then seen that the stylets penetrate between the cells of the outer tissues but ultimately terminate in a sieve tube element. The contents of the sieve tube element pass through the stylets into the body of the aphid. It has been found possible to sever the exposed portion of the stylet of an aphid that has been feeding, so leaving a stump through which the sieve tube sap slowly exudes. The flow may continue for hours or even days. Analysis of this sieve tube sap reveals sucrose as its main constituent.

The movement of nitrogenous substances in plants is rather less well understood than the movement of carbohydrates. In the first place nitrate taken up from the soil may travel in the xylem to the leaves where it forms amino acids and thence proteins; or it may be reduced to the level of amino acid in the roots, before being translocated up the xylem. When leaves become senescent their protein content falls. The proteins are hydrolysed to amino acids which are translocated out of the leaf through the phloem and so to other parts of the plant.

Direction and Rate of Translocation in the Phloem

Translocation in the xylem is powered by the transpiration stream and therefore moves from the root system up to the leaves. Phloem translocation by contrast can proceed in either direction. When a leaf is exposed to radioactive carbon dioxide in the light it forms radioactive sugars, the movements of which can be followed by making autoradiographs. Such studies show that the mature leaves are most active in photosynthesis, sugar from them being moved not only to the roots but also to the younger leaves at the apex which are still expanding. Although the youngest leaves are green and produce some sugars in photosynthesis they are, nevertheless, importers; it is only the older leaves that export products of photosynthesis. It follows that sugars leaving the mature leaves through the phloem may move upwards (to the growing apex) or downwards (to the root system); the same two-way pattern of distribution applies to materials leaving the cotyledons of a seedling.

Observations such as these lead to the generalisation that phloem movement is from regions where metabolites are present in high concentration to regions where they are in low concentration. From a region of production they move to a region of consumption. Thus sugars produced in photosynthesis may be translocated to the root system where they are used up in respiration or converted to some different substance so that the concentration of sugar remains low; they may, for instance, be polymerised to form cellulose in a growing tissue or to form starch in a storage organ.

Movement from regions of high concentration to low is a characteristic of diffusion, and one might therefore expect to find that phloem translocation was simply a matter of diffusion. However, it is known that phloem translocation can be stopped by killing the cells in a length of stem or petiole by scalding with steam. In addition, there are a number of records of inhibitor studies—experiments in which an enzyme poison was applied to a stem or petiole, with the result generally that translocation was slowed down or stopped. Finally, it has been found that translocation rates are influenced by a change in the temperature of the plant. These characteristics demand rejection of the idea that translocation is a simple diffusion process for diffusion would not require the presence of living cells or the activity of enzymes, and it would not be influenced by temperature changes. An even more important criticism is that the rate at which substances are translocated through plant tissues (which may be as high as 100 cm. per hour) is far higher than could be accounted for by diffusion alone.

How then are we to account for translocation in the phloem? This is something that many botanists would like to know, but we have no sure answer yet. Several hypotheses have been proposed, each of them seemingly plausible, and none has yet been decisively proved wrong. One hypothesis requires a mass flow of sieve tube contents through the sieve tube system; this proposal encounters difficulty at the sieve plate for it is not clear whether the sieve pores would allow an unobstructed flow of liquid through them. Electron microscope studies of the fine structure of these pores should lead to a better understanding of their nature and their contents.

It will be recalled that sieve tube elements are unusual in their cytology (p. 41). They are also unusually sensitive, attempts to prepare them for observation under the light microscope often resulting in coagulation of the cytoplasm within the sieve tube elements. The absence of a nucleus from the mature sieve element, and the conspicuous nuclei and dense cytoplasm of the neighbouring companion cells probably have some functional significance. It has been speculated that they may be concerned with the transfer of substances into and out of the sieve elements, for the sieve tube system is only a part of the translocation channel proper. Sugar synthesised in the light in a mesophyll cell of the leaf has to pass through several neighbouring cells (presumably through the plasmodesmata) before it reaches the phloem; entry into the sieve tube transport system may be facilitated by the companion cells. At the other end of its journey the sugar leaves the sieve tube system passing once again from cell to cell to its final destination.

11 GROWTH AND DEVELOPMENT

In everyday speech, the term **growth** means simply the process of getting larger, but botanical usage seeks to limit the term by excluding the osmotic swelling that may occur when cells are placed in water. Such a change in size is of a purely physical nature, and is not regarded as growth.

Growth is defined in terms of size, but the term **development** is used to distinguish the various phases of growth that may occur in the life of a plant: the resting stage, the period of rapid vegetative growth, the appearance of reproductive structures, senescence, and finally death. Growth and development usually occur simultaneously. A plant grows by the development of fresh roots, stems, and leaves. Likewise the growth of an individual cell is accompanied by the development of a thickened wall or a complement of chloroplasts. However, it should be recognised that developmental changes may occur within organs which, as a whole, make little or no growth. Thus in maturing or germinating seeds the embryo itself may grow and enlarge at the expense of the endosperm although the seed as a whole gets no larger.

At the cellular level, two processes are involved in growth and development: cell division and the enlargement of the products of division. Strictly speaking, growth can only occur by cell enlargement for the division of cells does not involve any increase in volume. However, although cells may become ten or fifty times larger as they vacuolate and differentiate it is obvious that this process alone could not account for the continued growth of a plant; there must be cell division as well to provide fresh cells capable of enlargement. Generally cell enlargement follows soon after cell division, as in a growing root or at the shoot apex. However, in the seta of the sporophyte generation of *Pellia* cell division is completed in the autumn, the rapid extension of the seta in the following spring being accomplished solely by cell elongation; it comes to a halt when the cells have finished expansion. The rapid initial elongation of radicle or hypocotyl in some seedlings is a consequence of the elongation of previously formed cells; so also is the rapid growth of the filaments of stamens.

Shoot apices generally remain meristematic for a long period producing fresh internodes and leaves and new shoot systems as they grow. For this reason shoot growth is said to be **indeterminate**. The final shape of a shoot system does not conform to a fixed and rigid pattern; one cannot, for instance, predict the number of branches on a mature oak tree with the same confidence that one could enumerate the number of fins on a fish. Some of the individual organs produced by the apex, however, have determinate growth. This is true, for instance, of the leaves of dicotyledons, of petals, and of fruits. Although the early growth of these organs involves cell division, they possess no permanently meristematic cells and their final growth is accomplished by cell enlargement. Their final shape can be forecast with more accuracy than can the shape of the whole plant that bore them; oak trees may differ markedly in height and branching pattern, but the acorns they produce are very similar.

The study of growth and development proceeds in part at a descriptive level, seeking to observe and describe the changes involved, and in part at an analytical level, trying to find out what factors determine, for instance, when a part of the apical meristem will produce a new shoot, how fast the shoot grows in relation to other parts of the plant, and whether it will bear flowers.

GROWTH RATE

Growth Rate of Unicellular Organisms

The growth of a population of bacteria can be followed by counting under the microscope the number of cells in a known volume of a suitably diluted suspension. When a culture of bacteria is inoculated into a suitable medium there may be an initial lag period before growth starts but the rate of growth soon rises to some level which is maintained until eventually the medium becomes exhausted of nutrients or poisoned by the accumulation of toxic products of metabolism. During the period of steady growth rate the cells grow and divide to produce more growing cells. Growth under these conditions is logarithmic, the number of growing cells increasing according to an exponential series. If there are x cells at time t_1, then when they have all divided there will be $x \times 2$ cells present; and after n divisions, $x \times 2^n$ cells. If r is the number of divisions per unit of time, then at t_2

$$\text{number of cells} = x \times 2^{r(t_2 - t_1)}.$$

The growth of bacteria is often expressed in terms of the **generation time**, the time from one cell division to the next. The generation time varies from one bacterial species to another and depends also on the supply of nutrients, temperature, and aeration. Under optimal conditions the generation time of many bacteria is of the order of 30-60 minutes. For unicellular algae, even with good illumination, the generation time may be as long as a day.

Growth Rate of Vascular Plants

How is the growth rate of a large rooted plant to be measured? Although it is possible to follow the technique for unicells, macerating the tissues with acid to separate the cells from one another and then counting cell number, this is a very tedious way to measure growth and one that is subject to errors arising from the wide range of cell size and shape found in plants. It is far easier to measure the dimensions of a plant or to weigh it, or weigh a part of it. A few

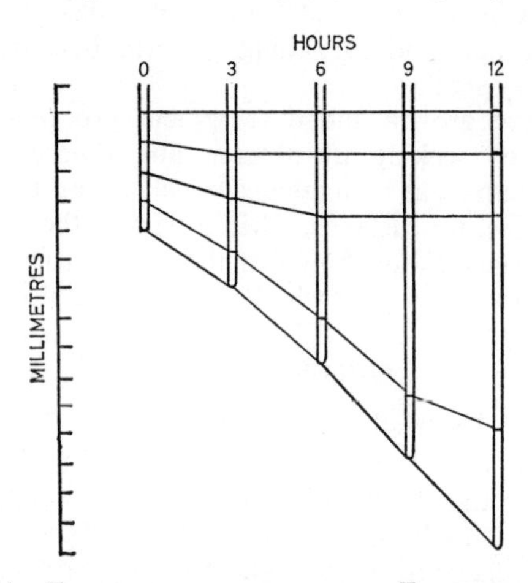

Fig. 134. Elongation of the root of *Zea mays* at 25° C.
Marks were made on the root at 1 mm. intervals and their position recorded at three-hourly intervals. It will be seen that the apical mm. made little growth in the first nine hours, but it then began to expand. The second mm. segment made the most growth, the third and fourth successively less, and in the fifth segment growth had already ceased. Data of Baldovinos, 1953.

examples will illustrate the use of these types of measurement in different situations.

Length measurement has the advantage that it is non-destructive, the same plant being available again and again for a series of measurements so that the whole course of growth can be followed on one plant. It has, obviously, the short-coming that it takes no account of changes in diameter and is therefore most appropriately used for studies on the growth of thin stems, coleoptiles, or roots where growth is mainly a matter of elongation. The growth of roots, in particular, has been studied in this way because the apical region of the root is readily accessible. Marks can be made on the surface of the root at equally-spaced intervals and root growth followed by measuring their subsequent movement. Fig. 134 shows some results obtained with maize roots. It will be seen that most subsequent growth takes place within the second millimetre segment, just behind the apical meristem itself. Because it is a cylindrical object with apical growth, the various stages of development in the root from cell division to final differentiation are spaced out along its length. However, it should be realised that this is a dynamic situation, individual cells passing through each of the stages in their own development: a cell that is cut off from a meristematic cell *now* will be enlarging and becoming differentiated in a few hours' time. The apical region of a maize root produces some 17,500 new cells per hour; each expands about ten-fold in length.

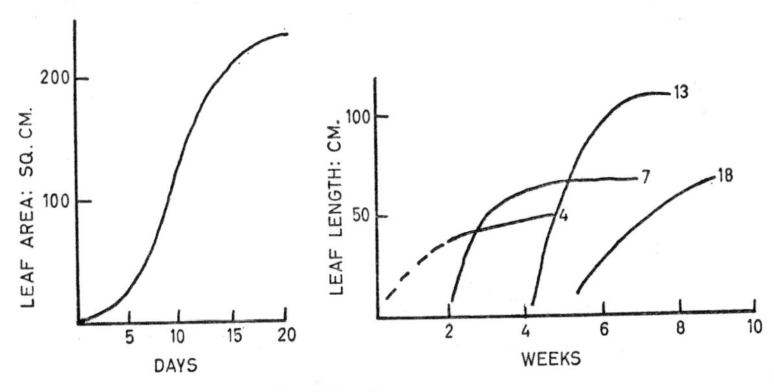

Fig. 135. LEAF GROWTH.
Left: growth in area of a cucumber leaf. *Right:* growth in length of the 4th, 7th, 13th, and 18th leaves of maize. After Gregory, 1921, and Whaley, *et al.*, 1950.

The fact that the photosynthetic capacity of plants depends to an important extent on their leafiness has led to much research on the factors governing leaf growth. The growth of grass or cereal leaves can be quickly assessed by simple length measurements, but other leaves present difficulties. A simple method is to draw an outline of the leaf on graph paper and count the number of squares within the outline, but for more accurate work a blue-print of the leaf is generally made and its area determined with a planimeter. It will be recalled that leaves are organs of determinate or limited growth. The area of a leaf increases slowly at first, then more rapidly until finally it slows down as the leaf reaches its mature size (Fig. 135). This succession of three phases—slow, fast, slow—was named by the nineteenth-century German botanist Sachs the grand period of growth.

Leaves lose water so quickly when they are detached from the plant that weight would not give a reliable estimate of area; but with fruits which generally have a thick cuticle and only lose water slowly, weight provides a convenient measure of growth. The agriculturalist and the market gardener commonly express the yields of their crops in terms of weight or volume; this does not, of course,

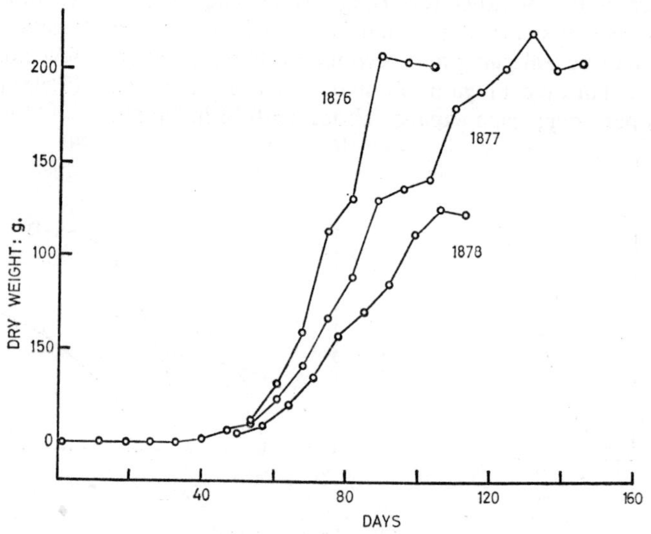

Fig. 136. DRY WEIGHT INCREASE OF FIELD-GROWN MAIZE PLANTS IN THREE SUCCESSIVE YEARS.

Note that the curves are S-shaped (sigmoid) in each year, despite the differences in growth rate and in final yield. The graphs are drawn with an arithmetic scale of weight; this does not permit display of the changes in dry weight that occurred early in germination. The initial dry weight was 0·33 g. per seed; during the first two or three weeks, as a result of respiratory activity, the dry weight fell to 0·26-0·29 g. before photosynthesis began and the plants started to put on dry weight. Data of Kreusler.

measure all the growth that the plant has made, but rather the useful outcome of that growth.

However, fresh weight and volume are not measures of great value to the physiologist who seeks to understand the metabolism and economy of a plant. Water contributes so large a proportion of a plant's weight that dry weight is a more appropriate measure if one wants to know about the amount of material that a plant has synthesised in the course of its growth. Before we come to consider what can be learned about the growth of whole plants from dry weight studies, it should be made clear that dry weight does not always increase during growth. When a pea seed germinates in the ground or a potato starts to sprout there is undoubtedly an irreversible increase in volume, but the growth of the new shoot is made at the expense of reserves which move from the cotyledons or tuber into the new growth. At the same time some carbohydrate is consumed in respiration so that the overall dry weight of the plant decreases, even though it is growing larger. There may be some uptake of salts from the soil but the weight of salt taken up in this way would be trivial in comparison to the weight lost in respiration. Only when a shoot comes above ground and turns green in the light will dry weight begin to increase. If the plant is kept in the dark and becomes etiolated its growth will be even faster, but this is still growth made at the expense of stored reserves and accompanied by a loss in dry weight.

The dry weight of a plant can only be determined on one occasion, so that a fresh sample must be dried again for each determination. Since individual plants differ from one another in their intrinsic growth rates and also, probably, in the minutiae of the conditions under which they are grown, it would almost certainly be misleading to take just *one* plant for the initial sample and *one* plant on each subsequent occasion. Several plants must always be taken for each sample. If the plants are rather uniform a small sample may suffice, but if the plants show much variability and especially if one is looking for small differences of growth, as between, say, two similar varieties of wheat, then many replicates will be needed and statistical analysis will be necessary to determine whether the observed differences between the varieties are significantly greater than the variations between individual plants of one variety.

The growth of a whole plant, as measured by dry weight, shows the same three phases that we saw in the growth of leaves. At first growth is slow, but then as photosynthesis gets under way and the number of dividing cells increases it becomes faster, reaches a peak level and ultimately begins to decline until eventually the plant reaches its mature weight (Fig. 136).

The rate of growth of a vascular plant depends on the size of the plant for this determines both the leaf area (and so the amount of photosynthesis and the quantity of material available for leaf growth) and also the number of growing cells. However, the relationship between growth rate and the amount of growth already made is a complex one. In a colony of unicells as we have seen, growth is exponential, each cell dividing to produce more dividing cells; but in the vascular plant more and more of the products of division differentiate and divide no further; nor do all the cells absorb nutrient from an external medium (as in bacteria) or synthesise it for themselves (as in unicellular algae). The growth of a vascular plant is a complex process involving the integration of many activities: the uptake of nutrients from the soil, photosynthesis in green parts of the plant, translocation to the growing regions, cell division in the meristems, and cell extension in their neighbourhood, the whole complicated by the occurrence of events like flowering, the formation of resting buds, leaf fall in the autumn, or the sudden resumption of growth when winter is over.

Growth Rate at Different Temperatures

For every plant there is an optimal temperature at which growth is fastest. This is often around 25-30° C. or higher for plants of tropical origin. The optimum is probably not due to inactivation of enzymes, for *in vitro* at least, many enzymes are still active at even higher temperatures (p. 215). The reduction in growth rate at these higher temperatures is probably due to a disturbance of the delicate balance of integrated metabolic activities that are required for adequate growth.

The slowness of growth at low temperatures can be safely attributed to a reduction in the rate of enzyme catalysed reactions. Temperatures below 0° C. kill off many plants, but some are frost-hardy; despite much research on this point, we still do not know how it is that one plant can survive conditions that are lethal to another.

PLANT MOVEMENTS

The mechanisms that bring about movements in plants may be classified as follows:

1. **Turgor movements**, which are due to changes in the water content of living cells rendering them more or less turgid. The opening and closing of stomata and the drooping of leaves under conditions of drought are examples. The diurnal variations in posture (sleep movements) of the leaves of *Phaseolus vulgaris* and other legumes (Fig. 137) are due to changes in the turgor of cells in special joints (pulvini) at the junction of lamina and petiole, and petiole and stem. If such plants are placed in the dark under constant conditions, the diurnal rhythm of leaf posture is kept up for several days, showing that there must be some internal time-keeping mechanism. Recent work has revealed that several other processes in plants, including growth in length and spore discharge in several fungi, are also regulated by a diurnal rhythm even when the plants are held under constant environmental conditions.

2. **Hygroscopic movements** are found in some dead cells or tissues which have specialised areas of thickening. Such movements are responsible for the loosening of the spore mass in the open sporogonium of *Pellia* (p. 455) and for the dispersal of gorse seeds (p. 383).

3. **Cytoplasmic movements**, like the beating of cilia and of flagella, cytoplasmic streaming, and the movements involved in mitosis and meiosis.

4. **Growth movements.** It was pointed out earlier that stems and roots grow in length as a result of cell elongation which normally occurs in the region just behind the tip although it may be at some

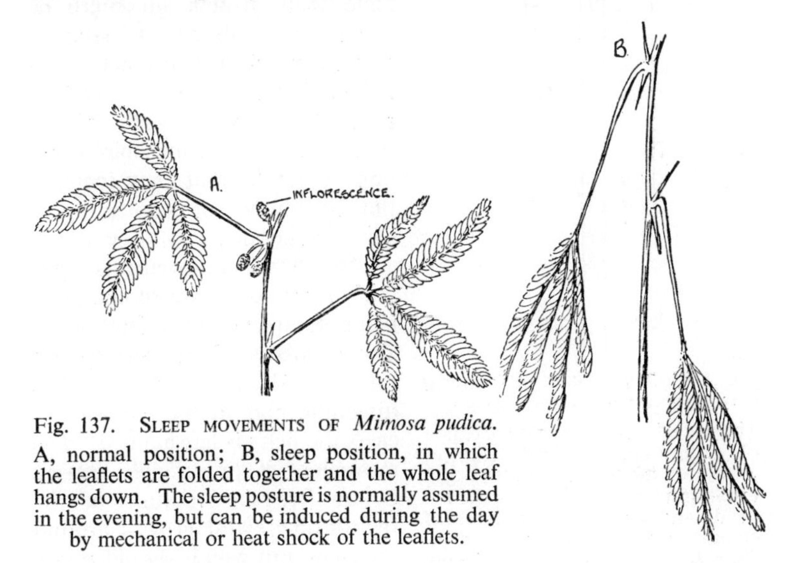

Fig. 137. SLEEP MOVEMENTS OF *Mimosa pudica*. A, normal position; B, sleep position, in which the leaflets are folded together and the whole leaf hangs down. The sleep posture is normally assumed in the evening, but can be induced during the day by mechanical or heat shock of the leaflets.

distance from the tip in the case of intercalary meristems. If there is any inequality of growth on the two sides of the organ this will produce a relatively large swing at the apex (Fig. 138). It is with such growth movements that we shall be concerned here. They are of three kinds: autonomic movements for which no stimulus is required; tropic movements where the organ gives a response towards a stimulus or away from it; and nastic movements where the response is governed by the structure of the organ rather than the direction of the stimulus.

Autonomic movements are shown by the apices of stems which do not retain a rigidly vertical position but incline slightly, first to one side, then to another as they grow upwards. The tip describes a very irregular helix as it grows (Fig. 139). This movement is known as **circumnutation.** No external stimulus appears to be required; so far as we know, the movement is entirely spontaneous. In many plants the amplitude of the movement of the stem apex is rather small, but in twining plants it may be considerable; the apex of one species of *Cuscuta* for instance describes a path with a diameter of about 10 cm. Most of the organs of a plant nutate to a greater or lesser degree as they grow. Tendrils nutate while they are still elongating, the movement coming to an end when they complete their growth in length or when they contact a support around which the tip begins to twine. The movements of tendrils and of the shoots of twining plants have an obvious biological importance in that they increase the likelihood of contacting a suitable support.

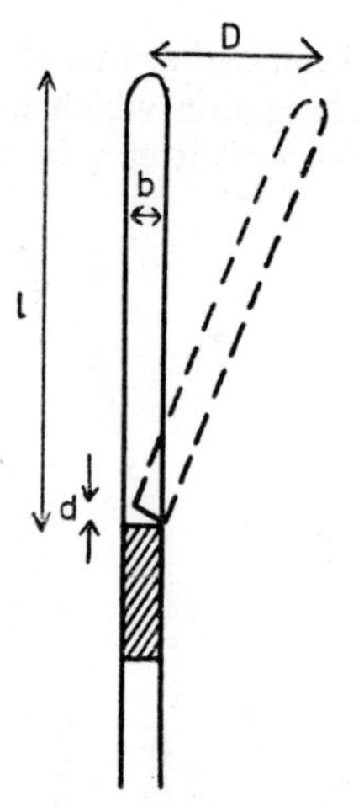

Fig. 138. THE ORIGIN OF GROWTH MOVEMENTS IN A PLANT ORGAN.

The shaded area represents the region of elongation. An inequality of growth on the two sides of the organ results in a big swing by leverage. Let the distance d represent the excess of elongation on one side over the other. Then D, which is the swing of the tip, is given by

$$D = l.\frac{d}{b},$$

where l and b are the length and breadth of the passively swinging tip.

Nutational movements are fairly rapid, one gyre of the helix being completed in a few hours. The members of any one species normally all nutate in the same direction, and in the majority of cases the helix is left-handed. The movement is presumably caused by an irregular rotation of the region of greatest growth around the stem, but why it should rotate in this way is not clear. The fact that movements comparable to those of angiosperm stems are to be seen in the unicellular sporangiophore of the fungus *Phycomyces* suggests that the rotation may somehow owe its origin to the molecular architecture of plant cell walls. In this connection it is at least interesting to find that the thickening in "spiral" xylem elements is generally left-handed.

Nastic movements are only made in response to a stimulus. Examples are the opening and closing of flowers. These movements may be induced by changes of temperature or of light intensity.

The best known thermonastic movements are those to be seen in the flowers of *Crocus* and *Tulipa*. If the unopened flowers are subjected to a temperature rise of a few degrees Centigrade they will open in a short while due to a larger increase in growth rate on the inner side of the perianth segments than on the outer. A fall in temperature has the reverse effect. Photonastic movements are shown by the capitula of *Bellis* (daisy) which open on exposure to light and the flowers of *Oenothera* (evening primrose) which only open at night.

In *Bryonia dioica* (white bryony) the tendril is spirally coiled when young. It straightens out and its tip nutates as it grows in length

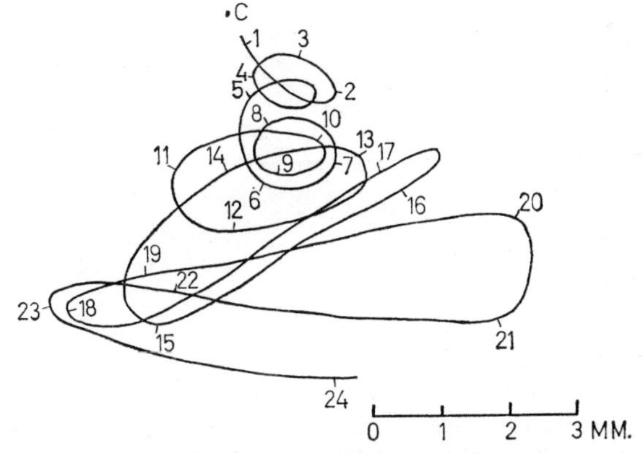

Fig. 139. PLAN VIEW OF THE PATH DESCRIBED BY THE TIP OF A COLEOPTILE OF *Triticum sativum*.

The letter C indicated the base of the coleoptile. The numbers give the time in hours since the start of autonomic movements. After Baillaud, 1962.

over a period of a few days. The apical part of the tendril is sensitive, and if rubbed or touched by a solid body, especially if the surface is rough, it bends towards the stimulated side. The bending results in a fresh part of the tendril coming into contact with the solid object, and so the stimulation is continuous; the tendril continues to bend, and by so doing encoils the support. The coiling around the support is a growth movement.

Contact with a solid body accelerates growth in these sensitive organs on the side of the tendril remote from the point of contact. Contact with drops of liquid, even of a heavy liquid like mercury, does not produce bending. When the apical part of the tendril has coiled around a twig or other support so that both ends of the tendril are now firmly fixed the proximal and distal parts coil in opposite directions (Plate 12). As a result the stem of the climber and support are drawn closer together and the tendril acquires a degree of elasticity. This reduces the risk that a tendril might snap if the climber is blown by the wind.

The movement of the tentacles of *Drosera* to entrap an insect (Plate 10) are largely nastic movements, although there is also an element of tropic response.

Tropic movements, like nastic ones, are made in response to a stimulus, but here the direction of the movement is governed by the direction of the stimulus. We shall consider only the two principal tropic movements—phototropism and geotropism.

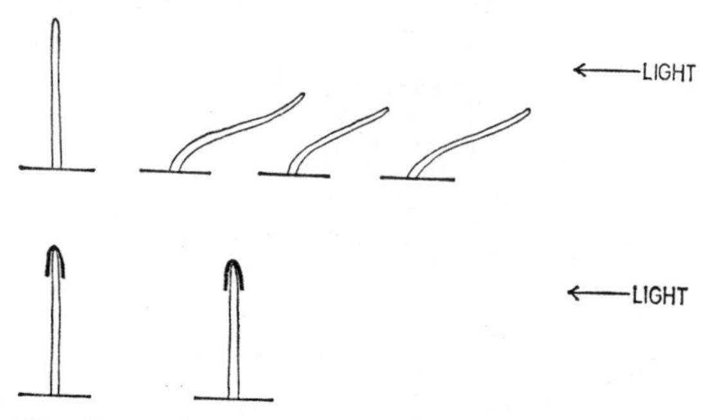

Fig. 140. DARWIN'S WORK ON THE PHOTOTROPISM OF COLEOPTILES.
In both diagrams the left coleoptile shows the initial condition; the light then shines from the right. The short horizontal lines show the level of the soil. *Above:* coleoptiles after exposure for eight hours in a box open on one side in front of a window. The curvatures towards the light are accurately traced. From Darwin, 1880. *Below:* the effect of a silver paper cap on the coleoptile.

Phototropism. When plants are exposed to unilateral illumination, their stems generally react by growing towards the light, while the petioles grow in such a manner as to set the leaves at right angles to the light. These are phototropic movements. Many roots are negatively phototropic, bending away from the light, but some are quite insensitive to light.

The response of plants to light was first investigated in detail by Charles Darwin with his son Francis. Their experiments, together with observations on other tropisms and on circumnutation were published in 1880 in a book *The Power of Movement in Plants.* Darwin worked with seedlings of *Phalaris canariensis* (canary grass). Seedlings are very convenient for experiments on phototropism for they are quickly and easily raised. As Darwin found, they are more sensitive to unilateral illumination if they are grown in the dark

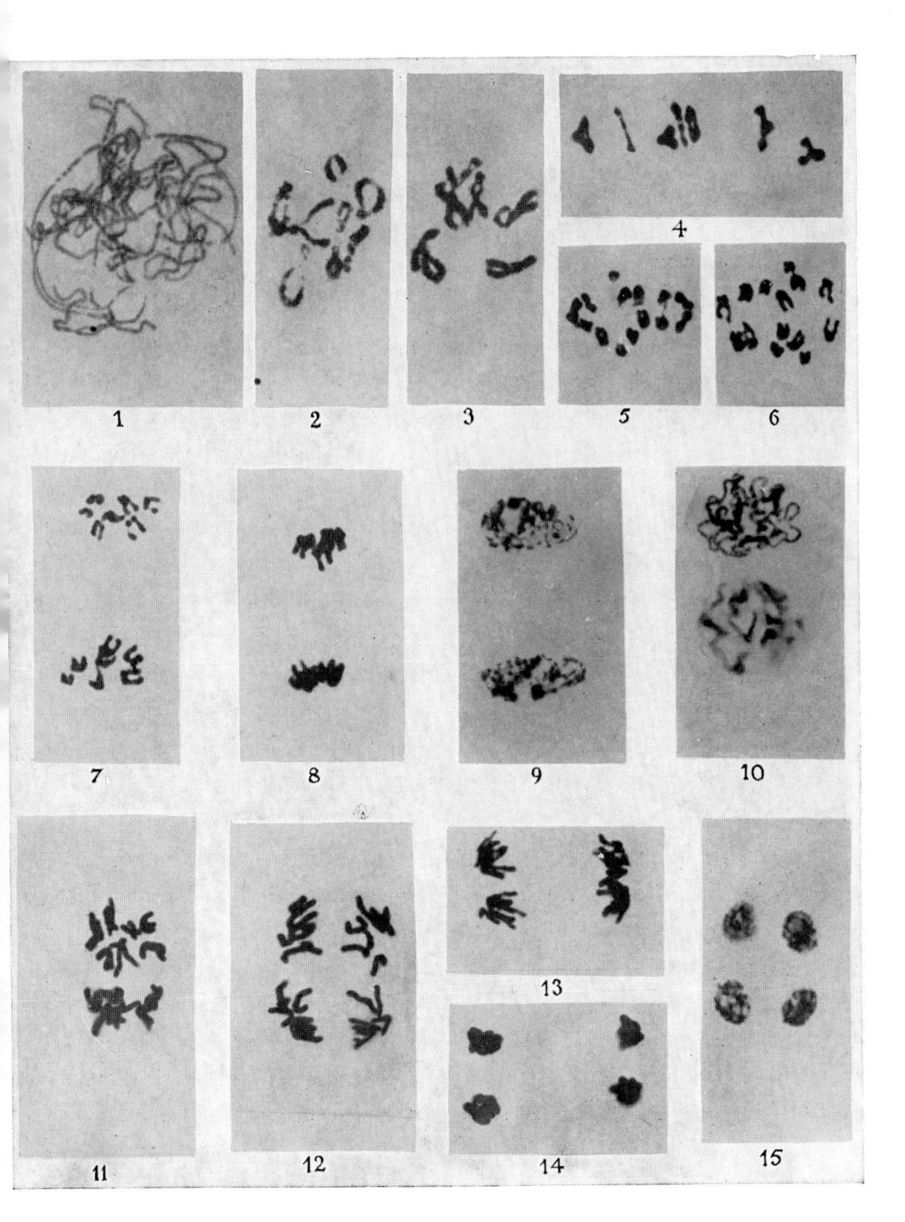

PLATE 9

STAGES OF MEIOSIS IN POLLEN MOTHER CELLS OF A *Narcissus* VARIETY, see pp. 165-7.

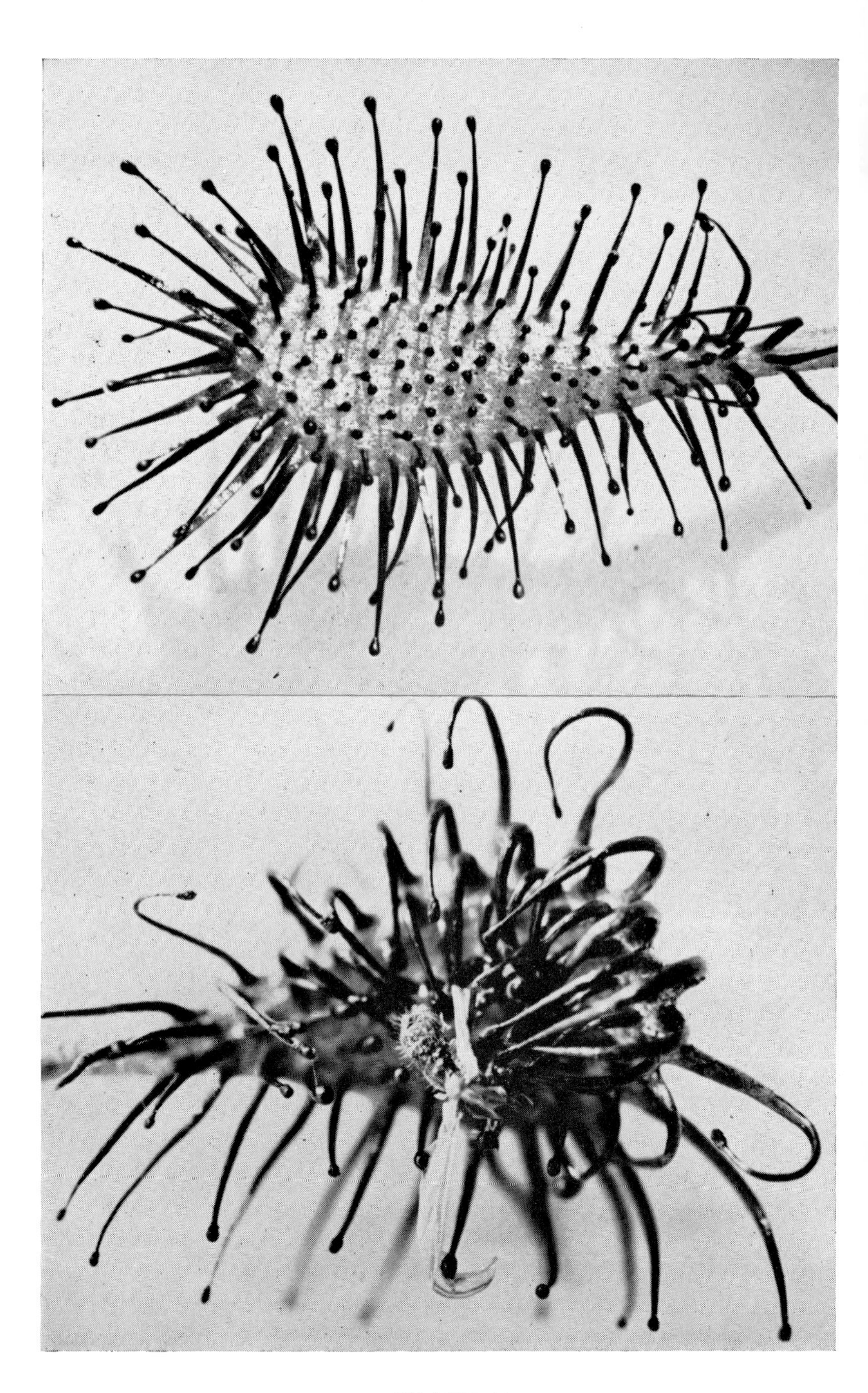

PLATE 10

Leaves of *Drosera intermedia*. The lower photograph shows a fly trapped by the sticky secretion of the tentacles. Tentacles from the more remote parts of the leaf are bending towards the fly. (× 6.)

than if they have been raised in the light. Darwin's choice of a grass seedling was a fortunate one in that the growing shoot is at first completely enclosed in a cylinder, the coleoptile, which is itself sensitive to light. The coleoptile is relatively simple in structure as compared to the apex of a shoot which is enveloped by growing leaves and branch primordia. It is an easy matter to expose the coleoptile to light and observe its reactions. When a coleoptile is illuminated from the side it comes to bend towards the light. The upper part bends first and afterwards the curvature extends gradually down towards the base. Such a movement on its own would result in the apex pointing eventually at the ground instead of the light. In fact the coleoptile ends with its upper part almost straight and pointing directly at the light (Fig. 140). It follows that the upper part of the coleoptile must have reversed its curvature as the lower part began to react. These observations led Darwin to suppose that the upper part of the coleoptile might somehow govern the movements of the lower part. In preliminary experiments the apical 1 or 2 mm. of the coleoptiles was cut off. Although the decapitated coleoptiles showed little or no curvature, Darwin was unable to exclude the possibility that cutting off the tips injured the plants so much as to prevent phototropism. An alternative to surgery was blind-folding; caps of very thin tin-foil were placed over the tips of *Phalaris* coleoptiles. In one experiment, of twenty-one coleoptiles capped and exposed to light for six–eight hours, seventeen remained quite upright while four became slightly inclined to the light. When the caps were removed from six of the upright seedlings, they curved towards the light showing that the tin-foil caps had caused no injury to the coleoptiles. Darwin concluded from these and similar experiments that the light stimulus was perceived by the tip of the coleoptile. Some influence was then transmitted from the upper to the lower part, causing the latter to bend. In modern terminology we should say that there are three phases in phototropism: (1) perception of the stimulus, (2) transmission through the plant to the region where (3) the response takes place. Phases (2) and (3) are considered in the next section (p. 294) but we may conclude this section with more recent work on the perception of the light stimulus.

Light in the blue region of the spectrum is the most effective in causing phototropism (Fig. 141). For the light stimulus to be received and acted upon, it must be absorbed by the coleoptile. The fact that the coleoptile responds mainly to blue light only implies that the light is absorbed by a pigment which absorbs blue light only: such a pigment will appear yellow in colour. There has been much discussion as to what this pigment could be. Two yellow substances have been proposed (a carotenoid and riboflavin), but the experimental evidence available does not present an overwhelming case for either. A strong source of light is not necessary for phototropism (as it is for photosynthesis), intensities less than that of moonlight being sufficient to cause curvature of some plant organs. Within certain limits the curvature produced is proportional to the total light energy received by the coleoptile, a short exposure to a

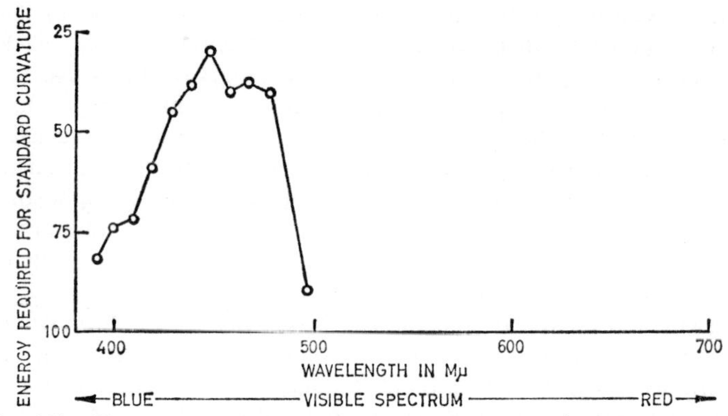

Fig. 141. THE ACTION SPECTRUM OF PHOTOTROPISM IN *Avena* COLEOPTILES. The curve shows the relative amount of light energy needed at each wavelength for a standard 10° curvature. Blue light at a wavelength of about 450 mμ is the most effective. Data of Galston and Baker, 1949.

strong light giving the same response as a long exposure to a weak one.

Geotropism

It is a commonplace that shoots will grow upwards and roots downwards even if they are placed in the dark. It is easy to make the hypothesis that this is a response to gravity, shoots being positively and roots negatively geotropic, but it is not so easy to test the hypothesis. It is perfectly feasible to switch lights on and off to test the response of plant organs to unilateral illumination but (short of working in a space rocket) we have no means of switching off the effects of gravity. What can be done is to compare the effects of a centrifugal force with that of gravity: if gravity does indeed play a role in the orientation of plants' organs then a centrifugal force should do likewise. This point was first taken by Knight who described in 1806 some critical experiments using an apparatus in which a water-wheel was made to operate a second, horizontally-placed wheel. In one series of experiments soaked seeds of *Phaseolus* were fixed to the rim of the wheel which then revolved like a gramophone. At eighty revolutions per minute the centrifugal field at the rim of the wheel was very close to 1 g, and the roots grew outwards and downwards at an angle to the plumb-line which Knight estimated at 45°. The roots thus oriented themselves along the resultant of gravity and the centrifugal force. This result is important for it shows that the root reacts to both gravity and the centrifugal force and furthermore that it reacts equally to them. The normal orientation of primary roots can therefore be ascribed to the influence of gravity.

For the experimental investigation of geotropism much use has been made of the **clinostat**. This is a device similar to Knight's wheel rotating in the vertical plane and powered to-day by electricity. The wheel is rotated slowly and plants are fixed near its centre rather than at its rim so that no appreciable centrifugal force is exerted on the plant as a result of the rotation. The object of the clinostat is to expose each side of a root or stem in turn to gravitational stimulation and to do this at such a rate that the organ, receiving contradictory stimuli on its opposite sides, never responds to gravity at all. The shoot of a plant placed on the clinostat with its axis horizontal then continues to grow horizontally; a shoot which is initially at an angle will eventually find the horizontal and then maintain this position (Fig. 142).

A root placed horizontally will respond to continued gravitational stimulus by a 90° curvature, but if it is given only a very short stimulus and then rotated on a clinostat (or returned in soil to a strictly vertical position) it may show little or no response. Experiments of this sort show that the response depends on the time of exposure to the stimulus. Roots laid horizontally for a few minutes will subsequently show a small but observable response. Roots placed at some angle (α) to the vertical require a longer period of stimulation for the standard response. The intensity of the stimulus is given by $g \sin \alpha$; a root at an angle of 30° requires twice as long an exposure as a horizontal root ($\sin 30° = 0{\cdot}5$; $\sin 90° = 1$). If, on the other hand, roots are exposed to more than 1 g on a centrifuge a proportionately shorter time will be sufficient. It follows that the response is governed by the intensity of the stimulus as well as its duration.

Geotropic curvatures, like phototropic ones, are growth curvatures and in like manner the curve is restricted to the growing zone of the organ (Fig. 143). In general it can be said that primary roots are positively geotropic, secondary roots place themselves at an angle to the vertical, while finer branch roots tend to lack any response to gravity. Although shoots are generally negatively geotropic and grow in an upright position, rhizomes (as in *Equisetum*, *Aegopodium*, *Adoxa*) have a longitudinal habit, keeping to a certain depth below the soil as they spread laterally. Such rhizomes respond to changes in the topography of the soil surface, rising when they meet a hill, and so on. The growing tip of the rhizome is presumably informed of the configuration of the surface above it by some mechanism that involves measuring the length of the aerial organs that is covered by soil (or conceivably it may be sensitive to such light as penetrates that far below ground). Nevertheless, the apical portion of a rhizome brought into the laboratory for experiment behaves as a diageotropic organ, growing horizontally. In *Narcissus* the pedicels of individual flowers are diageotropic and hence at maturity, whilst the stem of the infloresence is vertical, the pedicels are horizontal.

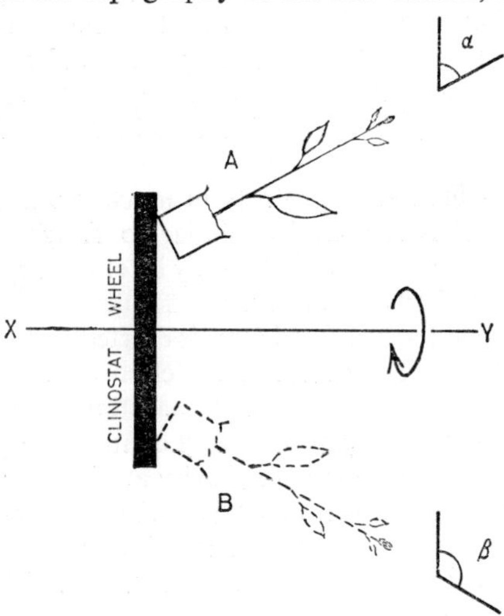

Fig. 142. ROTATION OF AN INCLINED STEM ON A CLINOSTAT.

Let XY be the horizontal axis of a clinostat to which is fixed a stem. A and B are the extreme upper and lower positions of the stem. If the intensity of the geotropic stimulus increases as the stem inclines away from the upright, then because β is greater than α, the curvature of the stem towards the horizontal, while it is in the lower half of its orbit, will be stronger than its curvature away from the horizontal in the upper half of its orbit. Equilibrium is therefore reached only when $\alpha = \beta = 90°$, with the stem parallel to the axis of rotation.

The leaves of many monocotyledons such as *Allium* are negatively geotropic and execute growth curvatures in the basal part of the leaf where the growing region is situated. In the stems of most grasses and of some *Dianthus* species, geotropic curvatures are brought about by the activity of meristems situated at the nodes (Fig. 144). If shoots of these plants are placed in a horizontal position they return to the vertical by curvature at one or more points near the base of the shoot.

The fact that a root can respond to the gravitational stimulus when it is moved out of the vertical by growing in such a way that it finds the vertical again means that it must have some means of perceiving its position with respect to gravity; and the same applies to other geotropically sensitive organs. What is the mechanism of perception? It must be a direct action of gravity on some cell component which either falls freely in the cell or at least becomes

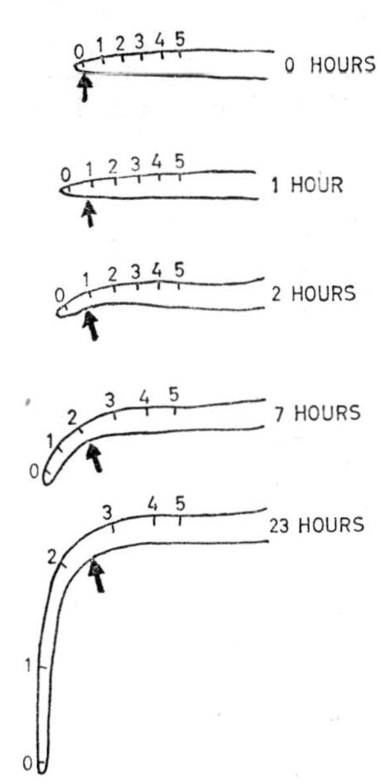

Fig. 143. SUCCESSIVE STAGES OF GEOTROPIC CURVATURE IN THE MAIN ROOT OF A SEEDLING OF *Vicia faba* AT VARIOUS TIMES AFTER THE BEGINNING OF STIMULATION.

The root grows beyond the arrow which represents a fixed point in the soil and curvature develops mainly in the region between marks 2 and 3. The situation shown here is a relatively simple one; roots and shoots sometimes curve initially beyond the vertical, and only when a second, opposite, curvature has set in does the growing point become vertically directed. After Sachs, 1874.

displaced. In the early years of this century several workers suggested that plants might perceive their orientation by the free fall of starch grains within their cells. Such free falling grains are named **statoliths**. They can be seen clearly in the root tip and in the starch-sheath of stems (Fig. 145). There is in fact a remarkable correlation between sensitivity to gravity in an organ and the possession of starch statoliths. Thus the roots of aerial shoots of ivy are negatively phototropic and grow towards the support up which the shoot is climbing; they are not sensitive to gravity at all, and have no starch grains—or at least none which can fall in response to gravity.

Fig. 144. GEOTROPIC RESPONSE AT THE NODE OF A GRASS STEM.

Even those monocotyledons which do not normally synthesise starch, such as *Iris* and *Allium*, have movable starch grains in the geotropically sensitive organs. The movement of cell organelles in horizontally-laid roots is being studied under the electron microscope in several laboratories.

HORMONES

We saw in the last section how Darwin's work on *Phalaris* coleoptiles in 1880 led him to the conclusion that once lateral

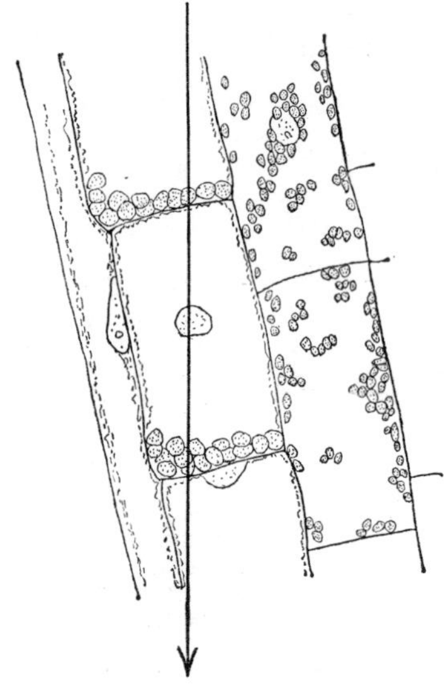

Fig. 145. PART OF A LONGITUDINAL SECTION THROUGH A NODE OF *Tradescantia virginica*.
The axis of the stem was held at 13° to the vertical (the arrow indicates the vertical). In the centre are cells of the starch-sheath in which starch grains have become displaced, and to the right, cells of the cortical parenchyma. After Haberlandt, 1900.

illumination had been perceived at the tip, "an influence" passed downwards to the region in which the response occurred. This work was followed up by several scientists over the next fifty years.

Boysen-Jensen (1910-11) discovered that the phototropic stimulus could be transmitted across a gelatin layer for when the coleoptile was excised and replaced with gelatin between it and the stump, the coleoptile still responded to the lateral illumination (Fig. 146, *a*). Later workers showed that decapitation of a coleoptile slowed the growth of the stump left behind, while replacement of the tip restored its growth. Evidently the apex of the coleoptile produced a stimulus that was capable of promoting coleoptile growth. A clue to its role in phototropism was given by experiments due to Paál in 1918 in which the coleoptile tip was replaced on the stump eccentrically for the coleoptile then curved even in the dark, one side of the coleoptile (below the tip) growing more than the other and so causing a curvature (Fig. 146, *b*). It would be easy to suppose from this evidence that phototropism operates in the same way, light somehow causing an uneven distribution of the stimulus

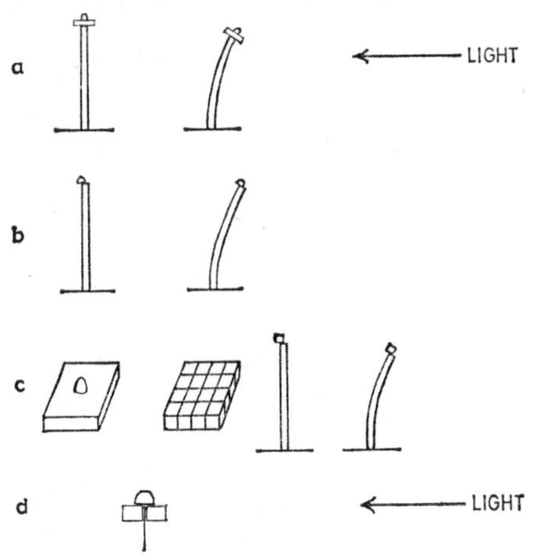

Fig. 146. EXPERIMENTAL STUDIES ON PHOTOTROPISM AND GROWTH HORMONES. (*a*) Boysen-Jensen (1910-11) showed that a phototropic stimulus (due to light coming from the right) could cross a layer of gelatin inserted between coleoptile tip and stump. (*b*) Paál (1918) found that when an excised tip is replaced on one side of the stump the coleoptile curves even in the dark. (*c*) Went's (1928) procedure for the assay of growth-substances in coleoptile tips. The growth-substances are collected in a sheet of agar which is subsequently cut up into blocks. Each block is then placed eccentrically on a decapitated stump, the resulting mean curvature being a measure of growth-substance activity. (*d*) Unilateral illumination of an excised coleoptile tip resting on two agar blocks separated by a razor blade. The block further from the light received 65 per cent. and the nearer one 35 per cent. of the growth-substance appearing from the tip.

from the tip. However, this sort of hypothesis could only be tested when some means of assaying the stimulus was available.

Went found in 1928 that if the tip of a coleoptile was excised and placed on a block of agar (a substance which is routinely used for preparing media for fungal and bacterial growth, see p. 533) then the agar block gradually acquired the ability to cause curvature of a coleoptile stump upon which it was afterwards placed eccentrically. This experiment provided evidence that the stimulant was in fact a chemical substance that could move from coleoptile tip into agar block and subsequently from the block into the stump. In further experiments Went allowed the substance from a series of tips to move into an agar block for sixty minutes. Later a second block of agar was placed upon the first to allow the substance to become diluted as it spread through the double volume of agar; this procedure was repeated again, giving a four-fold dilution. Representative portions of each agar block were then placed eccentrically upon coleoptile stumps and the resulting angle of curvature measured. Some representative figures for curvature are given below:

Number of coleoptiles placed on standard size agar block	Curvature		
	No dilution	Once diluted	Twice diluted
6	11·2°	5·5°	2·8°
12	—	11·2°	5·8°

It is clear that the angle of curvature is proportional to the concentration of the substance in the agar block. The proportionality only holds good for relatively low concentrations which produce curvatures of 12° or less, but this is sufficient to allow the method to be used as a bio-assay, *i.e.* a biological means of assessing the concentration of the growth-inducing substance.

It was now possible to assess the effect of illuminating a coleoptile tip on the distribution of the growth-inducing substance. Went showed that when an excised tip is illuminated more of the substance is received by a block of agar on the far side than on the side nearer the light (Fig. 146, *d*). Comparable experiments with coleoptile tips and root tips placed horizontally in the dark revealed that gravity also induces an unequal distribution. These experiments encouraged the view that plants contain a growth-inducing substance, the distribution of which is altered by phototropic or geotropic stimulation, in such a way that the organ grows more on one side than the other. However, many questions must be answered before we can feel that we really understand how these tropisms are brought about. If there is a growth-substance in plants, what is its chemical nature, and how does it affect growth? How do tropic stimuli influence its distribution? How is it transported through plants? These problems are still the subject of active research and no one feels they have yet been solved completely and satisfactorily. We can only indicate here some of the methods and approaches involved in this work and a few of the results that have been established so far.

In the first place, a substance produced as this one is, in small amounts in one part of an organism, and affecting the growth and development of other parts, is known as a **hormone**. We are concerned here with a hormone produced in the coleoptile tip which moves down the coleoptile and influences the growth of the region behind the tip. Plant growth involves both cell division and cell extension, but the two processes are not equally represented in the coleoptile; cell division ceases quite early in its life, subsequent growth being by extension alone. The hormone therefore acts upon the phase of cell extension. It is assayed nowadays by a straight growth test which is simpler to set up than Went's curvature test. One-centimetre-long segments cut out of the upper portion of young coleoptiles are floated on a solution of the substance under test. If it has growth-substance activity then, at the appropriate concentration, the segments will elongate more than if they were floating simply on water.

Auxins, Growth, and Tropisms

The account so far has been written as though we were concerned simply with one hormone, but there is of course no reason why things should be as straightforward as this, and we do not, in fact, yet know precisely what hormones are present in plants. Some claims have never been substantiated, while the recent work gives every indication that plants contain growth inhibitors as well as growth accelerators so that the "hormone" activity of a plant extract may be the net result of (perhaps several) growth promoters and inhibitors acting together. A substance that promotes the extension growth of coleoptiles and stems is generally termed an **auxin**. Two such substances have now been isolated from the tissues of angiosperms. The first to be discovered is the substance indoleacetic acid often abbreviated as IAA. The second, indoleacetonitrile (IAN) is apparently inactive in plants until it has been hydrolysed to IAA.

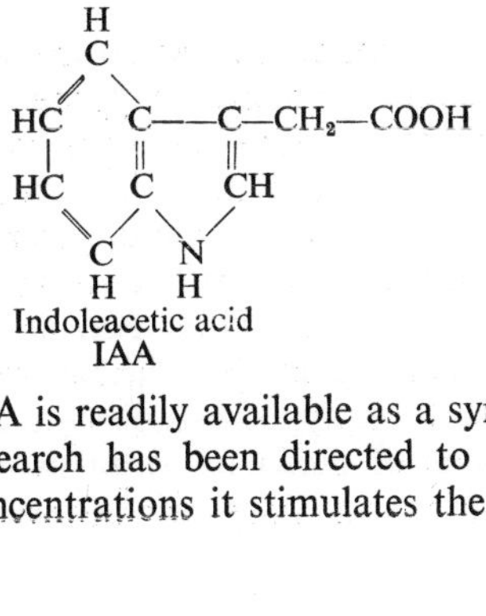

```
      H
      C
    //  \
  HC     C----C--CH2--COOH
  |      ||   ||
  HC     C    CH
    \\  / \  /
      C     N
      H     H
```

Indoleacetic acid
IAA

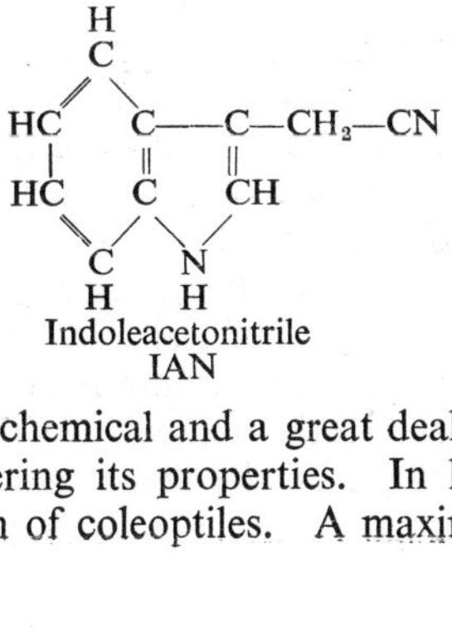

```
      H
      C
    //  \
  HC     C----C--CH2--CN
  |      ||   ||
  HC     C    CH
    \\  / \  /
      C     N
      H     H
```

Indoleacetonitrile
IAN

IAA is readily available as a synthetic chemical and a great deal of research has been directed to discovering its properties. In low concentrations it stimulates the growth of coleoptiles. A maximal rate is attained between one and ten parts per million (p.p.m.) of IAA, but if the concentration is raised further an inhibitory process sets in until eventually with concentrations as high as 1,000 p.p.m. coleoptile growth is completely suppressed (Fig. 147). However, the most striking fact about IAA is that its hormonal activities are not confined to stimulation or inhibition of shoot growth. It will, for instance, affect the growth of roots, stimulating the rate by a small amount at very low concentrations, but causing inhibition if more is applied. Fig. 147 brings out the fact that concentrations of IAA which stimulate shoot growth inhibit the growth of roots. It is

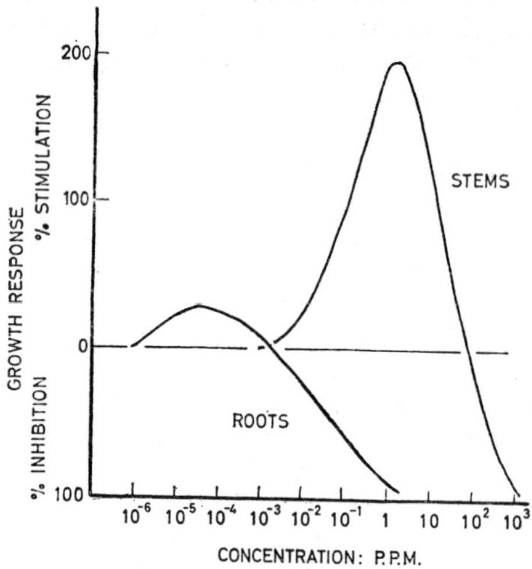

Fig. 147. RESPONSE OF STEMS AND ROOTS TO IAA APPLIED FROM THE OUTSIDE. The growth of both stems and roots is stimulated by certain low concentrations of IAA, but inhibited by higher concentrations. Diagrammatic: after Audus, 1959.

very tempting to suppose that this is somehow related to the way plant organs respond to tropic stimuli. We may suppose, for instance, that the gravitational stimulus somehow causes a redistribution of auxin in a horizontal organ so that the concentration on the lower side comes to be larger than that on the upper side. This would ensure greater growth on the lower side of the stem than on the upper and so lead to an upward curvature on the stem; and to the opposite curvature in roots because auxin inhibits their growth. However, the difficulty with this sort of hypothesis lies in our ignorance of the actual concentrations of auxin in living tissues. Attempts to measure IAA concentrations in tissues are bedevilled by the absence of any direct means of determining the amount of auxin in a tissue. The auxin must first be extracted from the tissue, and then assayed in the coleoptile straight growth test. At first the auxin was simply allowed to diffuse out from the tissue into an agar block, but in later work solvents such as ether have been used to extract the auxin from the tissue. This second procedure yields more auxin than does the first, so that we now have two sorts of auxin, the one freely diffusible and the other held or bound in some way. The respective roles of free and bound auxin have not yet been clarified and we are therefore uncertain as to what is the effective auxin concentration in a tissue. There is, however, ample evidence to suggest that auxin is more plentiful in young growing tissues than in older ones; in the coleoptile there is most at the tip.

It seems likely, from biochemical experiments, that IAA is synthesised from the aromatic amino-acid tryptophane which is present in proteins. A series of enzymes capable of facilitating this synthesis has now been recognised in several plants.

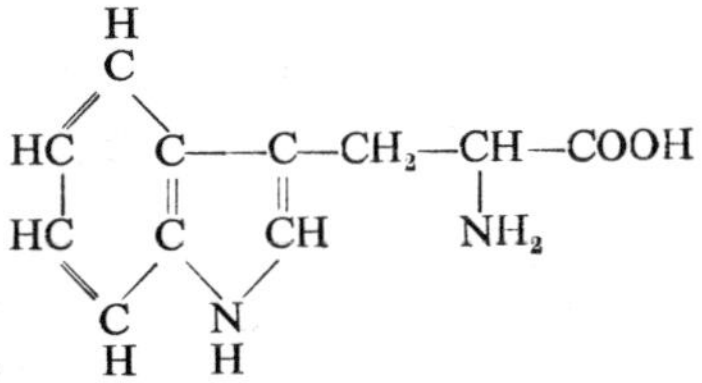

```
          H
          C
        //  \
      HC      C----C--CH2--CH--COOH
      |       ||   ||      |
      HC      C    CH      NH2
        \\  /  \  /
          C      N
          H      H
```

Tryptophane

Auxin Transport

A standard technique which has been used to study auxin transport in coleoptiles involves cutting off and discarding the apical 3 mm. and taking the next 10 mm. segment for experiment. If a block of agar containing auxin is applied to one end of such a segment and a block of plain agar placed at the other end, it is possible to follow the movement of auxin. It was early discovered that the movement is polar, going from the morphological tip to the base. This polarity is quite irrespective of which way up the coleoptile is placed during the experiment; movement is towards the morphological base even when the segment is upside down. Auxin transport is also polar in young bean petioles, but in the older petioles which have finished growth the polarity becomes less and less marked. In mature tissues no polarity of transport is evident.

It is generally supposed that auxin is produced at the growing apices of plants and translocated away from them. Enzymes capable of destroying auxins are known and perhaps as a result of their activity the concentration of auxin becomes less as it moves away from the apex.

Synthetic Auxins

One way to investigate the mechanism of auxin action is to synthesise some similar substances and examine their activity on plants. Such comparative studies may show which parts of the molecule of IAA are quite essential for auxin activity and which parts (if any) can be altered without harm. This sort of approach has been remarkably successful in the past, for instance in studies on the sulphonamide drugs, but it has not so far taken us very much nearer to an understanding of IAA activity. What it has given us, however, is a range of substances which have auxin activity just like IAA, and certain additional properties (like weed-killing) which are not all shared by IAA. Two of these substances are:

```
             CH2—COOH
     H        |                              H
     C        C                              C
   //  \    /   \\                         /   \\
HC        C        CH               HC           C—O—CH2—COOH
|         ||       |                ||           |
HC        C        CH               Cl C         C Cl
  \\    /   \    //                     \      //
     C        C                            C
     H        H                            H
 Naphthylacetic acid               2: 4-dichlorophenoxyacetic acid
        NAA                                 2: 4-D
```

Auxin Activities

We have considered so far the effects of auxins on the growth of stems and roots, and the tropisms which probably involve a redistribution of auxin in the tissue. However, this by no means exhausts the variety of ways in which auxins influence plant growth and development. Their role in the initiation of lateral roots is discussed below and they are also involved in the initiation of cambial activity, the abscission of leaves and flowers, fruit set and fruit growth. In addition, auxins may prevent growth, an example being the inhibition of bud growth (p. 310). This type of auxin activity has been put to practical use in the development of "hormone weed killers".

In horticultural practice it is often desirable to propagate plants vegetatively rather than by means of seed, partly because it is quicker but also because the offspring are then more uniform since vegetative propagation avoids meiosis (p. 163). Many plants have well-established natural methods of vegetative propagation such as runners (strawberry), bulbs (tulip), or tubers (potato). But for others, man has to take a hand. What he does usually is to cut off a young shoot, trim the cut end, and then place it in moist sand. All being well, such a cutting will produce roots and establish itself as an independent plant. Cuttings of some plants root themselves very readily (willow and *Ribes* are examples), but many plants are not so accommodating. Rooting may be encouraged by keeping the cuttings moist and by ensuring that they have some young leaves or sturdy buds. It is in fact significant that a woody twig which will not root while its buds are dormant in winter, forms roots with relative ease in the spring when the buds swell and burst; for it is developing buds (and not dormant ones) which produce auxin It was discovered in the 1930's that natural and synthetic auxins promote root formation. This can be seen by dipping young shoots of *Phaseolus vulgaris* (French bean) into solutions of IAA and then potting them in sand. The number of young root primordia visible after seven days depends on the strength of the IAA used. If young seedlings are immersed for some hours in a solution of 2 : 4-D (at about 100 parts per million) and then returned to water they produce more roots than the controls—but these roots are rather short and stunted, because 2 : 4-D inhibits the extension of roots at the concentration employed. NAA or simple derivatives of NAA are nowadays marketed as rooting agents; they have the advantage over IAA that they are less readily metabolised than IAA and so remain effective for a longer period of time.

In terms of quantity the most important application of synthetic auxins has been as herbicides. It was discovered in the early 1940's that 2 : 4-D would kill dicotyledonous weeds in cereal crops and had the advantage over the materials hitherto used (such as copper salts and nitrophenols) that it was not toxic to animals and would eradicate a wider range of weed species. Herbicides are sprayed on to the foliage of plants in aqueous solutions and penetrate more or less rapidly into leaf and stem tissues. Copper sulphate and nitrophenols are contact herbicides killing only those parts of the plant on which they alight. Extensive damage to the foliage is quite enough to kill off many annual weeds, but plants with underground organs from which fresh buds can arise such as creeping thistles (*Cirsium arvense*) and dandelions are able to survive repeated sprays. 2 : 4-D and similar herbicides have the great advantage that they are translocated within the plant, so that a dose applied to the leaves as a spray can kill the underground parts of the plant as well as the aerial shoot system. When 2 : 4-D is used as a herbicide it is used at a concentration of about 1,000 p.p.m. (cf.

Fig. 147). When a weed is sprayed with 2 : 4-D growth curvatures often become apparent after a day or two, with twisting and distortion of stems, petioles, and leaf blades. Some parts of the plant may grow in girth. The plant will not die until some weeks after it is sprayed. Even among dicotyledons there is considerable variation from one species to another in susceptibility to 2 : 4-D. The underlying causes for these differences—and for the resistance of the cereals to the sprays—are not yet fully established. Part of the answer probably lies in the morphology of the plants, the dicotyledon with its more or less horizontal leaves retaining more spray droplets than the cereal—but there are differences at the cell level as well.

Mechanism of Auxin Action

It cannot, unfortunately, be claimed that the research of the last thirty years has brought us to any satisfactory understanding of the ways in which auxin acts. Much of the research has been concerned with cell extension and it has been thought that perhaps IAA renders the cell wall more easily stretched by osmotic forces generated in the vacuole. However, it must be emphasised that this is only one aspect of auxin action and no one supposes that IAA acts in root formation (p. 301) or in apical dominance (p. 310) simply by its effects on the cell wall.

Gibberellins

The auxins were discovered as a result of experiments on growth and tropisms. The gibberellins, another group of plant hormones, came to light following observations of a Japanese plant pathologist working in Formosa on a disease of rice. When the fungus *Gibberella* infects rice plants they become a pale yellow in colour and generally fail to set seed. What is most remarkable about the infected plants, however, is that they grow taller than healthy ones. Workers in Japan supposed that some product of the metabolism of the fungus might be causing the rice to grow faster and they managed eventually to prepare cell-free extracts of the fungus which stimulated the growth of rice and maize seedlings. During the 1930's the extracts were purified and finally a series of active products, the gibberellins, were isolated. Gibberellins are complex organic compounds with four fused carbon rings. There is now evidence that some of them occur naturally in angiosperms.

The most striking effect of treating a plant with gibberellin is a promotion of stem growth. If dwarf plants are sprayed with weak gibberellin solutions the internodes may extend so much that the plants grow ten times as tall as controls. Thus treatment of dwarf French beans (*Phaseolus vulgaris*) makes them grow like runner beans (*Phaseolus multiflorus*). The increased growth is unfortunately of little economic value for it is not accompanied by any substantial increase in dry weight; treated plants may be bulkier, but most of the increased weight is simply water. The growth of leaves is less influenced by gibberellin than that of stems, while roots show no response at all.

DORMANCY AND GERMINATION

At some time in their life most plants pass through a phase of suspended activity, a phase in which there is little metabolic change. This may be a seasonal event occurring on the approach of a cold winter as in Britain or of a dry summer as in a Mediterranean climate; or again, as in fungi, it may be governed by the availability of nutrient substances. Seeds, buds, or spores in this state are said to be dormant. Although dormant seeds usually have a very low water content it does not necessarily follow that a supply of water is all that the seed needs to begin germination: there may be other factors involved in its dormancy. Dormant buds may have a quite high water content (as in onion or tulip bulb) and here dormancy must be imposed in some other way. We shall consider first the nature of dormancy in seeds and buds and then follow the course of events when a seed germinates.

Dormancy

The seeds of most cultivated plants germinate readily; that is to say that they will grow if they are supplied with water under aerobic conditions at a suitable temperature. For the gardener the test is whether the seeds he plants will come up; the laboratory worker uses a quicker and more reproducible test, placing the seeds on a layer of wet filter paper in a Petri dish, and determining what percentage of the seeds has germinated after incubation at 20° or 25° C. for a few days. When such a test is made on seeds collected as soon as they are shed from the parent plant, a low percentage germination may be found. Several factors may contribute to this dormancy of seeds: one that has already been mentioned (p. 131) is the existence of a hard seed coat through which water and oxygen can only permeate slowly.

The seeds of many plants germinate better if they are stored for a while before the germination test. The seeds are then said to undergo **after-ripening.** Anatomical investigation shows that some seeds are shed before the embryo is fully developed and that the embryo undergoes further differentiation (Orchidaceae) or growth (*Fraxinus*) during the period of after-ripening. However, it is only in relatively few seeds that we can actually *see* any changes and we are often left to infer that after-ripening has involved some biochemical change. Although we now have evidence that several kinds of biochemical change do take place during storage, the research has not yet progressed so far that we can point in detail to the precise reactions involved in breaking dormancy. The changes involved in after-ripening may be accomplished in a few weeks or they may occupy the greater part of a year or even longer. Many seeds after-ripen when they are stored dry but the seeds of some plants (including conifers and Rosaceae) must be stored in the imbibed state and at relatively low temperature. In nursery practice, the seeds are spead out between layers of moist soil over the winter months. This procedure is termed **stratification** (Fig. 148).

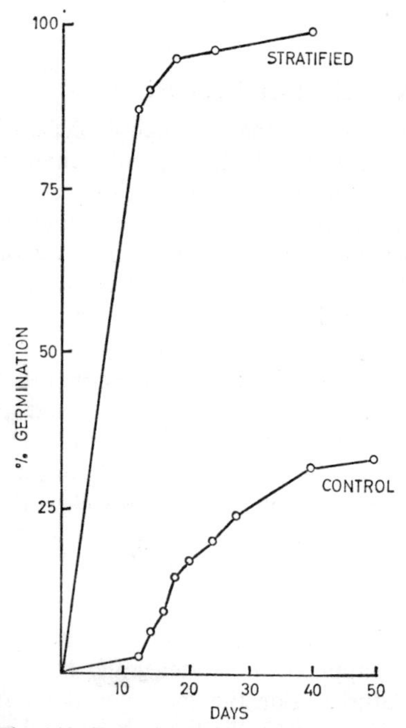

Fig. 148. Effect on percentage germination of stratifying seeds of *Pinus rigida* at 5° C. for various periods.
The control seeds were not exposed to the low temperature. Data of Crocker, 1948.

Simple laboratory experiments show that many substances prevent the germination of seeds. There can, for instance, be little germination of seeds exposed to high concentrations of potassium cyanide or salts of lead or copper since these are enzyme poisons, while in high concentrations of sucrose or other sugars the uptake of water by imbibition in early germination will be opposed by osmotic forces. The juice from fruits such as tomato and grape inhibits the germination of seeds, partly it seems on osmotic grounds, and partly because the juice contains inhibitory compounds; this inhibition prevents premature germination of the seed while it is still enclosed in the fruit. The seeds of some desert plants only germinate when sufficient rain has fallen to allow germination and growth of the seedling. It has been suggested that a germination inhibitor in the seeds is washed out by a heavy rainfall so allowing germination, but sufficient remains in the seeds after a light shower to prevent germination.

Some seeds remain dormant unless they are exposed to light. If such seeds are sown in the dark only a small percentage will germinate, but if they are given even quite a short exposure to light once they have begun to imbibe water, a higher proportion will germinate. Examples of such light-requiring seeds are *Bellis*, *Fagus*, *Taraxacum*, lettuce, and tobacco. Experiments in which the seeds are exposed to light of different wavelengths have revealed that they are most sensitive to red light of wavelength 660 mμ: light of other colours (different wavelengths) is less effective in promoting germination. When seeds are exposed to daylight it is the red component of the light that promotes germination. It was discovered in the 1930's that while red light promotes germination, infra-red (at a wavelength around 760 mμ) which is invisible to us, inhibits the germination of seeds. More recently it has been found that if lettuce seeds, for instance, are exposed to red and then given infra-red afterwards, the infra-red cancels out the promotive effect of the red. When seeds are exposed to a sequence of red and infra-red exposures the percentage germination is determined by the last exposure given; if the sequence ends with red there will be good germination: if it ends with infra-red fewer seeds will germinate.

However, the response of seeds to light is more complex than this suggests, for in some seeds the response to light depends on temperature, the seeds germinating perfectly well in the dark below a certain temperature. Further, a number of substances can act as partial or complete substitutes for a light requirement. The simplest of these substances is potassium nitrate; others are ethylene chlorhydrin, thiourea, and (for some seeds) gibberellic acid. The germination of many seeds (*Anemone nemorosa*, *Bryonia alba*, *Pelargonium zonale*, *Sorghum*) is quite indifferent to light or dark, while the germination of certain seeds (e.g. *Hedera helix*, *Gladiolus*, *Nigella*, *Phacelia*) is actually inhibited by light, the seeds germinating better in the dark.

It is not difficult to see the value to a species of these mechanisms that hold seeds dormant. If all the seeds produced by a plant germinated as soon as they became moistened, they might well all begin growth at about the same time and if conditions later proved unfavourable there would be little or no reserve of seed to re-establish the plant subsequently. Germination of all the seeds in the autumn, for instance, might be followed by a severe frost that would kill off all the seedlings. A requirement for softening the seed coat by the action of micro-organisms, for a period of after-ripening or for a particular light exposure spreads out the period of time over which the population of seeds will germinate, for individual seeds show some variation of detail in their requirements. Some may, for instance, have a particularly thick seed coat which will only soften after a long period of time. Evidence that the germination of seeds from one crop is spread out over a period is seen in the garden where weed seedlings keep on appearing even though care is taken to avoid the introduction of fresh weed seeds. As the soil is cultivated fresh seeds become exposed to conditions that permit germination.

Less is known about the dormancy of buds than the dormancy of seeds. One factor discussed later (p. 310) is the hormone emanating from the apical buds and preventing the outgrowth of laterals. This, of course, does not account for the dormancy of the apical bud itself. In some cases there is evidence for the presence of substances in the bud which inhibit the extension of coleoptile segments, or—what is more relevant—the apical growth of tree stems, and whose concentration is greater in early winter than in May and June when the shoots are making active growth.

The dormancy of the buds on some trees is only broken if the shoots are exposed to the cold temperatures of winter. Thus the buds of *Pinus* enter a condition of winter dormancy in September and this condition is only broken by winter chilling. Apple trees sometimes fail to come into leaf in a warm Mediterranean climate because the trees were not exposed to a sufficiently cold winter.

Germination

The morphological changes that accompany the germination of certain seeds have already been described (Chapter 6), but no connected account of the underlying physiological and biochemical events was attempted at that stage. When dormancy is ended a seed will germinate provided that it is supplied with water and oxygen and held at a temperature between 10 and 40° C. For each species there is an optimal temperature range at which germination is most rapid. For wheat this is 15-30° C., for oats 25-31° C., and for maize 32-35° C.

The dry seed contains numerous enzymes. Thus flour, which is made by grinding up dry wheat grains, can be used as a source of protease enzymes. However, despite the presence of these and other enzymes there is extremely little metabolic activity in air-dry seeds. The respiration of such seeds is so slow that it is difficult to measure and difficult to distinguish from the respiration of the micro-organisms that contaminate many seeds.

Once the seed begins to hydrate in early germination the enzymes present within it become active. The respiration rate rises rapidly (p. 223). In beans this initial phase of hydration due to colloidal uptake of water lasts for about a day and continues until the water content reaches about 60 per cent. At this stage the cotyledons and the root/shoot axis have swollen and taken up water, and the radicle has burst out of the testa, but neither root nor shoot has made any real growth: neither has increased in dry weight. Translocation of soluble sugars and nitrogenous compounds from the cotyledons to the root/shoot axis soon begins and a new phase of metabolic activity is heralded by the synthesis of enzymes that were not present in the dry seed or present only in small amount. Of particular importance is the synthesis of amylase in the cotyledons, for this catalyses hydrolysis of the starch they contain. The resulting sugars are translocated to the young root/shoot axis where they serve as a respiratory substrate and as a starting point for the synthesis of other cell materials (Fig. 127). Comparable changes occur in germinating cereal grains, only here starch is stored in the *endosperm* and then translocated to the young embryo.

In fatty seeds, enzymes capable of converting fats to sugars (p. 225) make their appearance after two–three days of germination. In the sunflower the fats are stored in the cotyledons and the resulting sugars move to the root/shoot axis, but in *Ricinus* the fat is stored in the endosperm, converted to sugar in this tissue, and then absorbed by the young embryo. The endosperm of *Ricinus*, like that of the cereal grain, senesces and dies when its resources are consumed early in germination. In some non-endospermous seeds (pea, bean) this is also the fate of the cotyledons, but in others (sunflower, cucumber) the cotyledons become green and leaf-like.

The early growth of the seedling is entirely heterotrophic, its life depending on the stores held in the cotyledons or endosperm. Once a root system develops the seedling becomes capable of absorbing inorganic salts from the soil but it can only become completely independent of the seed reserves if and when the shoot comes into the light. An exposure to light—either in the ovary (pea, *Acer*) or when the seedling comes above ground (sunflower, cucumber)—is a prerequisite for chlorophyll synthesis in angiosperm seedlings (though ferns and conifers can form chlorophyll in the dark). Illumination is also the signal for a variety of morphogenetic responses like straightening of the plumular hook. When the shoot turns green in the light and chloroplasts appear, the enzymes necessary for photosynthesis are synthesised and providing the light intensity is sufficient (Fig. 116), the germinating seedling becomes an independent, autotrophic, green plant.

MORPHOGENESIS

Morphogenesis is the study of the origin and development of form. It is in part a descriptive study and in part an analytical one seeking to understand the physiological processes that underlie the observed patterns of development. Prominent among the problems of morphogenetic interest are the time and place of origin of new organs, their relative growth rates and the way in which the behaviour of individual cells and organs is so controlled and integrated as to result in the harmonious development of the whole. To some extent the development of cells and organs is governed by internal factors (such as hormone distribution) but external factors such as illumination also have a role in determining plant form.

Differentiation

The fertilised egg cell of a vascular plant is a relatively small and simple structure, but in due course it develops into a large multicellular plant with clearly recognisable organs like leaves and roots. This development involves differentiation. There is differentiation of the plant into organs and there is differentiation at the cell level (for many of the products of cell division come to differ from one another in their size, shape, and physiological activity—see Fig. 92).

The term differentiation is sometimes coupled to the concept of **division of labour**, and it is indeed reasonable to point out that in many ways leaves seem well adapted for photosynthesis (whilst roots are not) and that the chloroplast is the seat of photosynthetic activity within the cell. To be able to allocate functions to the observed structural features of plants in this way gives a rather comforting notion that one understands the meaning and significance of differentiation. However, one must beware of the temptation to ascribe functions to all that one observes; many morphological features have no evident function, and even if they have, some experimental investigation is called for: guesses are not sufficient.

The morphogenetic aspect of differentiation concerns the origin of the observed differences in structure. Consider, for instance, the problem of cell shape. Parenchyma cells have one shape in the epidermis, another in the leaf mesophyll, and a third in the pith. To some extent these differences are a consequence of the mode of development of the tissue. In the pith the shape of cells is determined by the pressure of cell upon cell in a closely-packed tissue (p. 18), whilst in the leaf mesophyll the cells have only small areas in contact with one another because they make less growth than cells in the epidermis and palisade parenchyma and are therefore pulled apart. On the other hand, the difference between a parenchyma cell and a xylem tracheid cannot be ascribed simply to the behaviour of neighbouring cells or to differences in growth rates. Nevertheless, and here is the core of the problem, since these cells all arise by mitotic division from the same fertilised egg cell they must all have the same chromosome complement and so all have the same genotype (some evidence for this assertion will be found on p. 162). If the genotype is correctly to be regarded as embodying a set of instructions governing the production of enzymes and other proteins in the cell (Chapter 8), how can cells with the same genotype develop so differently? There is no easy answer to this question, although we are beginning to see where the answer is to be sought. The possibility is now being envisaged that only some of the information carried in the genotype is expressed and acted upon in any particular cell; the problem then becomes one of finding the mechanism by which information is selected or repressed.

Tissue culture experiments may throw some light on this question. When a stem is wounded a layer of cork cells covers the wound, but if a large enough area is damaged, as when a stem is cut across, a scar of callus appears. Callus is a mass of parenchymatous cells usually developing from the cambium and sometimes endowed with meristematic activity in its own right. Such callus tissues can be grown under culture conditions as a mass of relatively undifferentiated parenchymatous cells with a few scattered vascular elements. If now a bud from the same species of plant is grafted on to the callus, organised vascular tissues, continuous with those of the bud, make their appearance in the callus. Evidently the bud has the power of causing callus cells to differentiate into vascular tissue. The precise mechanism by which the bud exerts its influence is not yet known.

F. C. Steward at Cornell University has attacked another facet of this problem. As a plant first develops from a fertilised egg all of its cells are meristematic but in the course of its growth more and more cells lose the power of division and become differentiated. What is it that stops, say, parenchyma cells from dividing and causes them to remain quiescent? When small portions of the secondary phloem of a carrot root are transferred to culture solutions they will grow, forming a tissue that is little differentiated. However, Steward found that when individual cells were loosened from the tissue and allowed to grow on their own, some of them became organised and differentiated like a carrot embryo and, if suitably tended, eventually grew into normal carrot plants that flowered and set seed. Evidently the cells of the secondary phloem still have the power to divide and the potential ability to generate a whole plant: but when they are *in situ*, surrounded by other cells, they are forced to remain quiescent.

Correlation

The successive organs produced by a shoot apex as it grows do not develop in complete independence of one another, for the plant as a whole is an organised structure. One elm tree, the product of fifty years of growth and development, looks much like another fifty-year-old elm, but different from a Lombardy poplar. The organisation of *Ulmus* differs from the organisation of *Populus*. Clearly there must be some internal control over the degree of branching, the angle at which branches grow, the length of branches, the formation of buds, the disposition of leaves, and so on. The individual organs of the plant develop in orderly fashion, the growth of one being integrated or correlated with the growth of others.

Apical dominance is an example of correlative growth. The growth of an apical bud prevents more or less strongly the development of laterals below it. Thus lateral shoots only appear from the axils of pea or bean cotyledons if the main shoot is excised and likewise topping a tree allows the growth of laterals from the remaining shoot. Apical dominance is the principle that lies behind the pruning of trees and the trimming of hedges. Thimann and Skoog showed in 1934 that when the apical bud of *Vicia* was removed and a paste containing indoleacetic acid placed on the stump, the lateral buds made very little growth, although in controls with paste alone the buds grew vigorously. They concluded that in the intact plant, "growth-substance" (probably IAA) produced by the apical bud caused elongation of the main stem but inhibited the outgrowth of laterals.

The root and shoot of vascular plants are interrelated as regards nutrition for the root depends on the shoot for carbohydrate, while the shoot owes its supplies of water and mineral salts to the root system. The ratio of the dry weight of the root of the plant to the dry weight of the shoot is subject to change as the plant develops. The ratio falls when a plant comes into fruit and sets seed, and it is also reduced by anything that cuts down the photosynthetic activity of the shoot such as heavy grazing, frequent cutting, or shading.

Finally we may note that the development of one organ such as a leaf or a fruit may involve differential growth rates. Thus a leaf may become more deeply lobed as it develops, a fruit more pear-shaped, or a prothallus more heart-shaped. Such changes are brought about by relatively slow growth rates (or complete cessation of growth) in some parts of the organ or in some particular directions correlated with faster growth elsewhere (Figs. 149, 150).

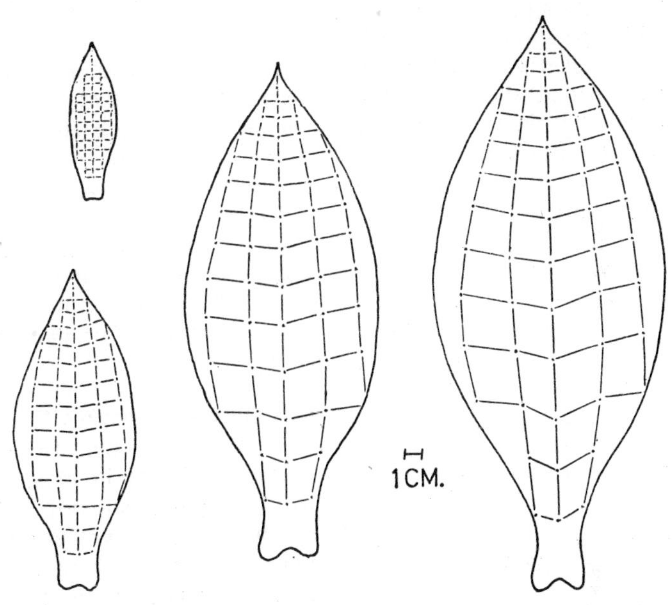

Fig. 149. SUCCESSIVE STAGES IN THE DEVELOPMENT OF A TOBACCO LEAF FROM THE TIME IT WAS ABOUT ONE-QUARTER OF ITS FINAL LENGTH UP TO MATURITY. The surface of the smallest leaf shown was marked out in 5 mm. squares. The appearance of the corresponding areas as the leaf matures indicates the differing rates of expansion as the leaf develops. The apical portion of the leaf grows relatively slowly and matures early, while the basal and marginal areas continued growth for a longer period and made more growth. After Avery, 1933.

Regeneration

Under the special conditions of Steward's experiments (p. 309) an individual carrot cell can regenerate a whole plant. Many plants display (rather less spectacular) powers of regeneration, producing individual organs or in some cases whole plants from a more or less massive group of cells.

Stem cuttings of many dicotyledons will grow roots from the callus that forms over the cut surface or from the pericycle (Fig. 151).

In many species the development of roots is promoted by treatment with a hormone (p. 301). Isolated pieces of willow twig form roots very readily from the morphologically basal (or proximal) part of the twig and at the same time shoots appear from buds at the apical (or distal) end. This polarity is retained even if a twig is placed upside-down in a moist atmosphere, the roots then growing from the upper (originally basal) end of the shoot. The shoot axis evidently has an inherent polarity.

Although shoots seldom arise from the intact roots of growing plants, isolated pieces of root are sometimes capable of producing new roots and shoots. Short pieces of *Taraxacum* (dandelion) root suffice (as the gardener knows to his cost) to propagate the plant. Such root cuttings behave again in polar fashion, but the polarity is opposite to that of the stem, shoots appearing at the proximal end.

Leaf cuttings of *Begonia* will produce roots and buds, while bulbils regularly appear on the leaves of growing plants of some *Bryophyllum* spp. and constitute a normal means of propagation (Fig. 152).

Fig. 150. SUCCESSIVE STAGES IN THE GROWTH OF A PROTHALLUS OF THE FERN *Pteridium aquilinum*.

Note that growth in width is more rapid than growth in length. After Albaum, 1938.

Morphogenetic Effects of Light

1. **Light intensity.** The importance of light in plant life has already been stressed in the sections on photosynthesis and phototropism, but these are by no means its only roles in plant growth and development. The morphology of leaves, for instance, is influenced by the intensity of the light in which they develop (see p. 151). However, the most striking effects of light intensity are seen when we compare plants growing in complete darkness (at the expense of reserve materials already present in their tissues) with those grown in the light. Dark-grown plants are said to show symptoms of **etiolation.** In peas and beans the internodes become very elongated, the leaves fail to expand much, the plumular hook (p. 134) fails to open, and the tissues contain fewer lignified cells than normal. These symptoms are typical of the etiolation of most dicotyledons but it should be noted that monocotyledonous plants with parallel-veined leaves behave differently. When bulbs of *Allium* or *Narcissus* are grown in the dark their leaves may become three or four times longer than normal. The etiolated leaves of angiosperms are yellow for they are unable to synthesise chlorophyll

or to form organised chloroplasts in the dark. When etiolated plants are brought into the light they rapidly become green and form chloroplasts. In legumes the plumular hook opens, the elongation of existing internodes ceases, and the internodes that are formed subsequently in the light are relatively short; leaves that are still growing continue to expand and the tissues become normally lignified. Etiolation can be prevented by a very low intensity of illumination—far weaker than is required for any significant amount of photosynthesis.

Fig. 151. Stem cutting of *Tradescantia* with roots appearing at the basal end.

2. **Light direction.** The topic of phototropism was discussed earlier.

3. **Light duration.** Over the greater part of the earth's surface conditions are not uniform throughout the year: there are differences in temperature, rainfall, light intensity, and so on. It is very generally found that plant development is geared to this seasonal cycle. Thus in Britain, snowdrops flower in winter, lilac in spring, grasses in summer, and *Chrysanthemum* in the autumn. Vegetative development is also seasonal. It is very easy to take this seasonal rhythm of plant behaviour for granted and indeed no major effort was made to investigate it until the beginning of this century. In 1920

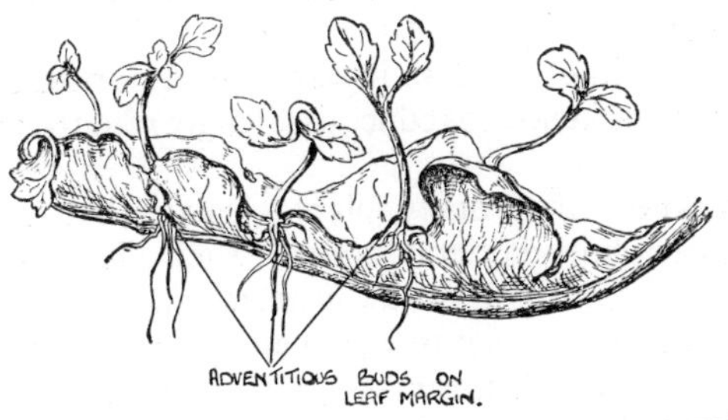

Fig. 152. Leaf of *Bryophyllum pinnatum* with adventitious buds.

Garner and Allard gave an account of experiments with a new giant strain of tobacco which had appeared (as a mutant) some years earlier. This strain was unusal in that it produced no flowers in the summer when grown in Washington, D.C. At the end of the growing season the plants were brought into a greenhouse for protection, and then during the winter they produced flowers and set seed. When spring came, flowering ceased and vegetative shoots developed. The problem before Garner and Allard, who wished to obtain seed of this new variety in quantity, was to determine what factor induced it to flower in the winter under greenhouse conditions. With this knowledge it might become possible to induce the plant to flower and set seed out-of-doors in the summer. The effect of temperature was soon eliminated for even when the greenhouse was held at summer temperatures throughout the winter, the plants still flowered in the winter months. Since the light intensity was lower in winter than in summer, experiments were set up to investigate the effect of shading the plants in summer, but this again had no material effect on the flowering date. In considering what other environmental factors could possibly control the time of flowering, Garner and Allard considered day-length. Although it "hardly seemed likely that the . . . length of the daily exposure (to light) could be responsible for the effects in question", they nevertheless set up experiments to test this hypothesis. During the summer season plants were exposed to various day-lengths by placing the pots of plants on trucks which could be shunted at the desired time into a darkened shed. In the first experiment tobacco was planted on March 6th and ten control plants were left outdoors in day-lengths of thirteen–fifteen hours through the summer months. These plants produced their first flowers in the last week of October. Fourteen test plants were allowed only five hours of daylight in each twenty-four-hour period from May 14th onwards and they flowered between July 8th and August 14th. The time of flowering was evidently controlled by day-length. Only when the days were relatively short (either because it was winter, or because the plants were artificially darkened to reduce day-length) did the tobacco come into flower.

We now know that many plants behave like tobacco, only flowering under short-day conditions. Such plants are known as short-day plants. Examples are *Chrysanthemum*, rice, cotton, and soya bean. These are plants which flower in our climate in the autumn or plants which normally grow under tropical conditions where day-length is about twelve hours all year round. Some plants by contrast only flower when days are long, that is to say when there are fourteen or more hours of daylight. Examples of such long-day plants are spinach, lettuce, and grasses which all flower in the summer in Britain (see Plate 11). If long-day plants are moved to the tropics (or more simply placed in a special growth-chamber which can provide short-day illumination), they will never come into flower. This control of plant development by day-length (or more correctly, as we shall see later, night-length) is known as **photoperiodism**. The length of the daily period of illumination is now known to govern the flowering date of many plants, although flowering in some plants such as rose and tomato is indifferent to photoperiod. The production of flowers is by no means the only aspect of plant development to be under photoperiodic control, other examples being the formation of bulbs and tubers, the fall of leaves from deciduous trees, and the bolting of stems.

Exposure to a few cycles of the appropriate photoperiod will not necessarily bring a plant into flower. Some plants must reach a certain stage of development before flowering is possible. Thus in rye, the apical meristem must first initiate at least seven leaves, while in soya bean the number is three or four. The primordia in the axils of these first leaves can only make vegetative growth but the primordia in the axils of the next group of leaves will produce flowers if the plant receives the requisite photoperiods; otherwise they remain vegetative. Photoperiodic stimulation thus acts as a trigger in the sense that it switches the whole future pattern of development, initiating a series of events that leads to the production of flowers. When a meristem begins to develop floral structures it changes in appearance, often becoming broader. The floral members are all organs of limited growth and the formation of the flower terminates the life of the meristem. Details of the formation and structure of the floral organs will be found in Chapter 12.

Many laboratories are now equipped with growth rooms in which plants can be grown to maturity under selected conditions of illumination and temperature. One aspect of recent work on photoperiodism concerns the effect of short interruptions to photoperiodic cycles. A short-day plant comes into flower when given cycles of say eight hours light followed by sixteen hours dark. What happens if we darken the plants for a while during the day or illuminate them at night? It turns out that a short black-out during the day is of no consequence as regards time of flowering, but that a flash of light in the middle of the night effectively cancels out the inductive effect of the long night: the plant behaves as though it had not had a long night. This is a remarkable situation for it suggests that what a short-day plant really needs is not a short day, but a long night during which some light-sensitive process essential for flowering is under way. From experiments in which short-day plants were exposed to short bursts of light of different wavelengths during their long night, it was discovered that red light (with a peak absorption at 660 mμ) was the most effective in cancelling out the night.

4. **Light quality.** Once it was realised that red light of 660 mμ had special significance in photoperiodism, experiments were undertaken to see whether light of this wavelength was especially active in other morphogenetic or biochemical processes. Sure enough, it turned out that many light-requiring processes specifically require this same red light (and, what is more, they are inhibited by infra-red light—see p. 305). To quote one example that has received intensive study, light at 660 mμ has the following effects on seedlings of *Sinapis alba* (white mustard): hypocotyl elongation is inhibited, the cotyledons enlarge, the plumular hook opens, tracheids appear in the vascular tissue of the hypocotyl, hairs form along the hypocotyl, and anthocyanin is synthesised. These symptoms indicate that etiolation is suppressed by red light. When we say that exposure to daylight suppresses etiolation it must be recognised that the red component of daylight is the most active, light at other wavelengths having little or no effect. Another response to light is the germination of seeds (such as lettuce, p. 305) and of spores (*Funaria*, *Dryopteris*), and here again experiment has shown that red light is the most effective in promoting germination.

All these morphogenetic and biochemical effects of red light have very similar action spectra, the peak of activity being at 660 mμ with a rather sharp fall in activity on either side of the peak. It follows that there must be a pigment in the plant which absorbs light most effectively at this wavelength. A group of workers at the U.S. Department of Agriculture laboratories have opened the way for further investigation of these intriguing problems by isolating the pigment in question. It turns out to be a bright blue protein, which they have named phytochrome.

Morphogenetic Effects of Temperature

Winter cereals are normally sown in the autumn and flower the following year. If sown in the spring they fail to flower. This behaviour contrasts with that of the spring variety of the same cereal which is sown in the spring and flowers in the same year. The winter cereal evidently needs a longer period (or exposure to winter conditions) for flower formation.

It has been found possible to by-pass the need for over-wintering and to hasten the flowering of winter cereals by soaking the seeds in water and then exposing them to a temperature of 1-5° C. for a few days. In this way the winter cereal can be induced to behave like a spring variety producing flowers in the same year from a spring sowing. This cold temperature treatment of seeds is termed **vernalisation.** Like photoperiodism, vernalisation has excited much interest and been extensively investigated in England, Russia, and the U.S.A. Vernalisation alone is not sufficient to ensure flowering. It initiates the flowering process, but no flowers are formed unless the plants are subsequently given long-day treatment. In winter rye flowering can be hastened by long days after either vernalisation of the seeds—or a few cycles of short days. In other plants, the short-day treatment is no substitute for vernalisation. It is evident that photoperiod and temperature regime may both influence the flowering process and experience shows that there are considerable differences between plant species in their response to these factors.

Low temperature treatment also induces flowering in many biennials. These plants grow vegetatively in the first year, producing leaves and generally accumulating sugar or starch in a tuber, bulb, or other organ. If the plants are kept warm, vegetative growth may continue for a long period, but if they are allowed to over-winter they flower and die in the following season.

AGEING, SENESCENCE, AND DEATH

Ageing

Shoot growth is characterised by the activities of apical meristems which produce a succession of leaves and shoots as they develop. This process of growth may continue (with seasonal interruptions) for months or years and we may ask whether it shows any signs of change as the plant becomes older. The transition from purely vegetative to reproductive development has already been discussed—but are there any other changes in the activities of the meristem as it gets progressively older? Are successive leaves, for instance, identical or do they show some progressive drift in their physiological or morphological characters? In looking for evidence of such changes in leaves, each leaf must be examined at the same stage in its own development, or there will be confusion between changes that occur within a leaf in the course of its own development and changes as between one leaf and the next.

Although rather few investigations have been made on the physiological characters of successively-formed leaves there is evidence of a progressive drift in at least one character—respiration rate. In barley, the respiration rate of leaves taken at the time of complete emergence shows a steady decline from the lower to the upper ones. Morphological differences between successive leaves have attracted much more attention because they are readily observed and often very striking. The differences in question may be quite subtle alterations in leaf shape or rather obvious changes in the number of leaflets per leaf or the degree of dissection of leaves (Fig. 153). In some instances the change is accomplished within the space of a few nodes and it becomes appropriate to speak of juvenile and adult foliage. Thus young gorse seedlings have hairy, laminate leaves but the apex produces few of these and there is a rapid transition to the adult leaf form which is a spine.

In ivy (*Hedera helix*) the apex produces juvenile foliage, which is five-lobed, for an extended period of time; but sooner or later a shoot growing up a tree or a wall begins to produce flowers and switches over at the same time to the adult leaf form which is rhombic.

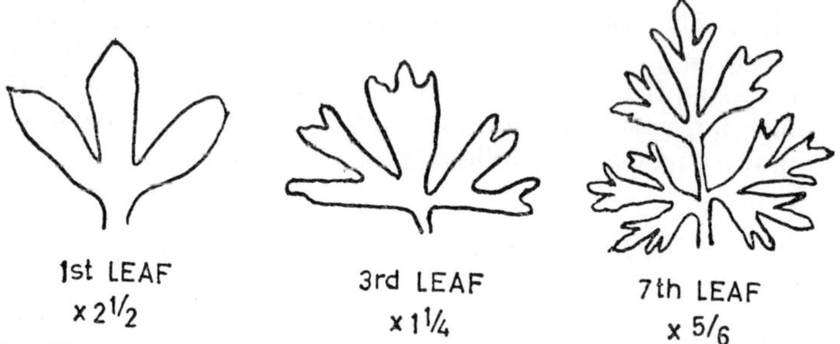

Fig. 153. INCREASED DISSECTION IN SUCCESSIVE LEAVES OF *Delphinium*. From Brown, 1944.

Whether the transition from juvenile to adult foliage is rapid or whether it is spread out over many nodes, the fact that there *is* a transition means that there must be some physiological and biochemical differences between successive leaves. These differences may be determined by the apices from which the leaves arose. One factor that could bring about such changes over a period of time is the progressive alteration of day-length during the growing season (see p. 313), but the control of leaf shape is certainly more complex than this alone would suggest and probably involves other factors as well, perhaps nutritional or hormonal.

Senescence is the last stage of plant life being followed only by death and autolysis of cells. It is a phase of particular interest because as the forerunner of death it may provide some information on the causes of death—and also because it is the stage at which fruits ripen and become ready for the table. As a phase, senescence is by no means as easy to characterise as is, say, germination.

The senescence of leaves is most readily recognised by a loss of chlorophyll, a loss which is irreversible; even young plants may lose their green colour when placed in the dark, but the colour returns when they are brought out into the light again. As the green chlorophylls disappear in senescence the tissues usually turn yellow, this being the colour of the carotenoids which were previously masked by the chlorophylls: such a colour change is to be seen in many leaves and in banana and citrus fruits. In some instances red anthocyanin pigments are synthesised as the chlorophyll disappears (some apples, Virginia creeper). Associated with the loss of chlorophyll is a fall in the protein content of the leaf. The proteins are hydrolysed and some of the products of hydrolysis translocated from the senescing leaf back to the rest of the plant.

The senescence of fleshy fruits is characterised by the changes known as "ripening". The fruits become soft (due to changes in the pectic substances of the cell walls), they develop an odour, and starch becomes converted to sugar (as in bananas). The respiration rate of fruits rises as they ripen; this is known as the **climacteric** rise in respiration.

In the early years of this century it was the practice of citrus growers in California to ripen their green fruit by storage in rooms heated with paraffin stoves. It was soon found that it was not the heat but the combustion gases which turned the fruit yellow, and the active agent was later identified as ethylene. There is now ample evidence that ethylene induces ripening in fruits, causing the climacteric rise to begin earlier than it otherwise would (and also that it causes some morphogenetic responses such as a downward curvature of petioles). Ethylene is effective in concentrations as low as one part per million in the atmosphere. A further and equally remarkable aspect of ethylene metabolism is that the gas is produced in small quantities by plant tissues. Care must be taken in storing unripe fruit for the inclusion of a few ripe fruit (which produce ethylene faster than the unripe fruit) may hasten ripening of the remainder.

Reference has already been made to the change in permeability of cell membranes at senescence (p. 186).

Longevity and Death

The life span of vascular plants varies widely from the ephemerals which complete their life-cycle from seed to seed in a matter of months, to some of the conifers which have lives in excess of a thousand years. The maximum ages recorded for many other trees (*Pinus, Ulmus, Salix*) lie between 100 and 500 years. Not all parts of the tree will share this long life, of course. Elm and willow are deciduous, shedding leaves in the autumn and bud scales in the spring as the new shoots expand. Pine, on the other hand, is an evergreen. Its needles do not fall in their first autumn but drop in irregular sequence after two or three years.

The death of some leaves before the death of the plant as a whole is not confined to woody species. In many annuals the lower leaves die as fresh leaves are produced higher up the shoot, while in bluebell the spring foliage dies down later in the season leaving the bulb below ground to propagate the plant in the following year. It is in the flower that one finds the most striking instances of short life. As horticulturalists well know, the petals of many flowers last only a short while once they are fully expanded. Finally we should note that individual cells differ in their life span. A cell that becomes a fibre may die as soon as its wall is fully thickened, while its parenchymatous neighbour remains living for very much longer.

While the death of the individual organs of a plant generally follows the phase of senescence, a wide variety of causes may result in the death of the whole plant. It may, for instance, succumb to extreme environmental conditions such as frost, drought, severe competition for light, or mechanical damage due to high winds; or as a consequence of the activity of parasites, insect attack, and so on. However, there are many instances where a plant dies under circumstances that do not allow us to conclude that it was killed by any external agency. We must then accept that the plant has died through some internal cause—such as the onset of senescence. This last seems particularly to be the case in monocarpic plants (Chapter 3), those which flower and fruit but once in their lives and die shortly afterwards.

In some micro-organisms the situation as regards death is far less clear-cut than in the angiosperms. When bacteria or blue-green algae reproduce asexually the parent cell is completely transformed into two daughter cells without any residue that could be called "dead". In this sense the organisms are endowed with potential immortality and will go on multiplying unless prevented, for instance, by a shortage of nutrients or an accumulation of toxic substances. Although green algae such as *Chlamydomonas* can reproduce themselves asexually, the parent cell does leave some residue (its wall) when zoospores are formed, but it remains true that with adequate lighting and a continuous supply of fresh nutrient medium a colony of *Chlorella* cells will pass through very many generations; barring accidents and any external cause of death it could continue growth indefinitely.

PLATE 11

PHOTOPERIODISM: PLANTS OF *Hyoscyamus niger* (HENBANE) GROWN UNDER GREENHOUSE CONDITIONS IN MANCHESTER AND PHOTOGRAPHED IN EARLY MAY. One plant (right) was covered each afternoon until next morning so that it received only eight hours of light per day; it has formed a rosette of leaves. The plant on the left is a control, fully exposed to the light for periods ranging from the 11-hour days of early March to the 15-hour days of May; the stem has elongated and now bears flowers. It follows that *H. niger* is a long-day plant.

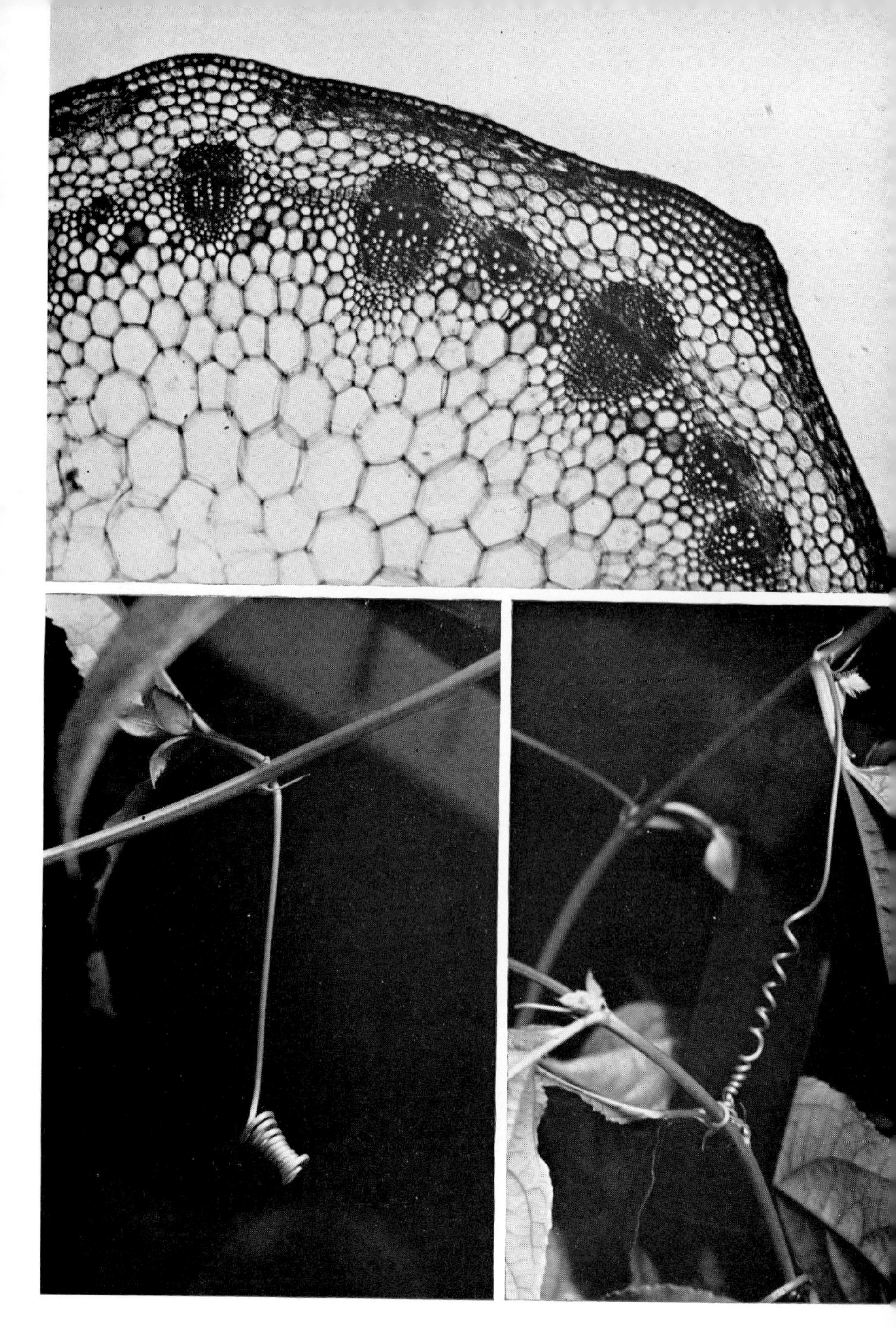

PLATE 12

Above: TRANSVERSE SECTION OF THE STEM OF *Calendula* (MARIGOLD). Of the six principal vascular bundles shown, numbers 1 and 4 (counting from left to right) are leaf traces; they are associated with salient ridges of cortical collenchyma and their metaxylem vessels are smaller than those of the other strands.

Below: TENDRILS OF *Passiflora*. The one on the left has failed to find a support and is forming a single coil. The one on the right has grasped a nearby stem at the bottom of the picture; with both ends of the tendril fixed the central part has subsequently twisted to form two opposite helices separated by a short straight portion.

The roots of some angiosperms can be excised and grown by themselves under culture conditions (p. 267). If the roots are allowed to grow for a few days and the tips then excised and transferred to fresh culture medium, they will make further growth. Repeated subculturing of the tips establishes a **clone**—a group of individuals which have identical genotypes (p. 639) because they have all been derived asexually from a single ancestral individual. Such a clone can be maintained for many generations and will then live far longer than the root system of an intact plant of the same species. It seems that the rapidly-growing isolated root tips are capable of long-continued growth while the root system on an intact plant has death imposed upon it.

A number of attempts have been made to delay senescence and death in sexually reproducing angiosperms. In annuals, the normal sequence of events is that after a period of vegetative growth, flowers are produced, seed is set, and the whole plant then senesces and dies. The onset of senescence can be delayed by systematic removal of the flowers as fast as they appear. The life of soya bean plants can be nearly doubled in this way. This is not a simple nutritive effect, the development of fruit denying metabolites to the rest of the plant, since the removal of "male" inflorescences in a dioecious plant such as spinach is just as effective as removal of flowers and fruit from the "female" plants. Spinach plants that were prevented from ever coming into flower by giving them a non-inducing photoperiod were said to live on "for an indefinite period of time". The senescence of individual leaves can sometimes be delayed by excising the shoot beyond the leaf and some success has attended efforts to delay senescence by spraying leaves with solutions of synthetic hormones and similar substances.

12 REPRODUCTION IN ANGIOSPERMS

STRUCTURE OF THE FLOWER

The **flower** is fundamentally a reproductive shoot concerned with the production of seed. Such attributes as scent and special colouration are common, but they are not essential. Note also that what passes as a flower in common speech is sometimes a compound structure, an assemblage of many flowers. A flower is built up on a stem or **pedicel**, the end of which is usually somewhat enlarged to form the **receptacle** (or torus), upon which the floral organs stand. The actual reproductive parts are of two kinds, the **stamens**, known collectively as the **androecium**, and the **carpels**,

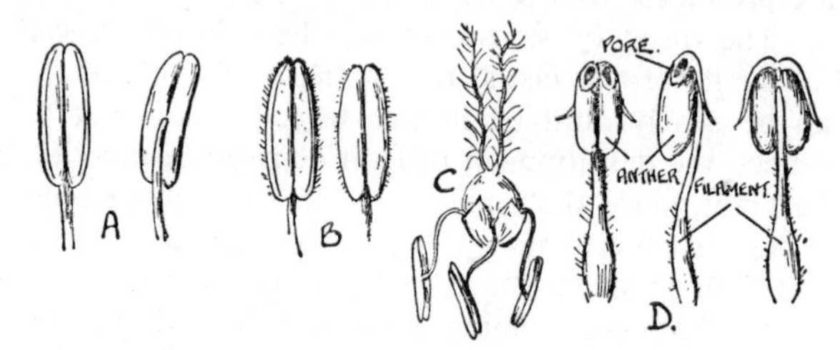

Fig. 154. STAMENS, EXTERNAL VIEW.
A, adnate, dorsifixed (*Nicotiana*); B, innate, basifixed (*Datura*); C, versatile, dorsifixed (*Triticum*); D, poricidal dehiscence (*Arctostaphylos*).

known collectively as the **gynaecium**. Most flowers have also some accessory often rather leaf-like structures known collectively as the **perianth**.

The Stamen

In most cases a stamen consists of a narrow stalk or **filament** (Fig. 154) containing a single vascular bundle, and bearing at its free end a swollen **anther** containing pollen grains. Although there is plenty of variation in detail, with some anthers producing little horns or tails, or having the anther attached to the filament by a flexible joint, there are relatively few plants in which the standard pattern of filament and anther cannot easily be recognised.

In section most anthers show four **pollen-sacs** or microsporangia (Fig. 155). The solid part of the anther where the vascular strand continues from the filament is often called the **connective**; sometimes it is enlarged or gives rise to special outgrowths. Within each pollen-sac a number of pollen mother cells (or microspore mother cells) divide to produce the pollen-grains (or microspores). The anther wall is parenchymatous, consisting of several layers of cells

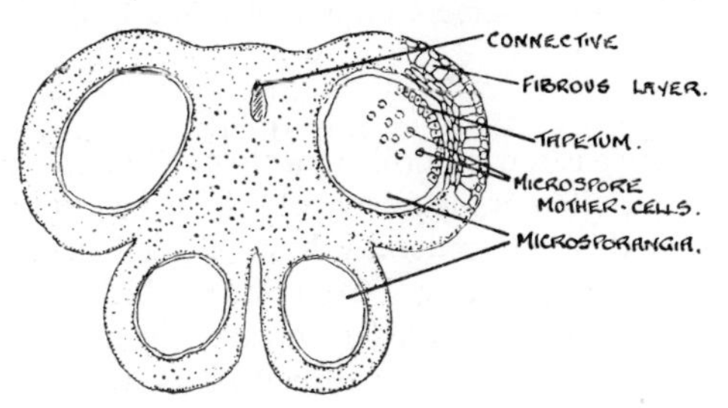

Fig. 155. TRANSVERSE SECTION, YOUNG UNDEHISCED ANTHER OF *Lilium*.

with different functions. The cells lining the pollen-sac have some special concern with the nutrition of the pollen mother cells, and this layer is distinguished as the **tapetum**. The outermost layer but one is called the **fibrous layer** because of the special thickenings of the walls of its cells (Fig. 156). The curvature of the anther wall which is responsible for the dehiscence (or opening) of the anther and the liberation of the pollen-grains is believed to be due to the unequal stresses set up in the fibrous layer as it dries. The great

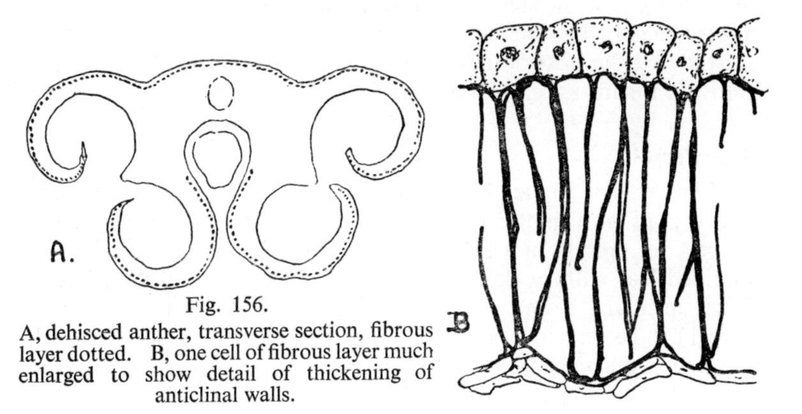

Fig. 156.
A, dehisced anther, transverse section, fibrous layer dotted. B, one cell of fibrous layer much enlarged to show detail of thickening of anticlinal walls.

majority of anthers open by two longitudinal slits, the two pollen-sacs on each side being torn open together (Fig. 156, A). There are other possibilities. Some anthers open by pores (Fig. 154, D) and in some cases these even have hinged lids. When the exact course of the cell divisions in a young anther is worked out, it is always found that the pollen can be traced back in origin to cells one layer removed from the surface of the plant. This is of some importance genetically, because it means that the pollen of a chimaera (p. 85) will all be derived from the same component (usually the inner one).

The Pollen

In all ordinary cases each pollen mother cell gives rise by meiosis (p. 163) to four pollen-grains, each of which has initially a single nucleus, though this will generally have divided before the pollen is shed. The four grains derived from one mother cell stick together for some time in a group called a **tetrad**. In a few families (*e.g* Ericaceae) the tetrad is actually dispersed as a unit, but in most pollens the grains have separated long before the anther opens. The grain has an outer coat or **exine**, which is extremely resistant to decay and to chemical reagents, and which is often elaborately sculptured, with spines, ridges, etc. In many pollens the exine has a pleated structure, with definite furrows which allow the volume of the grain to change considerably without any tearing of the wall. At certain points (often in the furrows) are germ-pores, thin places in the exine from which a pollen-tube may later grow. Germ-pores are of complex structure, and are reasonably constant in number and position for any given species. So varied are the forms of pollen-grains, in fact, that most grains can be identified, at least approximately, by simple microscopic inspection. This is important in studying the history of vegetation (p. 598) and also has applications in, for instance, the commercial analysis of honey.

The Carpel

The carpel is a much less obvious structural unit than the stamen, and it is often a matter of some difficulty to determine how many carpels are present in a flower. The carpel is to be regarded as an infolded leaf with ovules, the structures from which the seeds will arise, springing from it near the margins. The form of a simple carpel can be seen in a pea pod. At a very early stage in its growth the pod is an open trough of tissue, very similar to many a young leaf. As the pod enlarges the edges of the trough come together and fuse by a kind of natural graft. At maturity the pod has two seams or sutures along which it will easily split, and does in fact split naturally if left upon the plant. One suture carries the seeds and represents the two grafted edges of the carpel, the other suture is its midrib. Carpels just as easy to understand as this can be found in *Delphinium* and *Caltha*, where, however, each flower has more than one.

In most flowers the gynaecium consists of several carpels very completely fused together, and in these conditions the course of development is greatly disturbed, so that at no stage is it possible to see the carpels as separate leaf-like structures. In such cases the carpel is a useful theoretical idea rather than a structure to be dissected out.

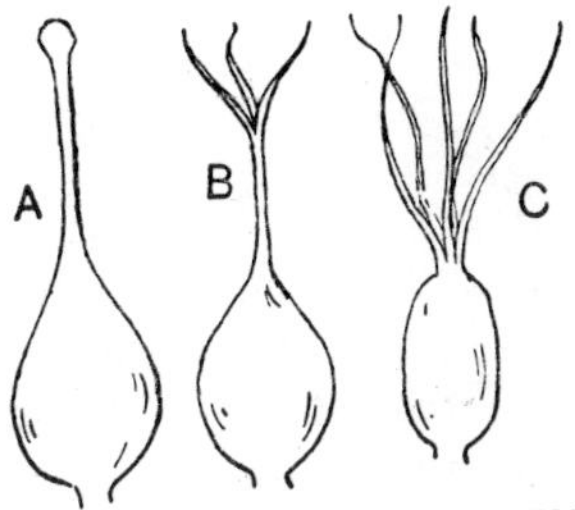

Fig. 157. DEGREES OF FUSION OF STYLE.
A, primrose; B, *Luzula*; C, *Stellaria*.

Every gynaecium has one or more specialised areas adapted for the reception of pollen. These regions are known as **stigmas**. A simple carpel like the pea pod usually has a single stigma at its tip. A stigma is often carried up on a stalk-like support or **style**, which is also part of the carpel. The hollow part in which the ovules lie is called the **ovary**, and the portions of carpellary tissue to which the ovules are immediately attached are called the **placentae** (plural of placenta). When there are several carpels fused into a **syncarpous** ovary, it is usual to find that the fusion of the styles and stigmas is less complete than that of the lower, ovary-forming parts of the carpels (Fig. 157); complete fusion of the stigmas is, however, perfectly possible (Fig. 157, A) and there will then perhaps be no external indication of the number of carpels present. There are two main ways in which carpels may be fused into a syncarpous ovary. When all the carpel edges are brought to the centre the ovary will have as many chambers (or loculi) as there are carpels (Fig. 158). This is often expressed by saying that the ovules are in **axile placentation**. Less commonly the carpel edges do not reach the centre, so that the ovary has only a single loculus (Fig. 159). The ovules are then in **parietal placentation**.

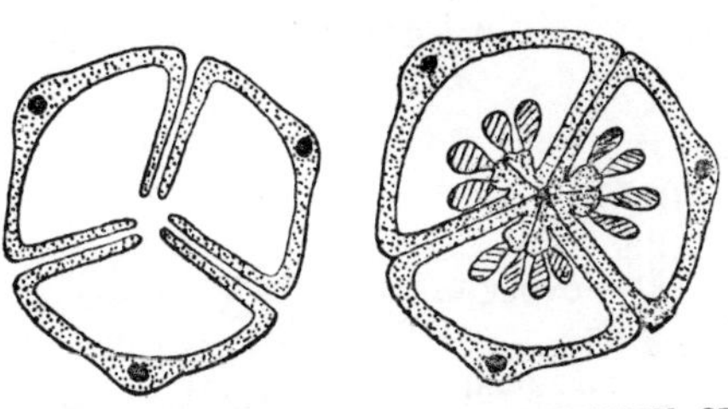

Fig. 158. DIAGRAMMATIC REPRESENTATION OF THE UNION OF THREE CARPELS TO FORM A TRILOCULAR OVARY WITH AXILE PLACENTATION, e.g. *Lilium*, SEEN IN TRANSVERSE SECTION.

There are two kinds of syncarpous ovary which will not yield the convenient kinds of transverse section we have just considered.

In many ovaries the number of ovules is reduced to one or two in each loculus, often indeed to one in the whole ovary. When there are few ovules they are usually attached at the base of the ovary, or sometimes they hang from its roof (Fig. 160). In neither case can the placentation (which will still be fundamentally axile or parietal) be satisfactorily made out from a transverse section across the middle of the ovary. There is also a type of single-chambered (or unilocular) ovary in which numerous ovules are carried on a central column of tissue which rises from the ovary floor and may or may not extend to the roof. This condition, which is relatively uncommon, is known as **free-central placentation**, and it is fairly clear from intermediate forms which exist that it has arisen from axile placentation by a failure of development in the tissue of the ovary partitions (or septa).

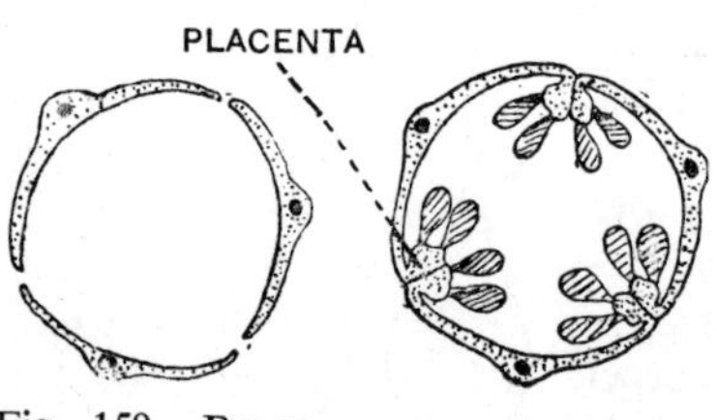

Fig. 159. DIAGRAMMATIC REPRESENTATION OF THE UNION OF THREE CARPELS TO FORM A UNILOCULAR OVARY WITH PARIETAL PLACENTATION, e.g. *Viola*, SEEN IN TRANSVERSE SECTION.

In extreme cases, where the ovary is unilocular and the fusion of the styles and stigmas unusually complete, the number of carpels

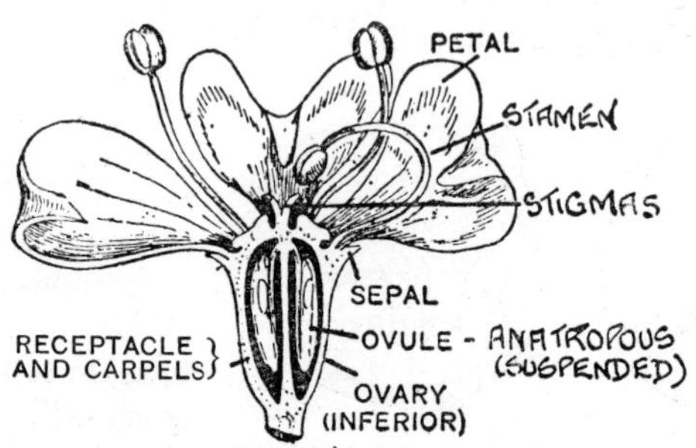

Fig. 160. FLOWER OF UMBELLIFERAE.
(Half-flower in vertical section.)

present can only be determined by a detailed study of the development and of the arrangement of the vascular strands (for a carpel has usually three principal veins). Fortunately, such difficulties are rarely encountered and the Cruciferae (p. 411) and Primulaceae (p. 433) are the only families of plants in which a British student will ordinarily be unable to determine the number of carpels himself.

The general rule is that the number of carpels is equal to the number of loculi, or to the number of principal style-branches or stigmatic lobes, *provided that this number is greater than one.* By far the commonest mistake is to conclude that there is only a single carpel, when in fact there are several. Outside the Leguminosae (p. 414) and the genus *Prunus*, there are very few flowers with only one carpel. Special provisions apply to Cruciferae (p. 411) in which some of the carpels are sterile, and to a few families such as Labiatae (p. 424), Boraginaceae (p. 438) and Linaceae, in which the carpel midribs grow inwards to form extra ("false") septa, so that the number of ovary chambers is *twice* the number of carpels, without, however, affecting the branching of the style. It is sometimes important to distinguish carefully the *principal* branches of the style. Three main branches, each forking into two, will indicate three carpels, not six. **Apocarpous** gynaecia, in which there are separate free-standing carpels, occur in a number of families such as Ranunculaceae (p. 430), Alismaceae, and Rosaceae (p. 416). The apocarpous condition, which is relatively uncommon, offers no special difficulty of interpretation.

The Arrangement of Floral Parts

In the great majority of cases the floral organs are arranged in concentric circles or whorls. The carpels are nearest the centre, with the stamens surrounding them, while the outer region is occupied by the **perianth**. Not every flower is complete, but if we establish the rules which govern the arrangement of the parts when everything is present, then the incomplete examples will present no difficulty. They can be explained by the simple omission of one thing or another.

Two principles apply very widely. The numbers of parts in the various whorls of a flower tend to be equal, and successive whorls tend to alternate, so that a member of one whorl bisects the angle between two members of the next. In determining the basic plan of a flower our main concern will always be to discover how far it departs from the simplest ideal condition, which is a system of equal-numbered alternating whorls.

Any type of floral organ may occur in more than one whorl. Many flowers, for instance, have two whorls of stamens. When the perianth has two whorls the separate parts (or **perianth segments**) may all be nearly alike, but often the outer ones can be distinguished as the **sepals**, making up the **calyx**, and the inner ones as the **petals**, making up the **corolla**.

It is convenient to represent the structure of a flower symbolically, as a formula. For this purpose each type of floral part is denoted by a letter: K for calyx, C for corolla (or P for an undifferentiated perianth), A for androecium, and G for gynaecium. The numbers of parts are shown by figures, one figure for each whorl. Thus A5 + 5 means two alternating whorls of stamens with five stamens in each whorl. It is normal practice to put into floral formulae a certain amount of additional information, but for the present we may use them in this simple form. Floral constructions such as: P3 + 3 A3 + 3 G3; K5 C5 A5 + 5 G5; K5 C5 A5 G5; K4 C4 A4 + 4 G4, are frequently encountered and call for no special remark. By far the commonest departure from this perfect mathematical symmetry is a reduction in the number of carpels, giving such formulae as: K5 C5 A5 + 5 G3; K5 C5 A5 G2. G2 is an especially common and widespread condition. It is, on the other hand, decidedly rare for a formula to run in twos all through.

The stamen is exceptional among the floral organs in having a very small area of attachment to the floral axis or receptacle. No very drastic rearrangement is required to make room for a few extra stamens. There are also biological reasons (see the section on pollination, pp. 345 and 349) why it should often be advantageous for a flower to produce large amounts of pollen. There are many cases where the number of stamens is large, and usually also variable as between one flower and the next. In formulae we use ∞ (the mathematician's infinity sign, but here read as "numerous"). Increase in number is commonest in the stamens, but sometimes occurs elsewhere, giving formulae like P ∞ A ∞ G ∞, and K5 C5 A ∞ G ∞. Where numerous parts occur it is often almost impossible to discover their exact arrangement. Certainly A ∞ does *not* mean that all the stamens are in one whorl.

Spiral Construction

In some families, of which Ranunculaceae, Nymphaeaceae, Magnoliaceae, and Cactaceae are the ones most familiar in Britain, some or all of the floral parts are in a spiral phyllotactic pattern and not in whorls at all. The practical recognition of spiral construction is not difficult but it is usually necessary to remove some of the parts. If, for instance, some of the stamens are taken out of a buttercup, the system of scars which is revealed will show clearly that the stamens are in sloping spiral lines just like those formed by the scales of a fir-cone. Although some flowers have a pure spiral construction throughout there are many in which a spiral arrangement of the inner parts is coupled with a tendency to form whorls, often imperfect, in the perianth. In these mixed flowers various Fibonacci numbers may occur, and one sometimes finds, almost always against a background of individual fluctuation, a predominance of some such combination as K3 C8 (the commonest situation in *Ranunculus ficaria*) or K5 C13 (in *Nuphar*).

Zygomorphy

Many flowers, if we ignore some finer details of their construction, are radially symmetrical in the manner of a starfish. If we take a flower K5 C5 A5 G5 there will be ten planes of symmetry; if we wish to cut the flowers into two mirror-image halves we can do so along any one of ten diameters. Flowers with radial symmetry are **actinomorphic**. There are, however, many influences at work which tend to make a flower lopsided or dorsiventral. Quite apart from anything else, any lateral flower is in a lopsided environment, for it has a stem to one side of it and a leaf to the other. It is not therefore at all surprising that many flowers are **zygomorphic**, with only one plane of symmetry. In a zygomorphic flower the upper and lower sides are different; if we wish to cut the flower into two mirror-image halves we can only do so along one diameter, ordinarily the one which is vertical when the flower is in its natural position. Zygomorphy occurs in very different degrees. The slighter forms involve little more than the curvature of some of the parts, or a difference in length between the stamens on the two sides. Slight zygomorphy is widespread; probably no family is entirely free from it. It involves no modification of the floral formula and creates no special difficulty of interpretation.

There is, however, a rather restricted range of families, some of them often met with, in which extreme zygomorphy, involving major changes in the construction of the flower, has become well established. These flowers are difficult, and beginners can make many mistakes with them. The important thing to grasp is that extreme zygomorphy often obscures the basic plan of a flower to such an extent that it becomes positively dangerous, for instance, to attempt to count the number of petals. Once a corolla has become very strongly hooded or two-lipped it is very likely that petals have branched or fused together in a most confusing way. The fundamental structure is then not to be determined by any quick examination of the flower, but only by a full investigation of the anatomy and especially of the development. Fortunately, we can easily simplify the situation. We may entirely set aside a rather mixed group of rare or isolated cases of extreme zygomorphy and also some families which are important but not often seen in Europe. If we confine ourselves to the floral constructions which will ordinarily and commonly come before the British student, we have only three specialised zygomorphic formulae to consider:

(*a*) P3 + 3 A1 G3. This is the structure of most orchids. Deciding whether a plant is an orchid is easy (p. 426). Working out the formula for yourself is extremely difficult.

(*b*) K5 C5 A4 (or sometimes A2) G2. This is found in a whole range of families, the petals being fused into a corolla tube. Examine a few specimens of Labiatae and Scrophulariaceae so that you know roughly what to expect, and when you meet some unknown flower which has the same general construction, keep to the formula! These flowers often *look* as though they had K2, or C4, or G4. All these things are mere deceptive resemblances; *genuine* departures from the formula are almost unheard of.

(*c*) K5 C5 A5 + 5 G1. This is the standard pattern in the Papilionatae (again an easy group to recognise; see p. 414). There are two main ways of going wrong. The calyx is sometimes two-lipped, which misleads the unwary into writing K2. The stamen filaments are joined, sometimes all ten together, but more often nine joined and one free. This must not be expressed as A10 or A9 + 1 (see p. 335).

The Fusion of Floral Parts

Many floral organs are perfectly free, so that an individual petal or stamen, for instance, can be taken off without disturbing or damaging its neighbours. Very often, however, the parts are fused together. There are in fact two kinds of fusion to consider. Sometimes two structures which were in the early stages of growth quite independent are pressed together, epidermis to epidermis, and join by a grafting process. This kind of true fusion always occurs in the growth of carpels, even free ones (p. 324) but it is rather uncommon in the outer parts of the flower. Examples can be found (the anthers of Compositae, p. 425; the carinal petals of Papilionatae, p. 414) but most of the fusions found in the androecium and perianth are **congenital fusions**, formed in an entirely different way, by common growth of the parts. In cases of congenital fusion organs which may in the first place arise quite independently are carried upwards by the action of a continuous meristem which runs underneath all of them. Congenital fusion involves no grafting process, no real junction of things which were originally separate; the word "fusion" is here being used in a somewhat abstract and theoretical sense. Every case of congenital fusion presents us with a difficult problem when we come to name the parts. Suppose, for instance, that young petals, by the action of a ring-shaped meristem in the receptacle, are carried up on a tube. Botanists will then say that the petals are fused (congenitally, of course, but it is not customary to specify this) and will talk about a corolla tube. This is purely conventional; we could just as well regard the thing as a tubular outgrowth of the receptacle, or as an entirely new development, a kind of spacer or distance-piece inserted between receptacle and corolla. Any argument as to which is the correct form of expression is quite futile and leads to no useful result. In dealing with cases of congenital fusion, botanists follow established customs which are now very unlikely to undergo any substantial change. To a great extent these customs arise from historical causes; the forms of speech which happened to be adopted when these matters first received attention have tended to persist. Considerations of practical convenience have also had great influence. To call what is conventionally treated as a corolla tube an outgrowth of the receptacle might be an improvement in pure descriptive accuracy, but it would create new difficulties in the use of floral structure as a means of classifying and identifying plants. On the whole, we had better stay as we are.

Fusion of parts is represented in floral formulae by the use of brackets. K (5) (read "K5 joined") means five sepals joined (congenitally, of course, though nobody bothers to say so), into a cup or tube which will (if we are lucky) have five obvious points or teeth. Fusions can involve members of more than one whorl. Among the monocotyledons P (3 + 3) is common and means a perianth tube with six teeth. One also meets such combinations as {C (5) A4}, read "C5 joined A4 epipetalous". This is a tubular corolla of five petals, though very likely not with five obvious teeth (you can see for yourself that the flower is zygomorphic), and with the stamen filaments springing from the corolla tube partway up. By convention the lower part of the tube is regarded as corolla only, without any stamen tissue. The stamens are therefore epipetalous (*i.e.* "upon the petals") and not otherwise joined to them.

There is one rule about fusions in the outer part of the flower which causes a great deal of trouble to beginners. Quite illogically, botanists refuse to recognise any fusion of calyx with corolla. It is *not done* to write {K5 C5} or {K5 C5 A5}, though there are plenty of flowers which look like this. By convention, the tubular or cup-shaped thing at the bottom of such a flower is *part of the receptacle*, giving us K5 C5. By much the same kind of absurdity as one finds in irregular verbs, it is, however, perfectly permissible to write P (3 + 3) or even {P (3+ 3) A3 + 3}.

Congenital fusion is a widespread effect which has played some part in the evolution of most flowers (for there is some degree of congenital fusion in every syncarpous ovary, though the final closure of the ovary cavity is brought about by true fusion) and is by no means confined to single flowers. It is perfectly possible to have fusions involving several flowers, or fusions of flowers with associated cataphylls, etc., or indeed, fusions of purely vegetative parts.

The Form of the Receptacle

In its simplest form (Fig. 161, A) the receptacle is merely a slightly enlarged ending to the pedicel, and the flower is then said to be

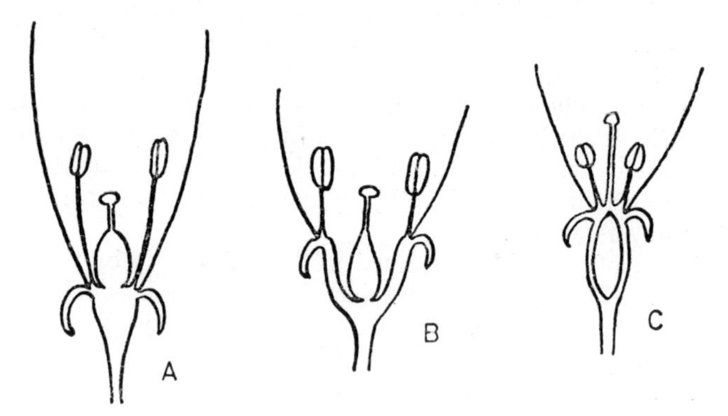

Fig. 161. FLOWERS IN LONGITUDINAL SECTION.
A, hypogynous; B, perigynous; C, epigynous.

hypogynous. In some cases the base of the receptacle is expanded sideways so as to make a flange, upon which the parts of the androecium and perianth are seated. In a more pronounced form this development brings about the production of a deep cup-shaped receptacle, with the carpels inside it, and the other floral parts standing on its rim (Fig. 161, B). Flowers which show this lateral expansion of the receptacle, even when it is very slight, are said to be **perigynous.** Perigyny, especially in its more extreme forms, is relatively uncommon, and characteristic of particular families, such as Rosaceae (p. 416). There are also many flowers in which the stamens and perianth appear to stand on the top of the ovary near to the styles. This is known as **epigyny** (Fig. 161, C). Most of the older books take it for granted that the epigynous flower has been derived from a perigynous form in which the receptacular cup has fused with the ovary wall. In reality, as explained above, such expressions amount to no more than a conventional manner of speaking. In most epigynous flowers there is no evidence that the apparent ovary wall contains any receptacular tissue at all—it might just as well bc regarded as a direct congenital union of the carpels with the bases of the stamens and perianth.

By a convenient convention the ovary in hypogynous and perigynous flowers is described as **superior**, that in epigynous flowers as **inferior**, and the position is shown in formulae by putting in a line which, as a matter of history, is intended to indicate the level at which the stamens are attached. Thus $G\,(\underline{2})$ is read as "G2 joined superior" (probably a hypogynous flower, but might be perigynous) and $G\,(\overline{5})$ as "G5 joined inferior" (which can only happen in an epigynous flower).

The Complete Floral Formula

All the conventions which are regularly used in floral formulae have now been described. They should be studied until the formulae can be handled with some fluency. Some writers have made complex additions to floral formulae, introducing special signs to indicate the placentation of the ovules or to show whether the flower is zygomorphic. All such elaborations are more trouble than they are worth, and the tendency is to abandon them. You may also encounter formulae in which fusions are shown by things like musical phrase-marks: $\overset{\frown}{C\,(5)\,A5}$, and so on.

Aestivation

Although it is perfectly possible to have a flower without anything of the kind, it is very common for floral organs, especially the flatter things like petals, to overlap at the edges, at least in the bud stage. This overlapping or **aestivation** is perhaps not very important from the functional point of view; it is mainly a matter of packing, and the actual direction of overlap may seem at first glance to be an accidental matter of no special interest. It turns out, however, that an unexpected degree of geometrical regularity exists, and that different families of plants are often characterised by different types of aestivation. Where two petals or sepals overlap one may be said to have an outside edge, the other an inside edge, and in some flowers these edges differ in structure as well as position. A pctal of *Hypericum* has two edges of quite different shape. In the sepals of *Geranium* spp. and of some of the wild roses the differences between inside and outside sepal-edges are very pronounced, and three different types of sepal can be recognised, with one outside edge, or two, or none at all. Less obvious differences of the same kind are widespread, and indeed the symmetry of many actinomorphic flowers (or for that matter of most zygomorphic ones) is only approximate. If details of aestivation are taken into account, then the division of a flower into mirror-image halves will often become impossible.

Floral Diagrams

It is convenient for purposes of comparison to draw a diagram which shows the arrangement of the parts in a flower in a conventional way, more like a map than a picture. The established customs

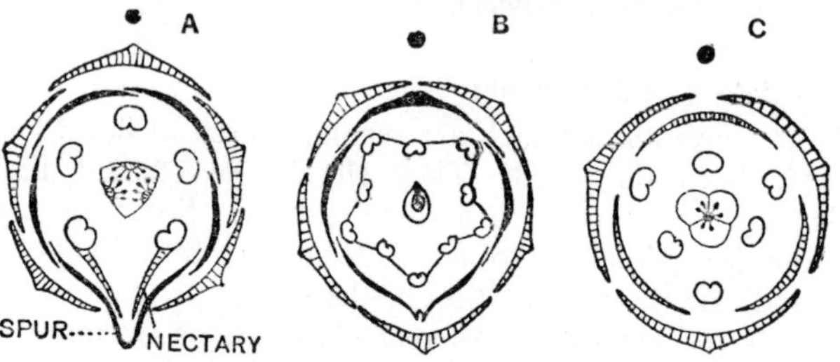

Fig. 162. FLORAL DIAGRAMS.
A, *Viola*; B, Papilionatae (monadelphous form); C, *Lilium*.

in this work are quite simple and are sufficiently illustrated by the examples given in this book. Every student should gain some experience in the preparation of floral diagrams from specimens. The following are the points most often overlooked:

(*a*) If a flower is strongly zygomorphic the diagram should be made obviously zygomorphic as well.

(*b*) Aestivation should be shown wherever the conditions allow it to be determined.

(*c*) All significant fusions of parts should be shown (those, that is, which would qualify for mention in a floral formula).

(*d*) The position of an organ is the position of its base. A flower might, for instance, have all its anthers hanging out at one side; this will not ordinarily be shown in the diagram, which is concerned with the bases of the filaments.

(*e*) It is usual to show, where appropriate, the relationship of the flower to the rest of the inflorescence (p. 337). Ordinarily there will be a sepal at the top of the diagram. Leguminosae are exceptional, and have the odd sepal at the bottom.

The shapes of the organs in the outer region of a floral diagram are quite arbitrary. It is usual to make some acknowledgement of conspicuous developments like a spurred petal, but there is no need for any approach to realism. Some people also draw a quite conventional transverse section of the ovary showing little more than the nature of the placentation. A diagram is much more valuable, however, if it includes a fairly accurate ovary section showing at least the principal vascular bundles.

The floral diagram is closely related to the floral formula. The diagram shows zygomorphy, aestivation, and placentation, which the formula does not. On the other hand, it leaves unspecified the superior or inferior position of the ovary, which we so easily put into the formula. Such comparisons ignore the main advantage of the formula—its suitability for conversational use.

Interpretation of Floral Structure

In the examination of an unfamiliar flower difficulties will sometimes arise of a kind which we have not so far considered. Students often make a mistake about the number of whorls present, especially in the androecium and perianth. Consider, for instance, the formula K5 C5 A10. This is not an absolutely impossible construction, and examples of it might perhaps be found. But it is not very likely, for whorls tend, on the whole, to be equal-numbered, at least in the outer parts of a flower. A really close inspection of those ten stamens will almost certainly show that five of them are a little longer or thinner or earlier in development than the ones between them. In other words, A5 + 5.

The perianth is more troublesome. In all ordinary cases we have only two whorls at the most (though a few families produce multiple perianth whorls). It is not usually difficult to decide how many whorls of perianth are present, but a little care is needed whenever it appears that the number of parts in a whorl is an even number. Suppose that we have C8. By an unfortunate accident of aestivation it might happen that four petals were tucked inside the other four, giving a quite misleading appearance of C4 + 4. In any species where this kind of uncertainty arises it is necessary to look at several flowers. The deceptive type of aestivation will never be quite constant. So in *Potentilla erecta* we write C4 (and not C2 + 2) because the system of overlapping is variable, but in *Tulipa* we write P3 + 3 (and not P6) because the overlapping is constant; there are *always* three outer segments and three inner ones. The greatest difficulties, however, are those which arise when only one perianth whorl is present. What is it to be called? Students are often perplexed by the apparent inconsistency of the treatment which is given to different flowers. The flower of *Anemone* looks as though it has a corolla but no calyx, so why do we write K6 C0? If *Alchemilla* has an obvious calyx but no corolla and if that state of affairs is admitted in the formula, why is the equally calyx-like structure in *Mercurialis* always called a perianth and never a calyx? All these questions have to be settled by comparison, by looking at the related plants. *Anemone* belongs to the Ranunculaceae (p. 430). When petals occur in the Ranunculaceae they are of peculiar construction and usually tubular. The petal-like structures of *Anemone* are flat; they might pass for petals in any other family but not here. Some Ranunculaceae have their own peculiar sort of petal and petal-like (but flat) sepals *as well*, which leaves little doubt about *Anemone*. *Alchemilla* is one of the Rosaceae, in which the calyx is of unusual construction and very easy to recognise (p. 416) and petals are usually present as well. So there is not much doubt about the situation in *Alchemilla*. *Mercurialis*, however, is one of the Euphorbiaceae, a large family in which there is never more than one perianth whorl. There is no evidence that any of these plants, or any of their ancestors, ever possessed any inner whorl that might have been called a corolla. So, although the structure looks like a calyx, we have really no good reason to call it that; it seems wiser to avoid committing ourselves. "Perianth" is as far as we can go.

There are many cases, particularly with petals, where floral organs are fused only at the extreme base. Such slight fusion is easily overlooked, yet it may be of great importance in assigning a plant to a family. The test is to hold a flower upside down and to slice away the base of the flower with a razor. If it is possible to reach a level at which the petals come away from the ovary and receptacle, but still remain attached to each other, no matter by how narrow a frill of tissue, then the petals must be treated as joined.

In some flowers there are rather conspicuous organs of indeterminate character inside the normal perianth, if any, and apparently additional to the floral parts which it is usual to include in the formula. When it is a question of fleshy lobes or protuberances, often with an obvious secretory function, and perhaps concerned in the production of nectar (p. 50) it is customary to refer to these structures (collectively, and without any regard to their actual shape) as the **disc**. Nectary outgrowths of small size are in fact very common about the bases of ovaries and stamens, and it is not surprising that larger and more conspicuous examples should occasionally be seen. Another class of outgrowth is the **staminode**, a structure which occupies a site where a stamen might be expected to occur, but does not itself produce pollen. Good examples can be seen in *Scrophularia*, with K (5) {C (5) A4} G $\underline{(2)}$ but with a staminode in the place of the "missing" stamen at the back of the flower, and in *Samolus*, which has five staminodes and five fertile stamens, unlike the other Primulaceae, which have only the five fertile stamens. Some corollas, and some of the P (3 + 3) perianths of the Liliiflorae, have a kind of inner frill, or sometimes a set of scales, known collectively as the **corona**. The true nature of these structures is quite obscure; the slighter ones amount to little more than folds in the corolla tube, as is common in Boraginaceae, but the "trumpet" of a daffodil cannot be explained so easily.

It is sometimes important to detect breaches of the common rule that successive whorls alternate. It is, for instance, one of the most constant features of the Primulaceae that their five stamens are on the same radii as the petals, an arrangement to which *Samolus* gives us an important clue. This matter should always be investigated by opening the corolla, laying it out flat, and tracing the principal vascular bundles upwards and downwards until the relationship becomes clear. Note especially that in zygomorphic flowers the filaments and anthers will almost always be displaced either towards the back of the flower or towards the front, but that the bases of the stamens will usually be found in regular alternation with the perianth segments.

The Inflorescence

It is possible to have a solitary flower, either terminal upon a vegetative shoot (e.g. *Tulipa*) or standing in the axil of a foliage leaf (e.g. *Fuchsia*). More commonly, however, there is a fairly distinct flower-bearing part of the shoot system, in which flowers are grouped together, usually with associated cataphylls, but without foliage leaves. Any definite flower-cluster of this kind is called an **inflorescence**.

In many inflorescences there is a clear and definite relationship between the branching of the stem and the arrangement of the cataphylls. It is then possible to deal with the structure systematically. Any cataphyll which is axillant to a pedicel is called a **bract**, and any cataphyll which is borne upon a pedicel below the flower is called a **bracteole**. These terms are strictly relative; a cataphyll which is the bracteole of one flower may at the same time be the bract of another. In most dicotyledons there are two bracteoles, standing right and left of the flower, while most monocotyledons have one only, standing at the back of the flower. Bracts and bracteoles are commonly represented in floral diagrams. In many of the more specialised inflorescences, however, there are cataphylls which do not bear any simple relationship to any particular flower. In such cases the word "bract" is applied in a very loose and irregular fashion to almost any inflorescence cataphyll. Any definite assemblage of bracts (using the word now in its wider sense) is called an **involucre.** In a few special cases where there are involucres of different grades the words "bracteole" and "involucel" are applied to the subordinate involucres (p. 421).

The branching of inflorescences can be divided rather sharply into two patterns. In **racemose** branching, which is fundamentally monopodial, a parent shoot gives rise to a large and indefinite number of lateral branches before its own growth comes to an end. In **cymose** branching, which is fundamentally sympodial, the parent shoot gives rise only to a small and definite number of lateral branches (rarely more than two, often only one) before its own growth comes to an end (normally by the production of a terminal flower). In many books an attempt is made to draw this distinction rather differently, by paying attention to the way in which the parent shoot actually terminates. The claim is often made that in a racemose inflorescence the main axis never ends in a flower, but only in a kind of abortive apical meristem which was (at least in theory) ready to continue with further growth. This contention is quite unsound. It is true that in many large racemose inflorescences growth is apparently brought to a halt by external factors, with obvious abortion of the apex. There are, however, many small racemose inflorescences in which there is a terminal flower which puts a definite end to any possible further growth of the main axis. In the last analysis, the difference between racemose and cymose inflorescences is only a matter of degree. It is useful to sort out the typical forms of inflorescence, because this can assist materially in the classification and identification of plants (Chapter 13). When the typical forms have been distinguished, however, there remains an untidy residue of transitional types, which have never been the subject of detailed study, and about which most books have little to say.

Racemose Inflorescences

The basic type of racemose inflorescence is the **raceme** (Fig. 163, A) in which flowers are arranged in a long sequence upon a central axis, each flower in the axil of its bract. Racemes, and also many inflorescences of more complex construction, are often referred to as spikes, but in botanical work there is a tendency to reserve the word "spike" for racemes in which the pedicels are of negligible length, a trifling distinction of little real value. It is important to note the regular sequence of flowers in a raceme. Seen from the side, the oldest flowers are at the bottom, the youngest at the top. Seen from above, if we take into account the enlargement of the older parts of the central axis and any possible elongation of the pedicels, then the older flowers will, in general, be further out from the centre of the stem than the young ones. This orderly arrangement of the flowers in plan view, though inconspicuous in normal racemes, becomes very important in racemose inflorescences with shortened axes.

Cymose Inflorescences

Cymose inflorescences are divided into classes according to the number of branches arising from each parent stem axis. In the **pleiochasium** (Fig. 163, B) there are more than two branches at each stage, almost always standing in a whorl. Pleiochasia are rare, the only examples commonly encountered in Britain being in *Euphorbia*. In the **dichasium** (Fig. 163, C) each axis gives rise to two branches, normally opposite to each other. Here the bracteole of one flower serves, as in all cymes, as the bract of a flower of the next higher order. In the diagrams these inflorescences are necessarily shown flat, but in reality they are three-dimensional. In a dichasium, for instance, if two branches stand north-and-south, then *their* branches will be east-and-west, and so on. In plan view pleiochasia and dichasia will not show the orderly arrangement of flowers according to age which we have noted in the raceme. The oldest flower of all occupies a central position, and the others are arranged round it in a pattern more complicated than anything which a raceme could generate.

In **monochasia** (Figs. 163, D, E) where each pedicel has only a single lateral branch, there is more scope for variation, because the relationship between the direction of one stage of branching and that of the next is not fixed. In the diagrams two possibilities are shown. Working in three dimensions it is possible to model at least four main types, all of which can be found in one plant or another. A consideration of the flowering order of a long monochasium will show that it is very similar to that of a raceme, with the oldest flower at the bottom. Evidently also, as in other cases of sympodial branching (p. 65), the sympodium is likely to grow straight, or nearly so. The only obvious difference between a monochasium and a raceme will then be in the position of the bracts, underneath the apparent pedicel in the raceme but opposite to it in the monochasium. Inevitably, some plants produce these inflorescences without any bracts at all. Some of the resulting uncertainties can be cleared up by detailed investigation; the bractless inflorescences of Cruciferae (p. 411) are regarded as

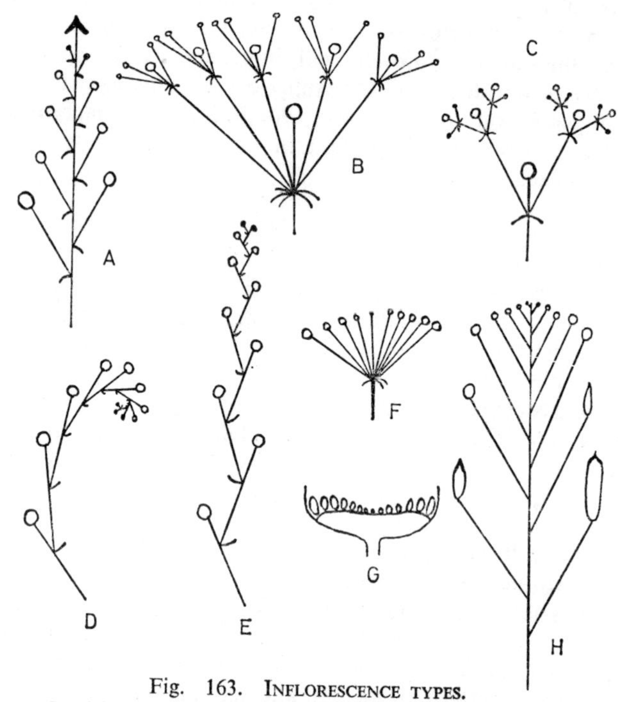

Fig. 163. INFLORESCENCE TYPES.
A, raceme; B, pleiochasium; C, dichasium; D and E, monochasia; F, racemose umbel; G, racemose capitulum; H, bractless corymbose raceme.

racemes on evidence which is really quite conclusive, those of Boraginaceae (p. 438) are generally treated as monochasia of the pattern shown in Fig. 163, D, though in this case a few experts have expressed the opposite opinion. Some frankly ambiguous cases remain.

Condensed Inflorescences

If, in any raceme or cyme, we suppose all internodes to be reduced to negligible length, except for the free part of each pedicel, then the resulting inflorescence will be an **umbel** (Fig. 163, F). All the apparent pedicels will spring from a common centre, and all the cataphylls will be brought to the same level so as to form an involucre. In most umbels there has in fact ceased to be any agreement between the number of flowers and the number of bracts, and it is no longer possible to trace any connection between a particular bract and a particular flower. The umbel is the prevailing type of inflorescence in a small number of plant families (racemose umbels in Umbelliferae, p. 419; cymose umbels in Amaryllidaceae, p. 439) and occurs sporadically elsewhere (e.g. *Lotus* in Papilionatae). It is usually easy to judge from the order of flowering whether an umbel is racemose or cymose. It is important not to confuse umbels with pleiochasia (p. 339) or corymbose panicles (p. 342).

If the condensation of the inflorescence is carried a stage further, by shortening the pedicels to vanishing point, then the result is a **capitulum** (Fig. 163, G). The end of the stem is necessarily enlarged to accommodate the flowers, forming a conical or disc-like structure which is called a receptacle, though it is clearly not equivalent to the receptacle of a single flower. A capitulum has a surrounding involucre, and in some capitula there is in addition a bract to each flower (p. 425). Capitula are especially characteristic of Compositae and Dipsacaceae, but there are a number of examples in other families, including some monocotyledons. Most capitula are apparently racemose, but some of those in Dipsacaceae show a flowering order which seems to indicate a cymose origin.

Compound Inflorescences

The basic types of inflorescence can be compounded in various ways. One may have an umbel of umbels, for instance, or a raceme of dichasia. In many compound inflorescences there is a progressive change in the manner of branching as one passes to smaller and smaller units. The difference in the number of lateral branches which we take as the distinction between racemose and cymose branching is after all an expression of the general vigour of the parent shoot. Many compound inflorescences, therefore, start in a racemose manner but produce branches which, as it were, "run down" by stages into dichasia and monochasia. It is convenient, without making any detailed analysis, to use the word **panicle** for any large compound inflorescence which branches, at least in the early stages, in the manner of a raceme. Some rather surprising compounds occur. A capitulum of capitula, for instance, is a perfectly possible thing (e.g. *Echinops*, a common garden plant). In some of the more extreme compound inflorescences difficulties of interpretation arise from the omission of some of the parts, or from widespread congenital fusion. In Betulaceae and Fagaceae (p. 432) one encounters, for instance, dichasia with the middle flower suppressed, and compound bract-structures resulting from the congenital fusion of several to many cataphylls. In grasses, where the inflorescence is built up from racemose units called spikelets (p. 428) there are examples (*Cynosurus*) in which some of the spikelets are completely sterile, appearing again as specialised bract-structures.

Descriptive Terms

In many inflorescences the lengths of the various stalks are so adjusted that the flowers are brought into a single layer which may be quite flat or gently domed. This tendency can be seen very clearly in *Sambucus* (elder) and *Crataegus* (hawthorn). Any such flat-topped inflorescence may be called a **corymb**; the umbel is almost always more or less corymbose by virtue of its construction, but there are also corymbose racemes, cymes, and panicles. In many racemes (*e.g.* Cruciferae) the corymbose effect is only transitory; the flowers are kept in a close grouping by a special spurt of growth on the part of the pedicel, but the fruits are spread out in a normal racemose fashion (Fig. 163, H).

There is a fairly definite biological type of inflorescence called a catkin. Typically this is a sausage-shaped group of many small inconspicuous wind-pollinated flowers. Most catkins hang down, and the main axis is sometimes remarkably flexible. It is, however, quite impossible to define the catkin in any rigid fashion (willow catkins, for instance, stand upright, and are insect pollinated) and there are examples which are treated as catkins by some people but not by others (e.g. *Urtica*). Nor is there any constancy in the structure of catkins; many are simple racemes but others (p. 434) are racemes of dichasia.

Specialised Inflorescences

The capitulum is often rather flower-like in appearance, and people who are not botanists are often surprised to find that a daisy head is not a single flower. In reality, however, it is very rare for any serious difficulty to arise in the interpretation of a capitulum. Although the individual flowers are often inconveniently small they are sufficiently complete to leave no room for doubt as to their true character. There are a few specialised types of inflorescence, however, in which the flowers, besides being closely packed, are so much simplified in structure that an uninformed observer is likely to have great difficulty in deciding where one flower ends and another begins. Some of these difficult inflorescences are dealt with in connection with the particular families in which they occur (catkins of Betulaceae and Fagaceae, p. 432; spikelets of Gramineae, p. 427), but others are more conveniently treated here.

The cyathium of *Euphorbia* (Fig. 164) should be examined with particular care, for a student who mistakes it for a flower will get into serious difficulties. The inflorescence of *Euphorbia* is usually a pleiochasium of some complexity, with whorls of (usually) five branches or three, reducing progressively as higher orders of branching are reached. The general layout offers no difficulty, but the branches, instead of ending in flowers, end in highly

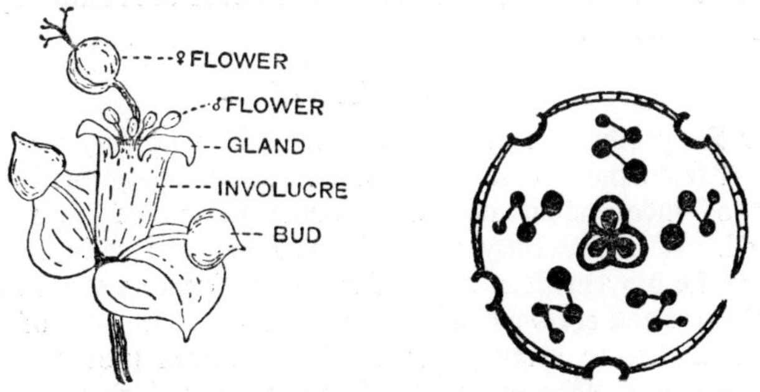

Fig. 164. General view and plan of the cyathium of *Euphorbia*.

specialised units called **cyathia**. Each cyathium consists of three parts:

(1) A cup-shaped involucre of five fused bracts. Upon the rim of the cup, between the free tips of the bracts, are kidney-shaped or crescent-shaped nectary glands. There may be five glands, but often some are missing.

(2) A single, often long-stalked, female flower, which in most species projects above the involucre or hangs over its edge.

(3) Within the involucre five zig-zag monochasia (one in the axil of each involucral bract) of male flowers, each consisting of a single stamen only.

Dissection will reveal some further refinements. Usually the male monochasia have their own bracts. When a stamen is taken out, it appears to have a filament which is jointed half-way up. Really this joint is the junction of pedicel and filament (some of the allied genera have a little perianth at this point).

Another unusual arrangement can be seen in the fig (*Ficus*). The structure here is fundamentally that of a capitulum which has been folded upwards to enclose a cavity. There is a hollow pear-shaped receptacle with the flowers on the inner surface, and opening to the outside world only by a small pore (much obstructed by involucral bracts) at the end opposite the stalk. Some of the other Moraceae do in fact have an open capitulum.

In several important families of monocotyledons there is a strong tendency for the stalk of the inflorescence to become fleshy, and sometimes the flowers are partially buried in this swollen axis. An inflorescence of this kind (or more strictly its stem only) is often called a spadix; associated with it there is often a large bract called a spathe. This type of development is rare in the British flora and is usually studied in *Arum* (p. 440., Fig. 171), a highly specialised plant with a number of features not found in most spadix-type inflorescences.

POLLINATION

For the production of seed it is normally necessary for pollen to travel from the anther to a stigma. As pollen-grains have no power of independent movement some means of transport is required. It is necessary to distinguish between **self-pollination**, which is the movement of pollen from an anther to a stigma of the same flower, and **cross-pollination**, which is the movement of pollen from an anther to a stigma of a different flower (not necessarily to a flower on a different plant). In genetical work these terms are used in a different sense. In connection with breeding experiments "cross-pollination" means pollination between flowers of two different plants, pollination between flowers of the same plant being "self-pollination".

Undoubtedly there are many instances where pollination takes place more or less accidentally through the joint action of gravity and wind. Wherever an anther is above a stigma, pollen is likely to fall from one to the other, and whenever a flower is shaken by the wind there is a chance that pollen will be thrown on to a stigma. Where flowers are closely grouped even cross-pollination must often result from accidents of this kind. Probably, however, no species relies entirely upon this casual type of pollination. Every flower seems to be committed, to some extent, to a definite system of pollination, involving in the vast majority of cases the action of some external agent to carry the pollen. The available pollinating agents are wind, water, and various kinds of animal. Most animal pollinators are insects, and no others are considered in this book, but in fact a considerable number of other animals (birds, bats, slugs, etc.) are known or suspected to be concerned in the pollination of particular species.

Anemophily

Pollination by wind is a simple but extremely wasteful process. The wind is practically random in its operations, and a stigma is a very small target compared with the rest of the world. Wind-pollinated or **anemophilous** plants are compelled to produce enormous amounts of pollen, almost the whole of which will be lost. This pollen is light and dusty, typically with small, smooth, rather featureless grains. Anemophily is found mostly in plants which are gregarious, covering substantial areas of land. It would obviously not be effective for isolated individuals. If each stigma is to stand a good chance of receiving pollen, then the air of a whole countryside must be thoroughly loaded. It is this large-scale effect upon the atmosphere which distresses people who are allergic to the pollen (hay-fever, etc.).

Anemophilous flowers have well-defined structural tendencies. Often they are unisexual, and when they are, there is often a great numerical excess of male flowers. The wind needs no allurement; it takes no account of colour or scent or sweetstuffs, and all the special features of animal-pollinated flowers are lacking, the only colour in many cases being that of the pollen itself. Anemophily, on the other hand, demands exposure of the parts, and it is usual to find stamens and stigma projecting well clear of any perianth or bracts which may be present. Stigmas are often feathery or adhesive. The predominant trend is towards reduction and simplification of structure, but there are some exceptional cases in which the pollen is violently ejected, as in *Urtica* (Fig. 165), where the stamens are bent inwards to the centre of the flower and then released with a flick action.

Fig. 165. MALE AND FEMALE FLOWERS OF *Urtica*.

Hydrophily

Water-pollination or **hydrophily** is very rare, and indeed most pollens are quickly spoilt if they get wet. Even the aquatic angiosperms nearly all have their flowers above the water-line, and the water plays no part in their pollination. There are two kinds of hydrophily. In *Elodea* and *Vallisneria* the solitary female flower is raised to the surface by a long stalk and the stigma is exposed just above the water. The numerous small male flowers break off and float to the surface where they open. These male flowers drift downwind against the female and a surface-tension effect tilts them so that the anthers touch the stigma. The pollen itself does not get wet. Afterwards the stalk of the female flower contracts spirally and draws the developing fruit under water again. *Zostera,* which is a totally submerged marine monocotyledon, has long filamentous pollen-grains with a specific gravity just equal to that of sea-water. These are carried by the tide and tend to wrap round any stigma they may strike.

Entomophily

If a plant is to be regularly insect-pollinated or **entomophilous**, three conditions must ordinarily be satisfied:

(1) The insect must be enabled to find the flower. There are two ways of doing this, and most entomophilous flowers combine the two. A characteristic scent may be emitted, and the reproductive parts may be associated with some organ which has a characteristic colour (the coloured structure need not be part of the flower—sometimes it is a bract).

(2) The pollen must be attached to the insect, firmly enough for transport but not so firmly that it will not come off at the end of the journey. Most entomophilous pollens are, in the mass, sticky, oily, pasty substances, but in some cases (*e.g.* orchids, p. 365) much more elaborate methods of attachment are found.

(3) The insect's visit to the flower must be sufficiently beneficial to ensure that the insect species maintains in successive generations those instincts upon which the plant species depends for its pollination. Usually the inducement which is held out is a supply of food, but there are other possibilities. Some flowers, for instance, are pollinated by insects which use the flowers as breeding grounds (*Ficus* and *Yucca*, p. 367).

There are some secondary considerations which have evidently had a great influence upon the evolution of entomophilous flowers. A pollinating insect will not necessarily arrive as soon as the flower opens, and delay is especially likely in bad weather. It is therefore likely to be advantageous if the pollen can be protected through a wet spell. In this respect an entomophilous flower, which can utilise the active movements of an insect for the removal of its pollen, is in a far better position than an anemophilous one, which must expose its stamens and stigmas freely. In fact, a high proportion of entomophilous flowers are so constructed that even heavy rain does not reach their inner parts. Another major factor in the situation is the need to exercise some control over the admission of insect visitors. Pollen is itself a rich food, and in many flowers it is supplemented by other attractions. Not every insect which enters a flower will be an effective pollinator. A pollen-eater, for instance, may never touch a stigma in its life. Accordingly there is a strong tendency to enclose the parts, to force the insect to adopt a standardised line of approach, and generally to create conditions which will favour one type of insect and at the same time discourage others. Only in exceptional cases, of which, however, there are a good many, does the pollination of one plant species depend entirely upon one particular insect species, but some degree of specialisation is very common. In general it is quite useless to discuss pollination in terms of some anonymous "insect", and even worse to assume that pollination in most angiosperms depends mainly upon the activity of bees.

Pollinating Insects

Many published statements about pollination are of little value because they assume that the insect is intelligent and that it will act as a human being might do in a similar situation. The experimental evidence is entirely opposed to this view. Insect behaviour seems to be almost entirely instinctive; a given situation automatically produces a standard response, which is pre-arranged in the nervous system and does not have to be learnt by the individual. If the situation is a natural one, the response will be reasonably appropriate, and may indeed appear to be very clever. In artificially contrived situations, however, quite inappropriate responses of an apparently stupid kind can readily be produced. In addition it can be shown that the senses and sensations of insects are significantly different from our own. In attempting to determine the reasons for an insect's actions, in trying, for example, to decide whether scent or colour is more important in attracting an insect from a distance, experiment is the only safe guide.

There have been many experiments upon the colour-vision of insects. Working with bees, butterflies, and a number of others it has been repeatedly found, by offering food in association with various coloured objects, that the insects can distinguish readily between a blue colouration and a grey of equivalent brightness. In other words, they see blue as a colour. Similar experiments with red invariably fail. Red, so far as most flower-visiting insects are concerned, is not a colour. It is indistinguishable from grey, and only very doubtfully distinguishable from green. This discovery perhaps does something to explain the rarity of pure red as a flower-colour in the wild plants of temperate regions, and the abundance of blues, mauves, and purples. Another point of some interest is the ability of many insects to see by ultra-violet light, to which the human eye is totally blind. This means that flowers which appear white to us are, from the insects' point of view, neither white nor all of the same colour.

Insects appear to be much less affected by the shape and size of flowers than they are by the actual colour. Some of the hoverflies, for instance, have an instinctive attraction to certain colours but, so far as can be discovered, no perception of size or shape at all. A hoverfly which is instinctively blue-seeking will fly towards any object which is about the right shade of blue, regardless of size, shape or position, or whether it is still or moving. Some butterflies are a little more selective, and will approach a coloured object if it lies within a certain size-range, but not if it is too big or too small. Even they, however, are uncritical about shape, making little distinction between circles, triangles, crosses, etc. In view of these results it is a little surprising to find how strongly the behaviour of an insect is influenced by the colour-patterns which so many flowers display. Many flowers have special markings, lines, and spots of contrasting colour which indicate the whereabouts of the entrance. Such markings are often known as nectar-guides. Many insects are strongly affected by these markings; presented with a coloured picture, or with a real flower covered by glass, they take up the correct position. There is a certain degree of standardisation about these patterns; there are, for example, many blue flowers with yellow centres, but perhaps not a single case of the reverse arrangement.

Much less is known about the response of insects to scents, but the available evidence suggests that scent is not ordinarily very important in attracting insects from a distance. Certainly scent can be very important when the insect gets close to the flower. In some experiments porcelain flower-models have been used; insects will approach these quite normally, but will not attempt to enter them unless the models have been provided with scent from a real flower. Scent in some flowers at least is not so much a means of attracting the insect as a means of stimulating it to perform the right actions upon arrival. The only known cases of long-range attraction by scent concern a special class of flowers which have (by human standards) offensive smells and which are pollinated by insects which would otherwise feed upon dung or corpses (Carrion-flowers, p. 362).

The feeding habits of insects are related to the form of the mouth-parts. Many of the smaller flies and beetles are pollen-feeders, and have really no provision for taking liquid food. Pollen-feeders are not necessarily ineffective in pollination, and indeed there is a distinct class of "pollen-flowers" (e.g. *Papaver*, *Clematis*) in which pollen, of which there must, of course, be a great excess, is the only food material offered to the visitor. Some of the larger flies are pollen-feeders, but most of them take nectar. Their tongues are rather short, often less than 3 mm. and rarely more than 5 mm. They require a rather open type of flower, so that they can get close to the nectar, and the nature of their mouth parts often requires that the nectar should be spread out on a flat surface; they cannot penetrate into narrow tubes or pockets. The honey bees are in the main nectar-feeding insects, though they take pollen as food for their young. Their tongues are of medium length (about 7 mm. in the hive bee, about 10 mm. in the larger bumble-bees) and are capable of being inserted into narrow spaces. A bee can take nectar from a thin surface film in case of need, but it can fill up much more quickly from a deep reservoir. The butterflies and moths have tubular mouth-parts of great length and can penetrate into deep pouches and pockets. To be of real use to these insects nectar (and most of them have no other source of food) must be supplied in considerable depth.

The effectiveness of an insect as a pollinating agent must depend upon the regularity of its visits to flowers of the same species. Observations upon insect behaviour reveal three main influences which tend to secure this regularity. At any given time and place the number of plant species which are in flower will often be very limited. To that extent the plants themselves compel the insects to restrict the range of their visits. Secondly, it appears that some of the insect species, especially among the flies, have more or less rigid colour-fixations. A particular species of fly, for instance, may be found to restrict itself to yellow flowers, while another species will only visit blue ones. This is not, of course, a restriction to one plant species, but it goes a long way towards narrowing down the range of choice. Thirdly, it can be shown in the case of bees that although workers from the same hive may be visiting several different plants, an individual bee will usually confine itself to a single species for several days at a time. Under garden conditions it is easy, by marking bees with spots of enamel between the wing-roots, to satisfy oneself that each insect returns again and again to flowers of the same type.

The Balance between Self-pollination and Cross-pollination

There can be no doubt that in many hermaphrodite flowers self-pollination occurs more or less regularly, either by the accidental effects mentioned on p. 344, or by more definite adaptations of behaviour (p. 355). It by no means follows, even when self-pollination occurs, that it will result in the production of seed, and indeed there are various influences which tend to secure, if a stigma is pollinated from mixed sources, that the seed which is produced shall be derived, so far as possible, from "foreign" rather than "local" pollen. There is also a large class of cases in which self-pollination is for various reasons unlikely or impossible. There appears, in fact, to be a general bias against self-pollination, which is sometimes prevented, and often rendered ineffective when it does occur. This bias shows itself in a great variety of ways, and in dealing with these it is necessary to remember that cross-pollination between flowers on the same plant has precisely the same genetical consequences as self-pollination. Both are forms of inbreeding. Inbreeding, if it is repeated, very rapidly reduces the variability of the population, and although it does not appear to be intrinsically harmful, it certainly increases the effect of any hereditary weakness which may happen to be present. In view of the genetical position it is desirable to make a sharp distinction between factors which merely favour cross-pollination, without necessarily preventing inbreeding, and factors which act positively to secure outbreeding with another individual.

Factors Tending to Prevent Self-pollination

(1) **Monoecism:** A plant which carries separate male and female flowers upon the same individual is said to be monoecious. There is clearly no possibility of self-pollination. In some monoecious plants (*e.g.* maize) the male and female inflorescences are rather widely separated, and this may reduce the proportion of inbred seeds to quite a low level (usually less than 1 per cent. in maize).

(2) **Dichogamy:** A flower in which the stamens and stigmas do not ripen at the same time is dichogamous. The great majority of hermaphrodite flowers show some degree of dichogamy. There are two possibilities. In a **protogynous** flower the stigma is ready to receive pollen before the anthers open. In a **protandrous** flower the pollen is shed before the stigma is in a condition to receive it. Of the two conditions protandry is much the commoner. Dichogamy is often associated with characteristic movements of the floral organs. A good example is *Chamaenerion* (= *Epilobium*) *angustifolium*. Here the flower is active for two days. On the first day the stamens stand out in front of the corolla and shed their pollen, but the stigma-lobes are still tightly pressed together so that no pollen can reach the receptive surface. The flower is therefore

functionally male. On the second day the stamens have withered and fallen back, and the stigma-lobes have opened. This is complete protandry, and it makes self-pollination almost impossible. Complete protogyny (which is a rare condition) is even more effective in this respect. In most cases, however, dichogamy is very far from complete, leaving a more or less extended "overlap" period in which self-pollination is perfectly possible. Also, even in a case like that of *Chamaenerion*, the sequence of flowers in the inflorescence is such that pollination can easily take place between adjoining flowers, making it very doubtful whether dichogamy is effective in reducing the frequency of inbreeding. What extreme dichogamy certainly does do is to make the plant more dependent upon insect visitors. The consequence of this appears in several familiar genera (e.g. *Epilobium*, *Geranium*). Each of these has large-flowered species which are completely dichogamous, and also small-flowered species in which dichogamy is partial at the most. It looks as though the smaller flowers, which perhaps cannot rely upon frequent insect visits, cannot afford to take the risk involved in becoming completely dichogamous. In some instances there are other considerations which seem to rule out the possibility of complete dichogamy. Evidently a pollen-flower (p. 349) is in a special position; if it were markedly dichogamous there would be no incentive for insects to visit the flower in the female condition.

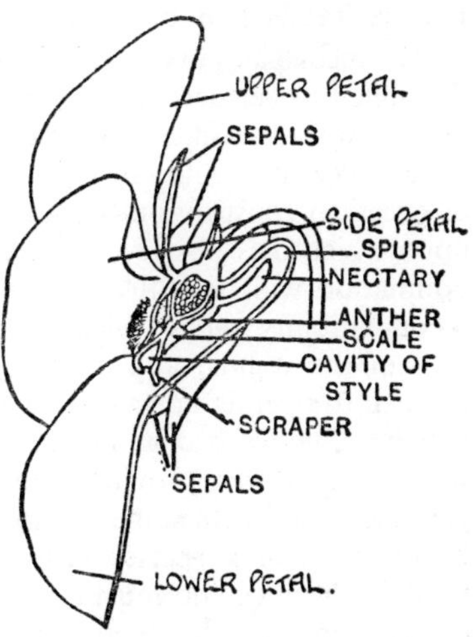

Fig. 166. FLOWER OF GARDEN PANSY (*Viola altaica*), SEEN IN VERTICAL SECTION, HALF-FLOWER.

(3) **Mechanical devices:** In some of the more specialised types of flower there are structures which act as non-return valves, the effect being to expose the stigma to an incoming insect, perhaps bringing pollen from some distant source, but to cover the stigma as the insect withdraws. In *Viola* (Fig. 166) the style ends in a knob, the actual stigmatic surface being in a pit upon the lower surface of this knob. The valve is a flap attached at the rear edge of the pit. An insect entering the flower pushes the flap back and exposes the stigma, but the act of withdrawal at once covers the

stigma. Under the hooded petaloid style of *Iris* is a flap which operates in a similar way, though here the stigmatic surface is on the face of the flap itself. There are also many flowers (*e.g.* orchids, p. 365) which possess no obvious valve-mechanism but which attach the pollen to the insect in a specially precise and definite way which makes self-pollination unlikely or even impossible. All these developments make the flower more dependent upon insect visits, and it is sometimes possible to trace the kind of relationship to flower-size which has already been noticed in connection with dichogamy. The smaller-flowered species of *Viola*, for instance, have no flap to the stigma.

Factors Tending to Prevent Inbreeding

(1) **Incompatibility:** This is a physiological effect, a failure of the pollen to perform its normal fertilising function. It can arise in various ways. Sometimes all the flowers of a species are similar in appearance, but pollination is only effective if there is a difference of genetical constitution between the pollen and the stigmatic tissue upon which it is placed. Where there is such incompatibility self-pollination will be entirely unproductive, for the pollen will carry incompatibility genes which exactly duplicate some of those in the cells of the stigma, and in these conditions the pollen will not be allowed to operate normally. Cross-pollination, on the other hand, will be effective except in the case, which must sometimes arise, where the flower providing the pollen possesses incompatibility genes identical with some of those in the stigma. This may happen by chance (for a species has not an unlimited variety of incompatibility genes), and must *always* happen when the two flowers are on the same plant. Incompatibility therefore renders all pollinations ineffective except certain selected types of cross-pollination between plants of contrasting genetical constitution. Incompatibility occurs in some plants of commercial importance. In planning a pear orchard, for instance, it must be remembered that all trees of a single variety have been produced by vegetative propagation from one original plant and therefore have the same genetical constitution, so that it is essential to consult the tables and choose varieties which are capable of crossing. Incompatibility reactions are widespread; they are, of course, only discoverable by experiment. There is no reason why incompatibility should not occur in plants which also display dichogamy, monoecism, or a mechanically refined type of flower, and some interesting combinations are known. A few orchids, for instance, in which self-pollination is in any case very unlikely to occur, nevertheless display an extreme type of

self-incompatibility in which the stigma is actually poisoned and killed by pollen of the wrong type. On the other hand, complete self-incompatibility is understandably rare among small-flowered species.

Many species in which complete incompatibility is unknown display partial effects of a similar kind. It is in fact a rather general rule that "foreign" pollen tends to be *quicker* in effecting fertilisation of the ovule than "local" pollen (that is, pollen from the same flower, or at least from the same plant). When local and foreign pollens arrive simultaneously upon the same stigma, which is a common occurrence, the outcome may vary according to the actual number of grains present. If there are enough foreign grains to fertilise all the ovules, then there will be no opportunity for the slower local pollen to contribute to the output of seed. If, on the other hand, there are only a few foreign grains, then there may be some ovules left over for the local pollen to fertilise.

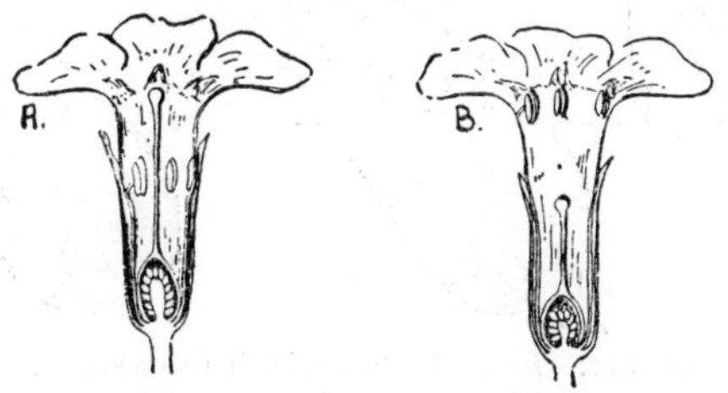

Fig. 167. DIMORPHISM IN *Primula*.
A, pin-eyed; B, thrum-eyed form in longitudinal view, half-flowers.

In a few genera (including, however, both monocotyledons and dicotyledons) a special kind of incompatibility has developed which involves the differentiation of the hermaphrodite flowers of one species into two or three distinct classes, differing in the length of style and some other features. Such a condition is known as **heterostyly**, the most readily available heterostyled flower being that of *Primula* (Fig. 167). Here there are two types of flower, known as pin-eyed and thrum-eyed, borne upon separate plants. Although the most obvious difference lies in the relative positions of stamens and stigma, there are in fact many other points of distinction (the pollen-grains are of different size, and differ also in the chemical composition of their contents, there are differences in the size of the stigmatic epidermal cells, and so on). There is nothing in these flowers to prevent self-pollination, or the transference of pollen between flowers on the same plant. Such pollinations, however, give a very poor yield of seed. The reproduction of the species depends almost entirely upon what are called the **legitimate pollinations**, in which pollen moves *from a stamen to a stigma of corresponding height*. This means, in *Primula*, pin-to-thrum or thrum-to-pin. So far as *Primula* is concerned, the position might be regarded merely as a modified incompatibility in which the incompatibility genes had the unusual effect of making the plants visibly different.

In some other instances, however (e.g. *Lythrum*, Fig. 168), there are three forms of flower, still borne upon different plants, still exhibiting many differences in pollen-structure, and still producing a normal yield of seed only from legitimate pollinations. This demands a more complicated explanation. For if we consider a

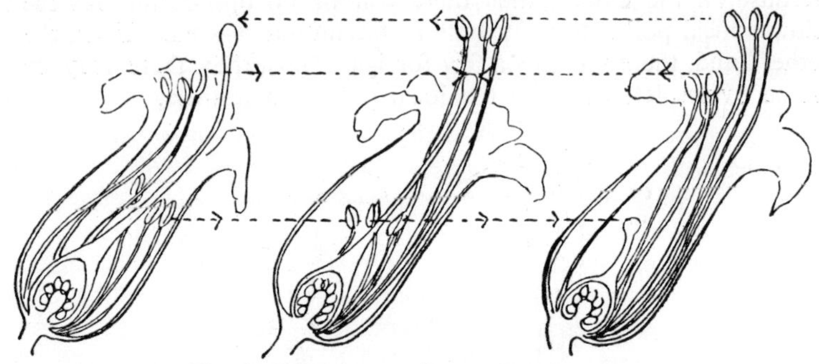

Fig. 168. *Lythrum salicaria*, TRIMORPHISM. Three types of flower.

medium-styled flower, the pollen in the long stamens and the pollen in the short stamens must be genetically similar, yet the short-stamen pollen will be effective upon a short style, though the long-stamen pollen will not be. In heterostyly the differences between the pollens are not always determined by the genes of the pollen itself. Breeding experiments have shown that the flower-forms are genetically determined, rather as sexual differences are genetically determined.

(2) **Dioecism:** A dioecious species is one in which some individuals have only male flowers while the remainder have only female flowers. Complete dioecism is decidedly uncommon. It prevails in a few families of woody plants (especially Salicaceae) but otherwise occurs only sporadically in particular species or genera belonging to a wide range of families.

There are many species in which the distribution of stamens and ovules is less constant than in simple dioecism, or in which there seems to be a gradient of sexual expression rather than a sharp distinction between different classes of individual. A few examples will show the kind of variability to be expected. In *Plantago lanceolata*, which is usually listed as a simple hermaphrodite, the normal anther is a broad creamy-white structure. In some places plants are found with much narrower, yellow-green anthers, producing pollen which is (all?) abortive, so that the plant is functionally female. *Fraxinus excelsior* produces male, female, and hermaphrodite flowers, and although it is doubtful whether such a thing as a purely male or purely female tree ever occurs, the proportions of the three types of flower can certainly vary widely from one tree to another. In many Labiatae there are two types of individual, but one has hermaphrodite flowers and the other female flowers. Male plants are unknown. In *Valeriana dioica* there is complete dioecism, but with four types of plant, not two. Each type of individual has its own form of flower, the possibilities being: pure female flowers with no anther-rudiments, functional females with rudimentary anthers, functional males with a stigma-rudiment, pure males with no stigma-rudiment. This gradient in sexual expression is coupled with a gradient in corolla-size. In some dioecious species there is a pronounced difference in the ecological requirements of male and female plants, leading to a corresponding difference in geographical distribution (*Petasites, Stratiotes, Elodea*). These plants give valuable evidence regarding the effectiveness of vegetative propagation as a means of dispersal.

Factors Affecting the Occurrence of Self-pollination

We have seen (p. 344) that self-pollination is often more or less accidental, and we have reviewed a whole series of arrangements which tend either to prevent this kind of accident or to make it ineffective if it should occur. There is, however, much to be said upon the other side. In some instances self-pollination, far from being accidental, results from marked peculiarities in the structure or behaviour of the flower. The biological significance of this seems clear; cross-breeding is no doubt in general to be preferred (for it gives a species significant advantages in vigour and adaptability), but where the provision for cross-breeding is unreliable it is desirable that self-pollination shall operate as a stand-by. In many species, in fact, the great majority of the seeds produced arise from self-pollination.

(1) **Movements of the Flower-parts:** In Compositae (p. 425) and in a number of other plants with branched styles, the stigmas curl outwards and downwards as the flower gets older, until they

touch either the anthers themselves or some other organ which has already been dusted with pollen. A similar effect is sometimes, though less commonly, brought about by movements of the stamens or (in cases with epipetalous stamens) the corolla. It is difficult to judge the true significance of some of these effects; that a withered stamen should fall against the stigma is not necessarily convincing evidence of a major evolutionary development. Some of the more definite effects are, however, distributed in an intelligible way; species with small flowers provide for self-pollination in a manner which is not adopted by their showier relatives. (*Malva sylvestris* and *M. rotundifolia* are often quoted in this respect.)

(2) **Cleistogamy:** A small number of species, belonging, however, to several families of dicotyledons, produce cleistogamous flowers. These are of simplified construction and are automatically self-fertilised in the bud stage, in fact they never open at all until they are destroyed by the development of the fruit. Cleistogamous flowers are always a supplementary development; that is to say, no species has *all* its flowers cleistogamous. Usually cleistogamous flowers appear later in the year than the normal flowers of the same species, and they often escape attention, for not only are they small and bud-like, but they are usually short-stalked and borne low down. In *Oxalis acetosella* and some other cases the cleistogamous flowers are actually produced underground. There is much variation in detail, but in extreme cases a cleistogamous flower shows little of the characteristic floral plan. (In *Viola*, for instance, the cleistogamous flowers show various stages in reduction from the normal C5 A5 down to C0 A2.) The number of pollen-grains is often quite small, and they are usually never liberated from the anther at all (p. 368).

(3) **The Need for External Agents:** There is a widespread tendency among entomophilous flowers to enclose the pollen and in various ways to protect it from wastage. In quite a few instances this has led to a situation in which a flower is capable of being effectively self-pollinated but requires a visiting insect for self-pollination just as much as for cross-pollination. This can happen in two ways. In many flowers, as in *Viola* (p. 362) or the Papilionatae (p. 363), the pollen is held enclosed for a time in a chamber formed by the anthers or corolla. The pollen at this stage may be very close to the stigma but is never actually in contact with it. Unless the mechanism of the flower is operated more or less normally, self-pollination, or indeed any pollination at all, is impossible. An interesting example arises in the cultivated lucerne (= alfalfa,

= *Medicago sativa*), where the flower is ordinarily "tripped" by a visiting insect. Some varieties will not self-pollinate unless tripped, others are self-tripping. There are also cases where the pollen-grain requires to be stimulated into activity by some substance which is present in the stigma but which cannot escape from an intact cell. In such a species the chance arrival of a pollen-grain upon a stigma leads to no result—what is required is the slight bruising of the stigmatic surface which the movements of an insect must almost always bring about. There is no reason to suppose that these hindrances to accidental self-pollination have any bearing at all upon the welfare of the species. The position appears rather to be that the pollen has been very effectively guarded against loss or damage, or against any danger of premature germination, and that these developments have been pursued even to the point where self-pollination can only rarely happen without cross-pollination taking place at the same time.

The Characteristics of Floral Tissues

The tissues of floral organs display a number of characteristics which are not often seen elsewhere. Some of these peculiarities are related in obvious ways to known floral functions such as the production of nectar. There remains, however, a formidable array of structures, some of them very complicated, which have no known functional significance.

The pigments which are responsible for most of the striking colours of flowers belong to two main series. The **carotenoids**, which range from ivory tints through yellow to orange and (rarely) red, occur in special plastids and are chemically rather stable, tending to give the same colour all over and a constant colour through the whole flowering period. The **anthocyanins**, which range from blue through purple to red, occur as a solution in the vacuolar sap. The anthocyanins are indicators, showing blue in alkaline media and red in acid ones. Flowers with anthocyanin pigmentation often show gradations in tint or a colour-drift (usually red-to-blue) as the flower gets older. Good examples can be seen in blue-flowered Boraginaceae where the buds are pink.

So little is known about the production of scent that in most flowers the origin of the scent has never been traced to any particular tissue. Many flowers, however, have special hairs, mostly arising from the corolla but often also from other parts, in which oily materials are produced. These hairs, of which it is not at all uncommon for a single flower to have several different kinds, are almost certainly responsible for some of the components of the scent; this cannot be the whole story, for some flowers with no glandular hairs at all still have an obvious scent.

The production of nectar is for the most part sharply localised in special structures known as nectaries, from which the nectar exudes as a glistening liquid. Some care is needed in the recognition of nectaries, because the place where nectar is stored is not necessarily the place where it is produced. Many flowers have special pouches, pockets, or spurs, in which nectar accumulates in varying amounts. Even where the reservoir is itself the nectary it is rather exceptional for the whole of its surface to be secretory; the actual nectary may be quite a small patch. Many reservoirs take no part in secretion at all; the pouched sepals of Cruciferae, for instance (p. 411), hold nectar arising from nectaries surrounding the bases of the stamens, while the spurred petal of *Viola* (p. 362) holds nectar produced by outgrowths from the connectives of two of the stamens. There are two main types of nectary construction. In some cases the nectary is little more than a patch of epidermis, usually without stomata, upon which the nectar appears as a surface film. In more massive nectaries, like the plug-shaped one which surrounds the base of the style in Compositae, there is a spongy parenchymatous body; the nectar passes from the cells into the intercellular spaces and from thence to the exterior by way of special stomata which never close. This structure is not very different from that of many hydathodes. The nectar itself is basically a sucrose solution modified to a varying degree by invertase action. It contains small quantities of other materials, which may give a characteristic flavour and may also have a slight antiseptic action, tending to discourage the growth of the yeasts and other fungi which are normally present in exposed nectar supplies.

There are a good many examples of **extra-floral nectaries**, nectaries, that is, which are not closely associated with flowers at all. Such structures can be seen on the stipules of *Vicia* species and near the junction of petiole and leaf lamina in some species of *Prunus*. Although there has been plenty of ingenious guesswork, there is no proof that extra-floral nectaries are of any benefit to the plants which produce them.

Those flowers which have no active secretion of nectar fall mostly into two classes: the pollen-flowers, in which the insect can eat excess pollen, and a type in which the insect has to pierce or bite the "nectary" to get the sugar out. There are, however, a few specialised cases where detachable food-bodies (really epidermal hairs) are formed. In view of the ease with which insects can be attracted to artificial flowers, even to bad imitations which would deceive no human eye, it is perhaps worthy of remark that no flower seems to be able to depend upon deception alone. The insect is *always* offered food, ordinarily for itself, sometimes (p. 367) for its young. The nearest thing to complete fraud comes in some orchids where a male insect is attracted to a flower which looks like the insect female, but even in this case food is given.

The epidermis of floral organs, and especially the epidermis of petals, often develops unusual characteristics. A high proportion of petals are papillate, with each epidermal cell rising like a little dome above the general level of the surface. A high proportion of petals, whether papillate or not, have a cuticle which is elaborately cracked or pleated, and the nature of this cuticular pattern may change very much from one part of the petal to another. In some petals there are, quite apart from any stomata which may be present, other intercellular spaces between the epidermal cells. These special intercellular canals do not open to the exterior, being bridged by membranes of unsupported cuticle. The meaning of all these elaborations remains a complete mystery.

The stigma is itself a specialised piece of epidermis, differing in many important respects from the surrounding tissue, from which it is usually marked off by a very sharp boundary. It is easy to over-estimate the extent of the stigmatic surface in a flower. It should be remembered that although anemophilous flowers often have a feathery stigma, the stigma of most insect-pollinated flowers is rather finely papillate. Quite a high magnification is usually needed to make the individual prominences visible, and under a hand magnifier the surface will ordinarily appear smooth matt or velvety at most. Impressive combs or brushes of hairs may be closely associated with the stigma, but they are very unlikely to be part of it. In the larger and more open actinomorphic flowers quite large stigmatic areas sometimes occur, and when a style has several arms it is common for a strip of stigma to run along each arm, usually on the upper surface only. Otherwise, and especially in some of the more strongly zygomorphic flowers, the stigmatic area tends to be very restricted. Even when a style ends in a conspicuous knob, it will often turn out that only a small part of this is stigmatic. Although it is probable that every stigma has some secretory activity, the amount of secretion is usually too small to attract attention.

The Significance of Zygomorphy

Any pronounced degree of zygomorphy, even if it is not associated with any great change in the general plan of the flower, has important consequences in connection with pollination. Upon a zygomorphic flower the position of the insect's body while feeding is roughly standardised. This makes possible a significant economy in the use of pollen, for instead of dusting the insect all over it is sufficient to apply pollen only to that part of the insect which will come into contact with the stigma. In fact, most zygomorphic flowers can be divided sharply into two classes: those which put pollen on the upper surface of the insect (most Labiatae and Scrophulariaceae) and those which put pollen on the insect's underside (most Papilionatae). In many zygomorphic flowers the increased efficiency in the use of pollen is reflected in an actual reduction in the amount of pollen produced; among the Scrophulariaceae and related families, all with K5 C5, one regularly finds A5 in actinomorphic forms but only A4 or A2 in zygomorphic ones. Similarly the Caprifoliaceae, which are actinomorphic or nearly so, have A5, the closely related Valerianaceae, which are zygomorphic, only A3 or A1. There are, however, some interesting cases where the tendency has been not so much to reduce the pollen output as to introduce mechanical refinements which, as it were, "ration" the pollen so as to make a given stock serve for a greater number of pollinations (orchids, p. 365; Papilionatae, p. 364).

Although some flower-visiting animals hover (humming-birds, some flies and moths), the great majority settle for a moment on each flower. In most zygomorphic flowers the lower lip of the perianth is developed to serve as a landing platform. What serves as a platform can also be made to operate as a treadle; some zygomorphic flowers have accordingly developed simple mechanisms worked by the weight of the insect (Papilionatae, *Antirrhinum*).

Although the symmetry of a flower usually determines in great measure its relationships with visiting insects, there are some interesting exceptions. A few flowers which are actually actinomorphic are so designed that they have, from the insect's point of view, several "entrances", each of which is like an independent zygomorphic flower in its general arrangement. The only familiar example is *Iris*, in which each (actinomorphic) flower is pollinated just as though it were a whorl of three zygomorphic ones. The opposite effect is found in many dense inflorescences; the flowers at the edge of a capitulum or umbel are often strongly zygomorphic, but they are parts of a radially symmetrical assembly, and in many respects they tend to behave as though they were actinomorphic. The ray florets of Compositae (p. 425) are a good example. Ordinarily the tendency is for actinomorphic flowers to have carotenoid pigmentation (p. 357) and for zygomorphic ones to have anthocyanins. Yet in the ray florets, which are strongly zygomorphic, carotenoids predominate. In this respect, therefore, the symmetry of the capitulum is more important than that of the individual flower. Zygomorphic symmetry does not often appear in inflorescences, but it is not unknown; some Euphorbiaceae, for instance, (not British) have strongly zygomorphic cyathia (p. 343).

The Selection of Insects

If one chooses a plant species and collects all the insects which visit its flowers over a period of time, then the resulting list of insect species is usually quite a long one. (It by no means follows, of course, that all of them are effective pollinators.) There are, however, considerable differences in the lists of visitors obtained from different plants; to some extent the flower can attract insects selectively, though relatively few flowers carry this so far as to depend upon a single insect species for pollination, and probably no flower in the world is completely free from the attentions of "unwanted" visitors which may damage it without effecting pollination.

Although there is little point in attempting fine sub-divisions, it is useful to recognise some broad categories of flowers which, however much they may differ in structure, display well-marked selective influences upon the insect population.

(1) **Open Flowers:** Actinomorphic flowers, typically white, cream, or yellow, often facing upwards, with food supply accessible to short-tongued insects, and pollinated by a wide variety of flies, beetles, etc. (Some, mostly with A ∞, are pollen-flowers, without nectar.) These plants can be arranged in a graded series; as the nectar becomes deeper and more sheltered, the tendency is to attract more of the larger and longer-tongued insects such as bees. Examples: *Ranunculus*, Umbelliferae, many Rosaceae, *Galium*, *Viburnum*, *Sambucus*, *Adoxa*, *Hedera*, many small Cruciferae.

(2) **Bee Flowers:** Flowers with deep nectar so placed as to require a tongue-length of 7-12 mm., predominantly blue or purple, often strongly zygomorphic, and sometimes arranged so that only strong or heavy insects can enter. Some of these plants (some of the agricultural clovers, for example) are absolutely dependent upon bees for the production of any appreciable crop of seed. Examples: *Delphinium*, many Labiatae and Scrophulariaceae.

(3) **Butterfly and Moth Flowers:** Deep nectar in a position which may demand a tongue-length of 12 mm. or more. Little tendency to zygomorphy, the mouth of the flower often very narrow, but never quite closed, the tongues of these insects being slender but

frail. Those pollinated by day-flying butterflies and moths predominantly red (*e.g.* some of the larger-flowered Caryophyllaceae, garden *Phlox*, etc.). Those pollinated by night-flying moths very pale, opening at dusk, and often wide-mouthed, with nothing but the time of day to protect the nectar from the "wrong" insects (e.g. *Lonicera*, *Calystegia sepium*, *Oenothera*, *Nicotiana*).

(4) **Carrion-flowers:** Pollinated by insects which would otherwise feed upon dung, corpses, decaying vegetable matter. Strong and offensive scents, colouration predominantly brown or purple, often mottled or spotted. Many actually trap the insects for a time, and in many an entire inflorescence acts as a single unit. Plants of this class are poorly developed in temperate climates. In warmer countries the flowers are often of great size, and display very peculiar features, especially a tendency to produce long dangling string-like appendages. Examples: *Scrophularia* (pollinated by wasps), *Arum* (p. 366), *Stapelia* (often seen in collections of succulent plants), *Aristolochia* (a common hothouse curiosity).

Examples of Pollination Mechanisms

It was the fashion at one time to study the pollination of even the smallest and simplest flowers in great detail and to attach some presumed functional significance to every little peculiarity of their structure and behaviour. Undoubtedly this went too far, and many trivial points were given an importance to which they have no real claim. Modern botanists are much more ready to recognise that in the pollination of many flowers a good deal happens that is not very precisely controlled. There are, however, certain cases in which the course of events is unusually complicated and sufficiently definite to justify one in speaking of a pollination mechanism. Even where remarkable events take place in a flower, however, their influence upon the reproduction of the plant is often far from plain. Some floral organs, for instance, are sensitive to touch. A stamen of *Berberis*, tickled in its axil, at once swings up against the stigma, while the stigma of *Mimulus* has two lips, which rapidly close together when touched. It is doubtful whether these plants gain anything by such performances. It will, however, be worth while to review a selection of cases in which a complex mechanism has a clearly established effect upon pollination.

In *Viola* the flower is strongly zygomorphic (Figs. 162 and 166) with the lower petal developed as a spur which contains nectar. The nectar is actually produced by two blade-like outgrowths, one from the connective of each of the two lower stamens. The filaments are very short and broad, as are the anthers also, and the stamens are held together at their edges by interlocking hairs. Each stamen has a triangular tip, and the five of these slope inwards to touch the style. The stamens, in fact, make a kind of box, into which the pollen, which is drier and dustier than that of most entomophilous flowers, is shed. The style has a thin flexible part at its base; the upper part of the style is therefore quite mobile, and when it is touched it disturbs the stamens, allowing pollen to sift out between them. The stigma is in a pit, which in the larger-flowered species of *Viola* is fitted with a flap-valve.

In Compositae the five anthers are fused into a tube surrounding the style. The pollen is shed into this anther-tube at a time when the style is short, and the growth of the style then pushes the pollen out at the top of the tube by a piston action. Self-pollination does not take place at this time because the stigmatic surfaces (Plate 13) are pressed together so closely that no pollen-grain can possibly get between them. In a high proportion of Compositae the style has brushes of hairs which undoubtedly make the removal of pollen from the anther-tube more complete. There are many cases in which the marginal flowers of a capitulum are female, and lack these brushes. So long as the ejection of pollen depends entirely upon stylar growth, it is naturally a gradual process. There are, however, some Compositae in which the stamen filaments are sensitive to touch. When stimulated, as they may be by a visiting insect, all five stamens bow themselves sharply outwards, thereby drawing the anther-tube rapidly downwards over the stationary style. Whether this is advantageous it seems impossible to determine; it occurs only in a small proportion of the family. In most Compositae, after the ejection of pollen is complete, the style-arms roll backwards to touch either the anthers or the (often hairy) style. There can be little doubt that self-pollination is thus accomplished with a very high degree of reliability.

In Papilionatae (Figs. 162 and 180) the stamens and ovary are at first enclosed in the two carinal petals which form the keel. These petals are free at their bases but lightly tacked together at their upper edges. The two next petals, the alae or wings, are usually folded together with the carinal petals at their bases. These four petals together constitute a landing platform; the insect may rest upon the keel directly, or if it stands upon the wings the thrust will be transmitted to the keel through the interlocking folds of the petal-bases. The pollen is shed in the first instance into the tip of the keel, and from this cavity it cannot escape so long as the flower remains untouched. Although the general arrangement of the flower is very constant, there are striking variations in the action of the pollination mechanism. In many Papilionatae there is a simple repeatable action; when an insect lands on the flower the stigma and stamens are uncovered, and make contact with the insect's underside, and when the insect leaves the petals rise to cover the reproductive organs again. From this two contrasting lines of specialisation can be traced. One form of development is to stake everything upon a single insect visit, by setting up forces which will eject the whole pollen-stock in one burst. This can be seen at its best in *Sarothamnus* (broom). Here the style is long and is highly tensed in the intact flower. An insect visit produces a violent reaction. It is strictly a non-repeatable performance, for once the spring is released there is no way of re-setting it. The opposite policy is to issue the pollen very sparingly. This can be seen in *Lotus*, *Lupinus*, etc., where pressure upon the petals produces a

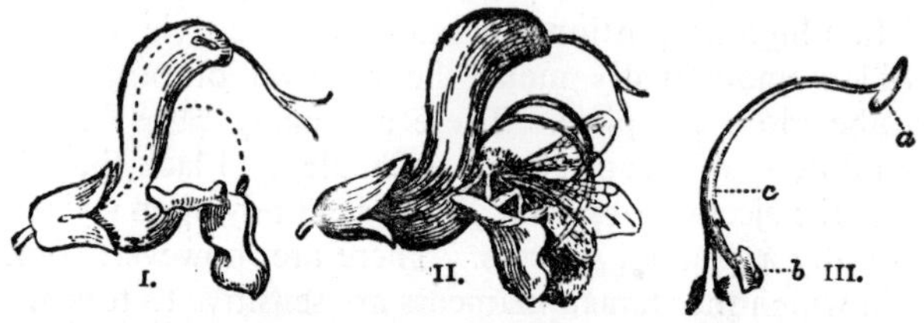

Fig. 169. I, FLOWER OF *Salvia* FROM SIDE; II, WITH HUMBLE-BEE EXTRACTING NECTAR, AND THE ANTHERS RUBBING AGAINST ITS BACK; III, SINGLE STAMEN, *a* BEING FERTILE ANTHER, *b* THE STERILE LOBE, *c* THE CONNECTIVE.

piston action and forces a thin ribbon of pollen out through the pointed tip of the keel.

In *Salvia* (Fig. 169) a system of pollination has developed which is very different from that found in most other Labiatae. Generally the flower in the Labiatae has four anthers close together under the hood of the corolla. These touch the insect's back, but this contact is secured only by a reasonably close agreement between the size of the insect and the size of the flower. An insect which is too small may walk under the anthers without touching them. In *Salvia*, however, there are only two fertile stamens, each with a long curved connective hinged across the top of a stubby little filament. The two lower half-anthers, which in the common species do not themselves produce any pollen at all, obstruct the insect's way to the nectar. When the insect pushes against the obstacle, the levers swing so as to bring the pollen down on the insect's back. This arrangement is coupled with marked protandry, the stigmas being brought down into the insect's path by later growth of the style.

In orchids there is a considerable range of complex pollination mechanisms, but the common British orchids are of a rather uniform pattern. The inferior ovary (Fig. 170) is twisted through 180° so as to bring to the front of the flower a special perianth segment (the **labellum**) which is structurally the uppermost. The labellum is more elaborate in shape than the other perianth members; it acts as a landing platform, and is extended backwards into a hollow spur from which the insect can obtain nectar, though only by biting the tissues. Only one stamen is fertile, though others are represented by staminodes (Fig. 170). Each half of the anther contains a **pollinium**, which is a mass of pollen-grains joined together by threads of sticky material. At its lower end each pollinium is attached to a little stalk or **caudicle**, which has at its base an adhesive disc (glandula in Fig. 170). The two discs lie side by side, enclosed in a

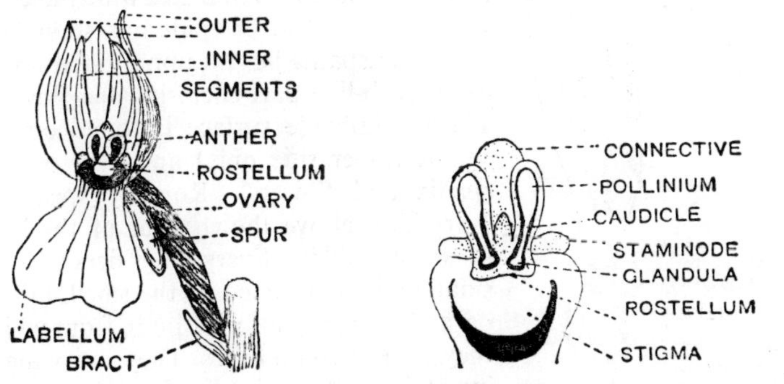

Fig. 170. GENERAL VIEW OF ORCHID FLOWER, AND DETAIL OF CENTRAL PORTION.

beak-like projection known as the **rostellum**. This rostellum is a most elaborate structure, sensitive to touch, and containing a reservoir of fluid which keeps the sticky discs in good condition. When an insect touches the rostellum the lower part folds back and the discs stick to the insect, which then carries the two pollinia like a pair of horns. If they remained in the same position and if the insect approached another flower in just the same way, the pollinia would, of course, strike the anther of the second flower. In fact, as they dry out, the caudicles bend forwards and outwards, so that if the insect maintains the proper line of approach the pollinia will pass to either side of the rostellum of the second flower and strike the stigmas, which are patches (single in some orchids, paired in others) upon the surface of the throat of the flower. Although an orchid ovary contains many ovules and requires many pollen-grains to fertilise them, the way in which the grains are bound together makes it possible for an insect to pollinate several flowers from a single pair of pollinia.

The inflorescence of *Arum* (Fig. 171) is a spike of unisexual flowers (male above, female below) enclosed in a large bract or **spathe**. The inflorescence axis or **spadix** has a club-shaped tip which produces a horrible smell, which is strongest at night, and carries two rings of prongs or tentacles which appear to represent sterile flowers. This inflorescence is a pitfall trap, the operation of which depends on a peculiar epidermal structure. The epidermal cells are shaped like the tiles on a tile-hung wall, so that an insect's claws find no foothold, and there are oil-drops which put out of action the sticky pads which many insects use in climbing smooth surfaces. An insect which tries to walk on this kind of epidermis soon falls off. The spathe has an upper hood and a lower bulb-like part enclosing the flowers. The unclimbable surface is found on the spathe (inner side only) and also on the spadix and flowers. Roughly speaking, everything above the equator of the bulb is unclimbable. Everything depends on small insects, attracted by the smell, falling off and dropping into the bulb, from which they cannot climb out. They are winged insects, but that does not seem to help them. The tentacles do not seem to play any part except to ensure that only small insects enter the bulb. There is no question of any "lobster-pot" action, and model inflorescences can be made which will catch insects perfectly well without any tentacles at all. Experiments with glass models show that the attraction of the insects is almost entirely due to scent. Models have been made of unnatural colours, or fitted with electrical heating-coils (for the rapid respiration of these inflorescences makes them noticeably warmer than their surroundings, and it has been suggested that this warmth may be attractive to insects). No matter what is done in other directions, however, the rule is that a model which is scented, either by being fitted with a natural spadix-tip or by being baited with decaying animal matter, catches many insects, while an unscented model catches none at all. The inflorescence is completely protogynous.

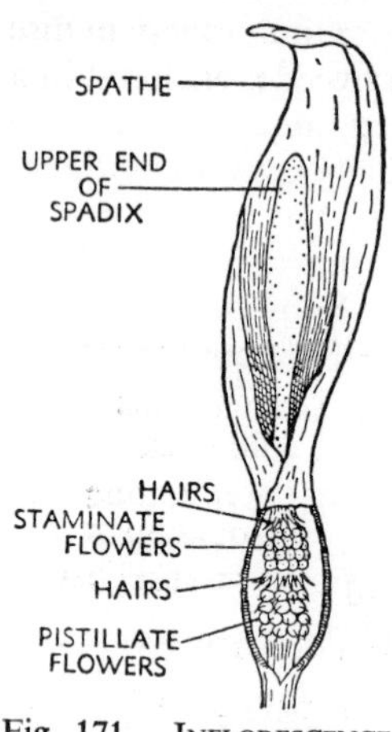

Fig. 171. Inflorescence of *Arum*, with part of spathe removed to expose flowers.

The insects are held overnight, a period during which pollination is possible being followed after an interval by dehiscence of the stamens. Nectar is secreted from the stigmas. By the morning of the second day the unclimbable epidermis has wilted, and is unclimbable no longer. The prisoners walk out, and many are caught again by other inflorescences (we know this because the plant fruits freely in the wild, but not at all if insect visits are excluded).

There are several interesting examples of pollinating insects which use the flower as a place for egg-laying and the development of the young. In *Ficus* (figs, etc.) the inflorescence is a hollow pear-shaped structure with simple flowers in a central cavity. These flowers are of three kinds: males, fertile females, and sterile females or **gall-flowers**. Pollination depends entirely upon minute gall-wasps, the females of which lay their eggs in the ovaries of the gall-flowers. A gall-flower produces a wasp, not a seed. The edible fig is a female inflorescence and will actually ripen well (though of course without seed) without being pollinated at all. In nature it would be pollinated by female wasps seeking to lay their eggs in the female flowers. Eggs in this position almost always fail to develop; in this particular species of *Ficus* gall-flowers are found only on another type of tree (the **caprifig**), the "fruits" of which are not edible. Figs produce seed, caprifigs produce pollen and wasps. On the caprifig the female wasps rear their young. On the fig they merely act as pollinators, conditions in the fertile female flower being unsuitable for the growth of the wasp-grub

In the fig the carrying of pollen is useless to the insect (for a gall-flower does not need to be pollinated) and appears quite accidental. *Yucca*, however, depends upon a moth which lays its eggs in the ovary of a normal flower and which quite deliberately collects pollen (from another flower!) and rams it into the funnel-shaped stigma. Without the moth (as in Britain) *Yucca* produces no seed. Where the moth is present seed is produced, because although the grubs feed upon the developing seeds (and are dependent upon pollination for their food supply) the balance is normally such that some seeds ripen in each fruit.

THE PRODUCTION OF SEED

The Male Gametophyte

The pollen-grain, and the structures which are developed from it, may be known collectively as the male gametophyte, for reasons which will become clear later (p. 442). At its first formation the grain is a single cell, but this soon divides unequally (Fig. 172), forming a large **vegetative cell** and a small **generative cell**. The cytoplasmic bodies of these cells are quite distinct, though no wall is formed between them. The generative cell, which originally lies against the wall of the grain, forces its way into the interior of the vegetative cell and there divides into two **sperms**. At the time of pollination, therefore, the pollen-grain may contain three cells. Often it contains only two, the division of the generative cell being delayed.

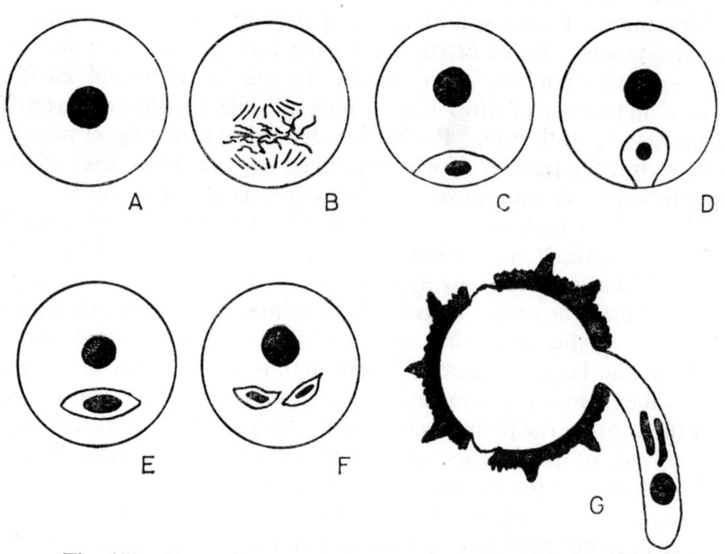

Fig. 172. DEVELOPMENT OF MALE GAMETOPHYTE IN ANGIOSPERM.
A, haploid microspore; B, mitosis; C, large vegetative cell and small generative cell; D and E, inward movement of generative cell; F, division of generative cell into two sperms; G, germination, with movement of nuclei into the tube. Exine and germ-pores shown only in last figure.

Most pollens are not exacting in their requirements for germination and will grow actively in a plain sucrose solution if the concentration is about right. It is a mistake to suppose that pollen-grains only germinate upon the stigma. Germination can often be observed in nectar, or on the surfaces of petals. This, of course, leads to no result, nor does the (probably quite common) case where a pollen-grain germinates on the stigma of some totally unrelated plant. A few pollens require to be started into activity by specific substances derived from the stigma, but this is exceptional. In cleistogamous flowers the pollen normally germinates in the anther, which never opens. Germination involves the production of a

pollen-tube, which is an outgrowth of inner wall or **intine**, emerging through one of the germ-pores. The tube has to grow from the stigma to the ovule, a distance which is usually only a few millimetres but is in the biggest flowers as much as 10 cm. or more. The cytoplasm and nuclei migrate down the tube, and in some cases the empty rear portion of the tube is shut off at intervals by the formation of callose plugs similar to those seen in sieve-tubes. The generative cell divides in the pollen-tube if it has not already done so. Pollen-tubes are sensitive to oxygen concentration and grow away from free oxygen; when a grain germinates upon the stigma this means that the tube will plunge into the stigmatic tissue. The nucleus of the vegetative cell is often called the tube nucleus, the implication being that it has some special control over the growth of the tube. Recent work has tended to discredit this view; the tube nucleus does not usually stay near the growing tip of the tube; on the contrary, it tends to trail along behind the sperms, and sometimes disintegrates entirely without any apparent detriment to the growth of the tube. Undoubtedly, the tube secretes enzymes which assist its passage through the tissues. Where a stigma has a cuticle, for instance (many do not), the cuticle can be removed after pollination and then shows holes where the pollen-tubes digested their way through it.

Within the style the tube grows along a definite track which is usually marked out in advance. Some styles are actually hollow, with a central canal, in which case the tubes may grow in a liquid film upon the epidermis lining the canal, with no real penetration of the tissue at all. Usually, however, there is a distinct **conducting tissue** (= transmitting tissue, = stigmatoid tissue) through which the tubes pass. This is a special parenchyma, often with elongated cells and thickened walls (Plate 13). Pollen-tubes ordinarily follow the line of the middle lamella; it is rare for them to enter a cell. By laying styles end-to-end it is possible to make tubes grow much further than they are ordinarily called upon to do, and there can be no doubt that the tubes actively parasitise the stylar tissue. It is very common for a tube to branch, especially in the later stages of its journey, and in some instances a pollen-grain may put out several tubes. Invariably, however, all the nuclei take the same route, and the branches which have no nuclei end blindly, without ever reaching the egg-cell in the ovule.

The Ovule

An ovule consists of a central parenchymatous core or **nucellus**, surrounded by a varying number of rather massive parenchymatous coverings or **integuments** (Fig. 173). Each integument begins as a collar round the base of the nucellus and grows upwards to form a close-fitting sleeve. The micropyle is the pore where the lips of the integuments meet (or sometimes fail to meet) over the tip of the nucellus. The majority of ovules have two integuments, which are then distinguished as inner and outer; there is, however, a substantial minority of angiosperms with only one integument. In a relatively small number of cases an ovule which has at first two integuments develops at a rather late stage a third integument, outside the others,

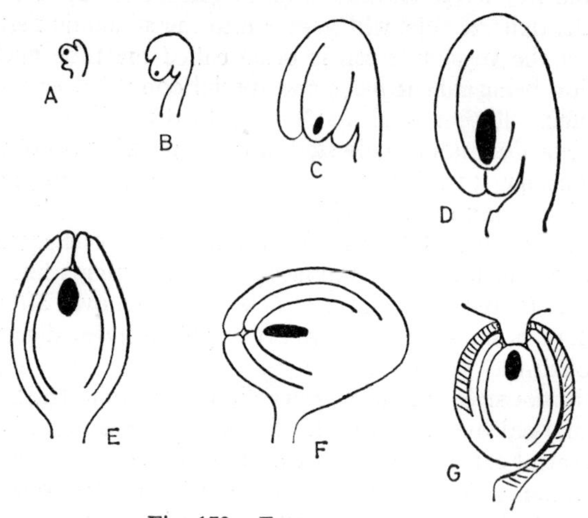

Fig. 173. FORMS OF OVULE.

A-D, four stages in the development of an anatroprous ovule with one integument; E, orthotropous ovule with two integuments, micropyle formed by inner integument; F, ovule of intermediate form, both integuments contributing to micropyle; G, ovule of Plumbaginaceae, anatropous but with the funicle (shaded) looped right over, and a plug of carpellary tissue intruding into the micropyle.

which never extends as far as the micropyle. Such an incomplete third integument is called an **aril**, and it may be conspicuous when the seed is ripe. The spice known as "mace", for instance, is the aril of the nutmeg. Although the nucellus and the integuments are closely pressed together they are not initially fused. In the later development of the seed, however, the situation is often extensively modified. The mature testa is often arrived at only by complex grafting processes, involving commonly the digestion of certain cell layers and the joining together of things which to begin with were not even next to each other.

Most ovules have a stalk which is called the **funicle**, and which contains a vascular bundle connected with the marginal bundle of the carpel. The internal vascular system of the ovule is usually very slight. Typically the strand from the funicle ends in a kind of vascular plate in the **chalaza**, which is the tissue lying just below the base of the nucellus. Exceptionally there are bundles running into the integuments or (rarely) into the nucellus. In the simplest case (the **orthotropous** ovule) the nucellus stands upright upon the funicle, so that the ovule has the funicle at one end and the micropyle at the other. Such ovules are not common. In the great majority of the angiosperms the entire body of the ovule is inverted by one-sided growth at an early stage, so that the micropyle lies close beside the funicle (the **anatropous ovule**). Intermediate forms are sometimes encountered.

The nucellus is a **megasporangium**. It is the counterpart of the **microsporangium** or pollen-sac, from which it differs in producing usually only a single spore mother cell, and in having no means of dehiscence, so that the spore is not liberated. The megaspore mother cell, like the pollen mother cells, is derived from the layer immediately beneath the epidermis. Typically the nucellus has embedded in its tip a single megaspore mother cell (Plate 14 and Fig. 174) which divides by meiosis (p. 163) to form a tetrad of megaspores. Ordinarily only one of these megaspores will function, and it is therefore hardly surprising that there is sometimes a partial failure of division, giving a row of three cells instead of four (two megaspores and a **diad cell**). With a good many exceptions, these three or four cells lie in a vertical row, and the functional megaspore is the one furthest from the micropyle.

The Female Gametophyte

The megaspore grows into a female gametophyte which is parasitic upon the nucellus, just as the male gametophyte is parasitic upon the style. The megaspore enlarges and very soon obliterates the other members of the tetrad. Its nucleus divides into two, which take station, one at the micropylar end and one at the chalazal end, and there divide twice more to give two groups of four nuclei, eight in all. So far no walls have been formed, and indeed there is no demarcation of distinct cells at all, within the wall of the megaspore. At the 8-nucleate stage, however, six of the nuclei organise individual cells, each with a wall, lying against the enlarged megaspore membrane. The three at the chalazal end are the **antipodal cells**; the corresponding group at the micropylar end consists of a single **ovum** (or egg-cell) and two **synergids**. This leaves two free nuclei, one from the micropylar group (the **upper polar** nucleus) and one from the chalazal group (the **lower polar** nucleus). The two polar nuclei move into a more or less central position.

At this stage the female gametophyte or **embryo sac** is ready to be fertilised, and without fertilisation it is normally incapable of further development.

Fertilisation

Until it reaches the placental region of the carpel it is unlikely that the growth of the pollen-tube is subject to any more detailed

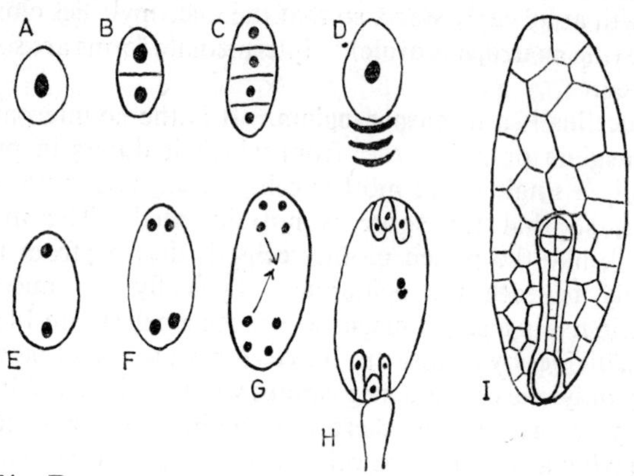

Fig. 174. DEVELOPMENT OF FEMALE GAMETOPHYTE IN AN ANGIOSPERM. A, megaspore mother cell; B, first meiotic division gives two diad cells; C, second meiotic division gives four megaspores; D, three megaspores (often one megaspore and a diad cell) abort; E-G, repeated mitosis in the remaining megaspore gives eight nuclei, of which two (polar nuclei) move to the centre of the embryo sac; H, mature sac with three antipodal cells above, two polar nuclei at right centre, ovum between two synergids below, pollen-tube touching ovum, having entered through micropyle; I, sac filled with parenchymatous endosperm, in which is embedded the pro-embryo, with enlarged basal cell in position of ovum, filamentous suspensor, and octants (four showing) of the embryo proper.

guidance than arises from the arrangement of the conducting tissue in which the tube finds its nutritive materials. In the final stages of pollen-tube growth, however, there is little doubt that substances produced by the embryo sac exert a specific chemical attraction. As a pollen-tube is incapable of crossing even a short air-gap, the approach to the ovum is often rather indirect. Usually the actual entry to the ovule is by way of the micropyle, but this is far from being an absolute rule. Entry through the chalaza occurs in some plants, either constantly or as an alternative procedure. Entry through the integuments somewhere at the side of the ovule is probably rather common. In any case, the pollen-tube has always to find a way from the placenta to the ovule. Although in most cases it goes up the funicle there are a good many plants in which other provision is made. The commonest thing then is an outgrowth of tissue from the placenta which touches the micropyle and in many cases actually projects into it, sometimes even touching the nucellus. Less commonly, the integuments, or even the embryo sac itself, may grow out of the micropyle to meet the pollen-tube on the placental surface, or sometimes even part way up the style. Whatever may be the appropriate course for the pollen-tube in a particular species, it is not always taken without hesitation, and some investigators have reported "aimless wanderings" on the part of the tube before it enters the embryo sac.

The two sperms are discharged into the embryo sac, the pollen-tube entering so that its tip is in contact with the ovum or synergids. Practically nothing is known about the details of this process. It has been suggested that the synergids may play an important part, and it is certainly common for one synergid (sometimes both) to be destroyed by the entry of the tube. This is, however, a most difficult field of study, the events being so rapid that large numbers of ovules have to be examined before the required stages can be found. The sperms themselves are often worm-like, and there is good evidence that they have some power of independent movement. One of them fuses with the ovum and the other enters into a triple fusion with the two polar nuclei. Usually the polar nuclei have fused before the sperm arrives, but it may sometimes happen that the sperm fuses with one polar nucleus and the other joins in later.

The Endosperm

The fertilised ovum or zygote gives rise to the **embryo**, while the triple fusion nucleus gives rise to the **endosperm**. The endosperm is a nutritive tissue, destined to be absorbed by the growing embryo. The life of the endosperm is often only a matter of a few days, for in "non-endospermic" seeds the endosperm has disappeared by the time the seed is ripe. The development of the endosperm is relatively rapid, and is usually well under way before the zygote has undergone more than two or three nuclear divisions. Endosperm is ordinarily a parenchymatous tissue, in the growth of which abnormal features are often observed. In many plants the endosperm passes through a **free nuclear stage**, in which the nuclei divide rapidly in a common mass of cytoplasm without any partitions being formed. In such cases cell walls are usually formed later, but sometimes the whole endosperm is swept away before there is time for walls to appear at all. Even in endosperms where cell walls are formed from the beginning there is a tendency for cells to become multinucleate, and haphazard nuclear fusions seem often to occur.

The Embryo

The angiosperms display a remarkable measure of uniformity in the development of their embryos. Such distinctions as embryologists have been able to make are of a highly technical kind, and of no general interest. There is not even, in the early stages of growth, any significant difference between monocotyledons and dicotyledons.

The zygote divides transversely several times, producing a row or filament of cells called the **pro-embryo** (Fig. 174, I). In this one can distinguish a **basal cell** (occupying the original position of the ovum), a **suspensor**, which is the main part of the filament, and which may elongate considerably, and an **embryonal cell**, which is the one furthest from the micropyle. The basal cell is sometimes enlarged, and may have some special physiological significance. The suspensor, by its elongation, thrusts the embryonal cell and the structures derived from it deeper into the endosperm. The embryonal cell divides in most cases into a system of **octants** (the figures obtained by cutting a sphere along three planes at right angles to each other), and each octant then divides periclinally. From this octant group almost the whole body of the embryo is developed. The portion attached to the suspensor becomes the root tip, to which the adjoining suspensor cell by further division often makes a small and probably rather unimportant contribution. The suspensor is not otherwise represented in the embryo proper. The side of the embryo which is furthest from the suspensor grows in a dicotyledon into the two cotyledons with the plumule between them. In a monocotyledon it forms a single massive cotyledon with the plumule emerging at one side of it.

Parasitism in the Developing Seed

In a developing seed there is a very complex physiological situation, with different tissues competing for nutrient materials and perhaps also for space. The various forms of parasitism which occur often involve visible modification of the parts. Sometimes one tissue is altered in such a way as to provide for the nutrition of another. In the nucellus, for instance, the cells next to the embryo sac are often enlarged, and enriched with starch and protein. It is also common for **haustoria** to appear, structures which grow into an adjoining tissue and actively parasitise it. In various angiosperms haustoria are developed from the antipodal cells, from the endosperm, from the suspensor, and sometimes from more than one of these sources. Even where there is no obvious structural modification it is clear that active parasitism is going on. By the time the seed is ripe, it is common for a good deal of tissue to have been completely absorbed. In relatively few seeds is there any significant remainder of the nucellus, and in a great many the endosperm has gone too. There are extreme cases in which the removal of tissue goes much further than this; in some plants the whole ovule is digested away so that the embryo lies naked in the ovary cavity.

Variations in the Reproductive Processes

The account which has so far been given of the events occurring in the pollen-grain and ovule covers only the behaviour which is regarded as normal for the majority of angiosperms. Without attempting to catalogue all the variations which can arise, it is important to make it clear that a high proportion of the angiosperms, probably not less than a third of the total number, are known to depart from the standard pattern at one point or another. Some of these abnormalities concern the pollen. In Cyperaceae, for instance, each pollen mother cell gives rise only to one pollen-grain (three nuclei aborting) instead of the usual tetrad. The main source of variation, however, lies in the development of the embryo sac. The sequence of nuclear divisions is often altered so that the embryo sac, instead of arising from a recognisable megaspore, comes directly from a diad cell or even from the megaspore mother cell. These abnormal sacs may have four nuclei, or sixteen, instead of the usual eight, and the endosperm may then arise by the fusion of more than three nuclei. Even a sac which is normal in origin will not necessarily be so in subsequent behaviour. In most grasses, for instance, the three antipodal cells divide further, until there may be a hundred or more.

There are many ways in which an embryo can be formed by processes other than the normal fertilisation of an ovum. Sometimes an ovum develops without being fertilised; an embryo can also arise (with or without fertilisation) from a synergid, or less commonly from an antipodal cell. It is also possible for cells of the nucellus, or sometimes of the integument, to intrude into the embryo sac and there to behave like suspensors, with embryos arising by a kind of internal vegetative budding of the parent plant.

Such developments lead sometimes to **polyembryony**, the presence of more than one embryo in a seed. A high proportion of orange-pips, for instance, contain multiple embryos, one being formed sexually, the others by vegetative budding of the nucellus. Polyembryony also arises sometimes because an ovule contained more than one embryo sac, or because a pro-embryo branched at an early stage in its growth.

In cases of persistent reproductive abnormality, however, there is often a complete failure to develop normal sexual embryos at all. The race is then **apomictic**, with each seed containing an embryo (usually only one) which is not the product of sexual reproduction. It by no means follows that apomixis relieves a plant of the need for pollination, because an endosperm will be needed to nurse the embryo. Some apomictic plants seem able to produce an endosperm without pollination, others apparently cannot.

The Timing of Reproductive Processes

The reproductive activities of each angiosperm species proceed according to a rather definite timetable. The plant flowers at a particular time of year, and each flower performs characteristic movements at certain times of day, having its special hours for opening, closing, shedding pollen, and so on. The regulation of these matters is a response to external conditions, particularly to light and temperature. Even closely related plants can differ considerably in their behaviour. There is a similar diversity in the timing of the internal reproductive processes, as for instance, in the interval which elapses between pollination and fertilisation. In some grasses, and probably in other plants also, the nuclear fusions in the embryo sac take place little more than an hour after the pollen-grain arrives on the stigma. At the other extreme some of the oaks have an interval of about fourteen months. Where there is a great delay, it is common for the pollen to arrive at a time when the ovules are in a rudimentary condition; in some of the orchids the ovules can hardly be said to exist at the time of pollination.

The Fruit

Pollination, fertilisation, and the development of embryo and endosperm, are all processes which involve the production of hormonal substances (p. 297) within the tissues of the gynaecium. Under the stimulus of these hormones, the ovary wall matures into fruit wall or **pericarp**. The hormones are important also in preventing the action of an abscission layer which in many cases would otherwise bring about the shedding of the flower. The extent to which fruit development depends upon the completion of the reproductive processes varies in different cases. Usually a flower falls if it is not pollinated, and even pollination is generally sufficient to induce only the early stages of fruit development, so that an incompatible pollination leads to early abortion of the fruit. There are, however, some interesting examples, including some of economic importance, in which the fruit develops normally though, for various genetical reasons, there is little or no production of seed. In bananas, oranges, and grapefruit seedless varieties are regularly grown. In some other instances, notably in tomato, it is practicable to induce the formation of marketable fruit by the use of synthetic hormone sprays, rendering pollination unnecessary.

In many cases the fruiting structure involves not only the gynaecium but also various associated structures such as perianth segments, floral receptacle, bracts, and bracteoles. Where these organs play a conspicuous part, and especially where they become fleshy and coloured, the whole assembly is sometimes called a false fruit or pseudocarp (*e.g.* strawberry and rosehip, both with fleshy receptacle, p. 417).

The Classification of Fruits

In many of the older books the classification of fruits is worked out in great detail, with special names even for the rarest types of construction. These elaborate treatments embody a good deal of futile pedantry for which there is no place in serious botanical work. It is still necessary, however, to draw some important structural distinctions and to establish convenient names for the types of fruit which are commonly met. **Dehiscent** fruits, which open in an organised manner to release their seeds, must be distinguished from **indehiscent** fruits in which the seeds either germinate within the pericarp or are released only by accidental processes of breakage and decay. **Succulent** fruits, in which some tissue is sacrificed as food for animal agents of dispersal, must be distinguished from **dry** fruits, which offer an animal no significant source of food other than that contained in the seed.

(1) **The capsule** is the commonest of all fruit types, being the usual product of a flower with several joined carpels. With only rare exceptions, capsules are many-seeded, and the great majority of them open by longitudinal splitting according to one of the patterns shown in Fig. 175. The capsule is fundamentally a dry fruit, the pericarp being usually quite dead and hard before the seeds are shed. Even where the pericarp is juicy the biology of the fruit in no way depends on the provision of food for animals.

Exceptional types of dehiscence are sometimes seen; in *Papaver* (poppy) and *Antirrhinum* there are pores in the pericarp, while in *Plantago* and *Anagallis* the top of the ovary comes off as a lid.

(2) **The follicle** (Fig. 176) is a rare type of fruit formed from a single free carpel and showing its true nature very clearly in its dehiscence. It opens by splitting which separates the two fused

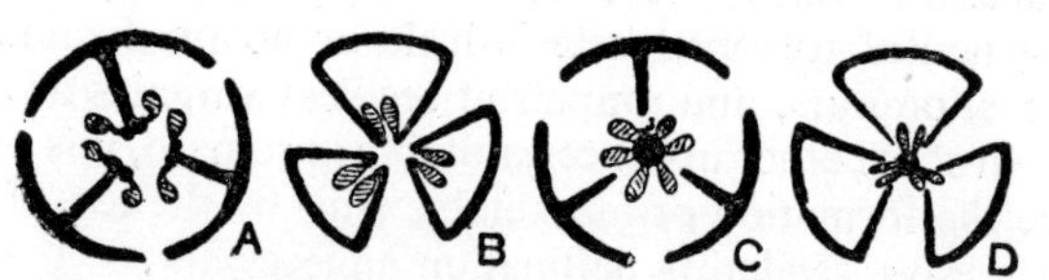

Fig. 175. DEHISCENCE OF MULTILOCULAR CAPSULES. A, loculicidal; B, septicidal; C and D, septifragal. (Diagrammatic transverse sections.)

edges of the carpel. Follicles usually occur in groups, and are with only rare exceptions many-seeded. Examples occur in Ranunculaceae, Rosaceae, and a very few other families.

(3) **The legume** is like a follicle but splits also along the carpel midrib. It is the usual fruit in Leguminosae; otherwise almost unknown.

(4) **The achene**, strictly speaking, is a one-seeded indehiscent derivative of the follicle. Achenes almost always occur in groups, and typical examples can be seen in Rosaceae, Ranunculaceae, and Alismaceae, the strawberry-pip being perhaps the most familiar. Achenes in this strict sense are of quite restricted occurrence, but the term is sometimes applied more loosely to cover a wide range of indehiscent dry one-seeded structures, such as, for instance, the characteristic fruit of the Compositae (p. 425) which is more correctly called a **cypsela**.

Fig. 176. COLLECTION OF FOLLICLES OF MONKSHOOD.

(5) **A nut** is any one-seeded indehiscent fruit with a woody or stony pericarp. It is important to note that most of the "nuts" of commerce are not nuts in the botanical sense at all (p. 380). Although a nut is one-seeded it is often derived from a multicarpellary ovary. In oak, for instance, the flower has G (3) with at least six ovules in axile placentation, yet the acorn, which is a typical nut, has normally only one seed.

(6) **A berry** is an indehiscent fruit in which the pericarp is fleshy or pulpy. Nearly all berries are many-seeded, and a few many-seeded

indehiscent fruits are included under this heading, although their pericarps are fibrous or even stony rather than succulent. It is always an essential part of the definition of a berry that the pips or stones, when they are extracted, are seeds only with no additional covering (compare with the drupe, below). The botanical use of the word "berry" has only a rather sketchy connection with common English speech. Many structures which are generally regarded as berries are botanically nothing of the kind, while fruits which come within the botanical definition are often not recognised as such by the layman (p. 380).

(7) **A drupe** (Fig. 183, E) is an indehiscent fruit in which the inner layers of the pericarp are stony, the outer layers usually fleshy, but occasionally fibrous. Drupes are uncommon, and usually one-seeded, the plum being a typical example. The pip or stone of a drupe is never a simple seed, but always a seed enclosed within a shell derived from the ovary wall.

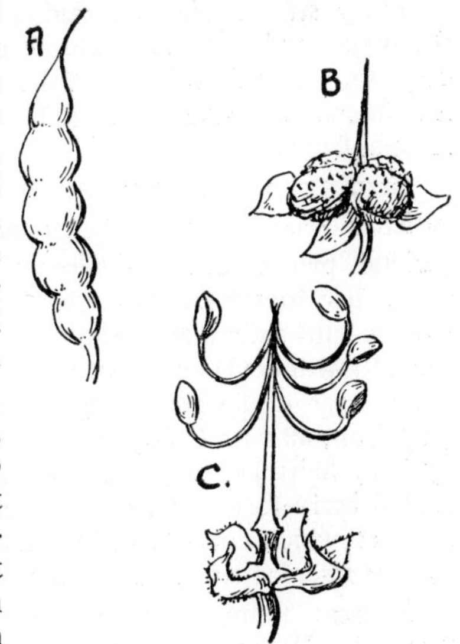

Fig. 177. SCHIZOCARPIC FRUITS. A, lomentum of *Hedysarum*; B, *Cynoglossum*; C, *Geranium*.

(8) **A schizocarp** (Figs. 177, 184) is a fruit which breaks into several pieces, which are almost always one-seeded. These portions (or **mericarps**) are dehiscent in some cases, indehiscent in others. There are two main types of schizocarps. Some are clearly of capsular origin with a whorl of two or more mericarps (*Geranium*, *Malva*, Labiatae, Umbelliferae). Others are pod-like fruits breaking transversely, an arrangement known as a **lomentum** (some examples in Cruciferae and Leguminosae).

Some Special Cases

In addition to the principal fruit types listed above a few other terms will sometimes be encountered. A **samara** is a one-seeded indehiscent fruit with the pericarp extended as a wing (found mainly in trees; *Acer*, *Fraxinus*, etc.). A **caryopsis** is similar to a nut but has the testa inseparably grafted to the pericarp (characteristic of grasses). A **pome** is the fruit of those Rosaceae (p. 419) in which the ovary is inferior (apple, pear, hawthorn). Separate recognition of the pome cannot be logically justified; it might as well be treated as a drupe, as are similar fruits in other families.

Occasionally the flowers of an inflorescence join in the production of a common fruit-mass which may then include not only the ovaries but also the stem, bracts, perianth members, and so on. The fig, pineapple, and mulberry are of this compound character.

Examples of Fruits

Every student should examine a range of fruits and make a thorough study of the features connected with dehiscence and dispersal. In this work the following brief guide will be helpful; it is intended to give the basic interpretation of the common commercial fruits.

Berries: Banana with $G\ (\bar{3})$, axile placentation, commercial varieties seedless. Gooseberry and blackcurrant with $G\ (\bar{2})$, parietal placentation. Bilberry with $G\ (\bar{5})$, axile placentation. Cucumber, loofah and vegetable marrow, and pumpkin, all inferior ovaries with axile placentation, number of carpels a little variable. Tomato with $G\ (\underline{2})$, often with additional carpels, placentation axile, outer layer of testa forming a clear jelly. Orange, lemon, and grapefruit, all with $G\ (\underline{\infty})$, axile placentation, the ovary loculi filled by juicy hair-like outgrowths from the ovary wall. Date, a one-seeded berry formed from a free carpel, the stone being the seed, most of which consists of endosperm, in which the main carbohydrate reserve (hemicellulose) appears as thickening of the cell walls.

Drupes: Plum, cherry, prune, peach, apricot, all single drupes with $G\ \underline{1}$. Walnut, a single drupe; when sold as a nut only the stone is present, but walnut pickle contains the whole fruit, taken before the stone hardens. Almond, a quite exceptional dehiscent drupe, in which the outer pericarp splits naturally to release the stone. Coconut, a single drupe from $G\ (\underline{3})$ but with only a single seed; usually only the stone is seen, the outer fibrous part of the pericarp having been removed as "coir", which is used for matting and cordage. *Rubus* (blackberry, raspberry, loganberry) has $G\ \underline{\infty}$, producing a collection of miniature drupes.

Nuts: the hazelnut or filbert and the sweet chestnut are the only nuts commonly sold as such in Britain. Acorn and beechnut are other familiar examples.

Structures incorrectly regarded as nuts: The coconut, walnut, and almond are drupe-stones as noted above. The Brazil-nut is a seed, the shell being the testa; the fruit is a globular structure with a hard shell, containing several seeds, and conventionally treated as a berry because it has no regular mode of dehiscence. The peanut or monkeynut is the seed of a modified two-seeded legume; at an early stage in its development this indehiscent fruit is thrust into thc soil by an unusual elongation of the floral receptacle. This gives rise to the alternative name of groundnut.

False fruits: The strawberry is a fleshy floral receptacle bearing numerous achenes. The rosehip is a fleshy receptacle with free achenes inside it, the flower being extremely perigynous.

Dehiscence

Every dehiscent fruit has some specialised tissues which are responsible for the movement of the pericarp (Plate 14). Most dehiscence movements depend upon the distortion of dead (often fibrous) tissue as it dries. Trials with a pea-pod, for instance, will soon reveal that the pod wall tears much more easily in one (oblique) direction than in any other; this is due to the presence of a layer of obliquely-running fibres which will tend to twist as it dries. In most cases also the line of weakness where the actual split will occur is marked out well in advance.

Dispersal

It is an obvious biological necessity for a plant to have some means whereby seed may be moved away from the immediate vicinity of the parent. As an external transporting agent is often required, some of the problems are similar to those which arise in connection with pollination.

Mechanical dispersal is found in "explosive fruits", from which the seeds are violently ejected. Nearly all these structures are capsules, schizocarps, or legumes, and it is quite clear that the propulsive force is simply an exaggeration of the tissue tension which normally causes the dehiscence or mericarp separation of such fruits. In many legumes the oblique fibres are stressed so that the valves suddenly separate and each coils up with a twirling motion which flings out the seeds. In the schizocarp of *Geranium* the mericarps are suddenly flung up by strips of fibres which tear away from the style (Fig. 177). *Impatiens* is a little unusual because the action of its "explosive" capsule depends upon the turgor of a living parenchyma instead of the stress in dead tissues. In *Ecballium* ("squirting cucumber") the berry ejects its seeds in a jet of liquid derived from the breakdown of the inner pericarp.

Dispersal by water is found in very few angiosperms, and is rarely connected with any obvious structural modification. Relatively few fruits or seeds will float for any length of time, and those that do are often damaged irretrievably by the water, especially if it be sea-water.

Dispersal by wind is common and takes place in a variety of ways. The principal forms are: (*a*) Seeds small enough to blow as dust are found in some parasites and some plants, especially orchids, which depend upon mycorrhizal association with a fungus. (Only if the young seedling has some special means of nutrition is the tiny seed with little reserve material likely to ensure survival of the species.) (*b*) "Censer mechanisms" in which the seeds are flung out by the sway and jerk of the plant in the wind, are common in the taller herbaceous plants, particularly those with capsules or follicles. (*c*) Tumbleweeds, not represented in Britain, are annual or biennial plants in which the whole shoot system comes away from the ground and bowls along before the wind, shedding seeds as it goes. There are some spectacular examples in steppe and prairie regions. (*d*) Winged fruits and winged seeds are fairly common but the system only reaches its fullest development in trees, presumably because unpowered flight is only really effective if started at a height. Some of the winged fruits and seeds, especially in warmer climates, are of great size. Most of them spin in the manner of a helicopter rotor, but there are some which perform a straight glide, and which perhaps should not be listed under wind dispersal at all, because they can travel in a calm. Some of these structures display considerable aerodynamic refinement, and were intensively studied by the pioneer aircraft designers. (*e*) Plumed fruits are seen in Compositae (p. 425) with a hairy pappus, in *Clematis* and *Anemone*, where the plumed structure is the style, and in some grasses with plumed bracts. Plumed seeds are found in Salicaceae, in *Epilobium*, and in many other examples. The flight of these objects depends upon their effectiveness as parachutes. In still air, or in the kind of non-turbulent airflow which may occur over water, they merely fall at constant speed. Over land, however, where any obstacle is certain to deflect the wind upwards, a dispersal unit with a very low rate of free fall has a good chance of getting into an up-draught, even though it starts at a low level. Plumed fruits and seeds are in fact common, and evidently effective, in plants of very moderate stature.

Dispersal by animals also takes place in a great variety of ways. The principal forms are: (*a*) Burrs are fruits (rarely seeds) equipped with hooks which catch in fur or feather. In species of *Galium*, in *Circaea*, and in some of the Umbelliferae, the hooks are outgrowths of the ovary wall, but there are many other possibilities. In *Geum* the hooks are formed by the styles, in *Arctium* by the bracts of the capitulum, in *Agrimonia* by the hollow receptacle of a perigynous flower. (*b*) Succulent fruits, in which an edible tissue is provided, not always by the ovary itself, owe the dispersal of their seeds to the activity of fruit-eating animals (in temperate climates almost all the animals involved are birds; in the tropics monkeys, bats, and some other mammals are also of great importance). In some cases the seeds are discarded by the animal, but this is by no means a strict rule. In general, the smaller and more numerous the seeds, and the larger the animal, the more likely it is that most of the seeds, and often all of them, will be swallowed. Although the gizzards of some birds are capable of destroying a high proportion of the ordinary seeds which enter them, the seeds of succulent fruits are especially resistant to the physical and chemical effects of the digestive organs, and germinate freely from animal excreta. There is perhaps a biological explanation here for the development of a stony pericarp layer in drupes. (*c*) Edible attachments to the seed are commoner than is sometimes supposed. Arils often function in this way. Alternatively the whole outer testa may be succulent as in pomegranate and *Iris foetidissima*, or there may be a **caruncle**, which is a special outgrowth of the integuments near the micropyle. Where the succulent tissues of seeds are extensive and conspicuous they usually attract birds as the succulent fruits do; there are, however, many cases of small and dull-coloured attachments which are attractive to ants, which will drag such seeds for long distances.

Different methods of dispersal are often combined. Thus in *Ulex* (gorse) the seeds are violently ejected by the dehiscence of the legume, but they also have an oily caruncle, and are liable to be carried about by ants.

The Effectiveness of Dispersal

Almost every angiosperm species quite obviously possesses means of dispersal which are effective in moving a fair proportion of the seeds beyond the actual area occupied by the parent. Apart from accidental wastage, which may be high, the process may involve a definite sacrifice; the dispersal of acorns, for instance, depends on animals which have no interest in acorns except to eat them, but which are often careless, forgetful, and untidy. Squirrels, for example, carry and store large quantities of nuts and seeds which they do not subsequently eat.

Long-range dispersal, over distances measured in miles, is a different matter altogether Apart from very rare accidents there are only three possible agents of transport: river, ocean current, and migrating bird. The bird is a less effective carrier than one might suppose. Externally, migrating birds are very clean; internally they rarely retain anything for more than three or four hours, and with an air speed which is usually less than fifty knots this is not enough for an ocean crossing. Setting aside weed species and others which have been distributed by human activity there appear to be only two groups (both numerically very small) of angiosperm species which have succeeded in spreading over great distances. There is a group of sea-shore plants, nearly all tropical, the seeds of which can travel by floating in sea-water and survive long voyages. There is also a group of fresh-water plants which appears to have travelled partly by river, partly in mud upon the feet of migrating water-fowl.

Although there are some curious and unexplained exceptions, the general distribution of angiosperms in the world is consistent with the view that dispersal is normally a short-range process, long distances being attainable only by repeated short moves in successive generations, anything but the shortest of sea passages constituting a serious barrier. In the southern hemisphere there are great differences between the floras of Australia and New Zealand, or even between the plants of Madagascar and those of the African mainland. In high northern latitudes, where the land-mass is practically continuous, many species spread most of the way round the world. The significance of these relationships is made clearer by the study of other groups of plants in which the dispersal units are smaller. Fungal spores, for instance, which are very much smaller than the seed of any angiosperm, are generally distributed in the atmosphere up to heights of over 20,000 ft, and fungal species are correspondingly more widely distributed on the ground.

13 CLASSIFICATION AND IDENTIFICATION OF ANGIOSPERMS

GENERAL PRINCIPLES

The basic principles of biological classification are universal, but it is traditional for a botanical student to approach the subject in the first instance through an examination of the flowering plants. Because the angiosperms are the only major group of plants in which the classification can be understood without the use of the microscope, and without any knowledge of fossil forms, they were the first group of plants to be effectively classified, and the factors which made them specially easy for the early botanists still operate to the advantage of the modern student.

Identification and Classification

As soon as plants are given names the practical problem of **identification** arises. We have a plant which is new to us; how do we find out what other people call it? This problem can only be solved by comparison. We must find a picture or a description or a named specimen which agrees sufficiently well with our unknown plant to satisfy us that the two are really the same—not of course exactly the same, for no two organisms will ever be identical, but sufficiently alike to justify the use of one name for both. The actual process of comparison is usually quite simple and straightforward but as the number of species of angiosperms in the world is about a quarter of a million it is really essential to have some guidance. How can we go quickly to the right page in the reference books? How can we avoid wasting time in fruitless comparisons which merely show that our specimen is *not* so-and-so?

Clearly the reference material must be arranged on some plan which makes it easy for the searcher to find his way. The aids to identification which modern books provide are very effective, but in order to use them to the best advantage it is necessary to understand the principles of their construction. In a limited field, such as the identification of plants of one country, a crude system of indexing by obvious structural features will do all that is needed. Suppose that we have a set of pictures of British plants, arranged so that we can, for instance, take out very quickly all those which refer to plants with yellow actinomorphic flowers and opposite leaves.

In this particular example the number of pictures taken out will be so small that there is no need for further refinement—a quick glance through the pictures in hand will give us an identification. Things will not always be quite so easy. With yellow actinomorphic flowers and *alternate* leaves the number of pictures taken out of the collection will be inconveniently large, and it will be necessary to break it down further, perhaps by putting plants with stipules into one group and those without into another.

This simple process of repeated sub-division can always be made to give an identification in a reasonable number of moves. Especially in working with pictures there is little point in pursuing the division to the very end; when the number of possibilities has been reduced to a handful it is often quicker to look at them all. Any system of indexing which works by this method of repeated sub-division of the material is called an **artificial classification.** Artificial classifications are used wherever routine identification of biological material is carried on; the police, for instance, have an artificial classification for fingerprints. In designing an artificial classification there is no room at all for theoretical considerations. In the long run, speed of operation is the only thing that counts.

It turns out, however, that plants can be (indeed must be) classified in another way, and that provision must be made for requirements which no artificial classification can satisfy. The nature of these problems can best be illustrated by reference to some familiar animal examples. If we are told that an animal has feathers, then we can say from experience that it will be warm-blooded, possess a beak, lay hard-shelled eggs, and so on. Even when the connection between different characteristics is not so rigid as in this example, there is very often a balance of probability. Not all birds can fly, but most of them can, and flight is one of the most important features of birds, even though it is not universal among them. This tendency for different characters to be linked, so that a group of organisms comes to make a very distinctive impression upon the mind, is not something which could have been predicted beforehand. It is a thing which had to be discovered. Common words like "bird" and "fish" represent the results of a great deal of prehistoric biological observation. Unfortunately, botanical distinctions of equal importance are a little less easy to appreciate, and common speech has never gone far in recognising groups of plants. In reality, however, clearly defined natural groupings exist everywhere among plants just as they do among animals. We have to consider the properties of this **natural classification.**

Clearly there can be only one natural classification, though different investigators may describe it in different ways, all more or less imperfect. As the classification is a fact of nature, we have no control over its form, and no reason to expect that it will be particularly simple or convenient. Exceptions are likely to occur, organisms which have departed in some unusual way from the ordinary habits of the group to which they belong. Every exception makes it more difficult to give precise definitions of the groups affected. The penguin, which is a bird but cannot fly, and the bat, which flies but is not a bird, would add to our difficulties in explaining the word "bird" to any visitor from another planet. Among animals, however, such exceptions are not very common and can be remembered fairly easily, so that it is safe to rely quite heavily upon general impressions. If an animal looks like a fish, then (unless it is a whale) it probably *is* a fish. Among plants, unfortunately for the beginner, the exceptions come in very much larger numbers. To observe that a plant "looks like a cactus" gets you nowhere; many kinds of plants look like cacti. With plants, you have to know just what to look for; vague general impressions are of very little use.

The natural classification of plants offers great difficulties to a student, partly because of the technical language which is used in describing it, but mainly because of the abundance of exceptions. Everywhere there are situations like this:

Ranunculaceae: Leaves alternate (but opposite in *Clematis*), flowers actinomorphic (but zygomorphic in *Aconitum* and *Delphinium*), flowers spirally constructed (except in *Aquilegia*), carpels free (but fused in *Nigella*). . . .

In the larger families of plants any attempt to state the characters of the family is apt to look like an attempt to catalogue every possible eventuality. Look at this:

Leguminosae: Trees, shrubs, perennial or annual herbs, often climbing. Leaves alternate or opposite or in whorls, simple or compound, with or without stipules, flowers actinomorphic or zygomorphic . . ., seeds with or without endosperm, germination epigeal or hypogeal . . . (and so on. There is hardly any end to this one).

In these circumstances it is reasonable to ask what is the best way of studying the natural classification, and whether the results of such a study can ever repay the effort involved. It is so easy to make good artificial classifications with no exceptions; what need is there for anything else? To answer these questions one must consider why a natural classification should exist at all. What is observed is a universal tendency for organisms which are alike in some features to be alike in others also. As a result, many character combinations which one might expect to find are missing. One does not, for instance, see a feathered animal suckling its young, though there is no very obvious reason why not. Because structural features are distributed in this uneven way, there are distinct groups of organisms, with equally definite gaps between them. For this state of affairs there are only three possible explanations. The whole thing might be a gigantic system of coincidences; in fact nobody is disposed to take this line. It might be a divine plan of creation. This is satisfactory to some people; whatever the merits of the explanation it clearly does nothing to diminish the importance of the natural arrangement. Most biologists, however, regard the natural classification as the product of an evolutionary process. If two organisms have some features in common, then that is probably because they inherited those features from a common ancestor. If they have inherited some characters from a common ancestor, then there is a prospect that they will have inherited others also. Those who take this view are in an extremely strong position, for the process of inheritance will explain not merely the existence of a natural classification but also many details of its construction.

For most people the natural classification is a sufficient proof that evolution has occurred, and it is also the best available chart of the way in which the different kinds of plants and animals have come into existence. In both capacities the classification must command our closest attention. To think of the classification as a scheme of evolution gives us also the key to the proper treatment of exceptions. If new kinds of plant arise by descent from existing forms, then however spectacularly a new type may depart from the habits of its ancestors, there can be no possibility of complete transformation, no danger that *all* the characteristics of the race will be lost. Can the leopard change his spots? Yes, occasionally a cub will be born with an abnormal pattern. Can the leopard change into a new sort of animal altogether, so distinct that the relationship cannot be recognised? No, of course not. This principle can be applied at all levels. In one of the examples above, five members of the Ranunculaceae have been listed as exceptions. To memorise them would be troublesome. The point is that there is no need to do anything of the kind. Not one of these plants will cause any real difficulty to anybody who knows the general pattern of structure and behaviour in the Ranunculaceae and who is prepared to look at the whole of his specimen. This is the usual situation; most exceptional plants are exceptional only in some special direction, their other characters following the normal pattern of the groups to which they belong. The rule, therefore, is extremely simple: on meeting an exceptional feature, *first pay proper attention to the rest of the plant.* Exceptions are often interesting, but it is a mistake to take too much notice of them too soon. They are of quite secondary importance, and should be treated accordingly.

Because of the evolutionary significance of the natural classification some people have been led to believe that a man cannot classify plants correctly unless he has the proper opinions regarding evolutionary theory. This is obvious nonsense. The classification represents the facts of nature. However strongly an investigator's ideas may influence his explanation of the facts, they cannot, unless he is dishonest, have any effect upon his description of the facts. As a matter of history, the main features of the natural classification were discovered by men who had no evolutionary beliefs at all, and in the mid-Victorian period when evolutionary ideas were provoking some of the fiercest scientific arguments on record the development of classification went on tranquil and undisturbed.

The History of the Classification of Flowering Plants

In tribal societies plants attract attention only as sources of food, clothing, baskets, cordage, medicines, arrow-poisons, building materials, and so on. As soon as economic conditions allow people a little leisure, the interest in plants expands. Rich men lay out gardens, poor ones write poetry or paint pictures. By 1500 B.C. an appreciation of the decorative qualities of plants was well developed in Egypt, Assyria, India, and China. Although these pre-botanical contacts with plants often require men to make skilful and accurate observations they very rarely lead to any significant attempt at biological classification. The tendency is much more to treat each plant on its own, as a special case. One reason for this is the way in which closely related plants tend to be geographically separated. People who know only the plants of their own country are unlikely to discover the natural classification for themselves. Nor does the need for a classification become pressing when the total number of plants known is very small; in this respect the early peoples all simplified their problems by ignoring entirely any plant which was inconspicuous or of no special value to them.

Promising attempts at scientific classification were made by Aristotle and Theophrastus in Greece, in the fourth century B.C., but there was nobody to carry on this work, and it was lost sight of for nearly two thousand years. All through the middle ages the study of plants in Europe was based on the work of Dioscorides, a very inferior writer of the first century A.D. Dioscorides was only interested in medicinal substances and his text was almost worthless to begin with. Repeated hand-copying did not improve the book, and in particular the illustrations, which had originally been fairly realistic, degenerated under the hands of the copyists into meaningless symbolic patterns.

Suddenly, in the period 1490-1535, several factors combined to transform the situation. Active geographical exploration led to a great surge of interest in foreign plants. The artists, who had recently solved the problems of perspective and exact representation, began to produce fine drawings of plants, the best of them quite equal to anything done since. Most important of all, the printing-press put these magnificent pictures into libraries all over Europe. For the first time it became possible to identify specimens with reasonable accuracy. This could not immediately lead to any development of classification. For one thing the technical language needed for effective description and comparison of specimens did not exist. The books continued to concentrate upon real or imaginary medicinal properties of the plants, and the texts consisted in great part of matter which we now regard as superstition or folk-lore. Public interest in plants was, however, greatly stimulated by the new publications, and this presently led to the establishment of botanic gardens. Here are some which have continued their scientific work down to the present day, with their dates of foundation: Padua 1540, Leyden 1577, Montpellier 1593, Oxford 1621, Edinburgh 1667 (not now on original site), Chelsea 1673. The accumulation of collections of dried plants began at about the same time. There was for the first time a brisk international exchange of specimens, and by about 1640 the best workers were already beginning to recognise some of the easier parts of the natural classification. The next fifty years saw rapid progress, in which British botanists played a major part. It was, for instance, an Englishman (John Ray), who first grasped the distinction between monocotyledons and dicotyledons.

Unfortunately, the pace of these developments could not be maintained. Difficulties were encountered which grew until they threatened to bring the progress of the science to a standstill. The root of the trouble lay in the rapidity with which new plants were being discovered. At the peak period the total number of plants known was being doubled every fifteen or twenty years, and the working methods of the seventeenth century were inadequate for the treatment of this unexpected flood of new material. Strictly speaking, there was at that time no system for the naming of species. Generic names were in use, and there was no difficulty in inventing new ones as required, but the plants in each genus were specified by expressions which were really short descriptions and not names in the modern sense at all. This was a survival of ancient custom. In the beginning generic names like *Iris* and *Narcissus* had served the simple needs of the ancient world. Later, when it was noticed that there were different kinds of *Iris*, these were roughly sorted out under such headings as "The large blue *Iris* of Germany", "The yellow *Iris* of watersides", and so on. This procedure, though a little long-winded, was extremely convenient. The descriptions were not standardised in any way. Nobody expected one to remember them word for word; every botanist did what he thought best in the language of his choice. Even in the most important genera there were until about 1650 so few recognised specific forms that there was little room for confusion, nor did anyone then have the slightest conception of the number of species which would ultimately have to be distinguished. Even before 1700, however, it was becoming extremely difficult to indicate clearly the particular plant under discussion.

There were various attempts at simplification and reform, but the decisive change came in thc period 1735-55 at the hands of Linné, a Swede, often known as Linnaeus (the Latin version). Linnaeus, who was a skilful propagandist, was able to gain general acceptance for two ingenious novelties:

(1) The name of a species was to consist always of two words only. The *Iris* forms became *Iris germanica*, *Iris pseudacorus*, etc. Such expressions had often been used before; what was new was their standardisation as *names*—previously they had been thought of as descriptions which just happened to be very short.

(2) A new system of artificial classification was introduced in which plants were sorted into groups according to the numbers of stamens and carpels. Anything with A5 G3 went into a group called *Pentandria trigynia*, and so on. Anything as crude as this is bound to cut right across the natural groupings, as Linnaeus himself seems clearly to have recognised. It is, however, a marvellously convenient way of indexing a mass of new material which you do not really understand, and as such it exactly met the need of the time.

The Linnean reforms made botany much easier for people of moderate ability, and undoubtedly led to some decline in the average standard of work. There was a great deal of undistinguished cataloguing, and relatively little regard for natural relationships.

For almost a hundred years the Linnean classification dominated the scene, though never to the total exclusion of other systems. Its overthrow can be traced to a group of French workers who began in the later part of the eighteenth century to develop further the natural classification as it had been described by Ray. The supporters of the Linnean system resisted for some time, but ultimately the value of the natural classification became clear, and in the period 1820-40 the Linnean classification was swept away almost as quickly as it came. The natural arrangement which then emerged has since undergone much detailed correction and improvement, but the basic outline has changed very little.

Botanical Collections

Effective work in classification and identification is only possible when facilities exist for comparing one plant with another. For direct comparison, which is always to be preferred, the specimens must be brought physically together. To have two specimens side by side upon the bench is the ideal. Seeing one plant in May and the other in August is not the same thing at all; in these conditions such comparison as may be possible will only be indirect. The first specimen will form the basis of some kind of record (notes, drawings, at the worst mere memory) which will be carried forward for comparison with the second. The risk of mistakes will be at least doubled, and if the second stage of the operation reveals a gap in the record it may be too late to go back to the first plant. If direct comparison is to be the standard, it is absolutely essential to build up collections of preserved specimens. With angiosperms the normal type of collection is the **herbarium**, consisting of dried and flattened plants attached to sheets of paper. Herbarium specimens have been accumulating for about five hundred years, and they are as permanent as books. Every civilised country now has large collections. These "public" herbaria display a common pattern of organisation: a building which houses the specimens (anything up to a million or two), a reference library, and a permanent staff. Such institutions, of which there are several in Britain, are publicly financed like museums or astronomical observatories, and their purpose is to provide for the accurate identification of specimens.

A student will at first have to work with such plants as he can obtain personally, supplemented perhaps by reference to a school or college collection. Even a student's work, however, is subject to the practical needs which have brought the large herbaria into existence. If any real progress is to be made plants will have to be kept for comparison with those obtained later. Every student in fact should make his own herbarium, and should adopt professional methods in the manipulation of his specimens. A herbarium sheet (Plate 15) is a flat piece of plain white paper, between $15\frac{3}{4}$ in. and $16\frac{1}{2}$ in. high and between $10\frac{1}{2}$ in. and $11\frac{1}{2}$ in. wide, labelled in the bottom right-hand corner. One can use an adhesive label or write directly on the sheet, but a horizontal rectangle about 4 in. $\times$ 3 in. is about the smallest space that should be allowed. A keen collector will often have printed labels with his name on; this gives a good appearance, but it is not a good idea to let the printer lay out spaces for the name of the plant, the date, and so on. Requirements vary too much, and one needs the freedom of a plain label. Drying the plants is a simple operation but it needs to be done methodically, and any carelessness will lead to an inferior result. It is necessary to have a press, which must be about the same size as the herbarium sheet. Nothing elaborate is needed, just two pieces of ply or hardboard, squeezed together by two or three webbing straps or by laying a suitable weight on the top board.

Plants can be dried perfectly well in ordinary newspapers, which is fortunate, because a large quantity of paper is essential for good work. It is important that the drying should be rapid, and this can only be secured by changing the paper frequently, say every day for the first week and twice a week thereafter. The damp paper coming out of the press is dried and used again. Only moderate pressure is needed. The plants must be firmly gripped so that leaves cannot crumple, but there should be no crushing of the tissues. Around a bulky specimen extra pads of paper will be needed to transmit the pressure evenly through the rest of the stack. A herbarium specimen should be in such a state that a fragment treated with hot water will yield almost as much information about microscopic structure as a piece of fresh material would do. A plant which has been pinched too hard or dried too slowly may still give a good idea of the general appearance, but will prove disappointing when any more detailed examination is attempted. Some plants offer special difficulties, mainly because they are unusually delicate, or because they live long enough in the press to grow a little or perhaps to shed their leaves or flowers. Most of these difficulties can be overcome. Flimsy water plants can be floated on to a support paper which then stays with them through the press and into the final mount. Plants that take too long to die can be given a preliminary bath in boiling water. In general, the conversion of a plant into a herbarium specimen ought not to involve the loss of anything but the colours. The final attachment of the plant to the sheet is best made with paper gumstrip (the self-adhesive plastic tapes cannot be trusted for long periods of time).

The object should be to show each species as completely as possible. Small plants are mounted entire, roots and all. Larger specimens may have to be cut, but still the basal parts should be shown. Plants which are tall, rather than bulky, as are many grasses, are often dealt with by putting the roots at bottom left and zigzagging the stem up and down the sheet. Some thought should be given to the display of each specimen, and care taken to show upper and lower surfaces of leaves, the back of the flower as well as the front. Trees offer special problems which can be partly solved by adding sketches or photographs to show the general shape of the plant (often best seen in winter), the nature of the bark, and so on. Complete representation of a species calls for the display of different stages of development, from the seedling onwards to the ripe fruit, for series of diseased and abnormal specimens, for the study of contrasts between plants in the open and plants from shady places, plants in tall herbage and plants in close-grazed turf, and in general for a survey of the whole range of behaviour. It is a poor collection which has only one specimen of a common and variable species, and it is only by active collecting that the range of variation is ever likely to be appreciated.

Specimens should be accompanied by the fullest possible information about the circumstances in which they were obtained. As a basic minimum the label should carry the name of the species, the collector's name, the exact locality, the date of collection, the nature of the associated vegetation, and also comments on the nature of the soil, the height above sea level, and the slope of the land in cases where these are in any way remarkable. It is also sound practice to add any relevant correspondence, newspaper cuttings, and so on. One very valuable item is a small envelope with spare fragments which can be used for detailed study (dissection of flowers, etc.) without disturbing the main specimen. Take an extra plant, and break it up after it is dry. A good herbarium contains an immense reserve of information which can be drawn upon at any time for all kinds of specialised purposes. If ever the need arises to identify a strange seed or pollen-grain, many of the reference specimens required ought to be obtainable from the herbarium sheets without delay.

It is important for a student beginning his herbarium work to understand quite clearly that he will learn much more by making a thorough study of the common plants of the district in which he lives than he will ever do by getting scraps of the greatest possible number of species. The deliberate hunting of rarities is particularly objectionable. In Britain no private individual has any business to take orchids, or any but the commonest ferns, or any plant which he knows to be specially uncommon. Herbarium specimens of orchids are almost useless, anyway, because too much depends on exact shape and colouring of the flower, and experts deal with these plants by making coloured drawings or photographs. In Britain it so happens that most of the other rarities are of no special interest in themselves. If you *must* have them, take spores or seeds and grow your own plants. The common plants tend to be more interesting because they grow in a much wider range of conditions and show much greater variability. Besides starting his general collection, a beginner should choose some very common and variable range of plants for special attention. A good set of brambles or dandelions or willows, even if, as is likely, the specimens cannot at first be completely identified, will provide valuable experience which less closely related plants cannot give.

There is little to learn in the actual taking of specimens. A digging tool is essential, and secateurs are better than a knife. The best work is done by taking the press to the plants rather than the other way round, but even people with cars are inclined to compromise on this point. The traditional container for plants is a **vasculum** (Plate 15), a shaped metal case with a shoulder-strap, a carrying-handle, and a hinged lid. It is an efficient design, and it is not at all easy to improvise a satisfactory substitute. Various sizes are made, a length of about 16 in. being appropriate for general work. Provided that a vasculum is fairly full (pack with spare herbage if necessary), is painted in a pale or metallic finish, and is kept as cool as possible, the plants in it will keep until next day. It is a great mistake to take wild plants out of a vasculum and stand them in water—they are better where they are. Most collectors now carry a few plastic bags. These are useful for small things but not in any way a substitute for a vasculum.

As it is not usually practicable to write herbarium labels in the country or to carry them through the press, it is necessary to have some system for relating each specimen to one's notes upon it. The best plan is to number each specimen with a tie-on price-tag, and to make an entry in the field notebook under the same number. On returning home, the final label is written at the first opportunity, while the details are fresh in the mind, the field number being transferred along with everything else. The tag is never removed from the specimen at all. In this way the final mount should show the field number twice over, on the label and on the tag. This procedure by no means eliminates the possibility of mistakes but it does give a useful safeguard against accidental interchange of labels.

The Identification of Specimens

The identity of a species is embodied in what is called a **type specimen**. In the simplest case the type specimen is the actual individual plant from which the species was first scientifically described and named. Sometimes there are several type specimens of equal authority; sometimes types have had to be chosen at a later date to replace a lost original. Type specimens are kept in the public herbaria. They are ordinary herbarium sheets but are distinctively marked by being given special folders (often red-edged) and are treated with special care (in particular, types are never allowed out on loan, as other specimens often are). There is only one way in which a specimen can be identified, and that is by comparing it with a type specimen and showing that they agree. In a difficult case, where all else fails, this doctrine may have to be carried to its logical conclusion, a direct comparison in the institution where the type is kept. In routine work the comparison will be indirect; the new specimen will be checked against other material which has been authenticated by previous comparisons going back to the type in an unbroken chain. With very well-known species there is so much reliable material to hand that the type specimen is never called for, and becomes a mere historical curiosity. The author of any reputable flora, however, will certainly have examined types, or specimens authenticated directly from them, in preparing many of his descriptions. Even a novice's identification, therefore, will often be quite closely linked with the type.

The ordinary worker, then, will make his identifications by comparing a specimen with some intermediate standard, the authenticity of which is derived from the type. The intermediate standard most commonly employed is a printed description. This has one great advantage for a beginner (if he understands the technical language) in that it directs his attention to the points of importance. Where there is a choice, however, it is not always wise to choose descriptions in preference to other available standards. In many respects good drawings are much more satisfactory, and named specimens are better still. It is the cost, and to some extent the bulk, of these other standards which forces one to rely so much upon descriptions. Descriptions have their own place as a source of botanical information, and identification from descriptions is good training for a student, and is an exercise often required in examinations, but there is nothing to be gained in ordinary work by artificially restricting one's sources of information.

In the reference books the plants are arranged in a natural sequence; the exact order will vary according to the author's opinions, but the families and genera are at least roughly standardised everywhere. Often there is a summary or **synopsis** of the arrangement adopted, and this is a valuable feature which should be used to the full. *Very little experience* is needed to enable one to go at once to the right part of the natural arrangement with at least a fair proportion of the specimens encountered. Some of the great plant families are met with over and over again, and a British student will find that even a rather sketchy knowledge of about a dozen families will enable him to cut out a great part of the working.

Even experts, however, can never hope to know enough to rely entirely upon the natural arrangement. Besides the ordinary alphabetical index, therefore, a book is usually indexed by a system of artificial classification, which is now invariably laid out as a set of keys. A **key** is really a series of questions. At each stage of the working one is offered a set of alternative statements, only one of which can apply to the specimen in hand. The correct alternative is selected, and leads one to the next choice, and so on until a name is reached. There are two principal ways of setting out a key in print. The commonest form is the numbered key, like this:

1.	Water plants with white flowers	15
	Land or marsh plants with yellow flowers	2
2.	Sepals 3, petals 7-12	*Ranunculus ficaria*
	Sepals 5, petals usually 5	3
3.	Leaves deeply lobed or divided	4
	Leaves entire or merely toothed	12

(Beginning of a key to species of *Ranunculus*, wording simplified from Clapham, Tutin, and Warburg: *Flora of the British Isles*, Cambridge University Press.)

The great advantage of this pattern is that the alternatives of a set (there may occasionally be more than two) are kept close together. Also, because of the numbering, it is easy to take a note of any point which has been reached, and return to it later without mistake. A less common type is the indented key, in which the lines are distinguished by letters and signs, and by being set in progressively from the left-hand edge of the page, like this:

A. Pod velvety
  B. Mature leaves almost hairless
    C. Leaflets 15-19 .. .. *Wisteria floribunda*
    CC. Leaflets about 11 .. .. .. *W. sinensis*
  BB. Mature leaves downy .. .. .. *W. venusta*
AA. Pod hairless
  B. Racemes up to 4 in. long.. .. .. *W. frutescens*
  BB. Racemes 12 in. long or more .. *W. macrostachya*

(Key to species of *Wisteria*, wording simplified from Bailey: *Manual of Cultivated Plants*, Macmillan.)

Indented keys have some advantage in speed of working, but large ones can confuse an inexperienced worker. Notice that the alternatives of a set may be rather widely separated (**A** and **AA** may not even be on the same page), and that letters are often repeated (**B** and **BB** are used twice in the example), which makes it easier to lose the place. The best way of learning the mechanics of keys is by making a key yourself. It need not be botanical—a key to one's friends is more amusing, and will teach the principles just as well.

Beginners often suppose that the main work of identification comes in the use of a key. They take their specimen through the key and arrive at a name, and then write that name down as the identification, or perhaps there may be a quick look at a description (just as a check, with the idea that the key has probably given the right answer). Anybody working in this frame of mind produces a steady stream of incorrect identifications. He is attributing to the key-work a degree of reliability which it does not possess; indeed, he often has more faith in the keys than the men who wrote them. The emphasis should be entirely the other way. Identification comes in the final comparison. The most that a key can do is to make useful suggestions, to point out comparisons which it would perhaps be worth while to try. For one thing (as you will find out when you try) writing a good key of any size is very difficult, and published keys are far from perfect. Again, everybody makes mistakes at times in the operation of a key, by skipping a line and so on. Difficulties often arise also from the incomplete specimen or the point which cannot be clearly decided. Suppose the key has "Fruit a berry/Fruit a capsule", and you have no fruit. Take a note of the place, assume a berry, and work out to the end. Return to the marked place, assume a capsule, and work out again. Your key has now given *two* suggestions. They cannot both be right. The object should be to gain some fluency in reading keys so as to be able to follow several lines, or even work backwards, without getting lost. Sometimes one can go straight through a key and come out with the right answer first time, but this should be regarded as exceptional good fortune, and a beginner who has had a few easy triumphs cannot afford to become over-confident.

In the early stages mistakes in the actual working of the key will arise mostly by overlooking some of the wording. It should be made a rule that every key-line must be read in its entirety. If something is said about the leaves of a plant that must be given proper attention before going on to read what is said about the flower, and so on. Also it should be a constant practice to read all the alternatives of a set before selecting any one of them To pick the first alternative without reading the others is asking for trouble. In an indented key, having read **D** and **DD**, see whether there is not a **DDD**. Sometimes there is—on the next page. When a little experience has been gained, however, it will often be found that whole sections of the key-work can be by-passed quite safely and with a considerable gain in speed.

There are two main ways in which this possibility arises. When you are getting fairly near the end of a key, there often ceases to be any point in struggling with difficult key-entries. If, in the branch of the key which lies ahead, there are only half a dozen plants, a quick inspection of the pictures offers better prospects than any but the most straightforward key-work. The most important form of short-cut, however, arises from the possibility in many cases of eliminating beforehand many of the names listed in the key. If a plant is marked as "Rare, Scottish mountains only" one is not likely to find five acres of it in Kent, and a key-line which leads in that direction can be abandoned at once. It often pays, before entering a key to species, to see how many can be ruled out by considerations of this kind. There are many genera with perhaps a dozen species of which only three or four are commonly met. In such cases there is little point in using the key at all unless it turns out that the specimen is *not* one of the common species.

Everybody arrives now and then at a point from which there seems to be no way forward. Every name suggested by the key proves to be the wrong one, and the worker hardly knows which way to turn. In this position there are three main possibilities to be examined. Often, especially with beginners, the trouble lies in some major error at an early stage in the working. Any assumption which seemed obvious at the time should be looked at again. Perhaps the plant is not a monocotyledon after all, perhaps the "flower" is really an inflorescence, perhaps the "leaf" is really a leaflet, etc. Another source of trouble which is commoner than many students realise is the freak specimen. Variation in numbers of parts is widespread; a flower which should have five petals will sometimes have six, a plant which should have opposite leaves will occasionally produce whorls of three. Colours are variable; in particular, species which normally produce coloured flowers are apt to yield white varieties. Size, especially the size of vegetative parts, is enormously variable. General measurements of height of plant are often given in the books but must not be taken too seriously. When due allowance has been made for serious errors, or for abnormality of the specimen, the suspicion must arise that the plant is one not listed in the book being used. In this respect the source of the specimen is important. A plant which occurs in every hedgerow is pretty certain to be listed in the flora, but an isolated plant on a rubbish-tip may very well not be. A foreign plant will not necessarily give rise to any special difficulty in working a key, indeed it may "come out" very easily, but the suggestion which the key makes will often be quite absurd.

The kind of information which one takes from a specimen varies very much according to the object in view. For purposes of classification, the recognition of true relationships, it is often desirable to use rather obscure and technical points which call for painstaking investigations. For the identification of an unknown specimen it is more important to use features which are easy to observe. Some key-writers are very inconsiderate in this respect, and will ask for microscopic examination of an ovary when the plant could perfectly well be keyed out on some obvious thing like orange roots or purple spots on the stem. In a key, it is not a virtue to follow the lines of the natural classification.

Another aspect of identification, which has its own requirements, is the attempt to recognise a plant which one has seen before. Here it is worth while to pay attention to features like smell and texture which can be remembered quite easily but which cannot be satisfactorily described or drawn. A plant like *Stachys sylvatica* can always be recognised by the smell alone, but this is not a possible method for identifying your first specimen because the smell is indescribable. When you meet a new plant, therefore, pass the foliage between your fingers and appraise the texture, crush a little and test for smell, take note of the exact colouration of the flower, whether the petals seem smooth or velvety, and so on. This kind of examination may at some future time save you a great deal of trouble and many mistakes.

One point of great importance which is often overlooked is the way in which problems of identification are apt to become easier when plenty of material is available. In a large genus like *Carex*, for instance, a worker trying to identify a single specimen from a book is in a very bad position. The key, which goes on for page after page, is full of distinctions like "Spikes small/Spikes larger" and "Stems slender/Stems rather stout". A single specimen gives no idea of the range of variation, and it is impossible to judge its position. But suppose that a collector takes every *Carex* he sees for a whole season. When he comes to identify the plants he will be able to form a good idea of what is a small spike or a slender stem by the standards of this particular genus. Indeed, as he will probably have in his collection a high proportion of the commoner species the task of identification will be to some extent replaced by the much simpler one of deciding, among a limited range of plants, which is which. In this way even a specimen which cannot itself be identified at the time may assist in the identification of others. All these benefits are denied to those who discard each plant after they have examined it.

Nomenclature

There survives from antiquity a basic stock of generic names like *Lilium*, *Rosa*, etc., mostly transmitted to us by way of Dioscorides and now in some cases certainly applied to the wrong plant. To these ancient names have been added others derived from three main sources. Some are descriptive names based on classical word-roots, sometimes Latin but more often Greek: *Eucharis* (= very graceful), *Aglaonema* (= bright thread). Some have been adopted from "barbarous" languages: *Pandanus* (Malay), *Alchemilla* (Arabic), *Sabal* (S. American Indian). Some are commemorative names, after royalty, eminent botanists, etc.: *Strelitzia* (after Charlotte Sophia von Mecklenburg-Strelitz), *Parkinsonia* (after John Parkinson), *Roystonea* (after Roy Stone).

The natural groups of plants form a hierarchy, in which at each level a number of smaller groups are brought together to make one large one. This kind of organisation is familiar among animals: the owls are joined with others such as vultures in a group known as the birds of prey, which in turn is combined with others to make the whole assemblage of birds. As a general rule the names of groups larger than a genus are made from generic names by changing the ending in a regular way. In the following table the various grades of association are set out in order, with the terminations usually employed:

Grade	Ending	Example
Order	-ales	Rutales
Family	-aceae	Rutaceae
Subfamily	-oideae	Rutoideae
Tribe	-eae	Ruteae
Subtribe	-inae	Rutinae
Genus	..	*Ruta*

Thus the Trifolieae are a tribe containing the genus *Trifolium* and some of its allies. The Rosaceae are a family containing *Rosa* and belonging to the Rosales, an order which also includes the family Crassulaceae in which there is a genus *Crassula*. The Spiraeoideae are a subfamily of Rosaceae including the genus *Spiraea*. There are a few of the larger groups which have irregular terminations, the name being formed, not from the name of any genus, but from some well-marked characteristic of the group as a whole. In these cases which mostly concern the more important and readily recognised groups, the status of each unit has to be learned. Thus Compositae (= "compound ones") and Cruciferae (= "cross-bearers") are families, Umbelliflorae (= "umbel-flowers") an order, Papilionatae (= "butterfly-flowers") a subfamily. The names of the larger groups, although in Latin, are not italicised or underlined like generic names. The words are all *plural* ("the Rosaceae *are* . . .") and custom allows the use of the English definite article as in the lines above. In a few cases "unofficial" anglicised singular forms are available to denote single members of a group. Thus an aroid is a species of Araceae, a composite is a species of Compositae, an umbellifer is a species of Umbelliferae.

No rule can be found which will settle the exact rank which should be given to any particular group of plants, and the treatment in different books will be found to vary a little. Some authors, for instance, make a family called Fumariaceae, while others reduce the same group of plants to the level of a subfamily (Fumarioideae) in the Papaveraceae. Such discrepancies are a little disconcerting at first, but they are not really important. There is usually no question of one being right and the other wrong. It is just a different way of looking at things.

Within a genus each species has its own **specific epithet.** This is not a complete name, and can never stand alone. The name of the species consists always of two words, the generic name followed by the specific epithet. Specific epithets are of several kinds. Some are ordinary Latin or Greek adjectives, the meanings of which can be found in the classical dictionaries. It is worth learning the commoner ones, like *palustre* (= marsh-dwelling), *hirsuta* (= hairy), *rubra* (= red), etc. Some of these occur in hundreds of genera. There is also a large class of geographical adjectives. Some of these end in *-ense* or *-ensis*, in which case the meaning is usually clear (*chinense*, *hongkongensis*), though sometimes an unfamiliar Latin version of the place-name is used (e.g. *vectensis* for the Isle of Wight). Others have independent terminations, as in *europaea*, *americana*, *japonica*. Note that *australis* means southern, not Australian. There are also many commemorative adjectives, usually ending in *-i*, *-ii*, *-iana*, or *-iae* (this last for a woman). Commemoratives are often written with a capital letter, e.g. *Lupinus Hartwegii* after Theodor Hartweg, *Rosa Banksiae* after Lady Banks (but *Musa Banksii* after Sir Joseph). Some specific epithets are nouns used in apposition, rather as one might say "Jones the postman". These are mostly generic names, often obsolete ones, and the use of a capital letter is common. Thus *Quercus Ilex* (*Ilex* = holly), *Sorbus Aria* (*Aria* being an old name for some similar tree), *Dolichos Lablab* (which comes from the local vernacular). In modern work it is common to use small letters for all specific epithets; it is therefore unnecessary to pay special attention to the capitals found in books. Adjectives change their terminations according to the ordinary rules of Latin grammar so as to take the gender of the generic name. The gender of a generic name is usually indicated by its termination, but note that trees tend to be feminine, whatever the ending: *Populus tremula* (not *-us*). Nouns in apposition keep their own ending.

There has been a great deal of confusion regarding specific names. Quite apart from actual mistakes authors are liable to disagree about a plant's proper position. A comparison of different books will often show that a plant has been moved from one genus to another, with consequent change of name, or that a different specific epithet has been used for some reason which is not clear. These matters are regulated to some extent by international agreement, but it has unfortunately proved quite as difficult to secure world-wide harmony in this sphere as in any other.

In a situation which is far from perfect there are two principles which make it easier to find one's way about and keep one's temper. In order that the origin of a name shall be traceable it is the custom to add to the specific name an abbreviation of the name of the author responsible for making the name in the first place: *Primula farinosa* L., P. *japonica* A. Gray, and so on (L. for Linnaeus). Where exact identification is concerned, as, for instance, on the label of a herbarium sheet, this abbreviation should always be given.

It is a very real safeguard in the rather numerous cases where two people have given the same name to two quite different plants. With regard to the stability of names it must be remembered that although there are some international rules about nomenclature there are practically none about classification. An author who makes a special study of a genus is likely to decide that it should be broken up into a whole group of genera, each with its own name (which the rules allow him to invent). This may change the names of nearly all the species. The author is within his rights, but the point is that he has no authority to compel anyone at all to follow his example. People who prefer to keep the old genus, and consequently the old names, are perfectly entitled to do so. This is often misunderstood; people are apt to submit too tamely to sweeping changes, not always very well-considered and often not supported by any new discovery about the plants. It is best to adopt a reasonable compromise; arrangements which have long been given up cannot be restored, but on the other hand there is no need to follow slavishly the whims of the man who wrote the latest book.

Within a genus it is often convenient to recognise **subgenera**, and within a subgenus one may have several **sections**. These units are named like genera, but their names do not enter into those of the species. Thus, for instance, *Artemisia maritima* lies in a section of *Artemisia* known as *Seriphidium*, while *Artemisia campestris* belongs to another section called *Dracunculus*.

The Nature of the Species

Note.—*This section makes use of genetical and cytological concepts which are explained in Chapter 22.*

When one examines the plants upon any one piece of ground there seems to be very little difficulty in sorting them into species. With rare exceptions a specimen is either one sort of plant or else it is another, and there are clear gaps between the kinds. Furthermore, within each species, although individual specimens will never be identical, the amount of variation which is visible in any restricted area of country will be quite limited. The early botanists therefore viewed species, and people with limited knowledge are still inclined to view them, as units between which there are clear-cut divisions, and within which there is only a rather trivial amount of variation.

More extended study does a great deal to destroy the clarity of this picture. The circumstances vary so much in different cases that it is quite impossible to arrive at any clear definition of the word "species". At one time this caused serious embarrassment, but we now know enough about the reproductive mechanisms of plants to understand a good deal of what is going on. The units which are called species, and which are given specific names, are of several different kinds, and the species in different genera are often of quite different status. Apart from the simple case where species show little variation and will not cross with each other, the main types of situation encountered are as follows:

1. **Species Connected by Hybrids.** In Britain there are, for instance, two native species of *Quercus* (oak). They have rather different preferences as to soil and climate, and over the greater part of the country one finds either one or the other. Structurally the difference between them is not great, but it is perfectly clear and definite. In some areas, however, the two grow intermingled, and hybridise freely. The hybrid itself is fertile, and will cross with either parent, so that the gap between the two species is bridged by quite an array of intermediates.

Hybrids are met in many genera, the greatest numbers in the British flora being in *Salix* and *Mentha*. Hybrids which are sterile, as a good many are, appear rather distinct, because they do not intergradc with the parents. The more distinct hybrids are often given a Latin name, preferably marked by a multiplication sign and accompanied by a note of the parentage thus: *Salix* × *rubra* Huds. (= *S. purpurea* × *viminalis*). References to hybrids in the older books are often untrustworthy, many troublesome plants having at one time or another been listed as hybrids on very inadequate evidence.

2. **True-breeding Hybrids.** Usually a hybrid, if it breeds at all, exhibits a segregation of genes and produces a very variable progeny. By modification of the chromosome complement, however, and especially by becoming polyploid, it is possible for a hybrid to become true-breeding, producing offspring which differ from the parent no more than do those of any ordinary species. The plant will then behave exactly like a normal species and its origin can usually only be established by finding the parent species, deliberately crossing them, and so "copying" the wild hybrid form. In Britain *Galeopsis tetrahit* and *Spartina townsendii* are known to have arisen in this way, and it is almost certain that other cases remain to be discovered.

3. **Apomicts.** Where apomixis is prevalent the chromosome complement of the parent is passed unchanged to the offspring. The resulting population is a **clone**, displaying the kind of genetic

uniformity which in the human race can be found only in identical twins, etc. An apomictic clone, however, may become a very large population covering a great stretch of country. It is likely to attract attention and to be given a specific name. In most apomictic forms normal sexual reproduction is rare, but it is probably never impossible, and any seed which arises sexually will start a new clone. In the genera which are affected by apomixis one usually finds a rather large number of apomictic clones, many of which differ from each other no more than do the individuals of a normal species.

In Britain great numbers of apomicts occur in *Alchemilla*, *Hieracium*, *Rubus*, and *Taraxacum*. Enthusiastic students of these plants have described and named enormous numbers of apomicts (there must be about 400 in British *Hieracium* alone). This is a perfectly proper field of study, but the feeling is growing that minor apomictic variants ought not to be given Latin names or allowed to rank as species. The apomictic genera are troublesome to ordinary botanists, who are inclined to deal with them by the use of "aggregate" names. It is easier to write *Rubus fruticosus* L. than to find out which apomict one is looking at out of the 386 listed in the latest monograph.

4. **Species with Free Assortment of Genes.** Probably no race of plants, not even an apomict, can indefinitely remain unaffected by mutation of its genes. In some instances a species shows clear evidence that contrasting genes are segregating among the population. Good examples in the British flora are *Capsella bursa-pastoris* and *Plantago coronopus*. In these species it is possible to see variation in a whole catalogue of characters. Any single local population is likely to have a definite emphasis in one direction or another, but there is no real line of demarcation anywhere in the species, and any two individuals, no matter where they come from or how different they may be in appearance, will normally cross freely and give rise to a bewildering array of new forms. In such species as these, any attempt to distinguish fixed varieties, etc., is futile. Such attempts have been made—all that happens is that a Latin name has to be invented for every gene-combination which is theoretically possible, a process to which no end can be seen.

5. **Species Containing Distinct Forms.** In a considerable proportion of species it is possible to recognise with some clarity two or more distinct forms, intermediates between which are rare, though not necessarily or even usually non-existent. Almost universally the forms differ in their ecological requirements; indeed,

in cases of this kind the physiological differences between the plants are often more clearly defined than the structural differences. This sort of differentiation is likely to appear in any species which occurs in contrasting situations. For instance, *Anthyllis vulneraria* occurs on coastal sand-dunes and also on inland chalk pastures. Plants from the two different environments will not be quite the same, though the differences are rather slight and only become really evident when the plants are grown side by side in a garden. Similarly *Armeria maritima* on a Scottish mountain is slightly different from plants of the same species in a coastal saltmarsh.

6. **Clines.** A cline is a gradient of variation. A good British example occurs in *Arum maculatum*, some individuals of which have spotted leaves. The proportion of spotted plants is highest in the south of England, and diminishes as one goes north into the southern counties of Scotland. This is a cline affecting the relative frequencies of two genes, but it is also possible to have a cline which affects the degree of expression of a character (increasing hairiness, for instance). Clines are not always geographical, but may be related to changes in environment. In *Cardamine pratensis*, for example, in which the chromosome number is unusually variable, it appears that the average chromosome number is higher on wetter ground. Clines are probably very common, but not very many have been discovered—it takes a lot of hard work to demonstrate a cline.

Learning the Families of Plants

There are by the usual reckoning about 450 families of flowering plants in the world. Their geographical distribution is such that no one country contains representatives of all of them. In particular, a great many are confined to the warmer climates, and a substantial number are confined to the southern hemisphere. In the British Isles we have a very scanty flora, with only about 130 families of truly native flowering plants. Even this number, however, can be pretty intimidating to a beginner. Another factor which tends to create a somewhat bleak and forbidding impression is the intensely technical and often rather trivial character of most of the information given in the reference books. Is it *really* necessary to remember for each of the hundred or more families of British plants whether the embryo is straight or curved, or whether the placentation is axile or parietal? Is there any way in which the student's task can be reduced to manageable proportions? This is a very real problem. Many students who try to learn their way about among the angiosperms eventually give up in disgust, usually because they have set about it in the wrong way and overloaded their minds with a mass of detail.

We have already considered (p. 388) the nature of the exceptions which abound in the natural system of classification. On the whole one cannot deal with the families in terms of strict rules. A plain statement that the plants of a given family have actinomorphic flowers is more likely than not to be defeated by some plant which (upon consideration of its other features) is obviously a member of the family but has become zygomorphic. It is much safer and in the long run much easier to form in one's mind a conception of the general trend of behaviour within a family, and at the same time to be prepared to discover that the "typical" member of the family does not exist, that almost every plant which belongs has an exceptional feature somewhere. In fact it is *never* safe to draw any conclusion from the observation of a single character. This cuts both ways—there are very few characters so important that it is absolutely impossible to do without them. If you have forgotten that the Cistaceae have (predominantly) parietal placentation, that is not necessarily a disaster; there are other ways of recognising the Cistaceae.

Our knowledge of the natural classification is based to a very great extent on the study of features which are of very little importance from other points of view. This is not surprising, for a character which is of little functional significance is likely to undergo little evolutionary change and so to remain as a convenient marker to show the origin of the plant. A typical example is the difference between the anthers of Malvaceae and those of Tiliaceae. The two families are very closely related with very similar floral and vegetative structures, but in Tiliaceae the anther has four pollen-sacs while in Malvaceae there is only one. This quite clearly is not a matter of life or death. Both arrangements are perfectly efficient, and none of the plants would gain or lose anything appreciable by changing its procedure. In itself, the difference is just an unexplained curiosity. It happens to offer the most reliable method for distinguishing between the members of the two families, and anybody who needs to identify specimens regularly will naturally take the trouble to remember which is which. For most botanists, however, the information might just as well remain in the library until it is needed. Most people in Britain do not meet enough of these plants to justify the effort of remembering. A great deal of the information in the books is of this kind. There is also a certain amount which records the results of investigations more detailed than one would ordinarily undertake. This applies for instance to some of the information given about seed-structure. The nature of the endosperm, the form of the embryo, the exact way in which the cotyledons are folded—these can all be of great value in showing clearly how the plants are related to each other, in sorting the genera into tribes, and so on. It by no means follows that the average working botanist who merely wishes to gain a general acquaintance with the plants will wish to go into all these technicalities, still less that they will ever be needed in the routine identification of specimens.

A student who is concerned mainly with the plants of his own country will find that many of the plants he meets, including some of the commonest, appear from his point of view as isolated representatives of their families. In Britain, for example, *Hedera* (Ivy) is the only native member of the Araliaceae. The British student may well be concerned with *Hedera* but will probably not need to consider the characters of the Araliaceae, of which incidentally *Hedera* is a decidedly untypical genus. The position is not very different when a family presents a number of common forms, so long as these form a single easily recognised series. The British student needs to know the characteristics of *Viola* rather than those of the Violaceae, those of the two closely related genera *Geranium* and *Erodium* rather than those of the Geraniaceae, and so on. Clearly also it is pointless for a beginner to trouble himself at all about rare plants until he actually encounters them.

Applying these principles to the British flora it is possible to reduce in a surprising way the number of families in which it is important for a student to learn something of the general family characters as distinct from the special features of the particular forms which he happens to meet. There is a group of just about a dozen families in which the ordinary British student will find that he is constantly encountering new species during his first year or two of field botany. A knowledge of these families is easily obtained, and is of almost daily use in dealing with unknown specimens. To these families of the first rank can be added a second series of about twenty families in which a British student can reasonably expect at an early stage in his work to see representatives of two or more genera which may not be obviously similar. In most of these "second-line" families the number of common British species is not large, but it is large enough to make it worth while to have some appreciation of the family as a whole. Of course it must be understood that the British representation of a family is no guide to its importance in the flora of the world. The Araceae, for example, which are very scantily represented in Britain, are in fact one of the largest families of all, while the Caryophyllaceae, which bulk very large in British botany and occupy many pages of the flora, are in reality a rather insignificant component in the earth's vegetation. The student who wishes to gain a general knowledge of the angiosperms should therefore not be guided by the arrangement given here, which is essentially designed for British, or at any rate north European, conditions.

In the following pages the families which are really very important in Britain have been dealt with most fully. The families of secondary importance have been more shortly treated, except for one or two which offer special difficulties or which have been given special prominence in teaching and examining. It would be pointless to repeat here the information which is given in the floras. The object is much more to point out the features which are especially important in the recognition of the families themselves and of some of the more important groupings within them, to prepare the student for some of the exceptional or difficult plants which may be encountered, and to give a warning wherever there is a special danger of making mistakes. Such a treatment can never replace in the slightest degree the actual experience of handling specimens.

In the last analysis the characters of a family are simply the characters of the plants which the family contains. The proper course is to examine a plant thoroughly and so to learn from it something of the group to which it belongs, not to look up the characters of the group in some book beforehand, and then check that the specimen obeys the rules laid down. Unfortunately there has been a tendency for specialised study upon a particular group of plants to generate its own technical terminology. Some of this is unavoidable, because structures are found which do not occur elsewhere, but a great deal of it is of no scientific value at all. Little is gained, for instance, by calling the perianth segment of a grass a **lodicule**. The modern trend in such matters is towards simplification, but many special terms are so deeply entrenched in the books that they can probably never be discarded. The principal terms are explained in dealing with the families in which they are chiefly used, but in working with reference-books it is always wise to look at the author's own explanation of the language he adopts. Even some of the most modern books on classification use rather old-fashioned terms (*e.g.* "pistil" for ovary) which it is not advisable to adopt in general botanical work.

THE PRINCIPAL FAMILIES OF THE BRITISH FLORA

1. CRUCIFERAE

General Character: Herbaceous plants, often of a coarse, scraggy, weedy appearance, with alternate leaves without stipules, though sheathing bases occur. Leaf-shape very variable. Some with branched hairs (visible with hand-lens). Some producing mustard oils giving a hot taste.

Flowers white or yellow, actinomorphic in a bractless raceme. The plan of the flower is most unusual. We may write the formula as:

$$K\,2 + 2\;C\,2\text{ (divided)}\;A\,2 + 2\text{ (divided)}\;G\;\underline{(2\text{ sterile} + 2\text{ fertile})}$$

and a diagram is given in Fig. 178. The inner sepals are often pouched at the base. The petals are apparently four, but these are neither symmetrical nor evenly spaced; they must be considered to form two pairs, an upper pair and a lower one. The petals are often **clawed.** That is to say, each petal is rather sharply marked off into two parts, a narrow basal **claw** which stands upright and carries the rest of the petal up above the (also more or less upright) sepals, and a broad terminal **limb** which spreads out sideways. (Clawed petals are found in some other families, but it is not really a very common type.)

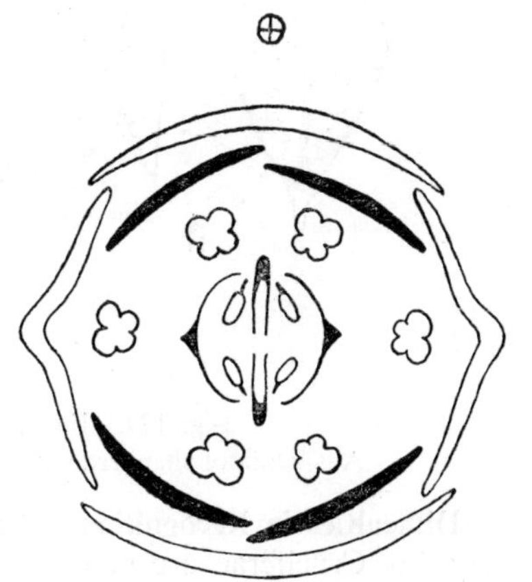

Fig. 178. FLORAL DIAGRAM OF A TYPICAL CRUCIFER. PETALS SHOWN IN BLACK, AND THE FOUR CARPELS SLIGHTLY SEPARATED.

The two stamens of the outer whorl are usually shorter than the four of the inner whorl. These inner stamens resemble the petals in being associated in pairs. It seems perfectly clear from a study of some related families that the ancestors of the Cruciferae must have had $K\,2 + 2\;C\,2\;A\,2 + 2$, and that the present situation is the result of evolutionary changes which brought about the duplication of the petals and the inner stamens.

Although the older books give $G\,(\underline{2})$ there is no longer any real doubt that the ovary contains four carpels. The inner two are completely flattened to form the **replum**, a longitudinal partition down the centre of the ovary. The replum has a kind of frame round its edge, but the central part consists of a thin double membrane in which a faint line sometimes marks the junction of the two carpels. The two outer carpels, often called the **valves**, form the greater part of the ovary wall. The ovules are attached to the frame of the replum in four rows as shown in the diagram, though for lack of space the "bodies" of the ovules often lie in a single row in the ovary chamber. The normal mode of dehiscence is by separation of the valves from the replum (Fig. 179), leaving the replum standing on the pedicel with the seeds hanging from it. Such a fruit is called a **siliqua** when long and pod-like (Fig. 179, B), a **silicula** when it is shorter and more pouchy (Fig. 179, A). Seeds non-endospermic, germination epigeal.

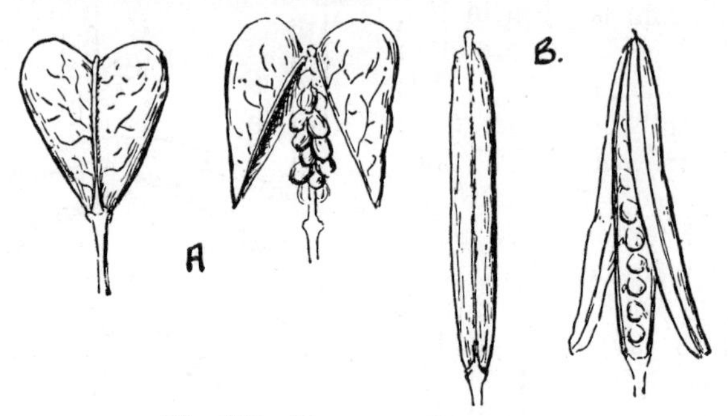

Fig. 179. FRUITS OF CRUCIFERAE.
A, silicula of shepherd's purse; B, siliqua of wallflower.

Difficulties in Recognition: Provided that flowers are available very few Cruciferae are at all likely to be mistaken for anything else. There are a few shrubby forms, a few with zygomorphic flowers, a few with unusual flower-colours, and a good many with unusual numbers of stamens (nearly always less than six, hardly ever more). None of these variations is likely to cause more than a moment's hesitation.

Very much more important is the variation which exists in the fruit. Many Cruciferae have entirely given up the usual method of dehiscence. When the fruit is long and many-seeded it then usually breaks transversely into short pieces, a fruit of this kind being known as a **lomentum**. When the fruit is short and few-seeded it may be quite indehiscent or it may split down the middle into two (usually one-seeded) pieces. When a specimen is entirely in fruit, therefore, its membership of the Cruciferae may be far from obvious.

A few plants in other families present a deceptively cruciferous appearance. Beware especially of Papaveraceae, recognisable by possessing latex (never found in Cruciferae), by having nearly always A ∞, and by having an ovary of a single chamber.

Classification: Relationships between genera are often very close. Division into tribes and genera rests largely on technical points, interesting only to specialists. Most people rely heavily upon artificial keys.

2. CARYOPHYLLACEAE

General Character: Herbaceous plants or soft-stemmed dwarf shrubs, with opposite simple leaves never lobed or toothed in any way. Flowers actinomorphic, white to pink or red, rarely yellow, never (?) blue. Inflorescence typically a fully-bracted dichasium.

Floral construction variable. Taking the basic formula as K n C n A $n + n$ G $(\underline{n})$ where $n = 4$ or 5, there are five ways in which this varies: (1) Some have fused sepals, in which case the petals are clawed as explained under Cruciferae. (2) Some have no petals. (3) Some are dioecious, either stamens or ovary being rudimentary (not usually quite absent). (4) Some have a reduced number of stamens. (5) Many have G $(\underline{3})$ and a few have G $(\underline{2})$. Such combinations as K 4 C 0 A 4 G $(\underline{4})$ and K (5) C 5 A 5 + 5 G $(\underline{2})$ are encountered. The styles are free to the base, the ovary single-chambered with free-central placentation, but the lower part of the ovary often contains incomplete partitions, so that a section cut too low down gives a misleading appearance of a divided ovary with axile placentation. The fruit is a capsule opening at the top into as many teeth as there are carpels or more often twice as many.

Difficulties in Recognition: Most Caryophyllaceae can be *provisionally* placed at sight upon their general appearance, but for certainty it is always necessary to examine the flower, because this characteristic caryophyllaceous habit is rather closely copied by some members of other families. Beware of Primulaceae, Gentianaceae, Polemoniaceae (all with fused petals), and Portulacaceae (with constant K 2). Beware also of *Linum catharticum*, one of the commonest sources of error, and worth learning on that account. Confusing features found in various Caryophyllaceae include elongated grass-like leaves, very small plants of moss-like habit, stipules (a few genera only), a good deal of variation in the inflorescence, and some fruits which are not of the usual form (few-seeded indehiscent types, some of them berry-like, also a few capsules which split further down than usual, or split at the bottom but not at the top).

Classification: A clear division into two subfamilies, the Alsinoideae with free sepals and the Silenoideae with joined ones. In the Silenoideae some of the genera are very closely allied, and species will appear in different genera in different books. The British flora is rich in small Alsinoideae, very troublesome to a beginner.

3. PAPILIONATAE

Papilionatae are here and in many other books treated as a subfamily of Leguminosae, the other subfamilies of which are not represented in northern Europe. Some writers raise the Papilionatae to family rank, making Leguminosae an order. The group may then be called Papilionaceae, or in American books Fabaceae.

General Character: Leaves alternate compound, with stipules and with a pulvinus to each leaflet, so that sleep movements are often possible. Margin of leaflet entire except in Trifolieae. Flower structure highly standardised (Fig. 180) with the formula K (5) C 5 A (5 + 5) G $\underline{1}$, strongly zygomorphic. The calyx is sometimes strongly two-lipped so that the number of sepals is not obvious. The odd petal stands at the back of the flower, an exceptional situation in dicotyledons. This upper petal is called the **standard** or **vexillum**, the two below are known as the **wings** or **alae**, while the two lowest are lightly tacked together at their edges to form the **keel** or **carina**. All the petals are free at their bases, though the wings are folded together with the carinal petals so that the four tend to move as a unit (p. 363). The stamen filaments are completely fused, sometimes all ten together to form a tube (monadelphous), more often the lower nine only to form a trough, the **vexillary stamen** remaining free (diadelphous), as in Fig. 180. The stamens and carpels are enclosed, usually very completely, within the keel. The fruit is a **legume,** like a follicle but splitting along both margins.

Difficulties in Recognition: Some have the leaf so modified that its compound character is more or less obscured. See pictures, etc., of *Lathyrus aphaca* and *L. nissolia.* The compound leaf with leaflet-pulvini is a rare type among angiosperms generally, but beware of Oxalidaceae. In none of the British Papilionatae does the structure of the flower vary enough to cause difficulty, nor is anything like it found in other families. There is no danger of encountering a legume outside the Leguminosae, but some Papilionatae have indehiscent fruits and some have a lomentum (p. 379).

Classification: Species may be troublesome but the tribal and generic distinctions are particularly clear and definite. Note, however, that *Lathyrus* and *Vicia* are very closely allied and have almost to be treated as a single series in the identification of species. Beware also of *Medicago lupulina* and *Trifolium campestre*, which are often confused (*Trifolium*: straight pod, petals persisting long after the flower has withered, stipules forming a sheath which girdles the stem/*Medicago*: coiled pod, petals soon falling, stipules not meeting on the side of the stem opposite the leaf).

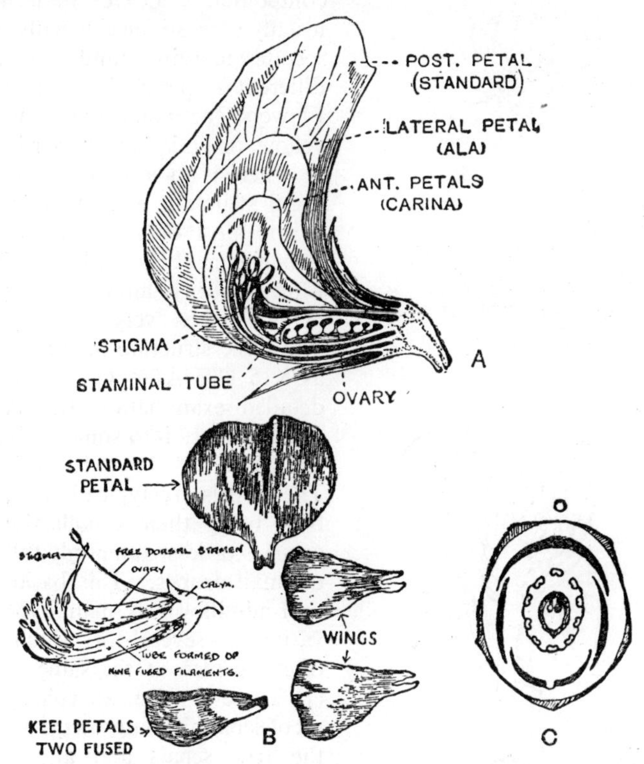

Fig. 180. PAPILIONATAE, FLORAL STRUCTURE.
Flower of pea, A, cut longitudinally in half; B, dissected; C, floral diagram.

The tribes most often encountered in Britain (they do not include all the British species) are distinguished by the following combinations of characters: (1) **Genisteae:** Mostly woody with a tendency to reduction of the leaf, vexillary stamen fused with the others (monadelphous). (2) **Trifolieae:** leaflets usually three, with lateral veins running right out to the margin, which is often toothed. (3) **Loteae:** Flowers in small umbels. (4) **Vicieae:** Distichous phyllotaxy, tips of leaves developed as tendrils, stem angled or winged with cortical vascular bundles in the internodes, germination hypogeal.

4. ROSACEAE

General Character: Very varied in general appearance. Trees, shrubs, or herbs, leaves simple or compound. Leaves alternate, usually with stipules, usually with serrate margins (and so very different from most Leguminosae). Flowers actinomorphic, white, yellow, or pink, hardly ever blue.

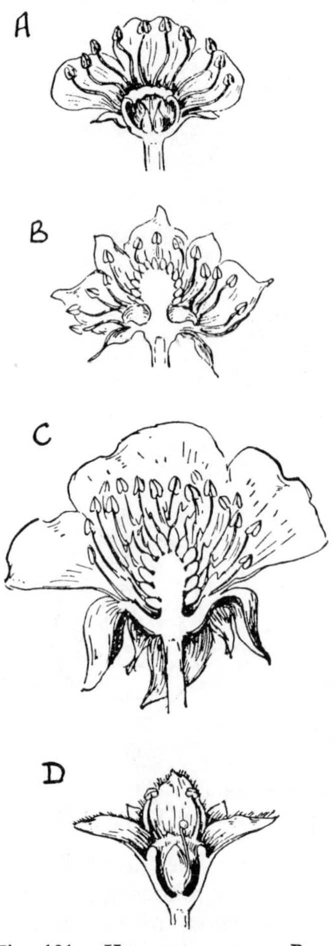

Fig. 181. HALF-FLOWERS OF ROSACEAE.
A, *Spiraea decumbens*; B, *Potentilla palustris*; C, *Geum urbanum*; D, *Alchemilla alpina.*

There is an enormous range of floral structure, making this one of the most difficult families for a beginner (Figs. 181 and 182). Flowers always more or less perigynous, often very strongly so. The basic structure may be taken as K 5 C 5 A ∞ G ∞. Upon detailed examination the A ∞ often resolves into some such system as A 5 + 10 + 10 + 5, etc. The carpels are typically free, the fruit being then a collection of achenes or less commonly follicles or small drupes. This basic pattern admits of six main types of variation, several of which can often be seen in the same plant: (1) There is often an **epicalyx,** a set of sepal-like outgrowths outside the true sepals and alternating with them. (2) There is sometimes a change in the general symmetry to give K 4 C 4 . . . , K 8 C 8 ., etc. (3) There are a good many with no petals. (4) The number of carpels can be reduced in varying degrees, sometimes to a definite number like 5 or 1. (5) The receptacle varies very much in shape. In some the part which bears the carpels is conical or globular (Fig. 181, B, C) with only a rather inconspicuous basal flange to carry the other floral parts. In others the whole receptacle is a deep cup, with the carpels enclosed within it and with the other floral parts on the rim (Fig. 181, D). Although the flower may then look from the outside as though it had an inferior ovary the carpels are in fact superior, being free from each other and from the wall of the receptacular cup. In some genera, however, complete fusion has followed, giving an inferior ovary of joined carpels with axile placentation (Fig. 183, A). (6) In many genera succulent fruiting structures are found: in *Fragaria* (Fig. 183, C) a solid juicy receptacle with achenes upon it, in *Rosa* a hollow fleshy receptacle with achenes inside it, in *Rubus* (Fig. 183, B) a collection of drupels (small drupes) upon a dry receptacle, in *Prunus* (with G $\underline{1}$) a single large drupe (Fig. 183, E), in *Pyrus* (with an inferior ovary) a special kind of fruit called a pome, which would probably pass for a berry if only the fleshy part were not so obviously derived from an enlargement of the receptacle (Fig. 183, A).

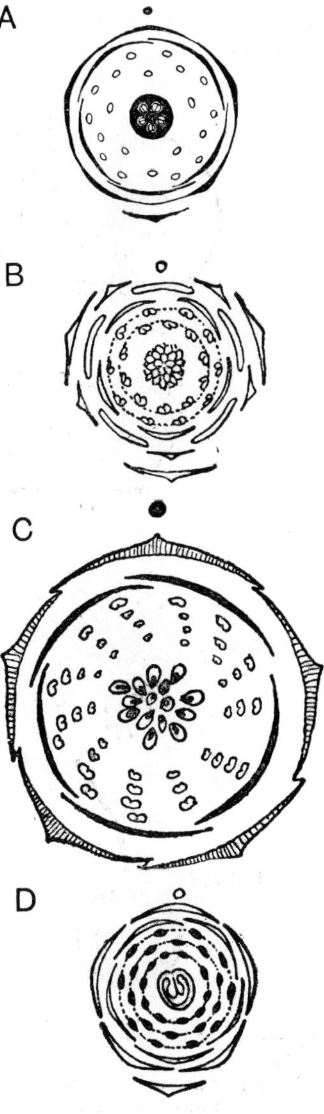

Fig. 182. ROSACEAE. FLORAL DIAGRAMS (after Engler).

A, *Pyrus communis*; B, *Potentilla palustris*; C, *Rosa*; D, *Prunus padus*.

Difficulties in Recognition: There is a possibility of confusion with Ranunculaceae (p. 430) for those who do not pay proper attention to leaves and stipules. Otherwise the danger is that of misunderstanding something which does belong to the family rather than that of including something which does not. The following points should be noted: (1) As is common in other families also, the woody members of the Rosaceae are liable to drop their stipules early in

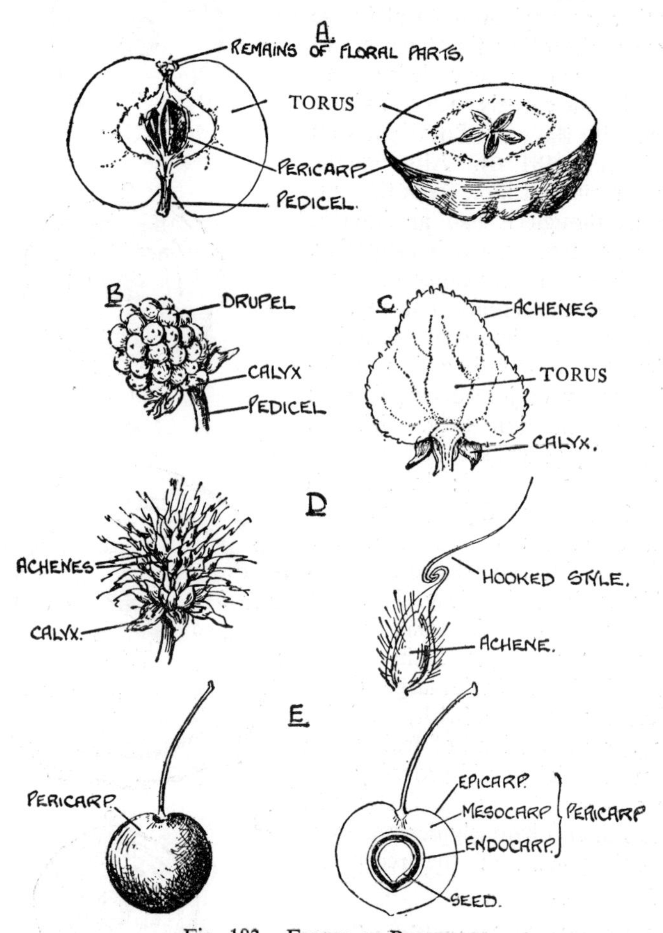

Fig. 183. FRUITS OF ROSACEAE.

A, pome of *Pyrus*; B, collection of small drupes (drupels) in *Rubus*; C, *Fragaria* (strawberry) with achenes on a fleshy receptacle; D, *Geum*, with a collection of achenes, each with a kinked style, the part above the kink breaking away to leave a hook; E, single drupe of *Prunus* (cherry).

the season. (2) The epicalyx (present in many of the herbaceous forms but hardly any of the woody ones) is highly characteristic. An epicalyx of a sort is found in a few other families, but does not usually then show regular alternation with the sepals. (3) Free carpels, with achenes or follicles, are of quite restricted distribution among the angiosperms. In the British flora free carpels are hardly seen outside Alismaceae, Ranunculaceae, and Rosaceae. (4) Extreme perigyny is rarely seen outside Rosaceae and a few allied families. It is important not to mistake a deep receptacular cup for an inferior ovary. (5) Most herbaceous Rosaceae have compound leaves. Some have a type of pinnate leaf in which very small leaflets are interspersed among the large ones, a thing not often seen in other families.

Classification: Divided into subfamilies and tribes mainly upon the form of the receptacle and fruit. Those with inferior ovary form the subfamily Pomoideae in which relationships between genera are particularly close. A number of genera in the family are notoriously "difficult" owing to the prevalence of apomixis and some other reproductive abnormalities. In *Alchemilla*, *Rosa*, *Rubus*, and *Sorbus* the identification of specimens should be handled with the utmost caution.

5. UMBELLIFERAE

General Character: Herbaceous plants, often biennials. Stems often stout and hollow. Leaves alternate, almost always compound or at least strongly lobed, with sheathing bases sometimes of great size. Flowers small, white or yellow, in large compound umbels.

Flower usually K 0 C 5 A 5 G $(\bar{2})$. Sometimes a more or less obvious K 5, but otherwise remarkably little variation in floral construction. Petals often deeply two-lobed, with an incurved point between the lobes. Above the attachment of the stamens is a fleshy nectary disc. The fruit is highly standardised (Fig. 184), falling when ripe into two one-seeded parts or **mericarps** which may remain for some time hanging from the central rod or **carpophore**. In transverse section each mericarp shows a characteristic pattern, with usually five **ribs** or **costae**, between which are **furrows** or **valleculae**. In the thickness of the wall are oil-ducts known as **vittae**, visible under quite a low magnification. These oil-ducts are continuous with others which run through all parts of the plant. Many Umbelliferae show marked chemical peculiarities. Some are aromatic, smelling of aniseed, etc., and a good many are dangerously poisonous. Unknown Umbelliferae should never be placed in the mouth or rubbed upon the skin.

Difficulties in Recognition: Little difficulty here—this is one of the easiest of all families to recognise, and was historically one of the first to attract attention. A few with simpler leaf shapes than usual, especially *Bupleurum* and *Hydrocotyle* (the latter sometimes placed in a separate family). *Eryngium* with blue flowers in an umbel so dense that it appears as a capitulum. *Astrantia* with a simple umbel almost enclosed by large petaloid bracts. In many the flowers at the edge of the umbel are strongly zygomorphic, at least in the corolla; in some of the less successful artificial keys the family is reached more easily if the flowers are treated as actinomorphic. Two common errors, arising from chance resemblances

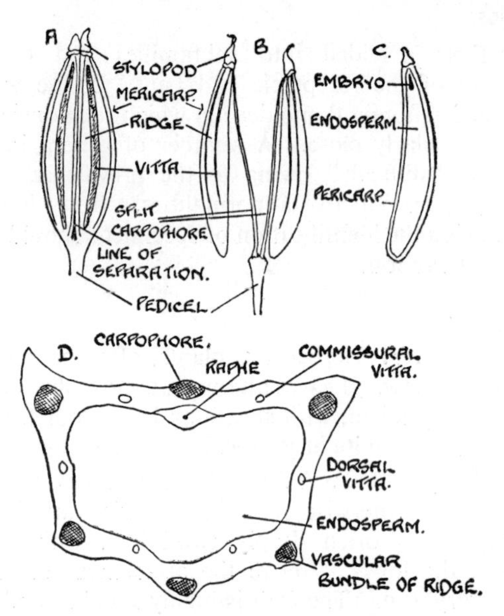

Fig. 184. FRUIT OF *Foeniculum*.
A, external; B, mericarps separated; C, mericarp in L.S.; D, mericarp in T.S.

in leaf shape, are to confuse *Sanicula* with *Geranium lucidum* in Geraniaceae, and *Hydrocotyle* with *Umbilicus* (= *Cotyledon*) in Crassulaceae. A few plants outside the Umbelliferac are superficially similar in their general habit of growth; the first point to check is the form of the inflorescence, which in the Umbelliferae is always a true umbel—plants with corymbose panicles do not belong.

Classification: Distinctions between tribes and genera turn mainly upon the shape of the mericarp in transverse section. It is best to cut a fruit which has reached nearly full size but has not hardened. Some genera are listed as having unisexual flowers;

care is needed here, because complete protandry is common, and the stamens often drop off long before the flower withers. In Umbelliferae "bract" and "involucre" refer to bracts of the major umbel, "bracteole" and "involucel" to bracts of the partial umbels.

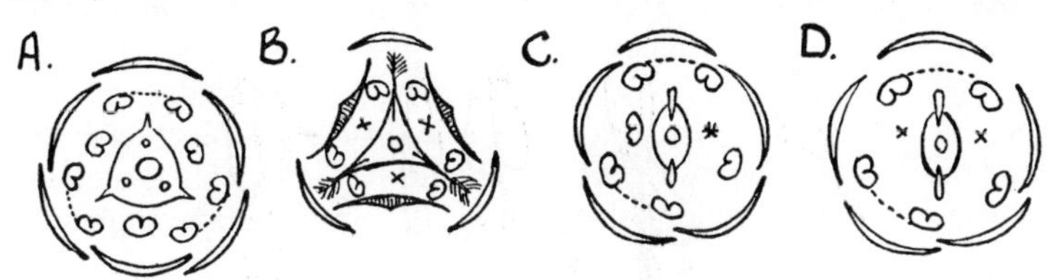

Fig. 185. FLORAL DIAGRAMS OF POLYGONACEAE.

Crosses mark positions of stamens believed to have disappeared in the course of evolutionary change, dotted links join stamen-pairs believed to occupy positions of original single stamens. A, *Rheum*; B, *Rumex*; C, *Polygonum lapathifolium*; D, *Polygonum amphibium*.

6. POLYGONACEAE

A family of minor importance in the world's flora, but constantly encountered in dealing with British vegetation. Herbaceous plants with alternate simple leaves, stipules fused into a sheath or **ochrea** which affords the easiest way of recognition. The ochrea is a thin transparent colourless membrane when young, drying later into a

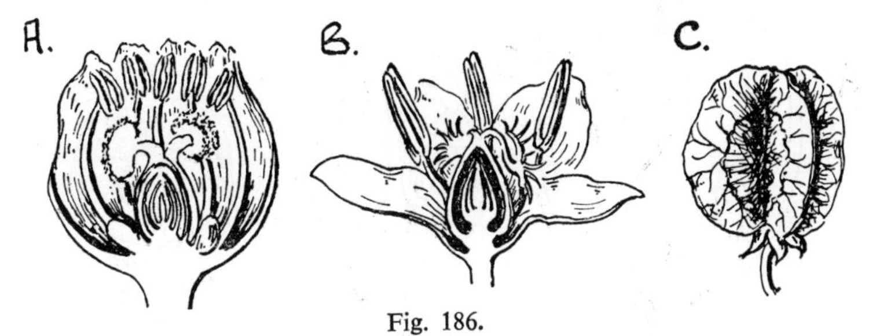

Fig. 186.

A, *Rheum officinale*, flower cut in half longitudinally; B, *Rumex acetosa*, ditto; C, *Rumex acetosa*, fruit with persistent inner perianth.

brown fragile papery sheath which is often torn by the growth of the shoot within it. Flowers small, green, white or pink, of very variable construction, but always with a superior one-seeded ovary of two or three carpels, and always lacking any pronounced differentiation between calyx and corolla (Figs. 185 and 186). Fruit a small nut-like structure often enclosed in persistent perianth-segments. Sometimes confused with Chenopodiaceae, but these have no stipules.

7. Ericaceae

General Character: All woody plants with simple usually evergreen leaves of leathery texture without stipules. Floral formulae mostly K 5 C (5) A 5 + 5 G $(\underline{5})$ or K 4 C (4) A 4 + 4 G (4), anthers

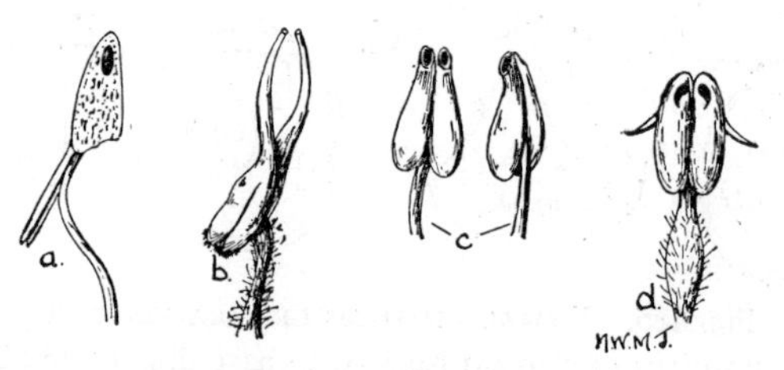

Fig. 187. Ericaceae, stamens.
A, *Erica tetralix*; B, *Vaccinium vitis-idaea*; C, *Rhododendron flavum*; D, *Arctostaphylos.*

usually opening by pores rather than slits. Shape of anther lobes very variable (Figs. 187 and 188). A few (*Vaccinium* and its allies) with an inferior ovary. Fruit a capsule or berry, usually many-seeded, placentation always axile.

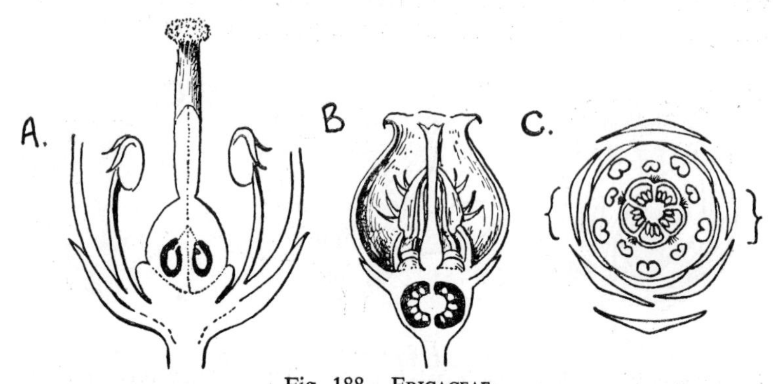

Fig. 188. Ericaceae.
A, *Arctostaphylos*, half-flower; B, *Vaccinium*, half-flower; C, *Vaccinium*, floral diagram.

A very natural group of plants with distinctive habits of life, mostly with mycorrhiza (p. 570), mostly avoiding calcareous soils.

Recognition: The combination of fused petals with stamens which are free or almost free from the corolla is rare, as is the dehiscence of the anthers by pores. These characters together point clearly to Ericaceae or some closely allied family. (The floras should be consulted regarding Pyrolaceae, etc.) Care must be taken to distinguish the species of *Erica*, with small needle-like leaves in whorls, from *Empetrum* (Empetraceae) often found growing with them, in which the leaves are alternate.

Classification: Generic distinctions mostly very clear. Beginners often confuse *Calluna* (stem surface hidden by small scaly leaves in opposite pairs) with *Erica* (needle-like leaves in whorls of 3 or 4, leaving the internodes bare).

8. SCROPHULARIACEAE

General Character: Herbs with simple leaves and no stipules. Flowers zygomorphic, usually K (5) { C (5) A 4 } G ($\underline{2}$). Ovary two-chambered, placentation axile, fruit a capsule with numerous seeds.

The phyllotaxy is very unsettled, some species having alternate leaves, some opposite ones, while many are in a transitional state, with the upper and lower parts of the stem behaving differently. Many species are parasitic, with attachments to the roots of neighbouring plants. These parasites often have rather scanty foliage; they vary considerably in their degree of dependence upon the host. Total parasites are found in the closely allied Orobanchaceae.

Difficulties of Recognition: The Scrophulariaceae are closely allied to a number of other large and important families from which they are separated upon rather technical points. In Britain it so happens that these other families are scantily represented, and some of them do not occur at all. Recognition of the Scrophulariaceae therefore offers little difficulty for the British student. Note that *Verbascum* has A 5 and is almost actinomorphic (but always with some difference between upper and lower stamens). Note also the special position in *Veronica*, apparently K (4) { C (4) A 2 } G ($\underline{2}$), believed in fact to be due to omission of one sepal and fusion of two petals into a single lobe, which appears larger than the others. In Scrophulariaceae with opposite leaves, especially in *Scrophularia*, the general appearance is sometimes strikingly similar to that of many Labiatae (following). Examination of the ovary will always clear up any uncertainty.

9. LABIATAE

General Character: Herbs or (mostly dwarf) shrubs with opposite simple leaves without stipules. Stem often squarish in transverse section, with the leaves on the flat faces, never on the corners. Flowers (Fig. 189) zygomorphic K (5) { C (5) A 4 } G ($\underline{2}$)

or sometimes with A 2. The ovary is at first two-chambered with four ovules in axile placentation, but at an early stage of development there is a secondary ingrowth of tissue from the midrib of each carpel. The ovary thus comes to have four chambers, each containing a single ovule. Each chamber swells outwards so that from the outside the ovary appears obviously four-lobed. The degree of lobing is variable, but in extreme cases the style (said to be **gynobasic**) appears to rise directly from the receptacle, with four almost completely independent swellings surrounding its base. In fruit each ovary chamber comes away as a one-seeded **nutlet**. The inflorescence is typically a raceme of small cymose partial

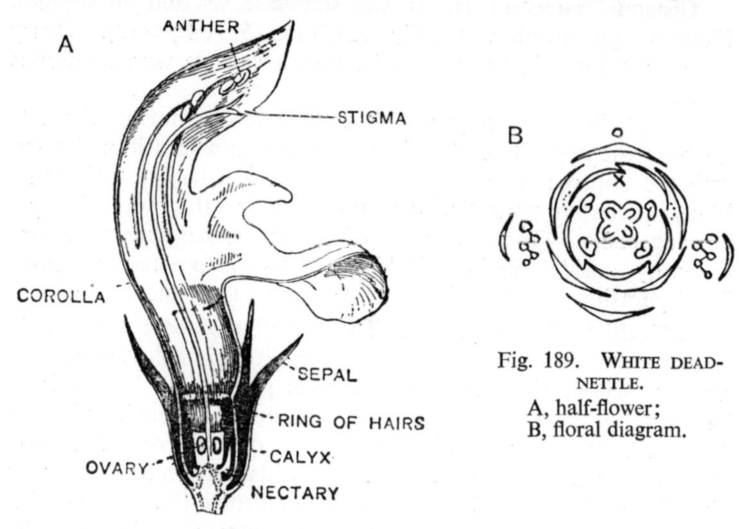

Fig. 189. WHITE DEAD-NETTLE.
A, half-flower;
B, floral diagram.

inflorescences. When, as often happens, the pedicels are short, the cymes of each leaf-pair present the characteristic appearance of a **verticillaster**, a false whorl of flowers (Figs. 190 and 191). A high proportion of the Labiatae are strongly aromatic.

Difficulties in Recognition: In British vegetation Labiatae can usually be recognised at a glance, but only because the plants with which they might be confused (Verbenaceae, some Scrophulariaceae, etc.) happen to be rather uncommon. It is never safe to give a final opinion without seeing the ovary. Note that *Urtica* (nettle) in Urticaceae has leaves on the corners of the square stem, and stipules. When the plants are not in flower beginners sometimes confuse *Helianthemum* (Cistaceae, with stipules) with *Thymus*.

10. Compositae

General Character: Predominantly herbaceous, leaves mostly alternate, mostly without stipules. Flowers (Fig. 192) small, in capitula. Calyx reduced to a **pappus** (a system of bristles or scales) or absent. Stamen filaments free, but anthers joined (**syngenesious**) into a tube surrounding the style. K pappus { C (5) A (5) } G $(\bar{2})$. An individual flower (floret) may be actinomorphic (**tubular**), or it may be strongly zygomophic (**ligulate**). Florets may be hermaphrodite, female (and then usually without any sign of stamens), neuter, or (rather uncommon) male. The florets in a capitulum may be all of the same kind, or there may be a differentiation into central **disc florets** and marginal **ray florets**. Although in many instances the disc florets are tubular and the ray florets ligulate, there is nothing to prevent the disc/ray distinction from appearing

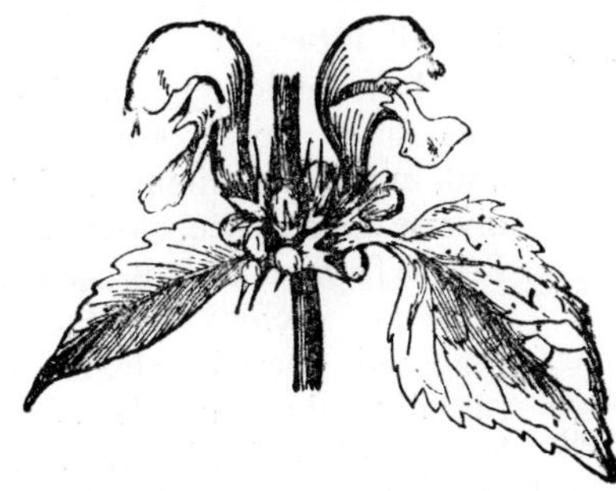

Fig. 190. Verticillaster of deadnettle.

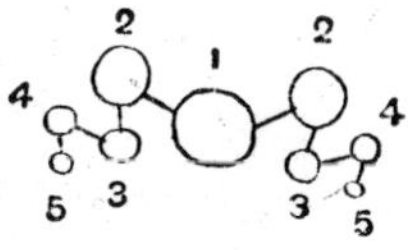

Fig. 191. Diagram indicating the relation of flowers in half of a verticillaster.

in a capitulum which has only tubular or only ligulate florets. The fruit is one-seeded (a **cypsela**, sometimes called an achene) and the pappus, if present, usually persists in the fruit.

Difficulties in Recognition: In many Compositae the capitulum has a small and rather constant number of ray florets, often 5. Such a capitulum looks rather like a flower, so that *Achillea* is sometimes mistaken for an umbellifer, and so on. Capitula occur in some other families, notably in Dipsacaceae (leaves opposite, anthers free) and Campanulaceae (great care needed; see pictures of *Jasione* and *Phyteuma*). When not in flower *Tragopogon* is apt to be mistaken for a monocotyledon.

Classification: Quite apart from the difficulties of dissection which arise from the small size of the parts, students are often confused by some of the special descriptive language. Every capitulum has an outer system of bracts known as the **involucre**. Some capitula have in addition an individual bract to each floret, or various scales, bristles, etc., interspersed among the florets. The books have therefore such expressions as "receptacle scaly", "receptacular bristles present", etc., and, most puzzling of all, "receptacle naked". All such expressions must be read as applying to the upper surface of the receptacle after the fruits have fallen, or after the florets have been artificially removed. It is sometimes necessary to determine whether the pappus-bristles are simple or feathery; mistakes are likely unless the bristles are dried before examination. Distinctions between genera and species are particularly troublesome in the Liguliflorae (latex present, florets all ligulate, nearly always yellow). A beginner may avoid some mistakes by noting that in dandelions the stem which supports the capitulum is hollow and unbranched.

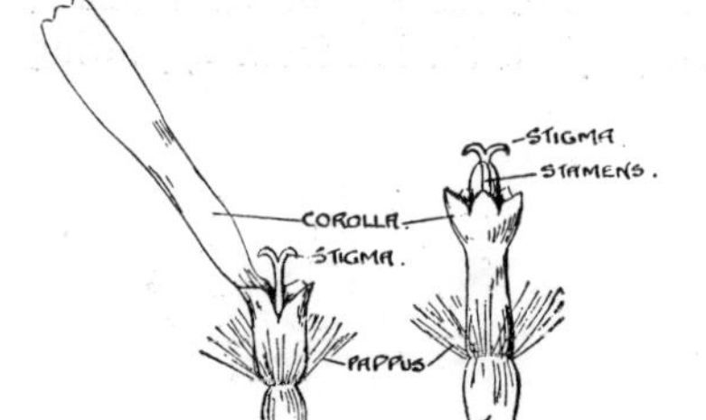

Fig. 192. FLOWERS OF COMPOSITAE. A ligulate (strongly zygomorphic) floret (left), and a tubular (actinomorphic) floret (right).

11. ORCHIDACEAE

Monocotyledons of highly specialised floral construction and, in warmer climates, of very diverse appearance. Most of the British forms are readily recognisable as orchids by the unbranched aerial stem with (usually only a few) *broad* hairless parallel-veined leaves, often spotted or mottled. P 3 + 3 A 1 G ($\overline{3}$), with one perianth segment (the **labellum**) very different from the other five. The inferior ovary, which contains numerous minute ovules in parietal placentation, is twisted through 180°, so that the labellum, which is structurally at the top of the flower, and shown so in the diagram (Fig. 193) actually points downwards. For the pollination mechanism, and the special construction of the anther, see p. 365. Orchids depend upon a mycorrhizal association, and some lack chlorophyll, being classed incorrectly as saprophytes.

12. CYPERACEAE

Monocotyledons of grass-like aspect, mostly on marshy ground. Flowers inconspicuous, wind-pollinated, usually more or less concealed by their bracts or **glumes**, often unisexual. Perianth usually 0, but sometimes represented by bristles or scales. Inflorescence consisting of distinct units which are known as **spikelets**, though in fact some at least are compound inflorescences. Classification depends largely on the number of spikelets (there may be only one), on the way in which they are combined into a larger inflorescence, on the distribution of the sexes between them, and so on. The Cyperaceae are an important component of the British flora, and students often have some difficulty in deciding what belongs to the family. The following points will be helpful. (1) Many Cyperaceae have distinctly triangular stems, often spongy but lacking any conspicuous central cavity. Such stems are otherwise rare in Britain. (2) There are some "leafless" Cyperaceae with a single spikelet and stems which are not triangular; these plants present a very striking appearance—see pictures of *Eleocharis.* (3) There should be no risk of confusion with the grasses (following) for these have cylindrical stems with a simple central cavity and a distichous arrangement of all their leaves, including their glumes. (4) The other British plants which might be confused with Cyperaceae fall into two series—large marsh-dwelling monocotyledons with distichous phyllotaxy (*Typha, Sparganium*), and smaller plants in which the flowers, more complete than those of most Cyperaceae, are rather freely exposed, and not organised into definite spikelets (*Triglochin*, some Juncaceae, *Plantago maritima*).

Fig. 193. FLORAL DIAGRAM OF A TYPICAL ORCHID.

Crosses show positions of sterile stamen-rudiments. The fertile stamen is towards the bottom of the diagram, with the stigmas shown as shaded areas on either side of it. Owing to the twist of the ovary, the living flower is actually inverted, bringing the labellum (the enlarged perianth-segment at the top of the diagram) to the front and the stamen to the back.

13. GRAMINEAE

A large and immensely important family, contributing staple foodstuffs for the majority of the human race either directly (as cereal grains) or indirectly, as fodder for livestock. The account given here does not apply to some of the foreign forms, especially the bamboos.

General Character: Herbs with hollow cylindrical stems, leaves in two rows with sheathing bases. Almost always a membranous ligule standing up against the stem at the junction of sheath and lamina. The grass shoot has swollen "nodes" which are in fact, in most cases, swellings of the basal part of the tubular leaf-sheath. The rigidity of the shoot depends to a great extent on the sheaths, the basal part of each internode being soft and meristematic. In some grasses the axillary branch grows up parallel to the main stem inside the leaf-sheath, giving a tufted habit; in others the young

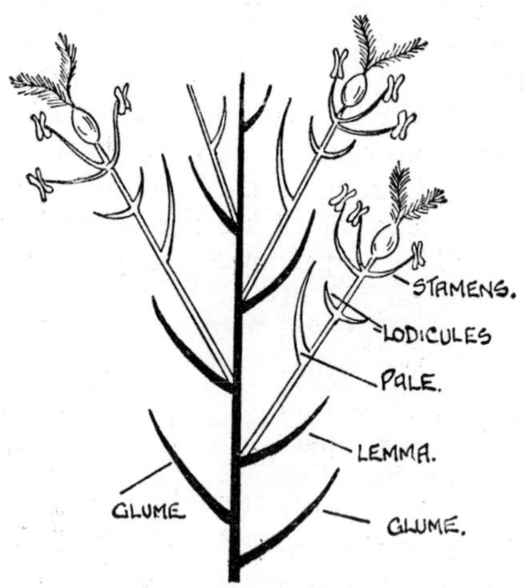

Fig. 194. SIDE VIEW OF A GRASS SPIKELET, THE RACHILLA WITH ITS GLUMES AND LEMMAS IN BLACK.
The lengths of all the internodes greatly exaggerated.

branch soon breaks out through the sheath and grows at an angle to the stem, which gives a turf-forming habit.

The flowers are simple, inconspicuous, and wind-pollinated, but mostly hermaphrodite. The inflorescence consists of definite units called **spikelets**; unfortunately all the parts of a spikelet have been given special names. In Fig. 194 all the internodes have been shown very long, so as to spread out the parts. The central axis, the **rachilla** (shown black), bears two rows of cataphylls. The two lowest of these have nothing in their axils and are called the **glumes**. Each of those which follow has a flower in its axil and is called a **lemma**. Normally each pedicel bears a **pale** or **palea**, which is really a bracteole, two **lodicules**, which are perianth-segments, three stamens, and an ovary. A floral diagram, which includes lemma and palea, is given in Fig. 195. This is the modern terminology, but in older books

Fig. 195. FLORAL DIAGRAM OF A TYPICAL GRASS.
The pale is the two-keeled structure backing on the rachilla. Two lodicules and three stamens are shown.

other expressions can be found. What we now call a glume has been known as a sterile glume or barren glume, what we call a lemma has been known as a flowering glume or fertile glume or outer palea or lower palea. What we call a pale has been known as an inner palea or upper palea. In reality all the parts of the spikelet are very closely packed, with short internodes.

The grass ovary carries two feathery stigmas and is one-chambered with a single ovule. The fruit is a **caryopsis**, a nut-like structure in which the inner layer of the testa becomes grafted on to the outer layer of the pericarp with complete digestion and removal of some of the cell layers between. Almost always the "fruit" as shed is accompanied by some of the associated bract-structures, which sometimes play an important part in dispersal. Germination is hypogeal, the seedling being highly specialised (p. 145).

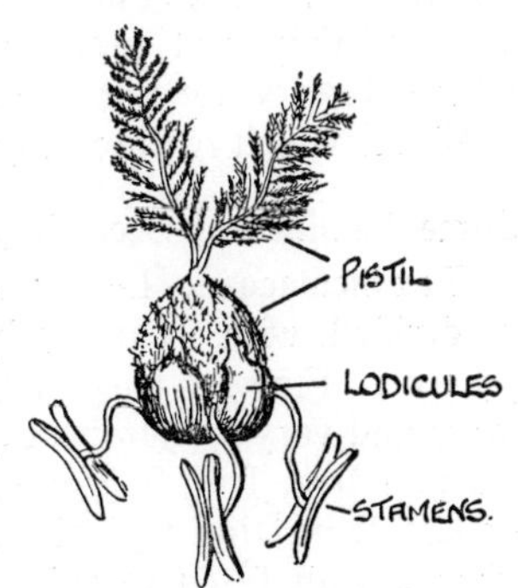

Fig. 196. *Triticum*, SINGLE FLOWER WITH LEMMA AND PALE REMOVED.

Classification: In British grasses the structure of the flower varies very little and plays little part in classification, though there are a few with only two stamens. The lodicules are very small, colourless, and often almost transparent; they can be seen against the base of the ovary when the lemma has been removed (Fig. 196). It is the function of the lodicules, however, to force the lemma away from the palea by swelling rather suddenly at the time of flowering. The flower then gapes widely open. Some grasses have no lodicules, in which case the stamens and stigmas all come out in a tuft together between the extreme tips of lemma and palea.

Far more important is the variation in the structure of the spikelet. There is a wide range in the number of flowers, in their sex distribution, and in the structure of the glumes and lemmas. The glumes may be of unequal sizes, or fused together, or provided with long bristles or awns, or there may be only one of them, and so on. It is important to notice that in a long spikelet some of the upper lemmas may have no flowers, or only abortive ones, but these must not be counted as glumes. Sometimes the rachilla is prolonged above the uppermost flower.

In most grasses the spikelets are grouped in a panicle with obvious stalks which are repeatedly branched. There are, however, a few which have a spike of spikelets, and some (*Phleum*, *Alopecurus*) in which many short panicle-branches are packed closely together to make a dense cylindrical mass.

Apart from the obvious difficulties of manipulation arising from the small size of the parts, the dissection of grass spikelets is a perfectly straightforward operation. Students who become confused usually do so by starting with too large a unit, often with a whole cluster of a dozen spikelets or more, under the impression that they have a single spikelet. It is advisable to choose for the first attempt a grass with large, many-flowered spikelets. A high proportion of the British grasses have only one or two florets, which is not enough to illustrate satisfactorily the general plan of spikelet construction. Because it is so easy to identify grasses from their flowering parts there is a tendency to neglect the vegetative organs. It is desirable to give proper attention to the leaves in view of the great practical importance of identification in turf where flowers are not generally to be had. Keys to grasses are available which require only vegetative parts.

Some Families of Secondary Importance in Britain

Ranunculaceae: Leaves usually alternate, often palmately lobed or divided, with sheathing bases, distinct stipules only occasionally present. Flowers (Fig. 197) predominantly actinomorphic, with large and varying numbers of parts mainly in a spiral arrangement. Carpels free, fruit a group of achenes or follicles. Some genera depart from this typical pattern (*Clematis* with opposite leaves, *Nigella* with fused carpels, *Aquilegia* with flower parts in whorls, *Actaea* with a berry, *Delphinium* zygomorphic, etc.). For the student, however, the main difficulty lies in the treatment of the perianth. When petals are present these are ordinarily tubular, and function as nectaries. The typical situation (*Helleborus, Eranthis*) is that in which the sepals are large and showy and petaloid, the petals quite inconspicuous tubular structures, two-lipped at the mouth. From this two main lines of modification can be traced. In *Caltha, Anemone*, etc., there are no petals at all, the sepals remaining petaloid. In *Ranunculus* the petals have become showy by a great enlargement of the lower lip, so that the upper lip now appears as a little nectary scale near the base of the petal. The sepals of *Ranunculus*, like those of most dicotyledons, but quite exceptionally in this family, are small and green.

Euphorbiaceae: A large and important family represented in Britain only by *Mercurialis* and *Euphorbia*, which are not at all closely related to each other. *Euphorbia* has the highly specialised type of inflorescence known as a cyathium (p. 343) and is likely to be very troublesome to anybody who tries to identify it without knowing this beforehand. The extremely simple flowers of *Mercurialis* are in fact much more typical of the family.

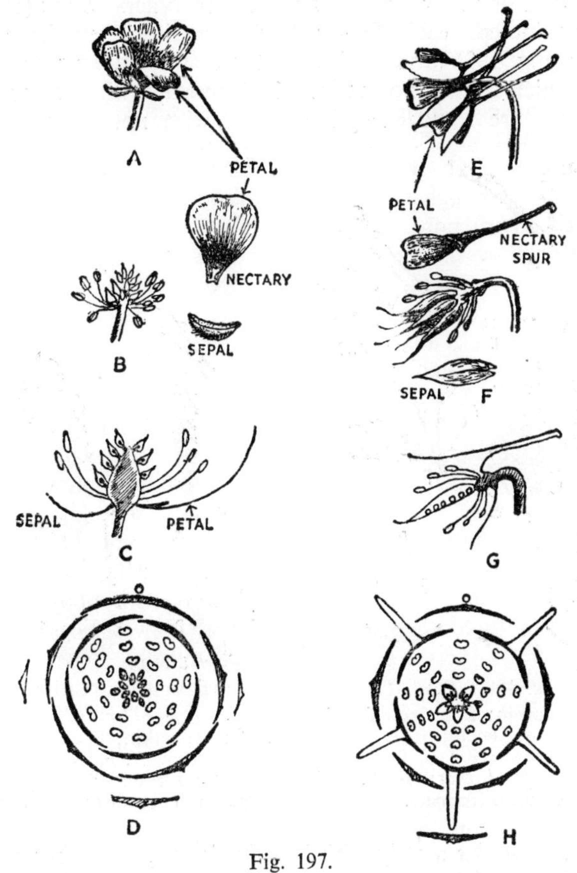

Fig. 197.
A, *Ranunculus* flower; B, some parts of A; note the nectary at petal-base, and the boat-shaped sepal; C, longitudinal section; D, floral diagram; E-H, ditto for *Aquilegia* (Columbine).

THE CATKIN-BEARING PLANTS: There follows a series of families of woody plants producing inconspicuous, mostly wind-pollinated flowers in **catkins**. All these plants have alternate simple leaves with stipules. The catkin-producing habit is especially characteristic of the north-temperate zone, and this is one of the few major series of angiosperms which is really well represented in the British flora. There are three main families to consider here:

(*a*) **Salicaceae:** Fruit a many-seeded capsule, seeds hairy and wind-dispersed, plants rigidly dioecious. Catkins always simple spikes, with one flower in the axil of each bract. *Salix* (Fig. 198) insect-pollinated, each flower having a little peg-like nectary. *Populus* (Fig. 199) wind-pollinated, the flower having a cup-shaped "disc" which secretes no nectar. *Salix* mostly with a rather narrow leaf (there are some exceptions), and with not more than five

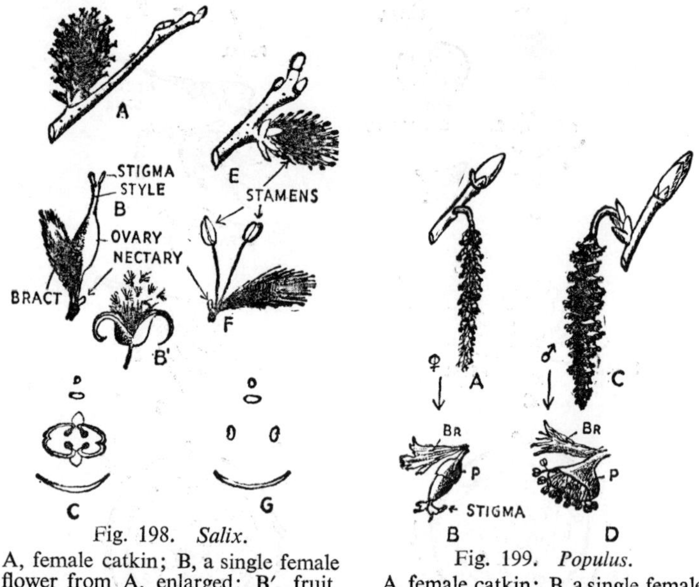

Fig. 198. *Salix.*
A, female catkin; B, a single female flower from A, enlarged; B′, fruit, liberating hairy seeds; C, floral diagram of female flower; E, F, and G, ditto for male.

Fig. 199. *Populus.*
A, female catkin; B, a single female flower from A, enlarged; C and D, ditto for male; P, cup-shaped perianth, or disc; BR, bract.

stamens. *Populus* mostly with broader leaves, numerous stamens, and the bracts of the catkins toothed.

(*b*) **Fagaceae:** Monoecious trees, never normally shrubby in Britain. Female inflorescence distinguished by the presence of a **cupule**, a massive cup composed of many fused bracts, and often spiny or variously lobed. Within the cup there may be one flower or a dichasium of three. Fruit a large nut. *Quercus*, *Fagus*, *Castanea* (Figs. 200 and 201).

(*c*) **Betulaceae** (including Corylaceae, which are sometimes separated): Monoecious trees and shrubs. Catkins predominantly compound, a bract often having in its axil a dichasium of three flowers (Figs. 202 and 203). By fusion of bracts and bracteoles compound scales are often formed, the apparent "bract" of the catkin being then a 3-lobed or 5-lobed fusion-product. Fruit a nut, usually of quite small size, sometimes winged. The nut of *Corylus* is exceptionally large for the family. The fruit is often accompanied by persistent and enlarged bracts and bracteoles

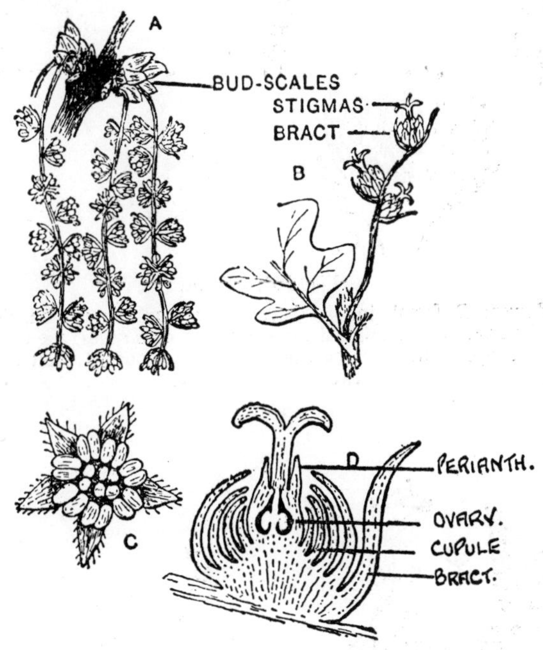

Fig. 200. *Quercus robur*.
A, male; B, female inflorescences; C, male flower; D, female flower in section.

(Figs. 204–209) but there is never any development which can be confused with the bulky cupule of Fagaceae. In *Alnus* the female catkins persist on the tree as black woody cones long after the fruits have fallen from them.

Primulaceae: Herbs without stipules, flowers actinomorphic normally K (5) { C (5) A 5 } G (5). Stamens opposite the petals, thereby breaking the ordinary rule of alternation (related families, not British, show stages in the elimination of an outer whorl of stamens. *Samolus*, which is British, has staminodes). Ovary with

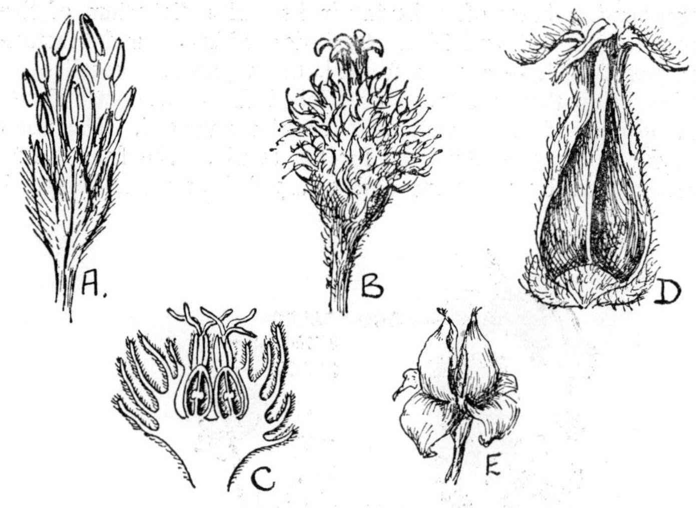

Fig. 201. *Fagus.*

A, male flower; B, female inflorescence; C, the same in section, showing the two lateral flowers of an original three-flowered dichasium, the central flower of which is suppressed; D, female flower dissected out; E, fruit consisting of two nuts in a cupule.

Fig. 202. *Betula*, MALE AND FEMALE CATKINS.

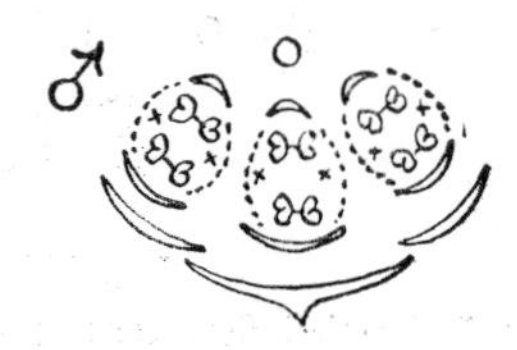

Fig. 203. *Betula.*
Diagram of dichasia in male and female catkin.

a single chamber, numerous ovules in free central placentation. The family offers two main difficulties to the student. There is no standard habit of growth, so that floral examination is constantly

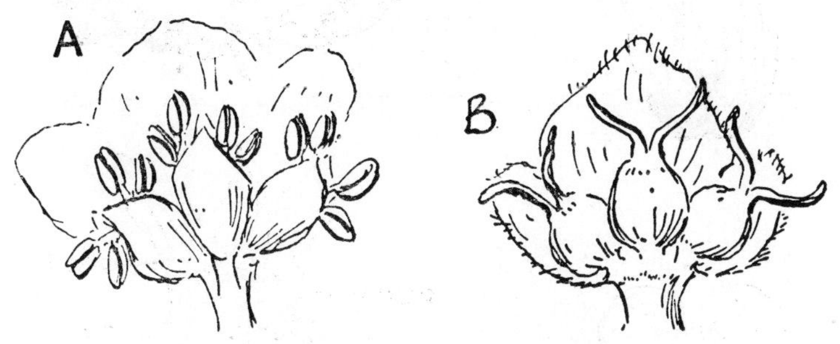

Fig. 204. *Betula*, DICHASIA DISSECTED.
A, male; B, female.

necessary, and the ovary gives no obvious indication of the number of carpels, the style and stigma being quite undivided. It is useful to remember that the combination { C (5) A 5 } with stamens opposite

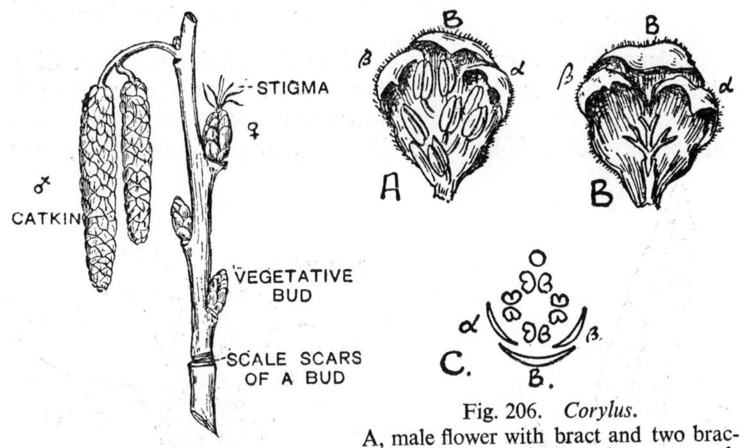

Fig. 205. *Corylus*, MALE AND FEMALE CATKINS.

Fig. 206. *Corylus*.
A, male flower with bract and two bracteoles; B, ditto, with anthers removed; C, floral diagram.

the petals will hardly ever be seen in Britain outside this family and the Plumbaginaceae (ovary one-seeded, style or stigma obviously five-branched). Some Primulaceae look very much like Caryophyllaceae, to which the family is in fact probably related.

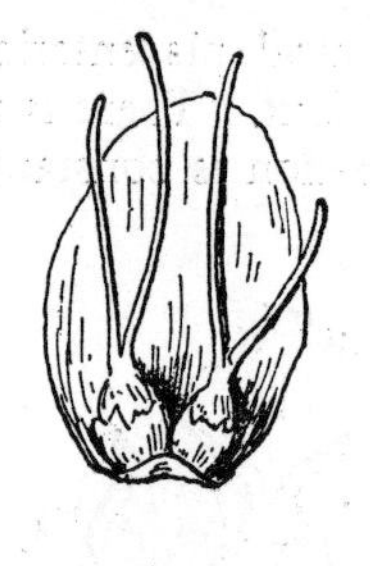

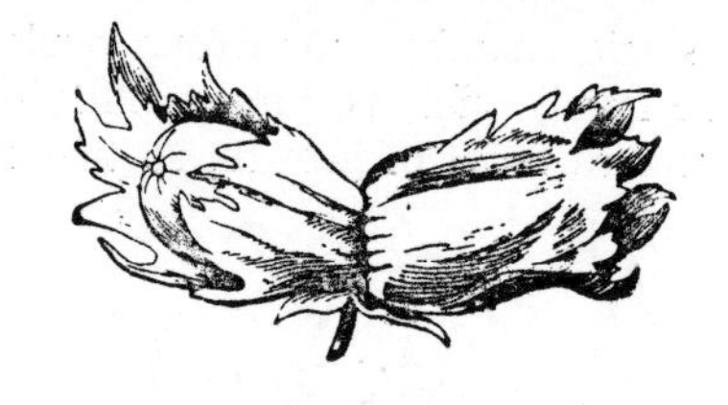

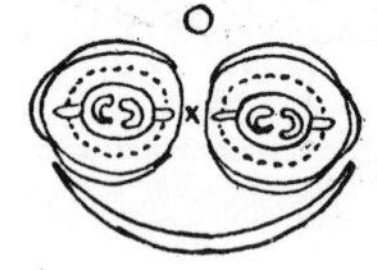

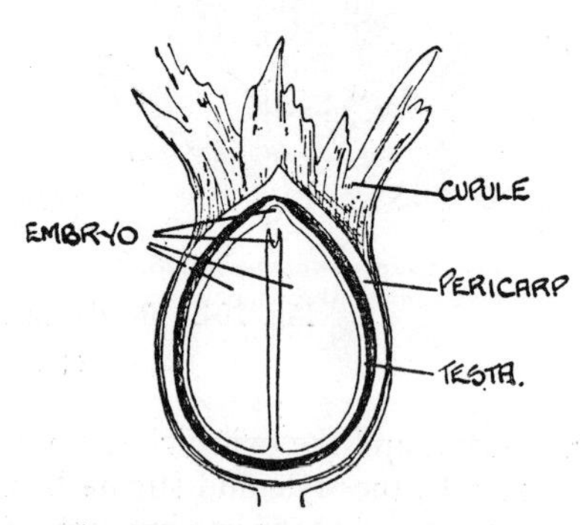

Fig. 207. DISSECTION AND DIAGRAM OF FEMALE DICHASIUM OF *Corylus*. The central flower of a group of three is suppressed, as in *Fagus* (see Fig. 201).

Fig. 208. THE FRUIT OF *Corylus*. Paired nuts, each with a cupule derived from the bracteoles of the dichasium.

Solanaceae: Very closely allied to Scrophulariaceae (p. 423), almost the only really constant difference being the presence in Solanaceae of internal phloem in the stem (never found in Scrophulariaceae). Most Solanaceae, however, are actinomorphic, with

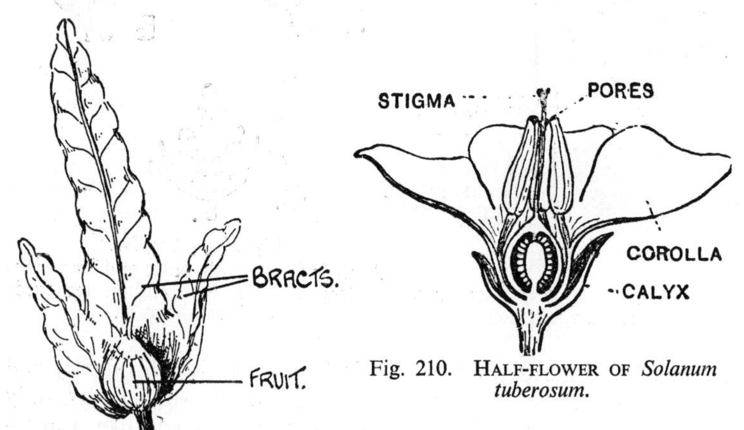

Fig. 209. *Carpinus* FRUIT.

Fig. 210. HALF-FLOWER OF *Solanum tuberosum*.

five stamens, and many of the common ones have berries, which are uncommon in Scrophulariaceae (Figs. 210–212). The Solanaceae are rich in alkaloids, and almost all of them are

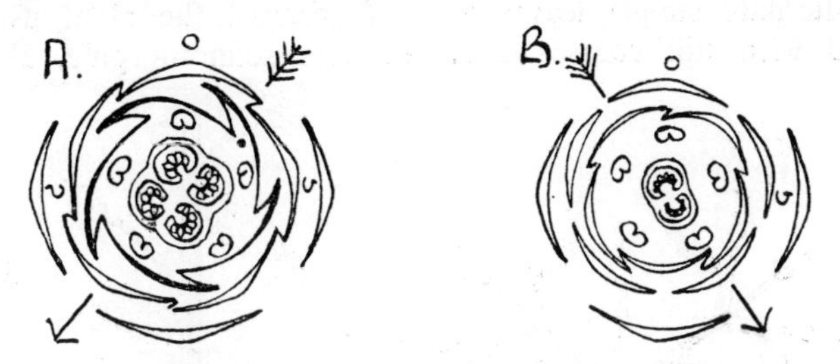

Fig. 211. FLORAL DIAGRAMS OF SOLANACEAE.

A, being *Datura stramonium* and B, *Hyoscyamus albus*. The large arrows show the orientation of the carpels, which in this family are placed obliquely. This is an unusual and interesting feature, but not a very convenient means of identification.

poisonous. Even species which are used for food (potato, tomato) are not necessarily safe in all their parts; potato leaves are decidedly poisonous. A number of important drugs are derived from this family. Solanaceae often produce unusual appearances in the inflorescence, where the normal axillary relationship is apt to be

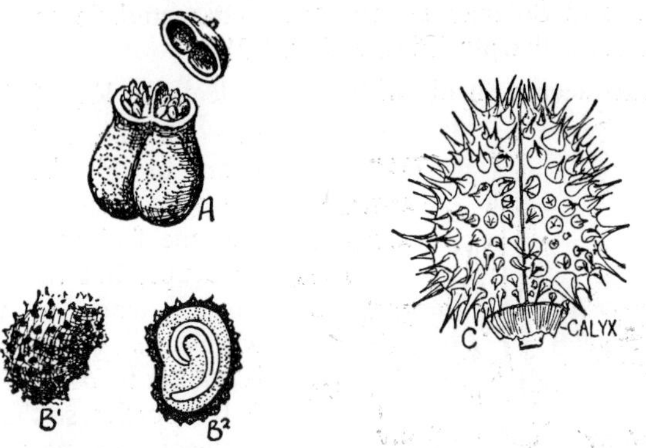

Fig. 212. FRUITS AND SEEDS OF SOLANACEAE.

A, *Hyoscyamus niger*, fruit; B, *Hyoscyamus niger*, seed, (1) entire, (2) in longitudinal section; C, *Datura stramonium*, fruit.

disturbed by fusion of the parts. Sometimes an axillary shoot is fused for some distance with its parent stem so that it seems to spring from the middle of an internode, sometimes bracts are carried up on their own axillary shoots so that the stem appears to fork without any axillant leaf (Fig. 213).

Boraginaceae: Herbs usually of very characteristic appearance, with alternate simple leaves without stipules, the plant usually covered with stiff coarse hairs. Flowers actinomorphic, almost

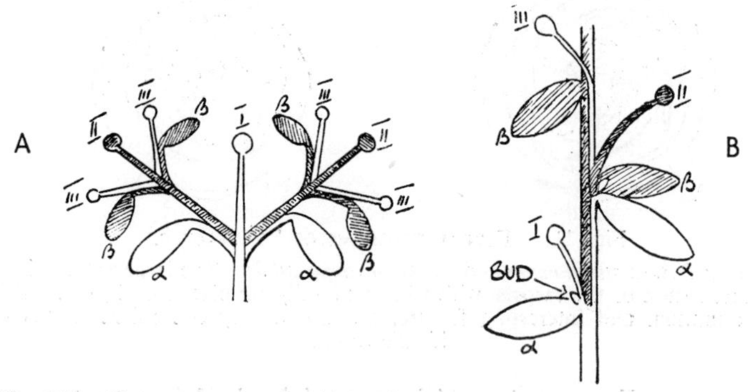

Fig. 213. TWO INFLORESCENCES FROM THE SOLANACEAE, SHOWING HOW THE AXILLARY RELATIONSHIP IS DISTURBED BY FUSION OF PARTS.

always blue or purple, in spirally-coiled monochasia. K (5) { C (5) A 5 } G $\underline{(2)}$ with the ovary constructed like that of Labiatae (p. 424). The Boraginaceae are closely allied to Labiatae, Scrophulariaceae, and Solanaceae, but their characteristic features mark them off quite sharply (Figs. 214 and 215).

Caprifoliaceae: Shrubs with opposite leaves. K (5) { C (5) A 5 } G $\overline{(2-5)}$. The condition of the ovary in this family is very unsettled. Placentation is axile, and the fruit usually a berry or drupe, but the number of carpels tends to vary even within a single species, and it is common for some of them to be abortive, so that a section of the ovary presents a puzzling appearance (Fig. 216). The family is closely related to several others and must be carefully distinguished from them. The main ones are: (1) Cornaceae, with free petals. (2) Rubiaceae, with almost constant G $\overline{(2)}$ and with much greater development of stipules, amounting in the British forms to the development

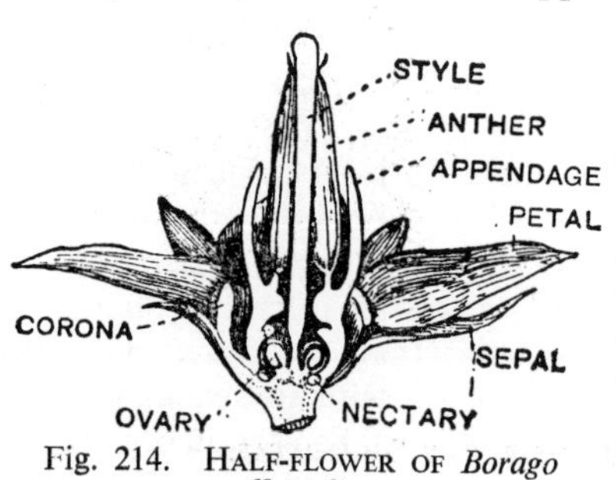

Fig. 214. HALF-FLOWER OF *Borago officinalis*.

of false whorls (p. 93). (3) Valerianaceae, herbaceous with constant $G(\bar{3})$ of which only one carpel is fertile, and with a flower which is unsymmetrical with less than five stamens.

LILIIFLORAE: A large order of monocotyledons, including among other things all the bulb-producing plants which are ordinarily encountered. Several families are recognised, but it is generally admitted that the traditional subdivision of the order is artificial and unsatisfactory. The main families are:

(1) **Liliaceae**, with $P\ 3 + 3\ \ A\ 3 + 3\ \ G(\underline{3})$, with the perianth segments petaloid and showy. Various degrees of fusion occur in the outer parts of the flower, giving $\{P\ (3 + 3)\ A\ 3 + 3\}$, etc. This is a large family, with great diversity of behaviour, and certainly

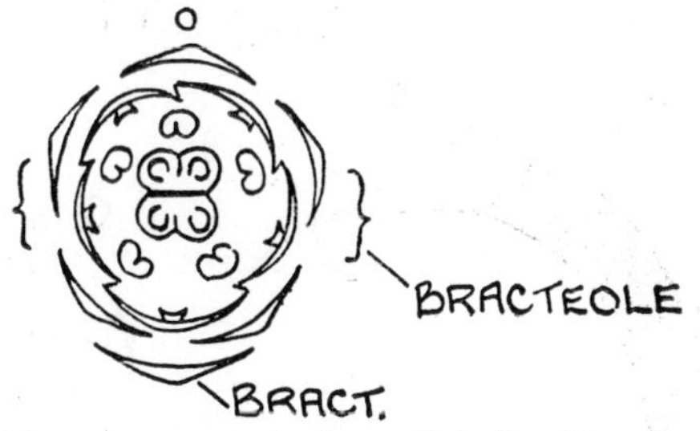

Fig. 215. BORAGINACEAE: *Anchusa officinalis*. FLORAL DIAGRAM.

includes plants which are only very distantly related to each other. (2) **Amaryllidaceae**, with $P\ 3 + 3\ \ A\ 3 + 3\ \ G(\bar{3})$, flowers usually in an umbel, which is sometimes reduced to a single flower. Perianth often with a corona, an additional inner frill or tube (see *Narcissus*). (3) **Iridaceae**, with $P\ 3 + 3\ \ A\ 3\ \ G(\bar{3})$, leaves often flattened vertically instead of horizontally (*Iris*). (4) **Juncaceae**, with the same formula as Liliaceae, but wind-pollinated with an inconspicuous perianth, and resembling Gramineae and Cyperaceae in habit of growth. *Luzula* is extremely grass-like, while *Juncus* is perhaps more varied in its general habit than any other genus in Britain. (5) **Dioscoreaceae**, twining plants with unisexual flowers and reticulately veined leaves, likely to be mistaken for dicotyledons.

ARALES (= **SPADICIFLORAE**): A large order of monocotyledons, characterised mainly by the inflorescence, a thick fleshy axis being covered with small flowers which are individually quite inconspicuous; so far as pollination is concerned the whole spike acts as a single unit. Leaves often reticulately veined. There are two families: (1) **Araceae**, represented in Britain by *Arum* (which in its pollination is more specialised than most aroids, see p. 366) and the reed-like *Acorus*, the leaf of which is liable to be mistaken for *Iris*. (2) **Lemnaceae**, free-floating water plants of minute size and simplified structure, rarely seen in flower and likely not to be recognised as angiosperms at all without some previous knowledge.

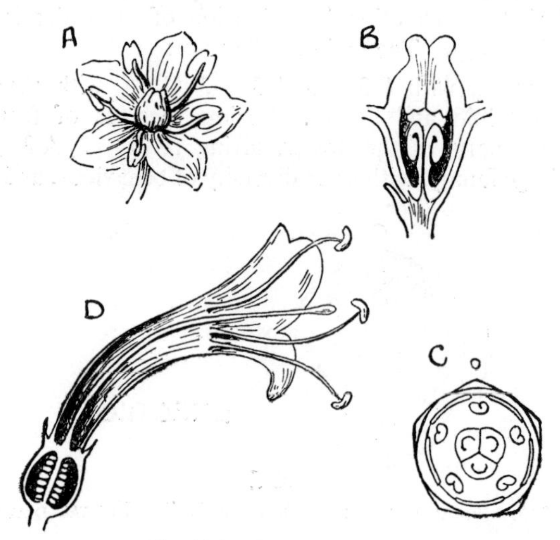

Fig. 216. CAPRIFOLIACEAE.
A, flower of *Sambucus nigra*; B, ovary cut longitudinally; C, floral diagram of *S. ebulus*; D, half-flower of *Lonicera periclymenum*.

BOOKS RECOMMENDED FOR VARIOUS PURPOSES

Identification of British Plants: Clapham, Tutin, and Warburg, *Flora of the British Isles, 2nd Edit.*, OR their shorter *Excursion Flora of the British Isles*. Hubbard, *Grasses*.

Pictures: Clapham, Tutin, and Warburg, *Flora of the British Isles, Illustrations*, OR (large works in several volumes) Syme, *Sowerby's English Botany*. Ross-Craig, *Drawings of British Plants*.

Explanation of Names and Terms: Jackson, *A Glossary of Botanic Terms*. Gilbert-Carter, *Glossary of the British Flora*.

General Reading about British Plants: Arber, *Water Plants*. Gilmour and Walters, *Wild Flowers*. Hepburn, *Flowers of the Coast*. Lousley, *Wild Flowers of Chalk and Limestone*. Prime, *Lords and Ladies*. Raven and Walters, *Mountain Flowers*. Skene,

The Biology of Flowering Plants. Summerhayes, *Wild Orchids of Britain.* Turrill, *British Plant Life.*

Distribution of Species in Britain: Matthews, *Origin and Distribution of the British Flora,* AND (large reference book) Perring and Walters, *Atlas of the British Flora.* For most parts of Britain a county flora is available. This will give information about distribution but not usually descriptions of the plants. The local librarian or museum curator should be consulted.

Wider Information about Families of Plants and Systematic Botany Generally: Lawrence, *Taxonomy of Vascular Plants.* Rendle, *The Classification of Flowering Plants* (2 vols.). Willis, *A Dictionary of the Flowering Plants and Ferns.*

Identification of Cultivated Plants: Bailey, *Manual of Cultivated Plants* (*Revised Edit.*). Rehder, *Manual of Cultivated Trees and Shrubs.* Jackson, *The Identification of Conifers.*

Identification of Foreign Plants: Normally one has to work with a flora in the language of the country, but there is a little flexibility; the usefulness of a French flora, for instance, does not stop short at the German frontier.

History of Botany, especially Classification: Arber, *Herbals* (*2nd edit.*). Blunt, *The Art of Botanical Illustration.* Gilmour, *British Botanists.* Gourlie, *The Prince of Botanists, Carl Linnaeus.* Grigson, *The Englishman's Flora.* Gunther, *The Greek Herbal of Dioscorides.* Hagberg, *Carl Linnaeus.* Hawkes, *Pioneers of Plant Study.* Hort, *The Critica Botanica of Linnaeus.* Raven, *John Ray.* Reynolds Green, *A History of Botany in the United Kingdom.* Woodward, *Gerard's Herball.*

14 SURVEY OF THE PLANT KINGDOM: INTRODUCTORY

Chapters 15 to 19 are each devoted to one of the principal groups into which the plant kingdom is divided. The reader will already be aware of the habit of classifying plant groups according to their position on a scale of evolutionary advancement. This is the idea behind any reference to the seed plants as the "higher plants" (*e.g.* p. 8), or to one group as being more highly evolved than another (*e.g.* p. 42). In the case of green plants, the customary order of groups is as follows:

	LEVEL OF ADVANCEMENT
Angiosperms (flowering plants)	HIGH
Gymnosperms (conifers, etc.: Chapter 17)	
Pteridophytes (ferns, etc.: Chapter 16) ..	
Bryophytes (mosses, etc.: Chapter 15) ..	
Algae (seaweeds, etc.: Chapter 18) ..	LOW

Even if there were no direct evidence of an evolutionary relationship between the groups, this arrangement would be logical in terms of several independent criteria. Structural complexity, for instance, is minimal among the algae and increases to its fullest development among angiosperms. An equally convincing trend which can be followed throughout this series is in the nature of the life-cycle. It will be recalled (see p. 168) that every sexual life-cycle has an alternation of haploid and diploid phases or "generations". The general pattern is illustrated in Fig. 217. The diploid phase ends with meiosis and the production of spores, and hence is known as the **sporophyte** generation; the haploid phase, which produces the gametes and ends with fertilisation, is called the **gametophyte** generation. Although Fig. 217 represents these two generations as equal in length, their relative length and prominence in the life-cycle may be very unequal. Among the algae, for example, many species have a life-cycle in which the greater part consists of the gametophyte generation, and the sporophyte is restricted to a single-celled zygote. Further up the scale, the bryophytes have an alternation of two multicellular generations, each one substantial in size and length of existence. At the top of the scale the angiosperms show maximum development of the sporophyte, with the gametophyte reduced to an almost negligible part of the life-cycle.

There is good reason to believe that the table of groups given above is not merely in keeping with the degree of structural complexity or the prominence of the sporophyte, but also indicates the order in which the groups have evolved. For although most living plants can be allocated without difficulty to their appropriate groups, there are clear relationships between each group and its neighbours in the list. For example, all seed-bearing plants whose ovules are not completely enclosed by maternal tissues are classed as gymnosperms. But the group of plants which share this feature shows great diversity in other features, including some members with strong resemblances to pteridophytes and others which have much

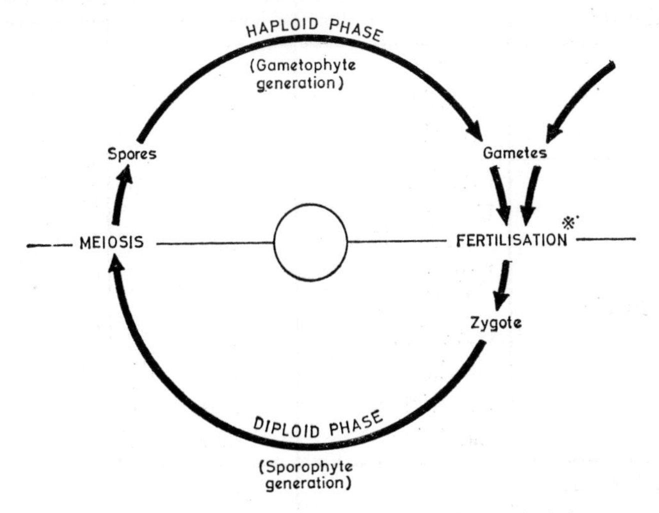

*The two gametes which unite frequently come from different individuals.

Fig. 217. GENERAL PATTERN OF A SEXUAL LIFE-CYCLE.

in common with angiosperms. Thus it is helpful to think of the green plants not as being divided into five separate groups, but as a continuous sequence of related forms in which five levels of organisation are customarily distinguished for purposes of classification. This is the pattern of relationships which one would expect to result from a process of gradual evolution, and common sense would suggest that this process began with simple plants and led up to more elaborate ones. Direct evidence in support of this suggestion is provided by the fossil record.

Fossils are the remains or impressions of dead plants and animals preserved in rocks. The preservation is in many cases so perfect and permanent that a detailed picture can be obtained of the morphology and structure of organisms, or more commonly parts of organisms, which lived many millions of years ago (see Plate 16). In addition it is often possible to estimate the age of particular rocks. With sedimentary rocks this is calculated from the thickness of the rock formation and the rate at which sedimentation is believed to

Era	*Geological system*	*Millions of years since rocks formed* (minimum)
Cainozoic		
Mesozoic	Cretaceous	70
	Jurassic	140
	Triassic	170
Paleozoic	Permian	195
	Upper Carboniferous	220
	Lower Carboniferous	255
	Devonian	275
	Silurian	320
	Ordovician	350
	Cambrian	420
Pre-Cambrian		520

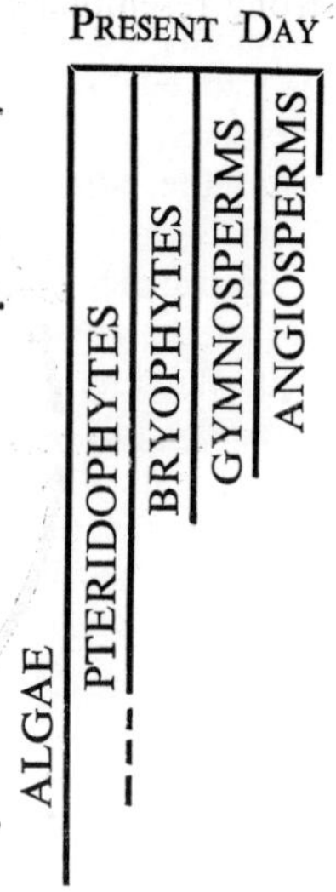

PRESENT DAY
ALGAE
PTERIDOPHYTES
BRYOPHYTES
GYMNOSPERMS
ANGIOSPERMS

Fig. 218. GEOLOGICAL TIME SCALE, SHOWING PERIODS DURING WHICH FIVE MAJOR PLANT GROUPS ARE KNOWN TO HAVE EXISTED.

No attempt has been made to indicate the relative abundance of the groups at different times.

have occurred. The radioactive minerals contained in some igneous rocks provide another method of dating, since the rate of disintegration is known and the proportion which has disintegrated can be measured. By a combination of these techniques an approximate time-scale for the various geological systems has been compiled (Fig. 218), and it can be used to determine the age of the fossils they contain. The store of information provided by fossils can therefore be of great value in studying the ancestry of modern plants, but its limitations should be clearly understood. For example, different types of plant are not equally likely to become fossilised. Those whose tissues are mostly soft are likely to decompose rapidly after death and leave no trace, but those with woody tissues and those strengthened by mineral deposits or a heavy cuticle decompose less rapidly and have a greater chance of preservation. Besides this, plants which grew in or near water are better represented among fossils than those from drier places. For one thing, immersion after death hinders decomposition by excluding oxygen; in addition, certain processes of fossilisation occur only in water. Many fossils, for example, are plant remains which settled to the bottom of a lake and became buried in sediment which has subsequently been compressed into rock and raised above water level by movements of the earth's crust. For these reasons the plants preserved as fossils form a very incomplete sample of prehistoric plant life, and any attempt to reconstruct the course of evolution from them is fraught with considerable speculation.

A further source of difficulty in interpreting the fossil record lies in the fragmentary nature of the specimens available, coupled with the fact that the older they are the less likely are they to resemble any living plant. An impression of an oak leaf from a recent rock formation can readily be identified as such, and can be classified as part of an angiosperm because of its similarities to living oaks. But the impression of a detached leaf from rocks 200 million years old may be impossible to identify or to allocate to a group because of its lack of a living counterpart.

However, in spite of the imperfections of the fossil evidence, it gives some idea of the relative ages of different groups. Fig. 218 indicates the oldest rocks in which fossilised remains of each group have been found, and shows that the oldest plant remains which have been discovered are those of algae. Most present-day algae consist of soft tissues only, but a minority are encrusted with calcium carbonate, and it is the remains of forms similar to these which testify to the existence of algae in Cambrian and pre-Cambrian times. It is significant that most algae live totally immersed in water and there is little doubt that plant life originated in water, and that for a long time there were no land plants.

Land plants first appear with any frequency in Silurian rocks, but recent discoveries of land plants in Cambrian rocks indicate a much earlier origin. These ancient land plants show some similarities to present-day pteridophytes. Among other characteristics, they possessed stomata, a cuticle, and a well-developed vascular system—all adaptations to life on land. It is difficult to believe that these features all evolved simultaneously with the migration from water to land. More probably, these early pteridophytes were preceded by simpler land plants of a more transitional form. Some of the present-day bryophytes have a structure which is much more in accordance with what is expected in a primitive land plant, but the earliest fossil remains of bryophytes which have been discovered date only from the Carboniferous period. However, all modern bryophytes are small plants and few of them have any hard tissues. The chances of such plants becoming fossilised are slim, so it is possible that bryophytes flourished in periods earlier than the Carboniferous, but no traces of them have been found. The simplicity of structure and prominence of the gametophyte generation in all living bryophytes strongly suggests that the group originated before the pteridophytes.

Plants related to present-day gymnosperms first appear in rocks of the Upper Carboniferous period, and angiosperms follow only in very much more recent rocks. In as much as a more recent origin implies greater evolutionary advancement, therefore, the fossil record fully supports the view that the angiosperms are the most highly evolved group of living plants. Their advanced status is also confirmed by the versatility shown by members of the group in occupying the most diverse habitats and frequently becoming the dominant type of vegetation.

The point has already been made that the older a fossil is, the less likely is it to resemble any modern species. This is a natural consequence of the fact that evolution does not simply add new species at the top of the scale but operates continuously at all levels of advancement. The vegetation of Triassic times, for example, was not like modern vegetation with the angiosperms missing. Certainly there were in existence plants recognisable as bryophytes, pteridophytes, and gymnosperms, but they were quite distinct from present-day members of those groups. Evolutionary changes since then have completely transformed the picture. Changes of a relatively modest nature have led to new species or genera within existing groups, while occasional changes of a more fundamental kind have created new families and even a new major division of the plant kingdom—the angiosperms. The reader should therefore guard against making unwarranted assumptions from the evolutionary hierarchy in which living plants are arranged. Although we may believe that gymnosperms, for instance, evolved from plants with some pteridophyte characteristics, there is no point in searching among present-day pteridophytes for the ancestors of gymnosperms.

In the foregoing discussion, mention of the fungi has been deliberately excluded, although fungi, like any other living organisms, are undoubtedly subject to evolutionary changes. In some morphological features fungi show similarities to algae, and it has been contended that they are related to that group; but there are no grounds for believing they are directly related to any other group of green plants. The course of evolution among the fungi themselves can make a rewarding study, and some of the criteria of advancement may be similar to those applied to the green plants, but there can be little doubt that thc fungi have evolved along lines which are separate from the main stream of plant evolution.

15 BRYOPHYTES

The bryophytes are a group of small plants including two main divisions, *Hepaticae* (liverworts) and *Musci* (mosses). Most species are capable of living on land, but a few live continuously submerged in water. On the strength of this feature of the majority, bryophytes are regarded as land plants, though they lack most of the adaptations to terrestrial life found in other groups of land plants, such as the possession of a cuticle, the ability to obtain water from any great depth in the soil or to raise it to more than a few inches above the soil surface. Bryophytes are therefore most abundant in permanently damp habitats such as bogs, wet woodlands, and the edges of streams. They are not uncommon elsewhere, however, since many species can withstand even prolonged drought, but growth is largely restricted to periods when the plants are wet. Bryophytes are to be found in almost all types of habitat, though they are rare in dry deserts and absent from sea-water.

In some features bryophytes show resemblances to the algae. Neither group possesses a true root system, and with a few exceptions among the mosses there are no vascular tissues either. Even the exceptional mosses have only primitive vascular tissues which cannot be regarded as true xylem or phloem. In general, the internal transport of water must be by passage from cell to cell in the parenchymatous tissues. This is a slow process, but the distances involved are small since the plants are not bulky and water can be absorbed over the entire surface. Liverworts are generally prostrate, or rise to a height of an inch or two above ground level by straggling over other vegetation. Terrestrial mosses may be erect and reach a height of about six inches, though most of them are much smaller. Thus, in these terrestrial forms no part of the plant is far from the substratum where water is most likely to be available. Submerged mosses are not faced with the same problems of water supply, and the largest British moss, *Fontinalis antipyretica*, which is common in freshwater streams and ponds, may reach a length of about three feet.

All bryophytes can reproduce sexually, though some do so only rarely, relying on other methods of propagation. An important feature of the sexual life-cycle is the alternation of two multicellular generations. No other plant group shows with such consistency the production of gametophyte and sporophyte which are almost

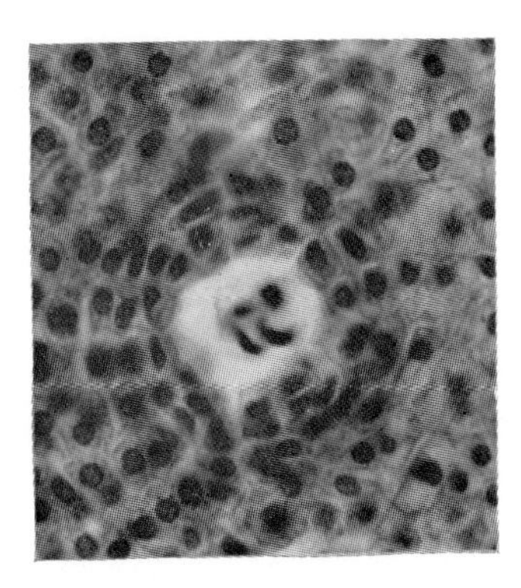

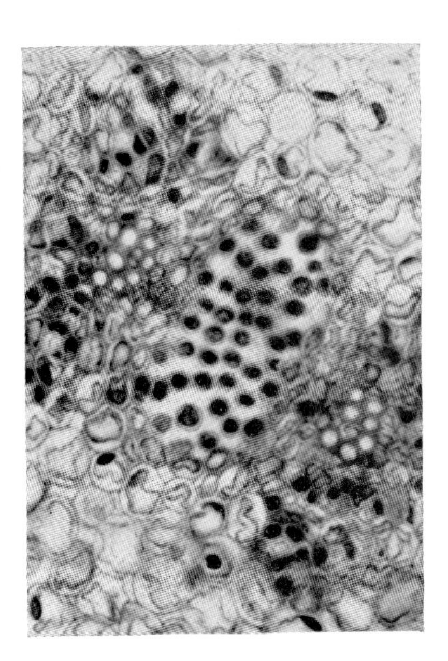

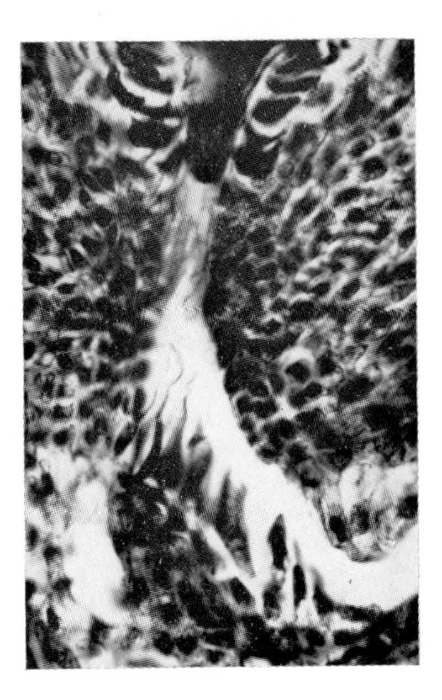

PLATE 13

TISSUES OF THE FLOWER OF *Centaurea scabiosa* (COMPOSITAE, ANATROPOUS OVULE) × 400 TO SHOW THE ROUTE TAKEN BY THE POLLEN-TUBE.

Top left: The tube will enter between the slanting cells of the stigmatic surface and grow away to the left in the thick tough wall substance between the cells of the conducting tissue, shown in L.S. at lower middle.

Bottom left: The conducting strands from the two stigma branches join into a single strand seen here, in T.S., as an oval central area. Small vascular bundles of the style on either side.

Top right: The conducting tissue ends as a tongue projecting into the micropyle. Four cells of the conducting strand are seen here in T.S., separated by a space from the surrounding integument.

Bottom right: This L.S. of the micropyle shows the end of the conducting strand, with hair-like cells at centre pointing upwards towards the embryo sac, part of which is visible at the top with its surrounding nutritive "jacket" cells.

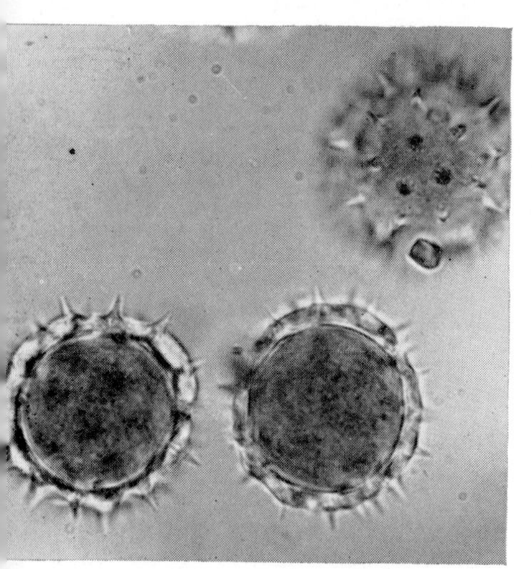

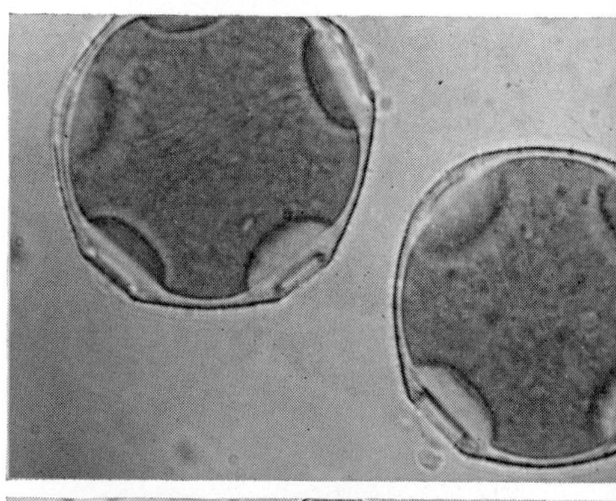

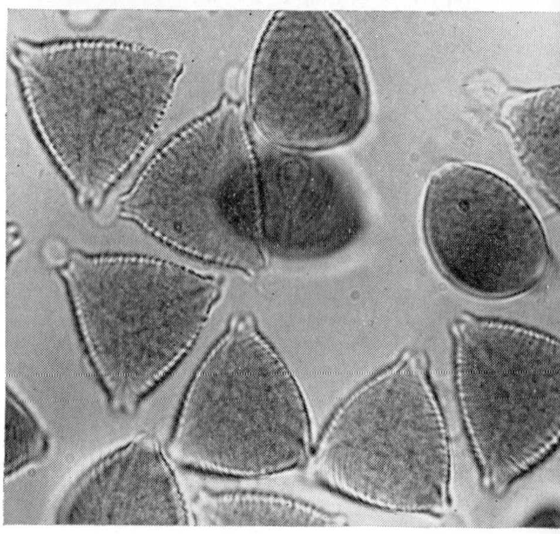

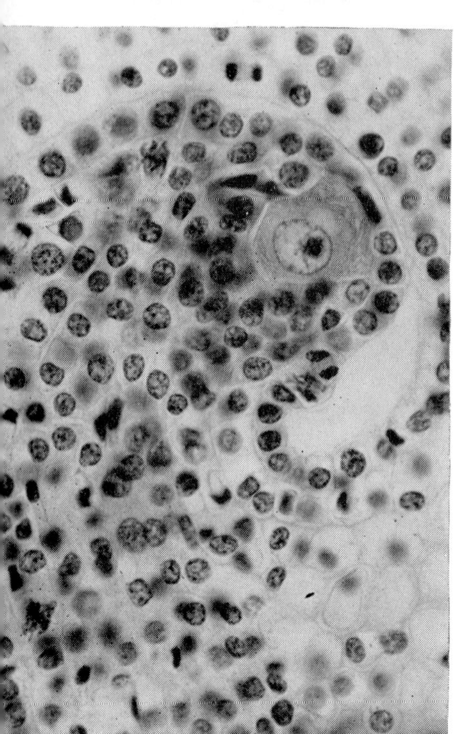

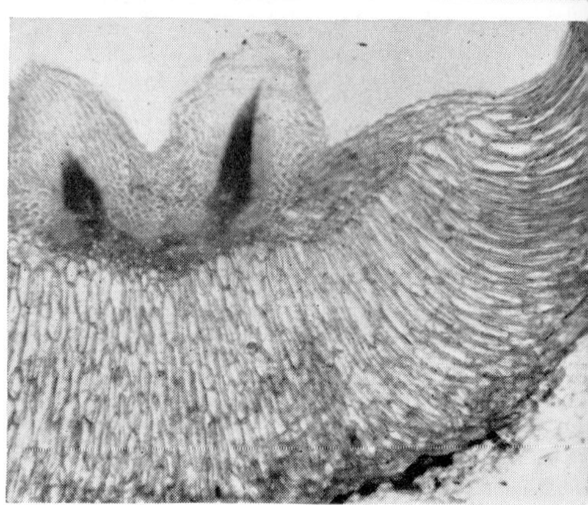

PLATE 14

REPRODUCTIVE STRUCTURES IN ANGIOSPERMS. Pollens, all on the same scale: *Dahlia* (*top left*) a spiny ball, two grains in section, one in surface view; *Campanula* (*top right*) with prominent germ-pores; *Cuphea* (*middle right*) a grain like a finely fluted triangular bun with a pore at each corner. Some of the *Cuphea* grains are standing on edge, and one of these, out of focus, just above the centre of the picture, has a germ-pore facing the camera. Young ovule of *Lilium* (*bottom left*) is growing upwards from the placenta and turning over to the right, with the megaspore mother cell in its tip; a slight bulge on the side of the ovule vertically below the mother cell is the first stage of integument-formation. Dehiscence-apparatus of pansy fruit (*bottom right*): a transverse section through the keel of one of the three boat-shaped valves of the capsule shows the stalks of two seeds above a thick pad of parenchyma with curved stress-lines; contraction of this tissue as it dries provides the power to open the fruit and throw out the seeds.

equally conspicuous. Throughout the group the sporophyte is an unbranched macroscopic structure growing out from the gametophyte to which it remains attached and on which it is to a large extent nutritionally dependent. These features of the sporophyte are diagnostic for bryophytes and could be used for placing a specimen in its correct group.

Sexual reproduction is oogamous, with the non-motile female gamete retained by the gametophyte in a special flask-like structure called an **archegonium**. The motile male gametes, **spermatozoids**, must swim over the surface of the plants to reach the archegonia and achieve fertilisation. Both liverworts and mosses may be either monoecious or dioecious. The production of motile gametes is a feature which bryophytes share with algae, but the structures in which the gametes are produced are generally distinctive. Most algal gametes are enclosed by only a cell wall before their release, whereas the gametes of bryophytes are produced in structures (antheridia and archegonia) which have an outer layer of sterile cells.

Alternatives to sexual reproduction include reproduction by fragmentation. The power of regeneration is well developed, and complete new individuals can be grown from fragments of others. Increase in numbers by this method is probably common in nature, but it does not lead to much increase in the range of distribution: the daughter plants are likely to grow near their parents. Some species of both liverworts and mosses, however, have an additional method of vegetative reproduction which allows considerable dispersal. Small packets of undifferentiated cells, known as **gemmae**, are developed on exposed surfaces and become detached. Each gemma is very light and may be carried some distance by air currents. If it lands on a suitable substratum it can then grow into a new individual.

The bryophytes are of little commercial importance and do not include any major crop plants. Bog mosses, however, after death may become compressed into peat which is a valuable fuel in countries where alternatives are not plentiful, such as Ireland. Species of *Sphagnum*, a genus of bog mosses, also make useful packing material, particularly for live plants which need to be kept moist in transit. A handful of wet *Sphagnum* retains its moisture like a sponge, and is similarly soft and resilient. In a less direct way, bryophytes are important as colonisers of bare earth, helping to prevent erosion and paving the way for the growth of larger plants.

Since bryophytes are unobtrusive both in size and importance, the variety within the group is often overlooked. It is true that recognition of species usually requires closer examination than when identifying a flowering plant. The identification of a liverwort may depend on the shape, distribution, and colour of the rhizoids, and a moss species may be distinguished by the details of shape and cell structure in the leaves. But with practice it is possible to name many of the commoner species in the field using only a hand lens. Anyone prepared to study the group will find rich reward, for in Britain alone there are more than 600 moss species and nearly 300 liverwort species, many of them with distinct preferences for particular habitats.

Hepaticae (Liverworts)

The liverworts owe their name to a supposed resemblance between some of them and the animal liver. Those concerned are the

Fig. 219. *Pellia*.
Thallus, X 3.

thallose liverworts, which have a gametophyte consisting of a green, branched ribbon or **thallus** with no division into stem and leaves (e.g. *Pellia epiphylla*, Fig. 219). The thallus grows flattened against the substratum, and branches dichotomously. Its general morphology is therefore reminiscent of many seaweeds, and this adds further emphasis to the similarities between bryophytes and algae. Each branch has its own apical meristem which can continue growth indefinitely. Individual plants do not reach great lengths, however, since the older parts die as fast as the branches grow. One of the largest (and commonest) British liverworts, *Conocephalum conicum*, may reach a length of 4-6 in., but this is well above average for liverworts in general.

On the underside of the thallus there are unicellular outgrowths called **rhizoids** which attach the plant to its substratum. They also play some part in the absorption of water, but this function is not restricted to the rhizoids. The thallus is very simple in structure. In *Pellia* it consists of continuous parenchyma (Fig. 220), but in some other thallose liverworts there are air chambers just within the upper surface opening to the atmosphere by pores. These pores generally have a fixed aperture and do not resemble the stomata of higher plants. Although some interior cells of the thallus are elongated in the direction of growth, there is no differentiation of proper vascular tissue.

Sexual reproduction follows a similar general pattern in all liverworts, though there is great variation in detail between one species and another. The description given below refers to *Pellia epiphylla*. It is important to remember that the plant whose morphology and structure have been described above is a gametophyte, with the haploid chromosome number. The production of gametes by these plants does not, therefore, involve meiosis. Male gametes are produced in antheridia, each of which is a spherical organ attached by a short stalk. The antheridia develop in cavities just below the upper surface in the central part of the thallus, and their presence can be recognised, usually about April or May, by small swellings (Fig. 221). Each swelling has a small central pore through which the spermatozoids are eventually released. A developing antheridium has an outer wall consisting of a single layer of cells, which encloses an increasing number of internal cells. When internal cell division ceases, there may be several thousand cells inside the wall. These are the **spermatocytes** (Fig. 222, A) and each one undergoes a remarkable metamorphosis from an angular cell forming part of a closely packed tissue, into a long sinuous spermatozoid which can propel itself by two flagella (Fig. 222, B). When differentiation of spermatozoids is complete, the antheridium is ready to discharge its contents. The wall of the antheridium splits open only when it is moist, absorption of water setting up tensions in the cells which eventually cause them to separate. The dehiscence mechanism therefore ensures that spermatozoids are released under conditions favourable for motility.

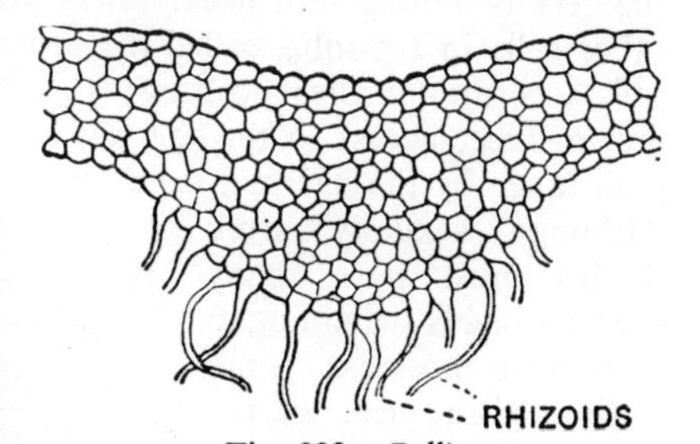

Fig. 220. *Pellia*.
Transverse section of central part of thallus.

Archegonia are found on the same thalli as antheridia, but their development begins a little later and in a different position. A

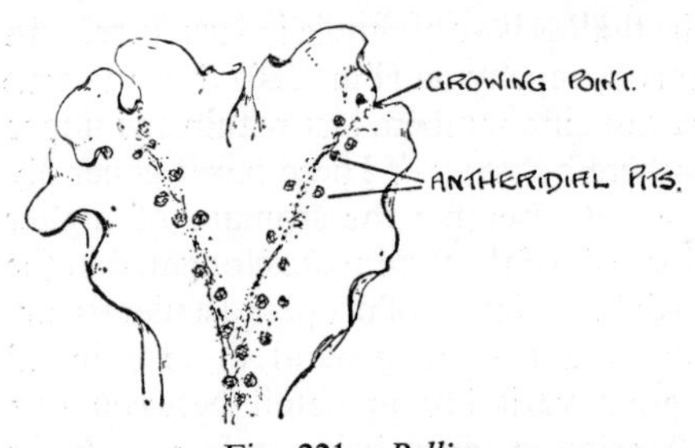

Fig. 221. *Pellia*.
Upper surface of thallus producing antheridia.

cluster of archegonia may develop near the apex of any branch, covered by a protective flap or **involucre** (Fig. 223). Each archegonium consists of a single large egg cell or **oosphere**, enclosed in a tube whose walls are one cell thick. The swollen basal part of the tube where the egg cell lies is called the **venter**, and the rest is a long thin **neck**. In a young archegonium there are other cells in the tube, called the ventral canal cell and neck canal cells according to their positions (Fig. 222, C), but these degenerate, giving direct access to the egg cell through the canal. This is the path taken by the spermatozoid which is to carry out fertilisation. Although a sexually mature thallus must have many spermatozoids swimming in its surface moisture, penetration of the neck of the archegonium is not left to chance. Spermatozoids are attracted by a chemical agent released by the archegonium, the exact nature of which is uncertain, though several substances have been shown *in vitro* to be effective. Directed movement of spermatozoids in response to a chemical stimulus is an example of **chemotactic** movement. Several archegonia in each cluster may become fertilised, but as a rule only one develops further.

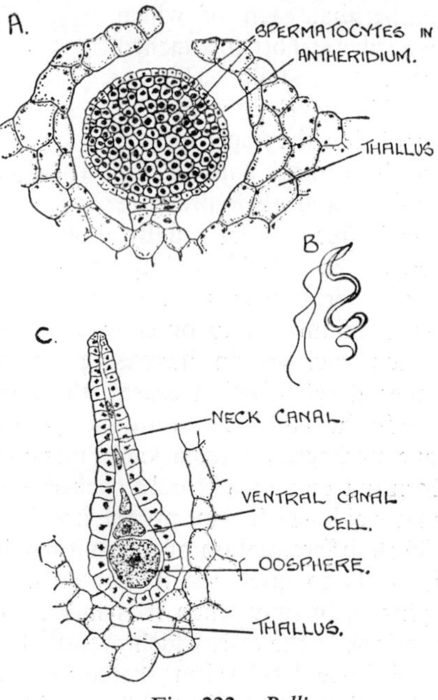

Fig. 222. *Pellia*.
A, section through antheridial cavity; B, spermatozoid; C, section through young archegonium.

Fertilisation produces a zygote with the diploid chromosome number, and is the beginning of the sporophyte generation. But the growth which follows as a consequence of fertilisation is not restricted to the new sporophyte. While the zygote begins to develop into the sporophyte, the cells of the venter, which is still part of the gametophyte, also resume active

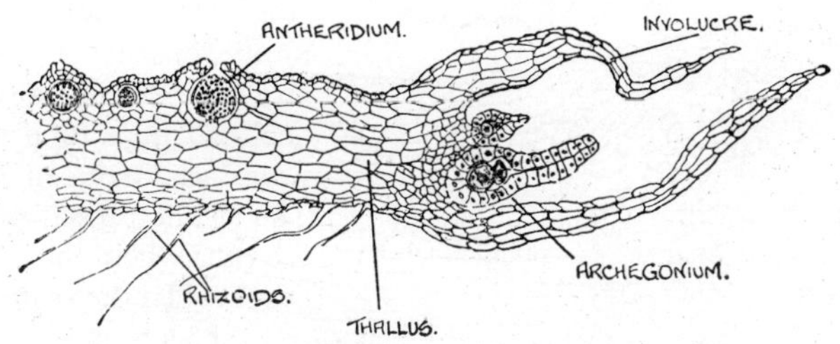

Fig. 223. *Pellia.*
Vertical section of thallus showing positions of archegonia and antheridia.

growth. They give rise to a sheath or **calyptra** which completely envelops the sporophyte through most of its existence. The whole structure composed of young sporophyte and calyptra is called a **sporogonium** (Fig. 224, A). During its early development, the sporophyte differentiates into three regions (Fig. 225). At the end

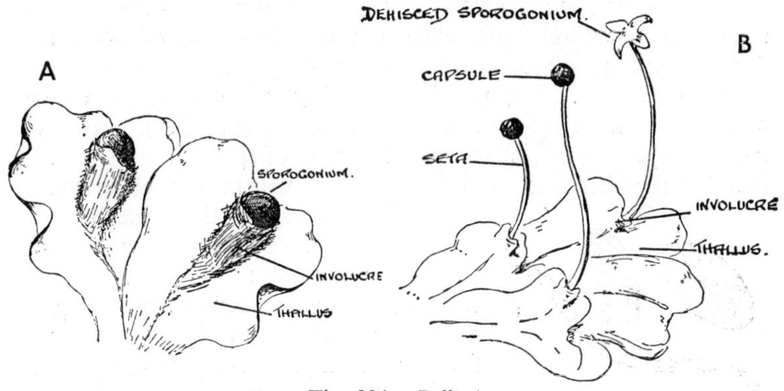

Fig. 224. *Pellia.*
Thalli with sporogonia, before (A) and after (B) elongation of setae.

corresponding to the base of the former archegonium is a mass of rounded cells firmly embedded in the tissues of the gametophyte. This is the **foot**, and its close union with the gametophyte is most important since the sporophyte is dependent upon the gametophyte for its nutrition. The foot therefore acts as an absorbing organ, receiving supplies from the gametophyte and transmitting them to the other parts of the sporophyte. Next to the foot is a cylindrical part of the sporophyte called the **seta**, made up of cells which remain roughly cubical until the sporophyte is ready to release its spores. The part furthest from the foot becomes the spherical **capsule** in

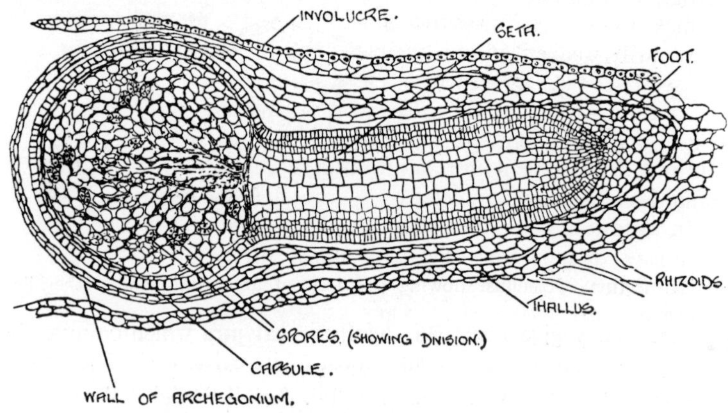

Fig. 225. *Pellia.*
Vertical section of thallus, passing through young sporogonium.

which the spores are produced. This has an outer wall several cells thick, and a central mass which develops into cells of two sorts. Some are the spore mother cells which undergo meiosis and produce tetrads of spores. The rest become long thin cells called **elaters** whose walls have helical bands of thickening (Fig. 226). Some of the elaters are loosely mixed with the mass of spores, but others are bundled together like the bristles of a brush into an **elaterophore** attached at the base of the capsule.

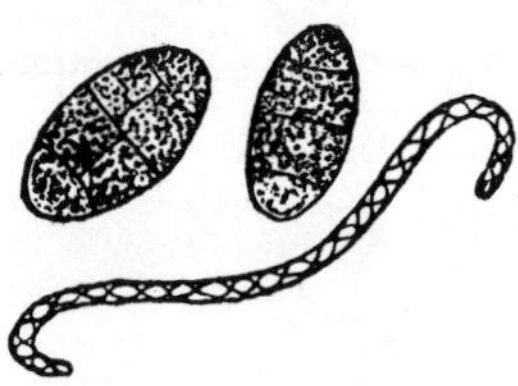

Fig. 226. *Pellia.*
Two spores and an elater.

Development of the sporophyte to the point of readiness to release its spores takes about a year, so that a zygote produced one spring yields spores the following spring. Liberation of spores is preceded by a dramatic elongation of cells in the seta, which forces the capsule through the calyptra and raises it up about an inch above the surface of the thallus. From an unobtrusive structure almost concealed within the gametophyte, the sporophyte rapidly develops into a conspicuous outgrowth with a glossy black capsule held up on the whitish seta (Fig. 224, B). Shortly afterwards the capsule wall breaks open by four longitudinal splits, exposing the contents. By this time the spores have already undergone several cell divisions, and at the time of release each one is a small multicellular gametophyte equipped with chloroplasts and ready to begin independent growth (Fig. 226). Dispersal of the spores from the capsule is assisted by the elaters which react to changes of humidity by sudden curling and uncurling, thus helping to flick the spores from the capsule. Some of the spores are temporarily wedged among the elaters of the elaterophore and are released later than the others, so ensuring dispersal in time as well as in space. Those spores which land on a suitable substratum may then continue development into adult thalli, and the sexual cycle is thus completed.

In addition to the thallose liverworts, Hepaticae include species which show differentiation into stem and leaves. These are the **foliose** or **leafy** liverworts. They usually have two opposite rows of prominent leaves with each leaf overlapping its neighbours like the slats of a Venetian blind. There is often a third row of smaller leaves also, which occur on the under surface of prostrate plants. Internal structure is very simple and undifferentiated, and the leaves are usually only one cell thick. The sexual cycle is comparable with that described for *Pellia*. Antheridia are produced in leaf axils and archegonia terminally.

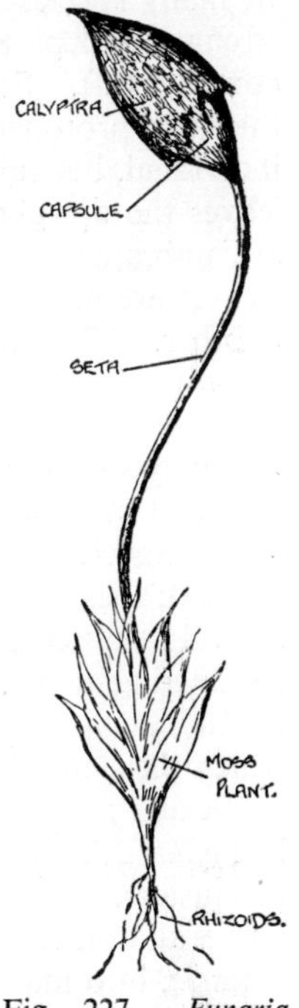

Musci (Mosses)

Unlike leafy liverworts, most mosses have radially symetrical shoots with only one type of leaf. The few exceptions with leaves in two ranks can usually be recognised by the presence of a midrib in each leaf, a feature absent from liverworts. The diagnostic differences between mosses and liverworts, however, are microscopic. The capsule of a moss has a central core or **columella** which does not develop into spores; the rhizoids are multicellular; and the spores do not develop directly into the leafy branches of the gametophyte. None of these features is found among liverworts. We shall consider the life history of a terrestrial moss such as *Funaria hygrometrica* (Fig. 227; Plate 16) which is common in Britain. The gametophyte generation begins with the formation and liberation of haploid spores. Those which land in a suitable place germinate into a branched

Fig. 227. *Funaria*. Gametophyte bearing sporogonium, before spore dehiscence.

multicellular filament called a **protonema**. Some branches of the filament are rhizoidal; they grow down into the soil and have no chloroplasts. Other branches spread over the surface, contain chloroplasts, and resemble the filaments of some green algae. A patch of bare soil on which many moss spores have germinated may become covered with a brilliant green layer composed of protonemata. Each protonema can produce several buds from which the leafy stems develop. In many species these stand erect, supported partly by their own strength and partly by growing side by side with other stems in a compact tuft. Several neighbouring stems may all be derived from the same protonema, and therefore at first are all parts of the same individual, but subsequent degeneration of the protonema frequently leaves the upright stems as separate plants. In *Funaria* the stems are unbranched, but in other species there is frequent branching. Leaves are normally attached in a close succession, overlapping one another. The lamina is one cell thick, but this may increase to several cells at the midrib. Near the base of the stem rhizoids are produced which, like those of liverworts, help to attach the plant and play some part in water absorption.

Most mosses have little or no internal differentiation of tissues. A few species have a central core of elongated cells in the stem. Some of these cells are thick-walled and give extra rigidity. Others are thin-walled, and there is evidence that they act as a primitive conducting tissue. The central strand is well developed in *Polytrichum commune* (Fig. 228), one of the largest British mosses, in which the stems frequently exceed 6 in. in height.

Sexual reproduction is similar in general features to the process in *Pellia*. Archegonia and antheridia are produced at stem apices in clusters. Monoecious mosses may have both archegonia and antheridia on each fertile branch, or there may be separation, as in *Funaria*, into male and female apices. Antheridia are club-shaped, with an elongated head attached to a stalk (Figs. 229 and 230, A), and each one produces a mass of spermatocytes enclosed in a wall one cell thick. The development and liberation of spermatozoids occur as in *Pellia*. Archegonia are larger than their counterparts in liverworts, with the venter several cells thick and a substantial stalk (Fig. 230, C). Both antheridia and archegonia may be intermingled with multicellular hairs called **paraphyses** (Fig. 229). These play no part in the production of gametes, but probably help to retain water at the apex by surface forces. This is necessary if fertilisation is to take place. Spermatozoids swim in the surface water and their dispersal is probably assisted by rain splash. Once in the neighbourhood of the archegonia they are attracted chemotactically to the necks.

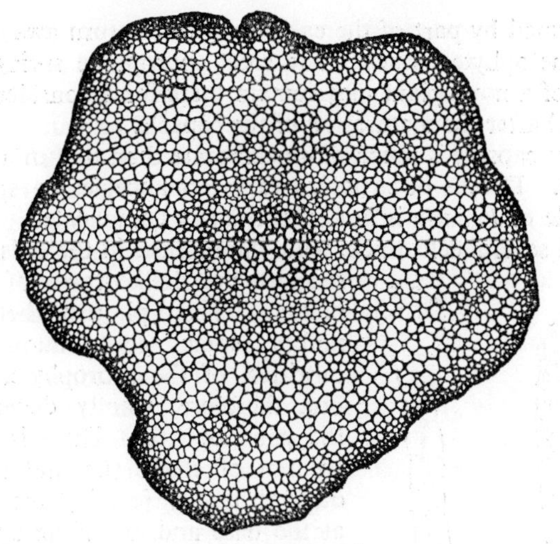

Fig. 228. *Polytrichum.*
Transverse section of stem of gametophyte showing differentiated central strand.

The early growth of the fertilised egg into a sporogonium consisting of capsule, seta, and foot, is accompanied by the formation of a calyptra from the cells of the venter. This is similar to the situation in *Pellia*, but elongation of the seta is not delayed as in that case. While the capsule is still relatively undeveloped, the seta elongates gradually, carrying aloft the capsule surmounted by a

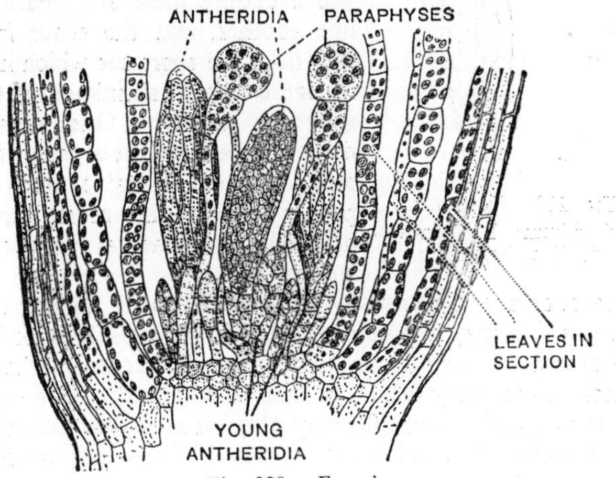

Fig. 229. *Funaria.*
Vertical section through apex of male branch.

"hat" formed by part of the calyptra which is torn away from the other gametophyte tissues. The erect sporophyte springing from the apex of a moss plant may remain there for a considerable time during and after the maturation of the capsule.

A moss capsule is much more elaborate than that of a liverwort (Fig. 231). Details of structure vary from species to species but the capsule of *Funaria* is not exceptionally complicated. It has an outer wall several cells thick, with chloroplasts in the cells and with stomata not unlike those of flowering plants. This photosynthetic tissue makes some contribution to the nutrition of the sporophyte, which is not, therefore, wholly dependent on the gametophyte. There is a central column of sterile (*i.e.* not spore-producing) tissue, forming the **apophysis** at the base and extending upwards as the **columella**. The apophysis includes the upper extremity of a conducting strand which passes up the seta and supplies the capsule with water. Between the columella and the photosynthetic outer wall is the fertile tissue in which meiosis occurs followed by the development of haploid spores. When mature these are separate from one another, and the space in which they lie is the **spore sac** which increases in size owing to shrinkage of the surrounding tissues. One outstanding difference between the capsule of mosses and liverworts is that a much smaller proportion of the moss capsule is devoted to the actual production of spores.

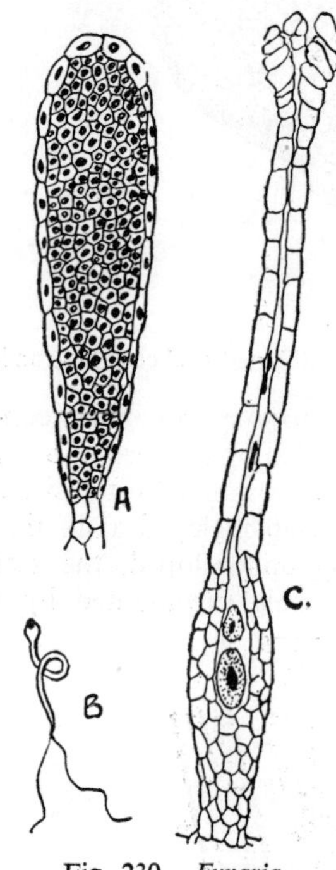

Fig. 230. *Funaria*.
A, antheridium; B, spermatozoid; C, archegonium.

The spores are eventually liberated through the apex of the capsule, which may not be at the top if the capsule is nodding as is the case in *Funaria* at maturity. The dehiscence mechanism in this moss, as in many others, is somewhat complex. The calyptra, not being part of the capsule, may drop off at any time after elongation of the seta, and this is a necessary preliminary to spore dispersal. At the top of the capsule proper is a cap called the **operculum**. It becomes detached when the spores are mature by rupture of a ring of cells called the **annulus**. Detachment of the operculum exposes the **peristome teeth** attached around the inside of the capsule wall just below the annulus. They are long and pointed, like the teeth of a comb, and are strips of cell wall material remaining from cells which have disintegrated earlier. *Funaria* has two sets of these teeth, one above the other. Teeth in the upper set are permanently arranged like the spokes of a wheel, their points meeting

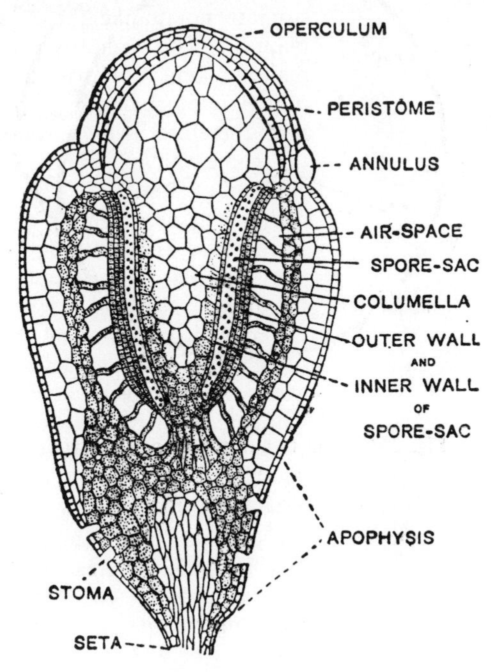

Fig. 231. *Funaria*.
Longitudinal section of capsule.

at the centre but with spaces between adjacent teeth. The lower teeth alternate with the upper ones and at first fill the spaces between them, so preventing the spores from being shed. However the material of which they are made is hygroscopic, and when it dries the teeth bend upwards and outwards, thus opening the gaps between the upper teeth. Spores are shaken out by movement of the capsule on the end of the flexible seta, and the hygroscopic mechanism ensures that the spores are liberated in dry weather when wide dispersal by air currents is most probable.

Comparison of the life histories of *Pellia* and *Funaria* shows that although they differ in some details they are broadly similar. The general pattern of the life history of bryophytes is shown in the following diagram:

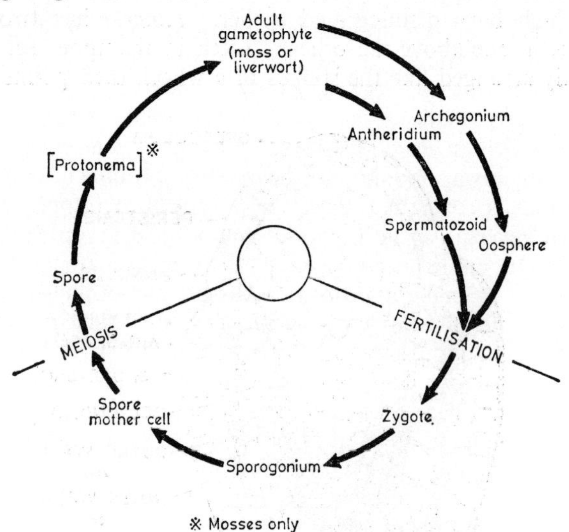

Fig. 232. THE LIFE-CYCLE IN BRYOPHYTES.

16 THE PTERIDOPHYTES

The pteridophytes are plants with an alternation of generations fundamentally similar to that seen in bryophytes, but with much greater elaboration of the sporophyte, which possesses xylem and phloem and is usually a branched leafy perennial. The gametophyte, by contrast, is in most cases a small, simple, and essentially temporary organism. So far as the relative prominence of the two generations is concerned, therefore, a typical pteridophyte shows a complete reversal of the situation seen in most bryophytes.

There are enough points of resemblance (stomata, spore-tetrads, archegonia) to make it probable that all pteridophytes and bryophytes have evolved from a common stock. The pteridophytes, however, even more clearly than the bryophytes, fall into several groups between which there is certainly no close relationship, and which appear from fossil evidence to have developed separately for some hundreds of millions of years. The living pteridophytes are mostly of small stature, are restricted as to numbers of species, and play only a subordinate part in the earth's vegetation. The fossil record reveals, in addition to the few surviving groups, other series of pteridophytes which have long been totally extinct, and some of these lost forms were of great size, with secondary vascular tissues, which are almost wholly lacking in the survivors.

Of the living plants we must recognise four main series, all with the same basic type of life-cycle, but differing sharply in reproductive details and in the vegetative anatomy of the sporophyte.

1. Psilophytes. A scanty remnant of a very ancient lineage, now occurring only in restricted parts of the southern hemisphere. Distinguished by the total absence of roots, together with other primitive and unusual features.

2. Lycopods. Sporophyte with numerous small simple leaves. Reproductive parts of the sporophyte more or less cone-like, each **sporophyll** (or spore-bearing leaf) having a single large sporangium in a roughly axillary position. A widespread and moderately successful group of plants, but with little resistance to atmospheric pollution or any disturbance of the vegetation, and therefore uncommon in densely populated areas; in Britain they occur mainly in mountainous districts.

3. Horsetails. One widespread genus (*Equisetum*) with a preponderance of marsh-dwelling species. Small leaves, of little photosynthetic significance, *arranged in whorls.* Photosynthetic tissue concentrated mainly in lateral branches of the stem.

4. Ferns. Differing from all other groups in having relatively large, usually compound leaves, each leaf being curled like a crozier when young. Fertile leaf or sporophyll usually with numerous small sporangia. By far the most abundant of the four series.

Detailed consideration of psilophytes is beyond the scope of this book, but we must give some attention to the other groups.

The Fern Sporophyte

Ferns are perennials, almost always with some kind of root-stock or rhizome. A few species form unbranched trees, though the

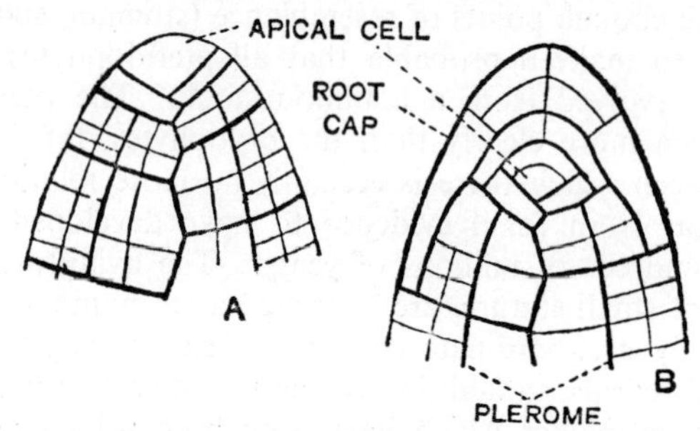

Fig. 233. Apex of A, rhizome and B, root of fern. (Diagrammatic longitudinal sections.)

"trunk" in such cases is largely composed of matted adventitious roots. Most ferns are readily recognisable as such, the rolling of the young leaves (hardly to be found in any other group of plants) being one of the best clues. There are, however, some specialised ferns of very untypical aspect. Some aquatic ferns are not at all fernlike in appearance, and some forest-dwelling species ("filmy ferns") resemble mosses in their general texture.

In most ferns every organ (stem, leaf, or root) has a single **apical cell**, from the division-products or segments of which all the tissues are produced (Fig. 233). In radially symmetrical structures (roots and the majority of stems) the apical cell is a tetrahedron or triangular pyramid; in a stem this has three cutting faces, but in a root the fourth or outer face is active in producing the root cap. In dorsiventral structures (leaves and some creeping stems) the apical cell often has only two cutting faces.

There is little that is in any way remarkable in the outer tissues (epidermis, cortex, mesophyll) of ferns. These tissue systems are basically parenchymatous, and similar in construction to the tissues of dicotyledons. In the stems and petioles there is a strong tendency for the outer cortex to become sclerotic, and the rigidity of these organs often depends far more upon lignified cortical tissue than upon the vascular system, which is mechanically weak in all ferns.

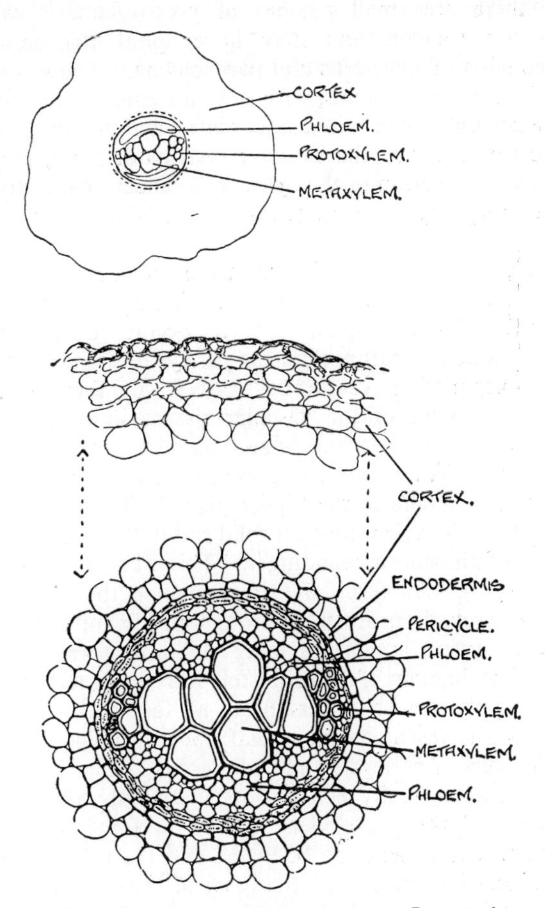

Fig. 234. Transverse section, root of *Dryopteris*.

In general the leaf lamina displays the characteristic features of shade leaves (poor differentiation between palisade and spongy mesophyll, chloroplasts in epidermal cells, etc.).

The vascular tissues of ferns are highly distinctive in their structure and arrangement. The xylem consists mainly of **scalariform** tracheids, a type which is relatively uncommon in seed plants. The side wall of a scalariform tracheid has bordered pits which are elongated sideways, the wall as a whole therefore presenting a ladder-like appearance. These tracheids are often of great size, and are embedded in a small-celled non-lignified xylem parenchyma. In addition there are small patches of protoxylem, in which the tracheids are smaller, and may have spiral thickenings. The phloem consists of sieve cells and parenchyma. The sieve cells are elongated with pointed ends, with sieve areas upon their side walls. There are no highly specialised sieve plates, and no companion cells. Fibres do not occur in the vascular systems of ferns, nor is there usually any lignification of the xylem and phloem parenchyma, nor, in the vast majority of ferns, is there the slightest sign of cambial activity.

The arrangement of the tissues in the root conforms closely to that seen in seed plants (Chapter 5). A majority of fern roots are diarch (Fig. 234), though other forms occur. Lateral roots arise from the endodermis rather than the pericycle, a rule which applies also to the origin of "adventitious" roots from a fern stem.

The arrangement of the vascular tissues in fern stems is so different from that in the stems of seed plants that a special terminology is needed. We cannot recognise in the ferns any counterpart of the vascular bundle in the higher plants. The simplest pattern is that in which the xylem forms a solid rod in the centre of the stem with a layer of phloem surrounding it. This is known as a **protostele** (Fig. 235, A, *a*). All ferns are protostelic in the early stages of growth; some remain protostelic throughout life, but in the majority the vascular system assumes a more elaborate form as the plant matures. The diagram of the protostele introduces us to two principles which apply almost universally to all fern stems. In the first place, the whole vascular system, leaf traces included, is completely clothed in layers of pericycle and endodermis similar in all essential features to those normally seen in roots. Secondly, the number and arrangement of the protoxylem groups in ferns is so variable that no general statement can be made, and the protoxylem clearly has little if any influence upon the form of the vascular system as a whole. In fact, we need not consider the protoxylem separately at all.

Protostelic stems are usually small, and the departure of the single leaf trace strand occasions little disturbance. In many ferns of greater size the departure of a leaf trace leaves an appreciable cavity in the xylem core. This cavity is lined with phloem, pericycle, and endodermis, and there is a tendency for such cavities to continue from one node to the next. This gives us a **solenostele** (Fig. 235, B, *b*), a tubular system with a central pith which meets the cortex at every node through the leaf gap. The layers of phloem, pericycle, and endodermis are uninterrupted inside as well as out. Some ferns, having achieved the solenostelic condition, maintain it to the end, others pass on to further elaboration.

An increase in the number of openings from pith to cortex produces a **dictyostele** (Fig. 235, C, *c*). In some ferns (e.g. *Dryopteris*)

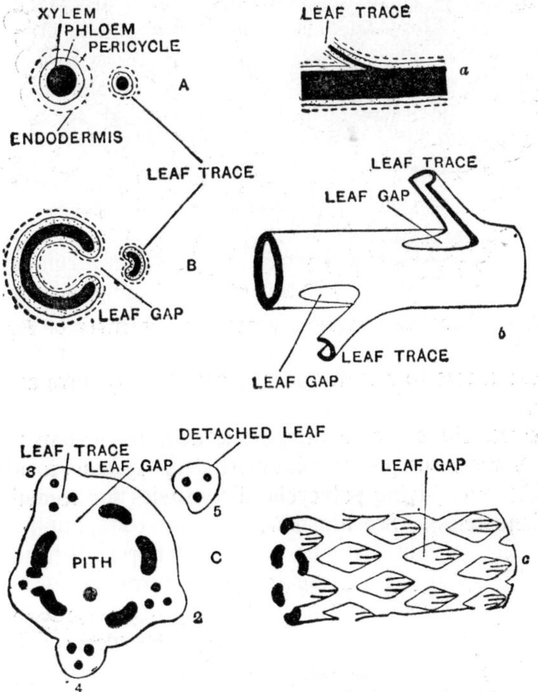

Fig. 235. DIAGRAMS TO ILLUSTRATE TYPES OF VASCULAR SYSTEM IN FERNS. A, *a*, Protostele; B, *b*, Solenostele; C, *c*, Dictyostele.

the dictyostele arises simply because the internodes are so short that several leaf gaps are visible in every T.S., but in other cases (e.g. *Pteridium*) there are **perforations**, openings in the stele which are independent of any leaf. In T.S. a dictyostele appears as separated **meristeles** (that is, partial steles); a meristele, because of its concentric structure and because it often has several widely-spaced protoxylem groups, is quite a different thing from a vascular bundle (Fig. 236). In many dictyostelic ferns there

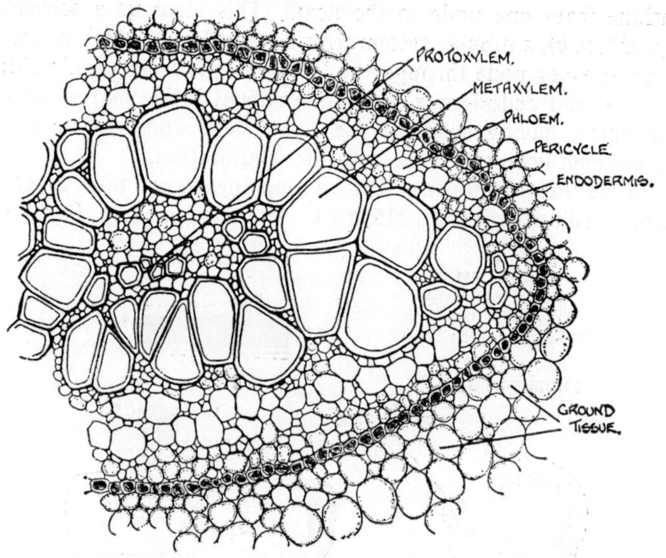

Fig. 236. Transverse section, portion of meristele of *Pteridium.*

are several traces to a leaf, and the petiole may have an elaborate structure.

The establishment of a dictyostele does not exhaust the possibilities. Some ferns produce internal stelar systems inside the pith of the first one, giving **polycyclic** dictyosteles (or sometimes polycyclic solenosteles). See Fig. 237.

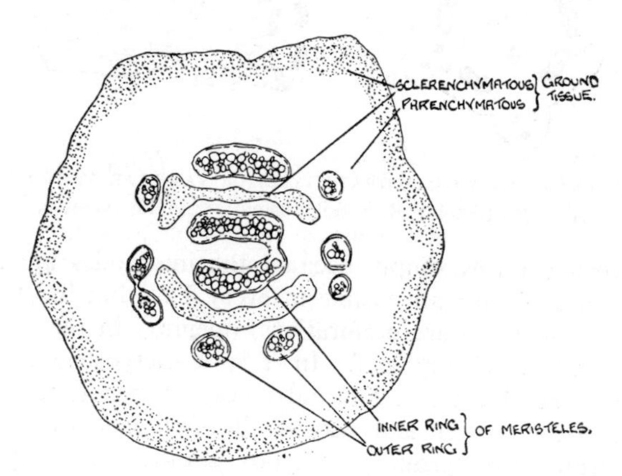

Fig. 237. Transverse section, rhizome of *Pteridium.*

Reproduction of the Fern Sporophyte

Some ferns, such as bracken, have active rhizome-systems, but in many others there is little power to spread vegetatively. Only a few species have more specialised means of vegetative propagation such as bulbils on the leaf. All ferns, however, produce **sporangia.**

The primitive pattern of fern sporangium is a globular structure as much as a millimetre in diameter, with a wall several cells thick, and a central cavity in which spore mother cells divide meiotically to form tetrads of spores. Such sporangia are found in a small number of living species. The output may be more than a thousand spores from each sporangium, and dehiscence (by a slit) involves no great structural refinement, the sporangial wall merely bending back a little as it dries. In the great majority of living ferns the sporangium is much smaller and more delicate, with a refined dehiscence-mechanism, and with a spore output of about sixty-four (in *Dryopteris* usually only forty-eight).

Fig. 238. PINNULE OF *Dryopteris* BEARING SORI.

Sporangia are produced in large numbers on the lower side of the leaf, or sometimes on its edge. A group of sporangia is called a **sorus** (Figs. 238, 239). The slight thickening of the leaf to which the stalks of the sporangia are attached is the **placenta**, and the membranous flap which often covers the sorus is the **indusium**. The classification of ferns is based primarily upon the arrangement of the sori and the shape of the indusia. In *Dryopteris* the sori are roughly circular, each covered by a kidney-shaped indusium, in *Pteridium* (bracken) there is a continuous sorus along the edge of the leaf-pinnule, and so on. In most ferns the leaves which produce sori are not otherwise very different from those which do not, but in some examples the fertile leaves (or sometimes parts of leaves) show a great reduction in the extent of the lamina.

In most sori the development of sporangia is spread over a period, so that sporangia of different ages stand side by side. In the development of the common type of sporangium the sequence of cell divisions is very regular (Fig. 240), giving a wall one cell in thickness, a **tapetum** or nutritive layer, and an **archesporium** or

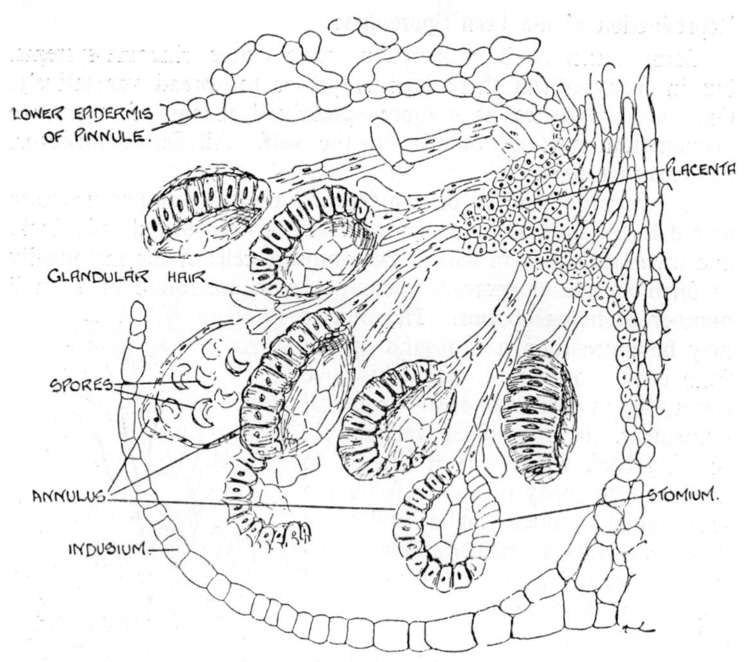

Fig. 239. VERTICAL SECTION, PINNULE OF *Dryopteris* THROUGH SORUS.

spore-producing tissue. The stalk commonly consists of two or three rows of cells. There is no vascular tissue in the sporangia themselves, though the placenta is vascularised. The head of the sporangium is encircled by a special row of cells, some of these cells having all their walls heavily thickened except the outer one, and forming the **annulus**, others forming a line of weakness at the **stomium** (Fig. 241).

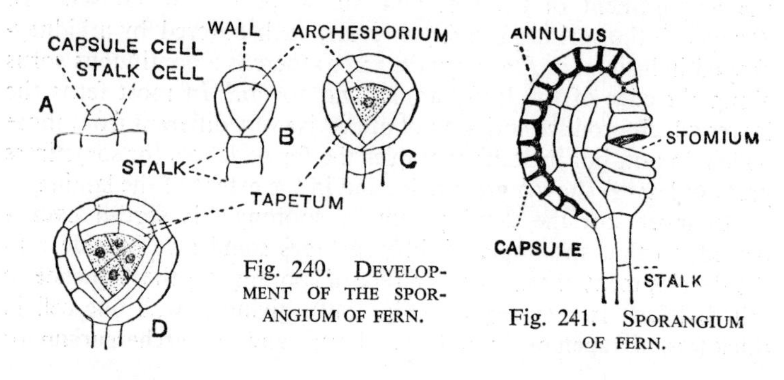

Fig. 240. DEVELOPMENT OF THE SPORANGIUM OF FERN.

Fig. 241. SPORANGIUM OF FERN.

The cells of the annulus play an important part in the liberation of the spores. As the sporangium ripens it tends to dry out. The annulus cells are full of water, but some of this evaporates through the outer wall, which is consequently drawn inwards. The cohesion of the water and its adhesion to the wall are strong enough (compare p. 188) to set up in the annulus a tension which ruptures the stomium, and indeed the body of the sporangium is torn almost in half across the middle, the upper portion being thrown right back like the hinged lid of a box. This movement is quite slow, but as drying continues a point is reached at which the water in the cells breaks suddenly, the upper part of the sporangium then returning to its original position with a jerk which throws out the spores to a

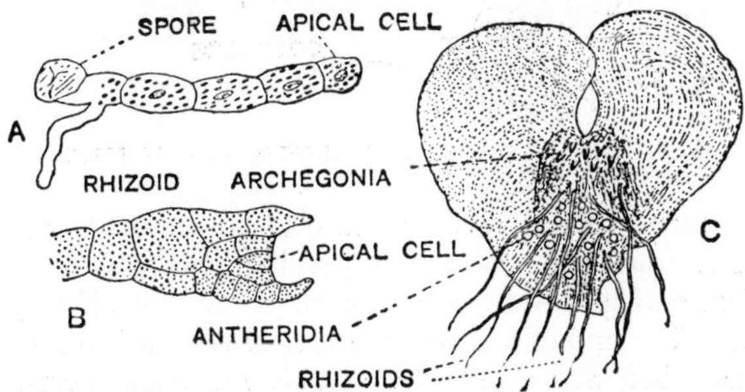

Fig. 242. GERMINATION OF SPORE AND DEVELOPMENT OF PROTHALLUS OF FERN.

distance of a centimetre or so, thereby setting them free in any passing current of air.

The Fern Gametophyte

The fern spore germinates on the ground to form a haploid gametophyte. Except that its rhizoids always remain unicellular this is rather like a moss protonema in the early stages of growth, and there are some ferns in which the gametophyte remains filamentous throughout life. More typically, however, the gametophyte grows (Fig. 242) into a heart-shaped **prothallus** about a centimetre across, having its apical meristem in the notch, and being attached to the soil by numerous rhizoids. The central region is several cells thick, and it is here that the rhizoids and reproductive organs occur. The prothallus is fully independent and autotrophic, but can flourish only in conditions of continuous dampness.

Archegonia and antheridia occur on the lower surface, between the prothallus and the soil. The archegonium is of simpler construction than that of most bryophytes (Fig. 243), with a shorter

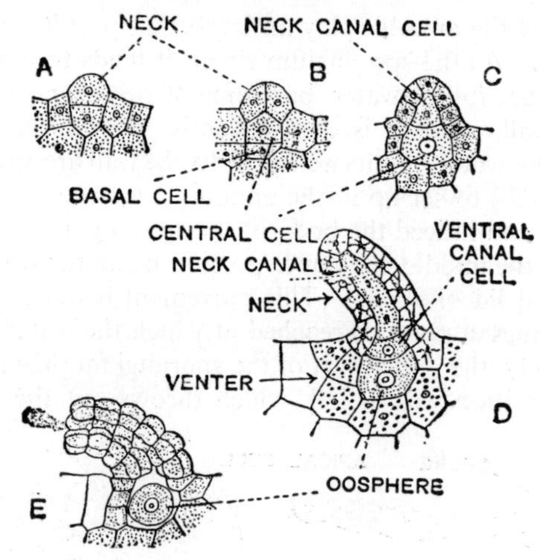

Fig. 243. DEVELOPMENT OF ARCHEGONIUM OF FERN.

neck and with its basal part sunk into the tissue of the prothallus. The antheridium (Fig. 244) is a peculiar spherical structure, in which funnel-shaped walls are formed, so cutting off ring-shaped wall cells. The antheridial wall consists of two such ring-cells, one above the other, and a cap cell. Inside are small spermatocytes,

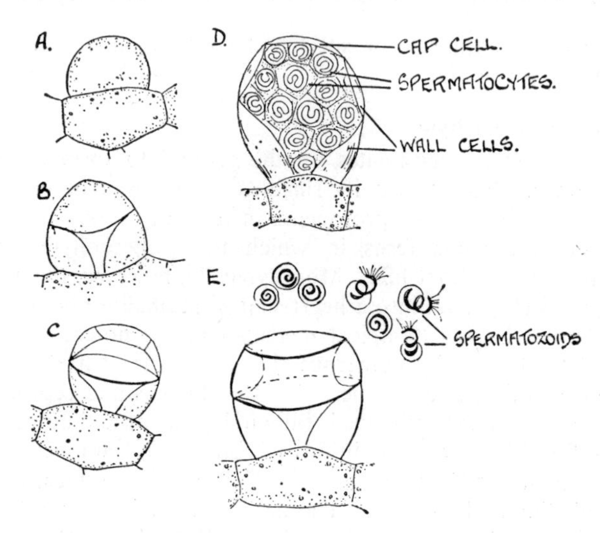

Fig. 244. DEVELOPMENT OF ANTHERIDIUM OF FERN.

each producing a male gamete or spermatozoid. The sperms differ from those of bryophytes in having numerous flagella instead of two.

Antheridia and archegonia are separated in space, the antheridia towards the base of the prothallus, the archegonia nearer the notch, and also in time, the antheridia appearing first. Although prothalli have organs of both sexes there is commonly cross-fertilisation between different individuals. The mechanics of fertilisation are similar to those seen in bryophytes, a sperm swimming to an archegonium, entering the mucilaginous drop which exudes from the archegonial neck, and ultimately reaching the ovum.

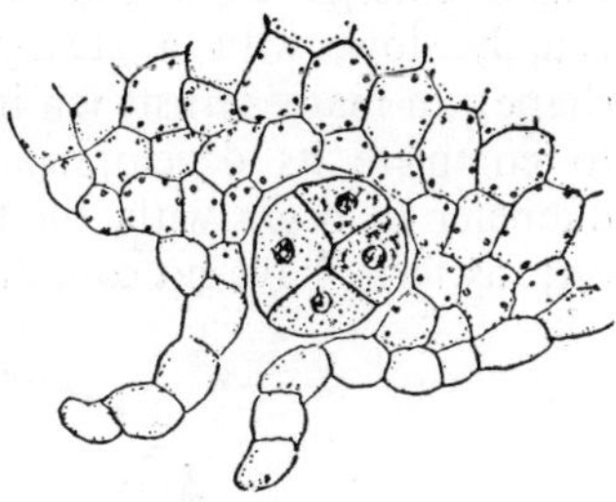

Fig. 245. FERN EMBRYO IN OCTANT STAGE.

The Fern Embryo

The fertilised ovum or zygote in most ferns divides by walls in three planes at right angles to give an octant stage similar to that in flowering plants (Fig. 245). In a very few ferns there is a preliminary division which cuts off a suspensor cell. Two octants facing in opposite directions form the apices of stem and root respectively (Fig. 246). The embryo also forms at an early stage a massive **foot**, which is an absorbing

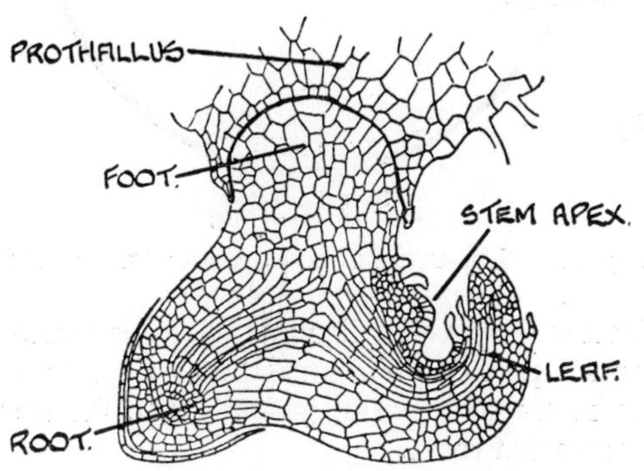

Fig. 246. YOUNG FERN-PLANT (SPOROPHYTE) ATTACHED TO PROTHALLUS.

organ, taking in nutrients from the adjoining prothallial tissue, and the first leaf, which is a smaller and simpler structure than the leaves of the adult sporophyte. Usually only one embryo matures on each prothallus, its first leaf or two characteristically projecting upwards through the apical notch of the prothallus. Once the young sporophyte is established, the prothallus in most ferns dies, though some have provision for the prothallus to spread vegetatively and perhaps form another embryo later.

The foot is a temporary organ, as is the first root. From a very early stage the young sporophyte becomes dependent on roots which emerge from the stem and leaf-bases. Development is usually slow, with a steady progression towards the adult leaf shape; in many ferns each individual leaf takes two or three years to complete its development. The stem is necessarily of small diameter to begin with, though it may become much stouter later on; as ferns have no cambium the original or basal piece of stem

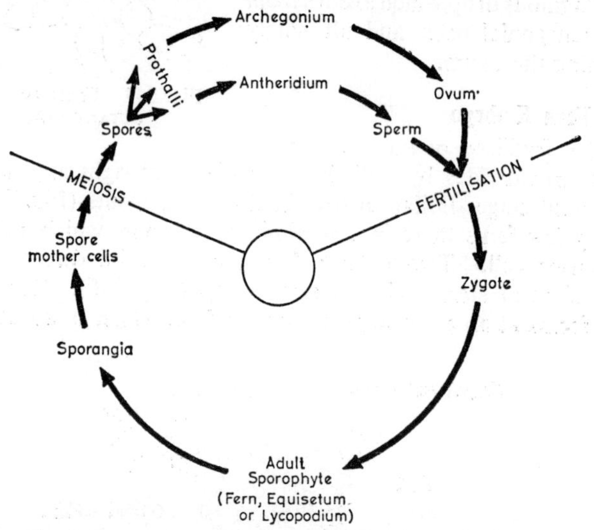

Fig. 247. LIFE-CYCLE IN HOMOSPOROUS PTERIDOPHYTES.

cannot, of course, increase in diameter once it is formed. Normally this first-formed part of the stem is lost. Even in a tree-fern the stem cannot be traced down to ground level, the trunk consisting largely of compacted roots.

Horsetails

The species of *Equisetum* are rhizomatous perennials. On aerial shoots and rhizomes alike the leaves are small scales, arranged in whorls, and those of each whorl fused into a tubular sheath (Fig. 248, A). Whorls of branches are formed, not quite in an axillary position but alternating with the leaves of the whorl, and these branches burst out through the lower part of the leaf-sheath. The stem has a large central cavity, and conspicuous cortical cavities as well. There is a ring of vascular bundles, the general plan being much more akin to that of dicotyledons than to that of ferns, though the xylem has no vessels and the phloem no companion cells.

The spore-producing organs are arranged in compact cones. In some species thc cones are carried on ordinary vegetative green shoots, but in others there are special reproductive shoots arising

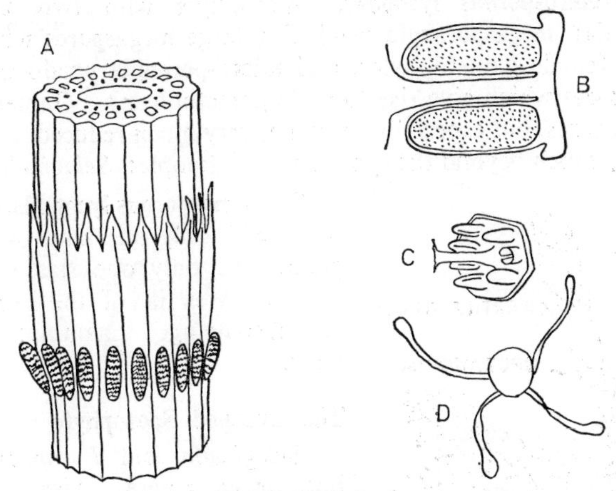

Fig. 248. *Equisetum.*

A, node with leaf-sheath and a whorl of young branches (shaded) just emerging; B, section of sporangiophore; C, sporangiophore with part of one sporangium cut away; D, spore with its elaters in the unrolled position.

directly from the rhizome, usually in the spring, and containing hardly any chlorophyll.

The cone consists of a mass of **sporangiophores**, each a peltate or umbrella-shaped structure with several rather massive sporangia hanging under its head. The spores are formed in tetrads by meiosis in the usual way. Each has an outer wall layer which splits spirally into four strips. These strips of spore wall act as **elaters**, coiling when dry, uncoiling when moist. (Compare liverworts, p. 454). Dehiscence of the sporangium is by a simple slit.

Although the spores all look alike, they produce two kinds of prothalli on germination. Some give large female prothalli, others yield much smaller male prothalli. The prothalli are lobed structures, very different in shape from the typical fern prothallus. Apart from the fact that one prothallus normally produces only one type of sex organ the reproductive history is very similar to that of ferns, and the embryology of the sporophyte includes the usual octant stage.

The Lycopods

The lycopods can be divided into two groups which differ sharply in their reproductive procedure. We shall consider the principal genus in each group:

1. Heterosporous lycopods. Sporophyte with two kinds of sporangia: **megasporangia** producing large **megaspores** which give rise to female gametophytes, and **microsporangia** producing small **microspores** which give rise to male gametophytes. Gametophytes of both sexes, but especially the male, very much reduced, and never growing much beyond the spore wall. Example: *Selaginella.*

2. Homosporous lycopods. Sporophyte with only one kind of sporangium, and only one size of spore, gametophytes all of the same type, and free-living. Example: *Lycopodium.*

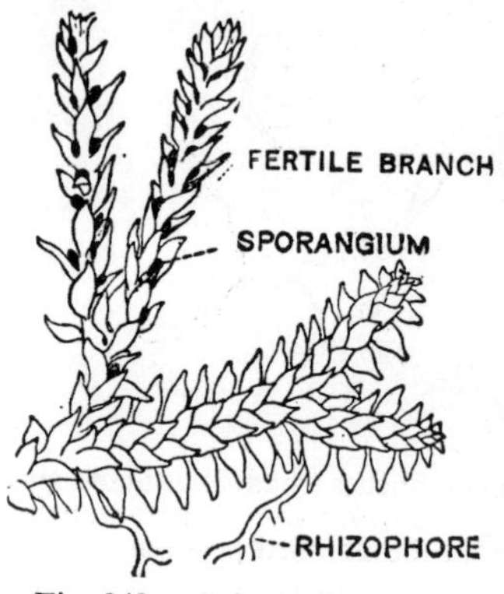

Fig. 249. *Selaginella helvetica.*

The Lycopod Sporophyte

Selaginella and *Lycopodium* are both large genera. Almost all the species have a creeping or trailing habit of growth. The plants root freely as they spread, though specialised rhizomes are rare. In many species roots arise directly from the stems, but some species of *Selaginella* root indirectly through the production of **rhizophores** (Fig. 249). A rhizophore is an organ intermediate in structure and function between stem and root; it is very root-like in appearance and behaviour but has no root cap and arises as a surface bulge. Rhizophores grow down to the soil and true roots emerge from them.

The leaves are always small and simple with an unbranched midrib. In *Selaginella* and other heterosporous forms, but not in *Lycopodium*, each leaf has a **ligule**, a little membranous flap seated in a pit on the upper surface of the leaf near the base. In most species of *Lycopodium*, and in a few species of *Selaginella*, the leaves are arranged in a regular spiral, but most *Selaginella* species, and a few of *Lycopodium*, have leaves in opposite pairs. *Selaginella* also very commonly shows a regular pattern of large and small leaves, the shoots being strongly dorsiventral. Some *Selaginella* species have lateral branch systems which are of limited growth and present an appearance strikingly like that of a fern frond.

The growth of organs is mostly by single apical cells similar to those of ferns. The arrangement of the tissues in the stem is also rather fern-like. In *Lycopodium* (Fig. 250) there is a cylindrical stele in which plate-like masses of xylem are buried in phloem. In *Selaginella* there are usually two or three meristeles (Fig. 251)

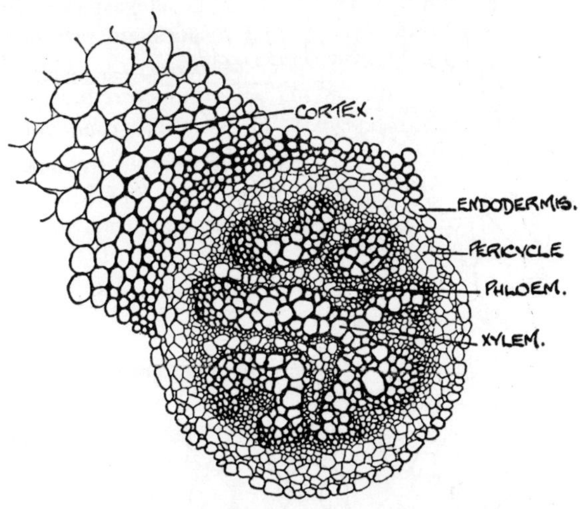

Fig. 250. *Lycopodium clavatum.* TRANSVERSE SECTION, STEM. Detailed drawing.

remarkable mainly for being suspended by cell-filaments or **trabeculae** in large air-spaces.

Reproduction of the Sporophyte

Each fertile leaf or sporophyll bears a single large sporangium, globular in *Selaginella*, kidney-shaped in *Lycopodium*, on its upper surface near the base (Figs. 252-254). In the heterosporous forms the sporangium is always between the stem and the ligule. In most species the sporophylls are closely grouped in distinctive cones.

Each sporangium has a construction similar to that seen in *Equisetum*, with a multicellular wall, a tapetum, and a mass of spore mother cells. Meiosis and the production of tetrads proceed normally in *Lycopodium* and in the microsporangia of *Selaginella*. In the megasporangium, however, there is abortion of many spore mother cells, and sometimes also of developing spores, so that the number of megaspores in the sporangium is variable and small. Perhaps the commonest situation is that in which one mother cell gives a full tetrad, so that the mature sporangium has four spores. There are, however, many *Selaginella* megasporangia with more than four spores, and some with less. It varies according to species, and

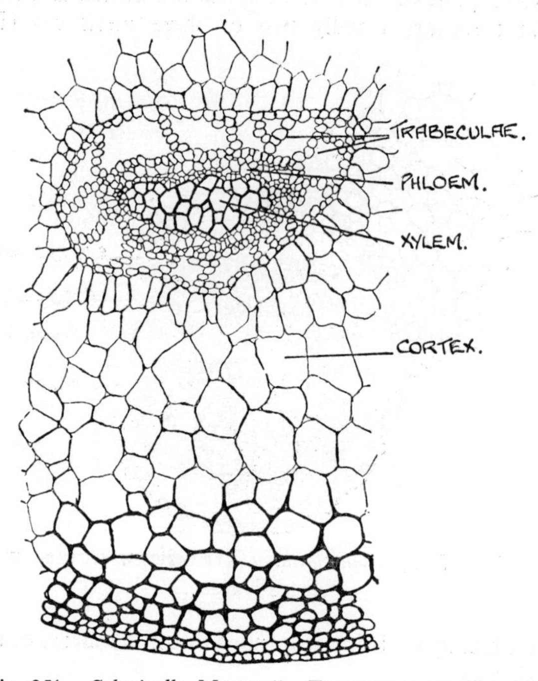

Fig. 251. *Selaginella Martensii.* TRANSVERSE SECTION, STEM.

according to nutrition. The megaspores are very large, and very rich in reserve materials, and their wall is often tremendously thick.

The Gametophytes

The prothalli of *Lycopodium* are small tuberous bodies with a fungal associate (compare p. 572); in some species they have green aerial lobes, in others they are completely subterranean and entirely nourished by the fungus. They have both archegonia and antheridia.

In *Selaginella* the female prothallus is a patch of tissue formed under the **triradiate ridge** which marks the side of the megaspore which was turned towards the centre of the tetrad. The spore wall cracks along the triradiate ridge, and the prothallus may protrude slightly, turn green, and even put out a rhizoid or two. It never

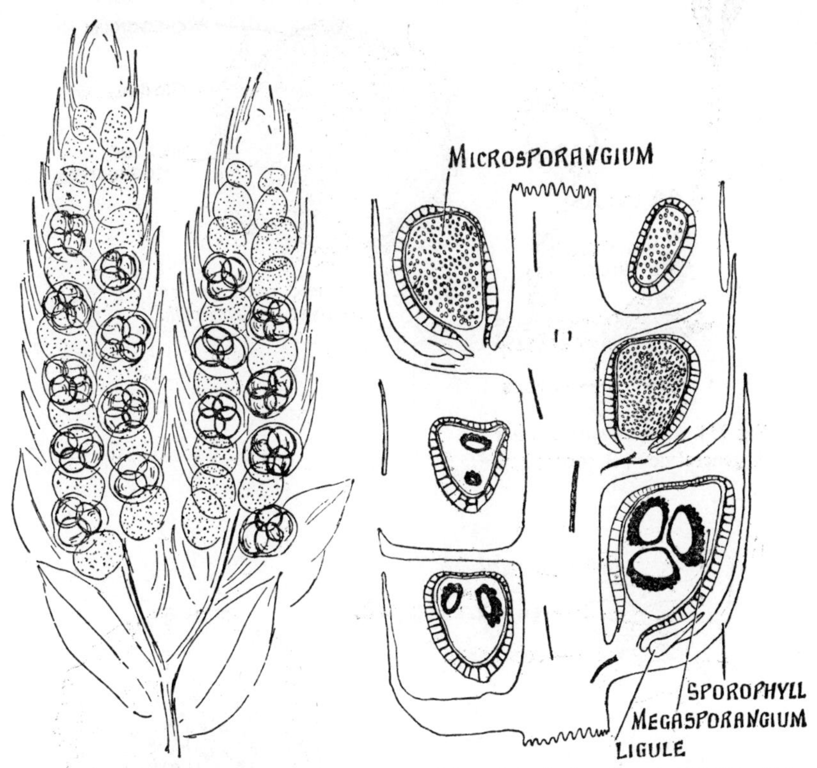

Fig. 252. *Selaginella:* FERTILE SHOOT SHOWING DISTRIBUTION OF MICRO- AND MEGASPORANGIA.

Fig. 253. *Selaginella*, LONGITUDINAL SECTION. CONE SHOWING MATURE MICRO- AND MEGASPORANGIA.

escapes from the spore wall, however. The archegonia, of which there are usually several, are similar to those of ferns, but with even less development of the neck (Figs. 255, 256).

The male gametophyte of *Selaginella* (Fig. 257) is also completely enclosed within the spore. Usually a single small and apparently quite functionless **prothallial cell** is cut off against the spore wall and then the whole content of the microspore organises into a single

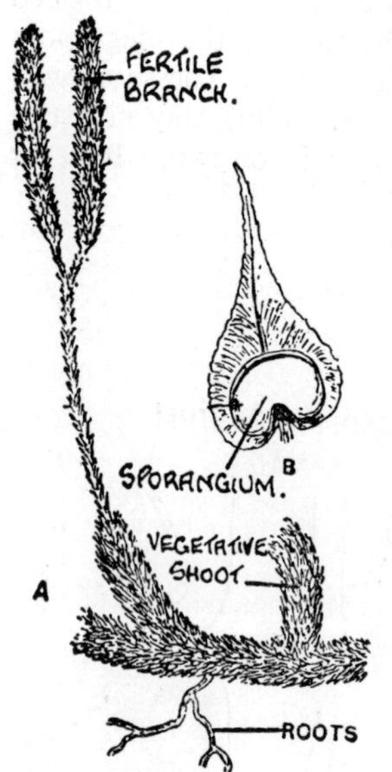

Fig. 254. *Lycopodium clavatum.*
A, general view; B, sporophyll.

Fig. 255. Section through female gametophyte of *Selaginella.*

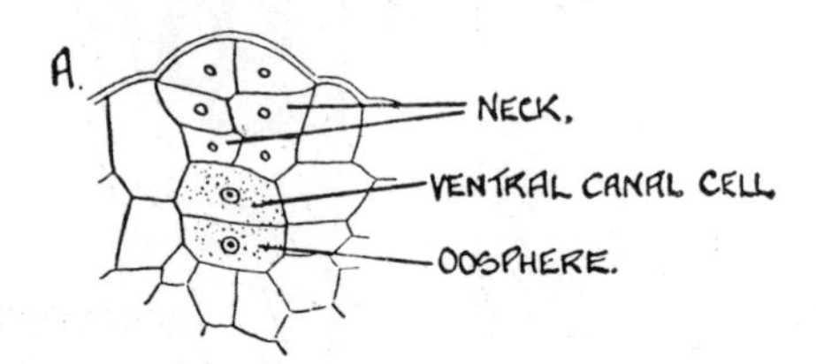

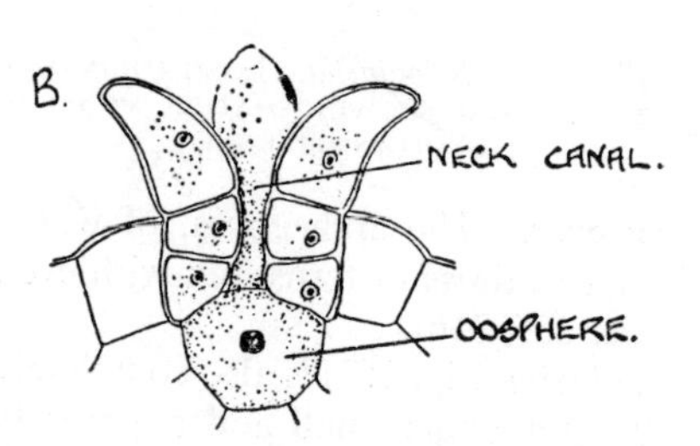

Fig. 256. Longitudinal section, archegonium of *Selaginella.*
A, younger stage; B, older stage.

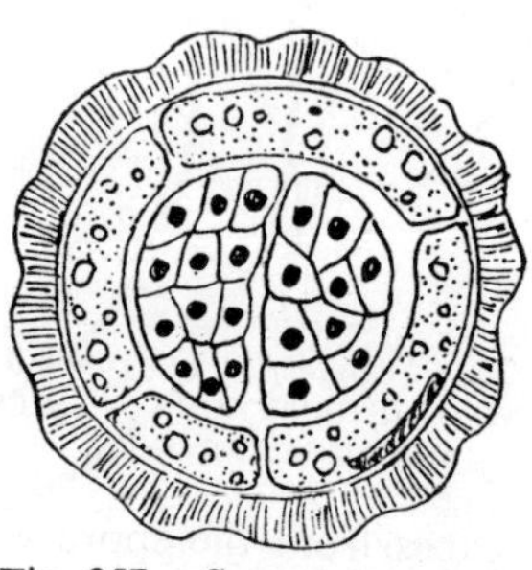

Fig. 257. Section through male gametophyte of *Selaginella.*
Note prothallial cell at lower right.

antheridium, usually with eight wall cells and an inner mass of sperm; each spermatozoid has two flagella.

It is usual for the development of the gametophytes in *Selaginella* to begin before the spores are liberated from the sporangia, but fertilisation usually takes place upon the ground, where great numbers of microspores (or male gametophytes) fall among a much smaller number of female gametophytes.

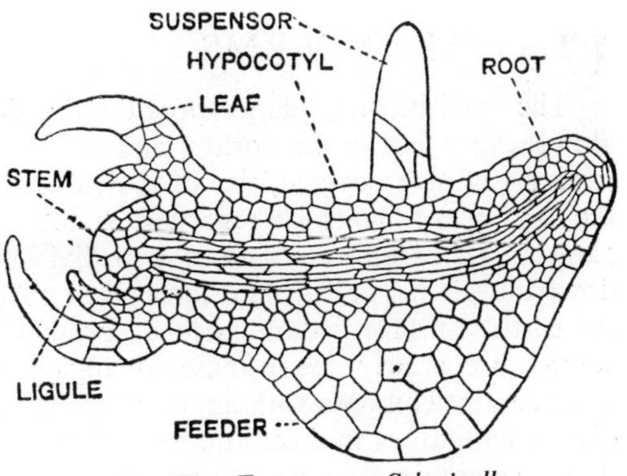

Fig. 258. EMBRYO OF *Selaginella*. (Longitudinal section.)

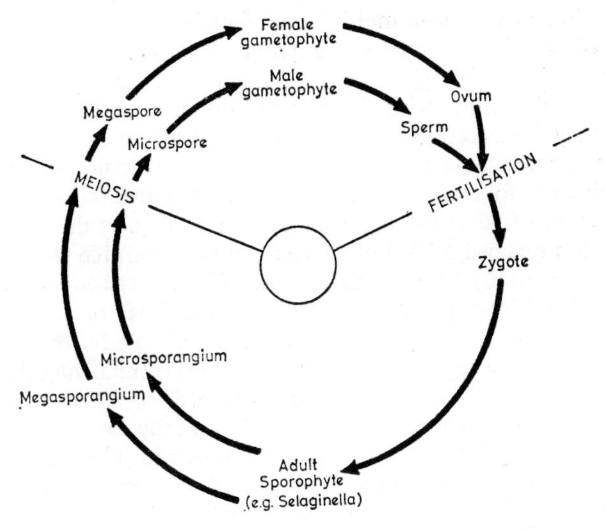

Fig. 259. LIFE-CYCLE IN HETEROSPOROUS LYCOPODS.

Embryology

Except that there is always a suspensor (Fig. 258) the course of development of the young sporophyte does not significantly differ from that of ferns.

17 GYMNOSPERMS

The seed-bearing plants provide the dominant vegetation of almost every part of the world's land area, and if success is reckoned in terms of area covered, size of individuals, and variety of species, the seed plants must be regarded as the most successful of land plants. The group consists of two divisions, the angiosperms or flowering plants, and the gymnosperms. Although a large part of the earth's surface is dominated by gymnosperm trees, the gymnosperms are clearly subordinate to angiosperms in some respects. They cannot compare with angiosperms for versatility in occupying diverse habitats or in sheer numbers of species, and it seems probable that the gymnosperms are well past their zenith, whereas angiosperms are still vigorously evolving.

As has been pointed out in Chapter 14, the various major divisions of the plant kingdom each represent a certain general level of development in a continuous evolutionary sequence. Gymnosperms include all those land plants with a dominant sporophyte generation and a large multicellular female gametophyte which is retained within the megasporangium or ovule. Although these features distinguish gymnosperms from other groups, there are clear relationships with both pteridophytes and angiosperms. With very few exceptions, the female gametophyte of gymnosperms produces archegonia which, though simpler in structure, show a clear resemblance to those of pteridophytes. On the other hand, the production of seeds by gymnosperms shows that in this respect the group has reached a level of development comparable with (though not equivalent to) that of angiosperms. There are two ways in which the seeds of most gymnosperms differ from those of angiosperms. At fertilisation there is, in gymnosperms, a simple fusion of a male nucleus with the egg nucleus. There is no accompanying fusion of other nuclei such as occurs in angiosperms (p. 373). Thus the nutritive tissue contained in a gymnosperm seed is wholly derived from the female gametophyte and is not homologous with the endosperm of an angiosperm, to which both male and female parents contribute.

The second difference between the seeds of most gymnosperms and those of angiosperms is the way in which they are borne. This

---

PLATE 15

Above: Collecting equipment including a portable wire-grid press and a vasculum, both by Flatters and Garnett of Manchester.

Below: Two herbarium sheets from the Manchester Museum, one of the principal British collections. Note the packet of fragments on one of the sheets.

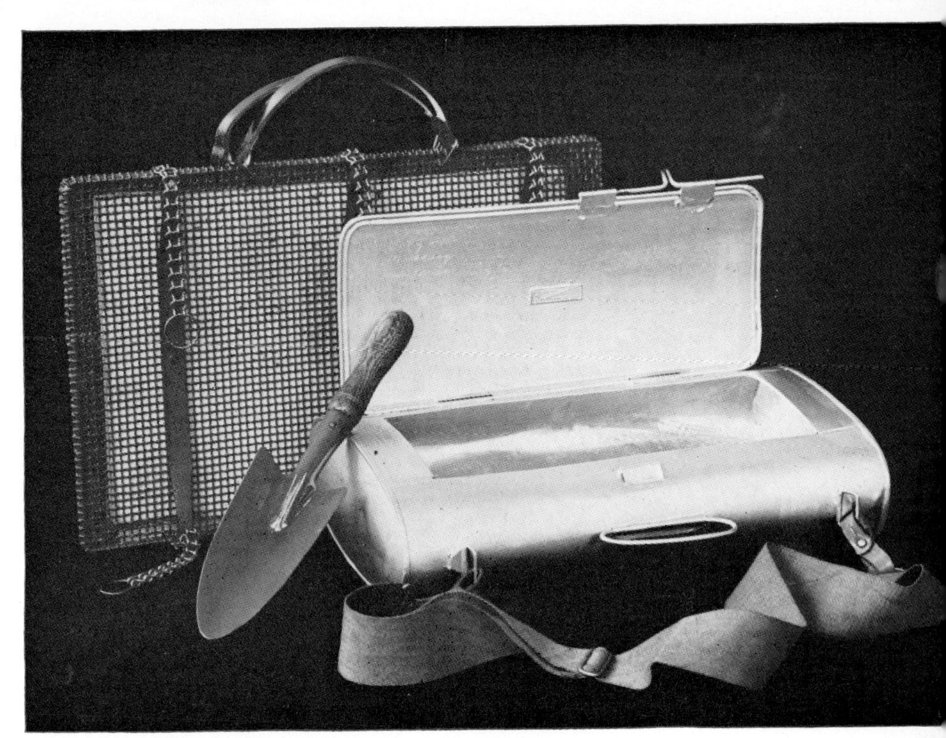

H. Sudre — BATOTHECA EUROPÆA — Fasc. I. 1903
16 – RUBUS GODRONI
FRANCE.

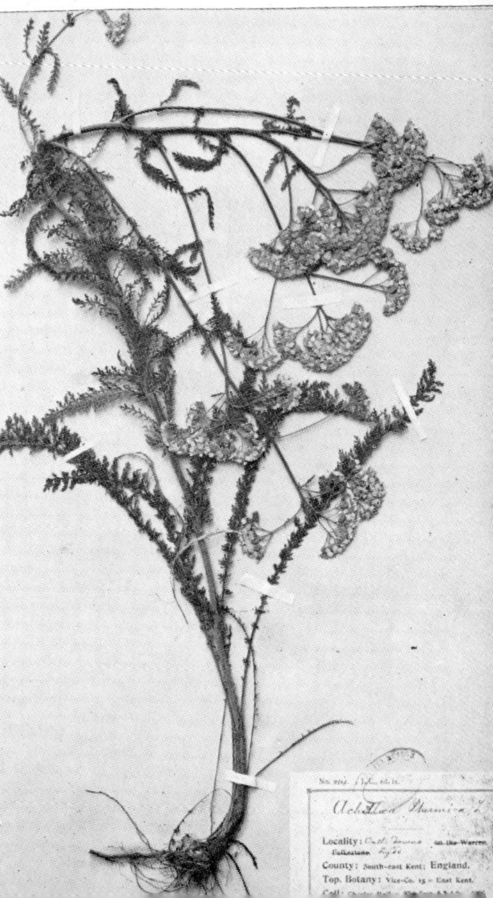
Locality:
County: South-east Kent; England.
Top. Botany: Vice-Co. 15 = East Kent.

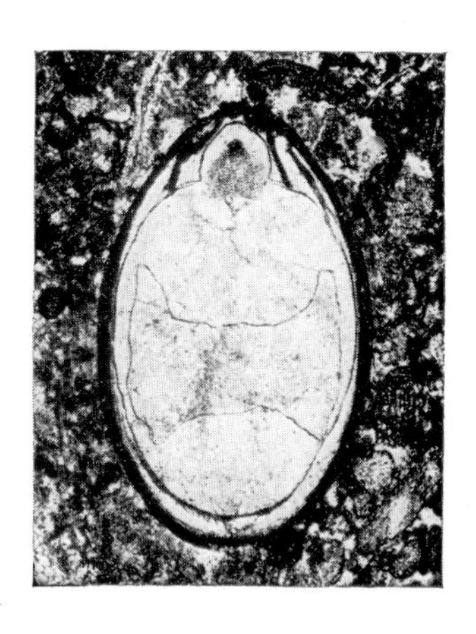

All Photos: Flatters and Garnett.

PLATE 16

Above left: LONGITUDINAL SECTION OF THE FOSSIL SEED *Lagenostoma ovoides*. Although it is more than 200 million years old the essentials of its structure are clearly preserved. *Above right:* FOSSIL IMPRESSION OF PART OF A FROND OF *Alethopteris lonchitica*, OF ALMOST THE SAME AGE. This plant was a pteridosperm, with fern-like foliage but reproducing by seed.

Below: THE MOSS *Funaria hygrometrica*, BEARING CAPSULES.

is implicit in the names themselves, gymnosperms meaning "naked seeds" and angiosperms "seeds in receptacles". This difference can be illustrated by reference to two familiar examples. If the scales of a large pine cone which is approaching maturity are prised apart, each one will be found to have two seeds developing on its upper surface. The exposure of these seeds does not involve cutting through any solid tissue, simply the separating of scales which are in close proximity with one another. In this sense, the seeds may be said to be naked. In contrast the seeds of most angiosperms are completely enclosed by maternal tissues. The garden pea, for example, has its seeds enclosed in pods which can be opened only by rupture of the tissues.

The "nakedness" of the gymnosperms is shown even more clearly at the time of pollination. The position of the ovules is such that pollen grains can gain direct access to them. In the young pine cone, for example, the scales with ovules on their upper surfaces are spread apart at the time when the ovules are ready for pollination (see p. 485). In angiosperms, however, pollen which is destined to carry out fertilisation is deposited on a stigma which may be some distance from the ovule, and the production of a long pollen-tube is necessary before fertilisation can occur.

Apart from these differences in the reproductive process, there are characteristic differences in cell structure and in construction of the tissues between angiosperms and gymnosperms (see Chapters 2 and 4).

The following four series of gymnosperms have living representatives:

1. *Conifers.* Shrubs and trees, many of which reach a considerable size. Frequently the dominant vegetation in temperate and subarctic regions. Of great importance as sources of timber.

2. *Cycads.* Perennials with a stout stem surmounted by a cluster of pinnate leaves. Occur sporadically in tropical and subtropical regions.

3. *Ginkgo.* A single tree species, native to China.

4. *Gnetales.* Three somewhat bizarre genera showing no close relationship either to other gymnosperms or to one another.

CONIFERS

Most readers will be familiar with a range of conifers, or at least with their products. Only three are native to Britain, namely the Scots pine (*Pinus sylvestris*), juniper (*Juniperus communis*), and yew (*Taxus baccata*); but many other species have been planted as timber trees or as ornamentals and are now well established. *Pinus sylvestris* is the source of the timber known commercially as European redwood or red deal, used extensively in carpentry. Whitewood furniture is made from *Picea abies* (Norway spruce), young trees of which are also sold as Christmas trees. *Thuja plicata*, the Western red cedar, yields a very durable timber which is resistant to most wood-rotting organisms and is therefore frequently used for timber buildings.

Among the features common to all these trees is the production of leaves with a small surface area in relation to their volume. All *Pinus* spp., for example, have long needle-like leaves; *Picea* spp. have leaves which are flattened but very narrow, and in *Thuja plicata* the leaves are small green scales lying close against the stem which bears them. Leaves with this relationship between surface and volume are commonly associated with habitats where water is scarce, the small surface area limiting the rate at which water can be lost by transpiration. It is clear, however, that leaf morphology among conifers cannot be simply explained as an adaptation to this single factor. Although many conifers do grow in dry habitats there are many others which do not. *Taxodium distichum* (swamp cypress), for example, a native of eastern North America, regularly grows in or near water, yet its leaves are as small as those of other conifers. Among the various factors which may complicate the relationship between structure and habitat in conifers are:

(*a*) conifer leaves, though individually small, are usually very numerous, and the total area over which transpiration can occur is not small;

(*b*) conifers have a type of xylem which offers relatively high resistance to the upward flow of water in the stem;

(*c*) nearly all conifers are evergreens, so that their leaves are subject to specially critical conditions in winter.

Relationships between structure and habitat are discussed further in Chapter 21.

There are few generalisations which can be made about the vegetative morphology of conifers. They show great diversity in size, shape, pattern of branching, and so on. As regards their anatomy also, although some useful generalisations can be made about cell structure (p. 36) and cell arrangement (p. 97), there is variation in detail from species to species. This variation applies to many of the tissues, but has been studied in particular detail in the secondary xylem, as an aid to the identification of timbers. With a little experience it is possible to distinguish between most of the common coniferous timbers by microscopic examination.

Reproduction

The following account refers to *Pinus sylvestris* which is common enough for readers to be able to verify much of the description by direct observation. In general features the account applies to many other conifers also, but details of the reproductive process are peculiar to individual species or groups of species.

The reproductive structure is called a **cone** or **strobilus**. Pine trees, like most conifers, are monoecious, having on each tree separate male and female cones. These produce microspores and

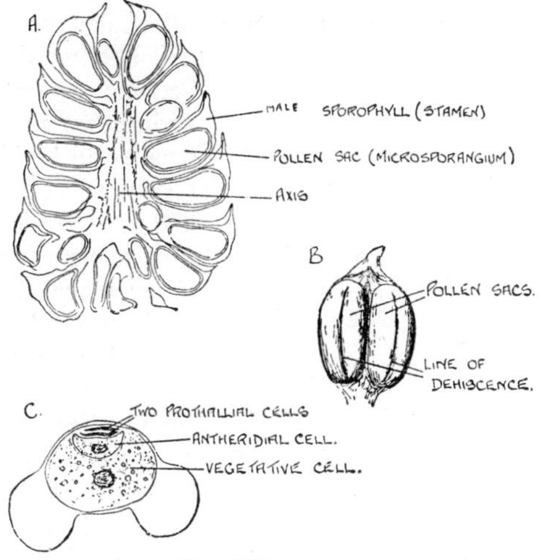

Fig. 260. *Pinus.*
A, L.S. of male cone; B, lower surface of microsporophyll; C, mature pollen grain.

megaspores respectively, which are homologous with the structures in *Selaginella* (p. 477) known by the same names.

Development of Male Cones

Male cones are initiated towards the end of the growing season at the base of terminal buds. Only when these buds expand in the following spring do the male cones become obvious. It can then be seen that a single bud may have a cluster of perhaps ten or more male cones, each in the axil of a bud scale. The cones enlarge during the spring, each one becoming an egg-shaped structure about $\frac{1}{4}$ in. long. A cone has a central axis from which project numerous scales, the outermost parts of which fit together to form the surface of the cone (Fig. 260, A). Each scale is a **microsporophyll** and is equivalent to a stamen in an angiosperm flower. It has two pollen sacs or **microsporangia** on its lower surface (Fig. 260, B), in each of which develop many pollen mother cells which undergo meiosis. The products of meiosis are the **microspores**. They represent the beginning of the male gametophyte, which in gymnosperms is very limited in size. The single haploid nucleus of the microspore first divides into two, one of the nuclei passing to the side of the cell where it becomes walled off and degenerates. Then the same process is repeated. The two small cells which degenerate are the **prothallial cells**, so called because they appear to be the rudiments of a multicellular prothallus. The surviving nucleus then divides once more. The two resulting nuclei become separated by a wall giving two unequal cells, a smaller antheridial cell and a larger vegetative cell (Fig. 260, C). While these successive nuclear divisions have taken place, the microspore wall has developed a double-layered structure. The two layers become separate from each other at two places, and distention of the outer layer produces two inflated air sacs (Fig. 260, C) which are conspicuous features of the mature pollen grain.

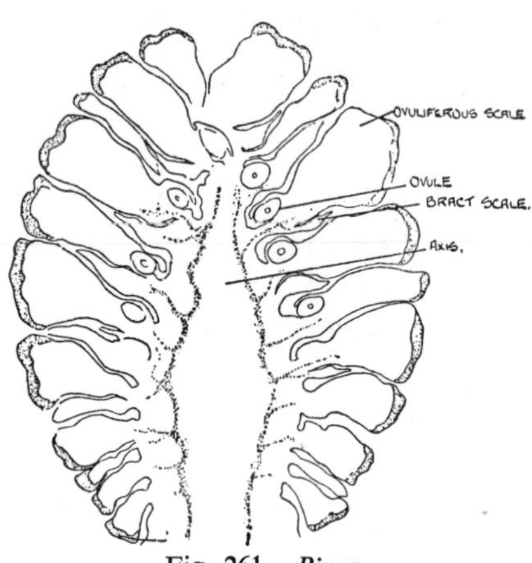

Fig. 261. *Pinus.*
L.S. of young female cone.

When pollen dehiscence approaches, the cone scales separate and each pollen-sac splits longitudinally. Pollen grains are shed between the scales, and the extra surface provided by the air sacs assists dispersal by wind.

Development of Female Cones

Unlike the male cone, which completes its development from initiation to pollen dehiscence within a year, the female cone undergoes a course of development extending over three years. During the first year it grows to about the size and shape of a large pea. It is attached to a short stalk growing in the axil of a scale leaf not far behind a shoot apex. A longitudinal section of the cone at this stage gives the appearance shown in Fig. 261. As in the male cone there is a central axis bearing a number of closely packed scales. Some of these (the **ovuliferous** scales) produce ovules on their upper surfaces. Below each ovuliferous scale is a smaller **bract** scale. It seems probable that each bract scale is a modified leaf and the ovuliferous scale is a shoot in its axil, though the homologies of the parts of the female cone have been a subject of prolonged disagreement.

During the first year of the conc's cxistence, each ovuliferous scale develops two ovules side by side. They first appear as swellings on the upper surface, each of which differentiates into a parenchymatous **nucellus** invested by a single integument except for an aperture, the **micropyle**, at the end facing the cone axis (Fig. 262). The female gametophyte is derived from a cell in the nucellus situated just below the surface. This megaspore mother cell undergoes meiosis, with the products arranged as a row of four megaspores in line with the micropyle. Of these, only the spore furthest from the micropyle continues to develop; the others degenerate. The surviving megaspore grows into a substantial multicellular female gametophyte completely enclosed within the nucellus. This gametophyte is homologous with the prothallus of a pteridophyte, though it is never released from the parent sporophyte. It is, nevertheless, often referred to as the female prothallus.

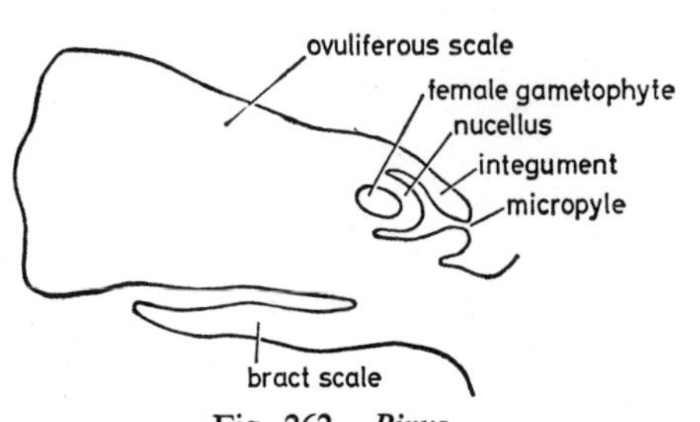

Fig. 262. *Pinus.*
L.S. of part of young female cone, passing through ovule.

At this stage, or somewhat earlier, pollination occurs. *Pinus sylvestris* sheds its pollen in early summer, at which time the first-year female cones have their scales gaping apart from one another. Pollen grains can therefore pass between the scales and reach the inner recesses of the cone. At this time also, each ovule secretes a drop of fluid through the micropyle, in which pollen grains are likely to settle. This "pollination drop" later dries up or is absorbed by the tissues, and as the meniscus retreats along the micropyle the pollen grains are drawn towards the nucellus. Those pollen grains which reach the nucellus have a chance of carrying out fertilisation, but this process does not take place until the following summer. An interval of several months between pollination and fertilisation is not uncommon in conifers, but the full year shown by *Pinus* is among the longest periods. After pollination, the cone scales close up and do not move apart again until two years later when the seeds are ready to be shed.

In the period immediately after pollination, the pollen grain sends out a pollen-tube into the nucellus, but at the time it does not penetrate far. Note that here we are dealing with a process which has no parallel in the pteridophytes or bryophytes, where motile gametes propel themselves all the way to the female gamete. In *Pinus* the female gamete remains surrounded by maternal tissues through which a passage is forced by the intrusive growth of the pollen-tube.

In the winter following pollination, the short pollen-tube does not lengthen. Growth is resumed the following spring and the tip

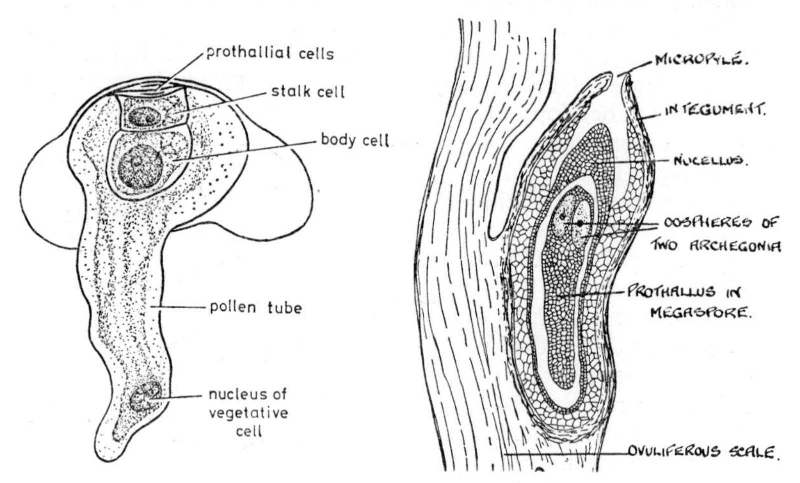

Fig. 263. *Pinus*. Germinating pollen grain.

Fig. 264. *Pinus*. L.S. of mature ovule. Oospheres = egg cells.

of the pollen-tube advances towards the female prothallus. The nucleus of the vegetative cell is situated near the tip of the pollen-tube. The antheridial cell divides into two, giving a **stalk** cell and a **body** cell (Fig. 263). The function of the stalk cell is unknown: it takes its name from its appearance of a stalk attaching the body cell to the side of the pollen grain. The nucleus of the body cell divides again and the two products, which do not become walled off, are the male gametes. They pass down the pollen-tube and join the vegetative nucleus at the tip.

Meanwhile, during the second year of the female cone's existence, two or three archegonia develop at the micropylar end of each female prothallus (Fig. 264). They do not protrude from the surface and are simple in structure, with a prominent egg cell enclosed in a single-layered venter and a barely recognisable neck (Fig. 265). Both the egg cell and the zygote derived from it are extremely large by comparison with the corresponding cells in angiosperms. This is so throughout the gymnosperms. In *Pinus* the oval egg cell is frequently ½ mm. or more in length, which is about ten times the diameter of even a large angiosperm egg cell. In cycads (p. 489) the egg cells reach even greater sizes, a length of 2 mm. being not uncommon.

When the archegonia are fully formed, the ovule is ready to be fertilised. This is accomplished by the tip of the pollen-tube reaching the neck of an archegonium, allowing one of the male

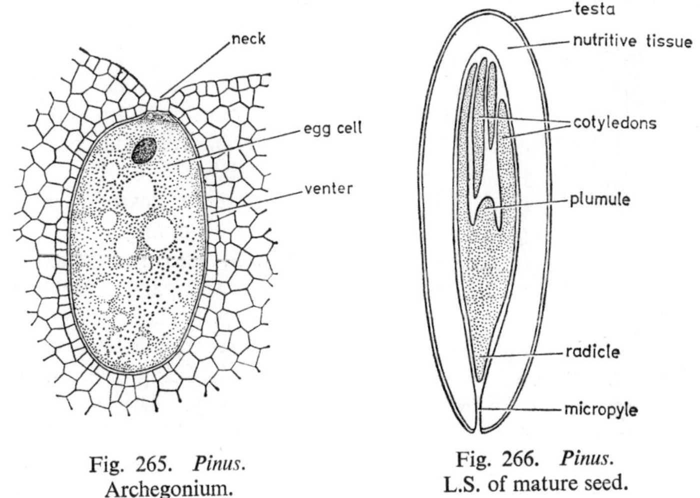

Fig. 265. *Pinus*.
Archegonium.

Fig. 266. *Pinus*.
L.S. of mature seed.

gamete nuclei to enter and fuse with the egg cell. Although more than one archegonium may be fertilised, only one normally gives rise to an embryo.

Development of an embryo from the fertilised egg is curiously indirect. The diploid nucleus divides into four nuclei, each of which gives rise to a short series of cells. The terminal cell in each series is a potential embryo, and several embryos may begin to develop, but eventually all except one of them abort. Meanwhile, tissues which were surrounding the fertilised egg have developed into other parts of the seed. Fig. 266 shows a longitudinal section of a mature seed. The embryo lies centrally with the radicle towards the micropyle and a cluster of linear cotyledons at the other end, encircling the small plumule. The possession of several cotyledons is common among conifers, in contrast to other gymnosperms and to angiosperms, where one or two is more usual. Surrounding the embryo is a layer of nutritive tissue derived by enlargement from the rest of the female gametophyte. The testa is derived from the integument of the ovule, and at maturity of the seed there is little or no trace of the nucellus. In addition to the tissues shown in Fig. 266, the surface layer of the ovuliferous scale remains attached to the testa, and when the seeds are shed, each one is equipped with a papery wing formed from this layer (Fig. 267), which assists dispersal. The seed of *P. sylvestris*, excluding the wing, is only about 4 mm. long, and consequently difficult to dissect. Other species of *Pinus* have larger seeds with the same general structure. *P. pinea*, for example, a native of southern Europe, has seeds ½ in. long which are the pignola nuts or pignons of commerce. They are sold for human consumption, and also provide useful material for the botanical examination of pine seeds.

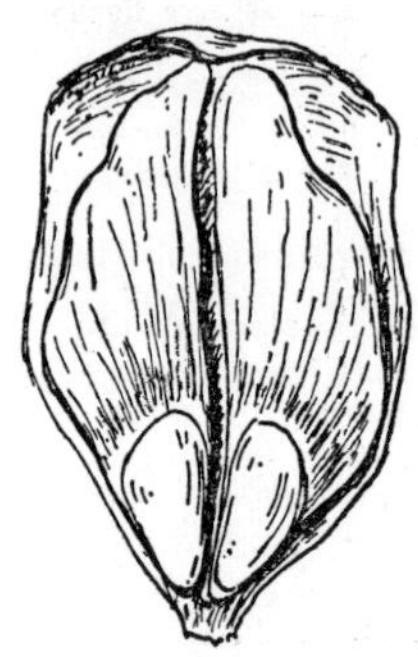

Fig. 267. *Pinus*. Ovuliferous scale bearing two-winged seeds.

The movement of the scales of a mature pine cone in response to changes of atmospheric humidity is well known. When the air is dry the scales move apart, and when it is humid they close up. These movements occur in third-year cones while still on the tree, and result in seeds being shed mainly when the weather is dry. Dry weather is often windy also, so the seeds are given a good chance of being blown well away from the parent tree. This both helps to increase the range of distribution and reduces the likelihood of the seedling being overshadowed by the parent.

"Coneless Conifers"

Some genera which are customarily included among the conifers in fact have no structure recognisable as a female cone. *Taxus*, for example, bears its seeds singly, each one invested in a fleshy red aril (p. 370). There are no structures resembling female cones, and very little direct evidence which might suggest that *Taxus* was descended from cone-bearing ancestors. For this reason some authors consider that *Taxus* and its allies should be regarded as an order separate from the conifers.

Despite the lack of resemblance between the seed of *Taxus* and the cone of *Pinus*, the ovules of the two genera have comparable structure. Before fertilisation the ovule of *Taxus* has a recognisable nucellus, integument, and micropyle. After fertilisation the fleshy aril grows up from the base of the integument and almost completely encloses the hard seed inside. Thus, while the winged seeds of *Pinus* are dispersed by wind, the seeds of *Taxus* are dispersed by birds which are attracted by the red arils. They digest the flesh of the arils but reject the seeds.

CYCADS

The cycads are a small group of plants with representatives in several tropical or sub-tropical regions, notably central America, South Africa, and Australia. Although clearly gymnosperms, they are of special interest because of their various resemblances to pteridophytes, which indicate that they are among the more primitive gymnosperms. The economic importance of the group is negligible, though the pith of some species stores large quantities of starch which is sometimes collected to make certain types of sago and arrowroot.

The larger cycads are small trees with a stout, usually unbranched trunk and a crown of pinnate leaves. Their general habit is not unlike that of tree-ferns (p. 462), and like them they have trunks containing a large proportion of soft tissues. There is a wide central pith and an outer layer of old leaf-bases, but there is also a considerable amount of secondary xylem. The smaller cycads also have a single erect stem, but this is underground and the crown of leaves is produced at ground level. The habit of these cycads is comparable with that of the fern *Dryopteris*.

Cycad leaves show two features which are common among ferns, namely, their pinnate shape and the way they are, in some species, rolled lengthwise when young.

All genera of cycads produce pollen in cones, and all except one have female cones also. The exception is *Cycas*, from which the group takes its name, and in which the megasporophylls form a loose cluster of irregular shape. Fig. 268 shows a single megasporophyll of *C. revoluta*, which is distinctly leaf-like in some respects. Its distal end has a pinnate lamina which is purely vegetative, and the ovules are borne laterally towards the base. It is not difficult to imagine the gradual evolution of this sporophyll from a pinnate fern-frond bearing sporangia at its margin. Further reduction of the vegetative lamina and in the number of ovules, accompanied by aggregation of sporophylls around a common axis would produce a recognisable cone. The megasporophylls of the several species of *Cycas* show various stages in this probable evolutionary sequence.

The development of the male gametophyte shows yet another affinity with pteridophytes. Nuclear divisions in the germinating pollen grain resemble those in *Pinus*, but the two nuclei formed by division of the body cell nucleus become walled off instead of remaining as free nuclei. Each of the two cells then grows into a large globular spermatozoid with a spiral band of cilia (Fig. 269). Although these spermatozoids are strikingly different in size and shape from those of pteridophytes and bryophytes, the fact that they are produced at all suggests a connection with plants dependent on external water for fertilisation to occur. The amount of swimming which a cycad spermatozoid has to do is very limited. In a mature ovule there is a space, the **archegonial chamber**, between

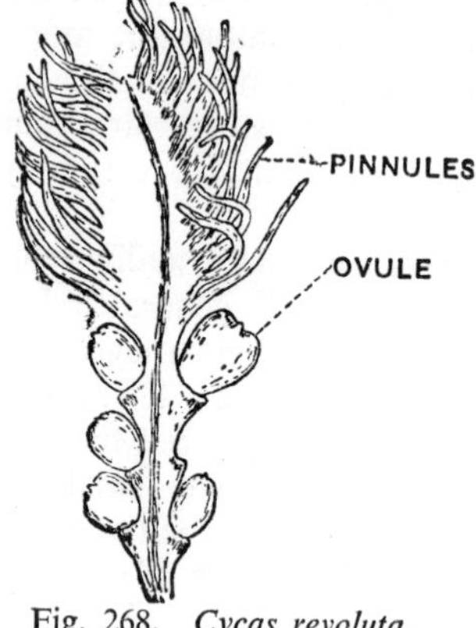

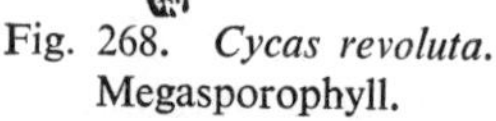
Fig. 268. *Cycas revoluta*. Megasporophyll.

Fig. 269. *Cycas*. Spermatozoid.

the female gametophyte and the nucellus (Fig. 270). Spermatozoids must reach this chamber if they are to fertilise. When the pollen grain germinates on the far side of the nucellus, it puts out a pollen-tube into the nucellus, but the spermatozoids do not pass into the tube as in angiosperms. The tube does not even grow towards the archegonia. It often grows laterally as though avoiding the female gametophyte. During the period of pollen-tube growth, and perhaps as a result of enzymes secreted by many tubes, the part of the nucellus directly above the archegonia is digested away, giving access from the micropyle to the archegonial chamber. At this stage the basal end of the pollen-tube, in which the spermatozoids have remained, swells and finally bursts, releasing its liquid contents and the spermatozoids themselves, which have to swim only a short distance to the necks of the archegonia. Thus although the pollen-tube may be indirectly concerned with bringing the male and female gametes together, it is not, as in angiosperms and conifers, the actual vehicle for this process.

GINKGO

Ginkgo biloba, the maidenhair tree, is the sole remaining species of an ancient lineage. Though a native of the Far East, it thrives elsewhere and may be found in many gardens. Its fan-shaped leaves with a deep central cleft are very distinctive.

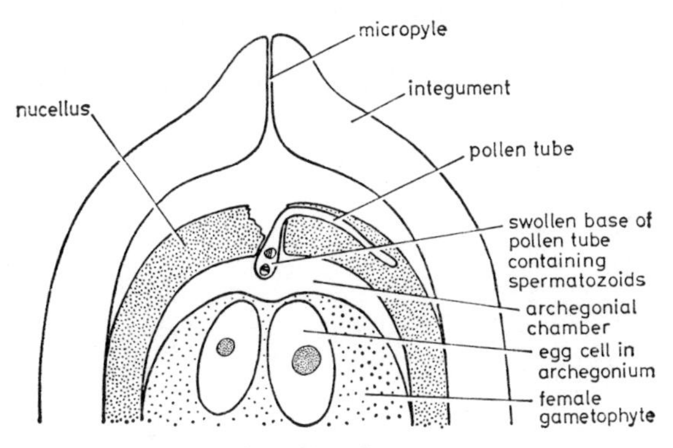

Fig. 270. *Cycas*.
L.S. of ovule shortly before fertilisation.

Ginkgo is of particular interest because it combines a vegetative structure like that of conifers, with primitive reproductive structures, including motile male gametes, like those of cycads.

GNETALES

This group includes three genera. *Ephedra* has more than thirty species, all of which are low shrubs with very small leaves, found in dry deserts in many parts of the world. *Welwitschia* has a single species found only in desert regions of south-west Africa. This unusual plant consists of a massive, almost spherical stem with a long tap root and two broad leaves of indefinite length growing from opposite sides of the stem. *Gnetum* has a number of species, most of which are tropical climbing plants with broad leaves. These brief descriptions emphasise the great differences between the genera: some authorities consider that each one should constitute a separate order. They have in common some advanced features of structure and reproduction which bring them close to angiosperms in certain respects. *Gnetum* itself has vessels in the xylem, laminate leaves like those of many dicotyledons, reproductive organs resembling flowers, and no archegonia in the female gametophyte. There is thus a defensible case for regarding *Gnetum* as a primitive angiosperm, though by custom it is included with the gymnosperms.

18 ALGAE

It is obvious even to a casual observer that bodies of water such as ponds, streams, lakes, rivers, and the sea can support the growth of a profuse and varied assortment of plants. Some of these, such as watercress and water buttercups, are clearly related by their structure and methods of reproduction to familiar land plants, and may be classified accordingly. But many others show no such relationships and are included in a large group called the algae. While the majority of algae habitually live in water there is an important minority of terrestrial forms also. It is easier to define the algae by what they lack rather than by what positive features they have in common since there is great diversity within the group. They do not reproduce by seeds and there is little differentiation of their internal tissues. It is therefore clear that they stand apart from the seed plants and pteridophytes. Although many of them have a sexual cycle with regular alternation of generations, the sporophyte is never an unbranched, dependent structure such as is found among bryophytes. In addition, algae never produce the tetrads of thick-walled spores after meiosis which are common in these other groups. On the other hand, algae possess genuine chlorophyll (as distinct from bacteriochlorophyll—p. 578) and show autotrophic nutrition, so that they are clearly separated from the fungi and bacteria. Within these wide and somewhat negative limits, at least 1,500 genera are recognised, and the number of species which have been described, about 20,000, probably falls far short of the total number in existence.

In size, algae range from single cells visible only with a microscope to multicellular seaweeds which may reach a length of 150 ft. In their life-cycles algae show greater diversity than any other group except perhaps the fungi. Some species have no known sexual process. Of the others, the majority have a prolonged haploid phase, and a diploid phase which may be very restricted indeed (e.g. *Chlamydomonas*, p. 496). In complete contrast, some advanced algae such as *Fucus* (p. 513) are diploid with the haploid phase reduced to an extent equal to that in angiosperms. Between these extremes there are species with an alternation of multicellular haploid and diploid phases which may be similar or dissimilar, and other variants of the generalised sexual cycle (see p. 443).

The basis of the customary classification of algae, however, is neither their structure nor their life history but the photosynthetic pigments contained in their cells. It may be recalled (p. 236) that the chloroplasts of higher plants contain pigments of two sorts—chlorophylls and carotenoids. There is a remarkable consistency among higher plants both in the number and relative quantities of these photosynthetic pigments, but the algae show much greater variety. Algae of all classes contain chlorophyll a and β-carotene, but there may also be other chlorophylls and carotenoids which are unknown in higher plants. In addition some algae contain pigments of a chemically distinct group, called phycobilins, which are also unique to the algae. Although the taxonomic distribution of these various pigments is not as clear cut as was formerly believed, the classification based on pigmentation is generally satisfactory. It is frequently found that species which contain similar pigments show resemblances in other respects also, such as the chemical nature of their cell walls and their reserves, and the morphology of their spores and gametes.

At least nine classes of algae may be distinguished on the basis of their pigmentation and associated biochemistry. Some authorities recognise more than nine. In this book we shall give some consideration to the seven classes which include most of the commoner species.

CHLOROPHYCEAE

These algae have photosynthetic pigments which are the same as those of higher plants. They are therefore usually green in colour, and the class is generally referred to as the green or grass-green algae. Further resemblances to higher plants are the formation of starch as the principal reserve, and of cellulose as a major constituent of the cell walls. Many species produce motile cells at some stage or stages in the life-cycle, and these are frequently pear-shaped with two flagella of equal length attached at the narrower end.

Green algae are predominantly inhabitants of fresh water, though there are some marine species also. They are very common in most fresh-water lakes, ponds, and streams, and are widespread in the soil. They are largely responsible for the green colour which develops in outdoor water-tanks if the water becomes stagnant. None of them is a large plant, though their size ranges from minute single-celled individuals to macroscopic plants several inches long.

Since there are such close biochemical resemblances between the green algae and higher plants, and since it is generally accepted that plant life originated in water, there is good reason to believe that the ancestors of land plants belonged to the Chlorophyceae. But as is pointed out elsewhere (p. 446), evolution is continuous in all groups, both primitive and advanced, and there is little likelihood of finding among present-day Chlorophyceae exact replicas of the plants from which land plants evolved.

Although the photosynthetic pigments of Chlorophyceae are identical with those of higher plants, the plastids containing the pigments are not. The variation in size, shape, and arrangement of chloroplasts is one of the most prominent features of cell structure in the class. In many cases each cell has only a single large chloroplast, and the situation typical of higher plants, where each cell may have numerous discoid chloroplasts, is very rarely found. The form of the chloroplasts is more or less constant for each species and is a useful aid to identification. Each chloroplast usually contains at least one conspicuous body called a **pyrenoid** (see Fig. 271). This has a core of protein around which plates of starch become deposited. Although its function has been a matter of disagreement, it seems very probable that the pyrenoid is concerned with the production of starch from the immediate product of photosynthesis.

We shall now consider a selection of common members of Chlorophyceae. Comparison between them will show the wide variety of structure and reproductive method present in the class.

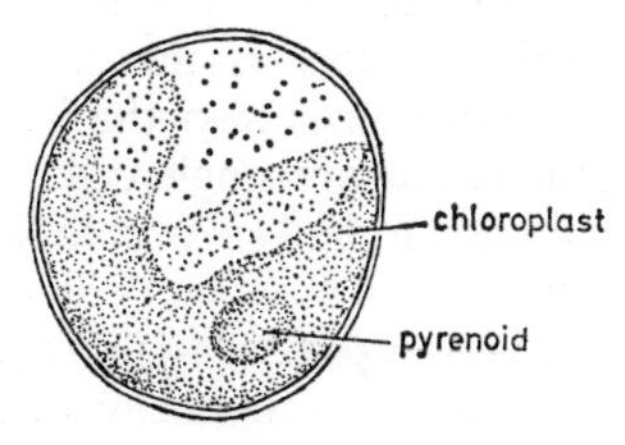

Fig. 271. *Chlorella.*

Chlorella (Fig. 271)

The outstanding characteristic of this genus is its extreme simplicity. The individual is a single, spherical cell which may grow to 10μ in diameter, but is frequently much smaller. These cells are found in many different habitats, submerged in fresh-water ponds and ditches, in soil, on the surface of tree-trunks and flower-pots, and as symbionts in lichens (p. 572) and in some invertebrate animals such as *Hydra*.

Each cell has a single chloroplast of irregular shape, usually flattened against the cell wall. There may or may not be a pyrenoid.

Sexual reproduction has not been observed. The only known method of reproduction is by division of the protoplast into two, four, eight, or sixteen spores which are liberated by rupture of the parent wall and then become independent individuals. Neither the spores nor the adults into which they develop are motile, though when growing in water they easily remain in suspension and are carried about passively by currents.

Though morphologically simple, *Chlorella* has a photosynthetic system which is biochemically identical with that of an angiosperm. Because of the ease and speed with which it can be grown in the laboratory under controlled conditions, *Chlorella* has been used extensively in investigations of the mechanism of photosynthesis. Its speed of growth and high protein content have also led to the suggestion that *Chlorella* might make a useful addition to world food supplies. However, the technical problems of culture on a large scale are formidable, and even if these were overcome there would remain the problem of creating a palatable foodstuff acceptable to the consumer.

Pleurococcus (Fig. 272)

This is another widespread genus whose members are almost as simple in structure as *Chlorella.* The principal difference is that *Pleurococcus* shows some tendency to form small multicellular aggregates. The plants can be found in many damp terrestrial habitats, such as the surface of tree-trunks, walls, and fences. *Pleurococcus* is also the algal component of some lichens. Some individuals are single cells, but these multiply by division and it is common to find small colonies of two, four, or more cells in which the several cells are closely associated with one another. If conditions are very moist, irregular colonies may develop in which there are short chains or filaments of cells joined end to end.

Cell structure resembles that of *Chlorella,* with a single irregular chloroplast and usually no pyrenoid. Multiplication by cell division is the only known form of reproduction. There are no motile cells.

Chlamydomonas (Fig. 273)

Individuals belonging to this large genus are all unicellular, but they show much greater complexity than *Chlorella* both in their structure and their life history. They are common in fresh-water ponds and ditches. More than 300 species have been described, but it is known that the appearance of cells can easily be modified by variation in cultural conditions, and it is possible that some "species" are simply variants produced in this way. The description which follows refers to *C. debaryana,* a common species in Britain. The various structures referred to occur in most other species, but their shape, size, number, and arrangement may differ.

Each plant consists of an egg-shaped cell with a small protuberance at the tip of the narrower end. Usually, when the cell is living in water, two flagella of equal length are attached at the base of this protuberance and the cell is motile. By a lashing action, the flagella propel the cell with the pointed (anterior) end foremost. The cells may also be cultured on a solid agar medium in which case they produce an aggregate of many cells enveloped in copious mucilage, and flagella are not produced. This condition is known as a **palmelloid** phase. It occurs under certain conditions in nature, perhaps as a response to drying up of the water in which the cells normally live. When a palmelloid culture is flooded with water, the cells rapidly develop flagella and become motile.

At the base of the flagella are two **contractile vacuoles** which undergo a repeated alternation of slow distension and sudden collapse. These vacuoles are believed to have an excretory function,

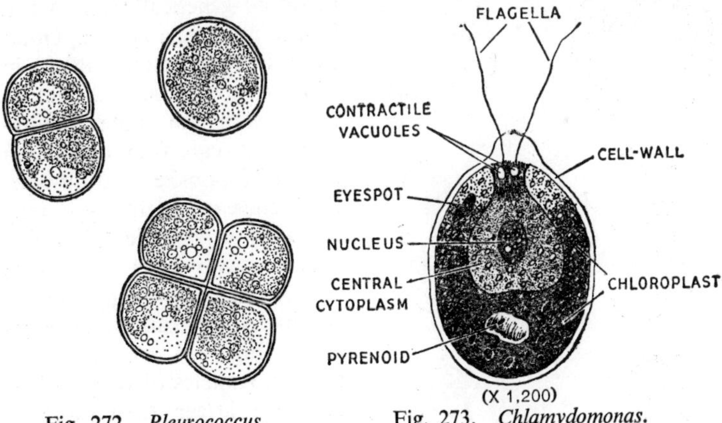

Fig. 272. *Pleurococcus.* Fig. 273. *Chlamydomonas.*

and the sudden collapse to represent the expulsion of waste products from the cell.

Also near the anterior end of the cell is an orange or red **eyespot**, shaped like a biconvex lens and usually lying against the cell wall. This structure is sensitive to light and plays a part in controlling the direction of motion of the cell. In general, *Chlamydomonas* will swim towards light of moderate intensity but away from very bright light. This is an example of **phototactic movement**, that is movement of a whole organism in response to light (cf. phototropic movement in which only part of the organism responds).

The most prominent feature of the cell is the single green chloroplast which is basin-shaped and occupies most of the posterior part of the cell. Embedded in it is a conspicuous pyrenoid. The single small nucleus lies near the centre of the cell.

Asexual reproduction takes place by the protoplast becoming detached from the cell wall and dividing into two, four, eight, or sixteen parts, each one a replica of the parent. These are called **zoospores,** the prefix zoo- indicating that they are motile (Fig. 274; A, B). They are liberated by breakdown of the parent cell wall and then become independent plants. This is the common method of multiplication and can lead to rapid increase of numbers under suitable conditions.

Alternatively there is sexual reproduction. Gametes are often morphologically indistinguishable from vegetative cells, though they may be smaller. Some species are **homothallic**: that is, two gametes derived asexually from the same ancestral cell (and therefore genetically alike) can fuse to produce a zygote. Other species are **heterothallic,** in which case all genetically similar cells are of the same mating-type and can fuse only with cells of opposite mating-type. Difference of mating-type may be purely physiological, in which case the two sorts of gamete are similar in appearance. Mating is then said to be **isogamous** (Fig. 274, C). In other species, gametes of one mating-type are larger than those of the other: mating is **anisogamous** (Fig. 274, D). In all cases the product of gametic fusion is a non-motile zygote which may develop a thick wall and can survive long periods of drought. Mature zygotes often contain a red pigment called haematochrome, and heavy deposits of fat. These obscure the events preceding germination, but it can eventually be seen that the contents of the zygote have divided, usually into four or eight zoospores which are liberated by breakdown of the zygote wall. In a heterothallic species, half of these zoospores are of one mating-type and half of the other. This segregation indicates that meiosis occurs in the zygote, and the sexual life-cycle can therefore be represented as in Fig. 275.

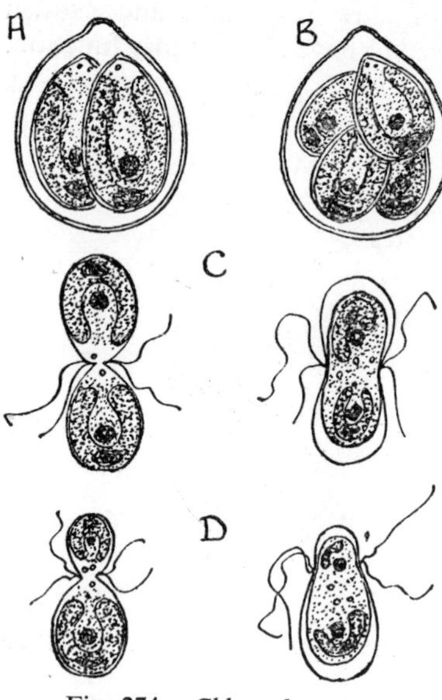

Fig. 274. *Chlamydomonas.* A and B, formation of zoospores; C, isogamous mating; D, anisogamous mating.

It will be seen that the only diploid phase in the cycle is the zygote: at all other times the organism is haploid.

Pandorina, Eudorina, and Volvox

These three genera are considered together because they have a common type of organisation. The individual is a form of **coenobium**, that is a multicellular organism with some integration of the component cells, but with each cell having a considerable degree of independence also. The cells are flagellated and resemble *Chlamydomonas* or similar algae. Members of all three genera are widespread in Britain in fresh-water lakes, ponds, and ditches.

Pandorina (Fig. 276). The coenobium consists of sixteen (or sometimes eight or thirty-two) cells closely packed into a spherical arrangement with very little free space in the centre. The individual cells are somewhat conical, with the apex pointed inwards and the flagella protruding from the outward-facing base. The whole cluster

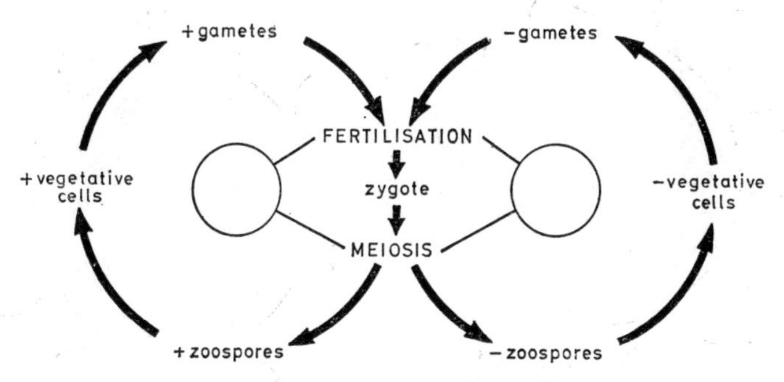

Fig. 275. *Chlamydomonas*. Sexual life-cycle.

is enclosed in a sphere of mucilage. Each flagellum extends through this mucilage and the greater part of its length is free to move in the surrounding water. The coenobium is propelled by the concerted action of all the flagella. In some species there is a recognisable polarity of the coenobium, with large eyespots at one side and smaller ones (or a complete absence of eyespots) at the other.

Reproduction may be asexual or sexual. In asexual reproduction the coenobium first ceases to be motile. The sixteen cells then each divide into a coherent cluster of sixteen smaller cells, and the sixteen clusters separate and become new coenobia.

Sexual reproduction begins with cell divisions as in asexual reproduction, but the products are dispersed as separate cells which can act as gametes. *Pandorina* is heterothallic and there is slight anisogamy. The zygote has a thick wall and meiosis probably precedes germination, though usually only a single zoospore is released. If, as seems likely, this is a product of meiosis, the other three products must degenerate. The zoospore has two flagella, and after a period of motility it settles down, loses its flagella and produces a new coenobium by cell division.

Eudorina (Fig. 277). There are usually thirty-two cells in the coenobium, though there may be sixteen or sixty-four. The cells are spherical and are arranged around the periphery of a sphere of mucilage with flagella extending out into the surrounding water. Each cell appears well separated from its neighbours, but close examination shows that there are fine cytoplasmic connections between them. As in *Pandorina* there is sometimes a difference in

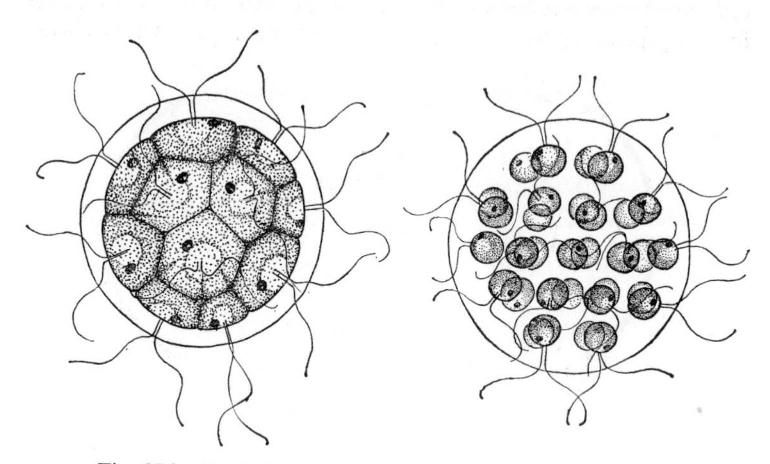

Fig. 276. *Pandorina.* Coenobium.

Fig. 277. *Eudorina.* Coenobium.

size of eyespots on opposite sides of the coenobium, and this may be accompanied by polarity in size and reproductive capacity. In some species the anterior cells are smaller and remain purely vegetative; posterior cells are larger and they alone take part in reproduction.

Asexual reproduction is similar to that in *Pandorina*, but sexual reproduction is more advanced. There is a clear distinction between large, non-motile female gametes and small motile male gametes. When the difference is as pronounced as this, sexual reproduction is said to be **oogamous**. In *Eudorina*, the female gametes do not leave the coenobium which produces them. Although this is commonly the case in oogamy it is not an essential feature of oogamy (see *Fucus*, p. 513). Coenobia may be monoecious or dioecious.

Each female gamete develops from a vegetative cell without division. The formation of male gametes, however, involves division of a vegetative cell into sixty-four slender, flagellated cells which are liberated in a coherent cluster from the parent coenobium. They then separate and can swim individually to carry out fertilisation. The zygote, like the female gamete, is retained in the parent coenobium but eventually liberates a zoospore which is probably a product of meiosis. This zoospore can develop into a new coenobium by cell division.

Volvox (Fig. 278). *Volvox* shows greater advancement than *Pandorina* or *Eudorina* both in vegetative and reproductive features. The coenobia are comparable with those of *Eudorina* but are very much larger, with as many as 50,000 cells in each. These cells are arranged in a single layer around a sphere of mucilage which is soft in the centre but firm at the periphery. The cells are flagellated and connected with one another by cytoplasmic strands. It is not unusual for a coenobium to reach 0·5 mm. in diameter, in which case it is clearly visible to the naked eye.

Only a restricted number of cells in the posterior part of the coenobium are capable of reproduction. Asexual reproduction begins with the enlargement of a vegetative cell into a **gonidium**. This then divides repeatedly by walls perpendicular to the surface of the coenobium, producing first a saucer-shaped layer of cells and later an almost complete sphere within the parent coenobium (Fig. 278, B-E). Note that the outer (flagellated) surface of the coenobium is continuous with the inner surface of this daughter sphere. There is then a remarkable inversion of the daughter sphere so that what began as the inner surface becomes the outer. This is accompanied by detachment of the daughter sphere which then becomes a miniature replica of its parent. Daughter coenobia produced in this way are either released through a pore at the position of the original gonidium, or remain inside the parent and are released only when the parent coenobium disintegrates. It is sometimes possible to find coenobia containing daughters which in turn contain grand-daughters.

Sexual reproduction is oogamous, and species of *Volvox* may be monoecious or dioecious. Female gametes, like gonidia, develop from vegetative cells without division. Each is a large cell with many pyrenoids but no flagella. Other cells give rise to male gametes by repeated cell division: a single vegetative cell may produce a cluster of as many as 512 spermatozoids. This cluster is spherical and undergoes inversion as in asexual reproduction, after which the slender, flagellated spermatozoids are released. Female gametes are fertilised without becoming detached from their parent coenobia. The zygote is eventually liberated and later undergoes meiosis. One of the products is released as a zoospore and this develops by cell divisions into a new coenobium. Coenobia formed directly from zygotes are generally small, and maximum size is

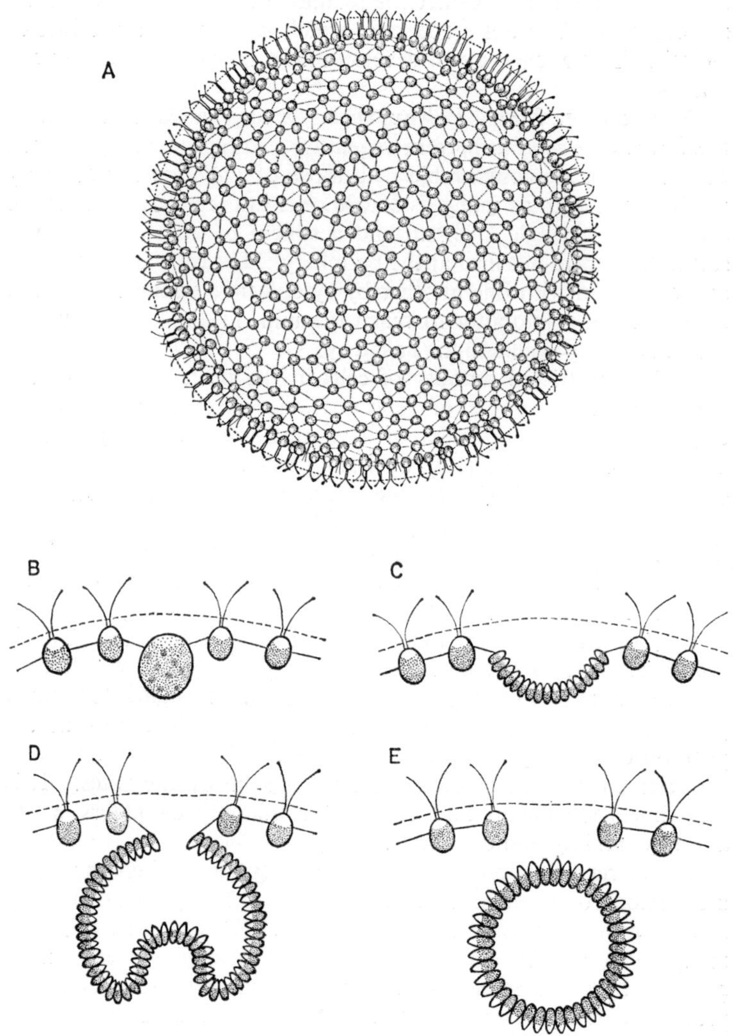

Fig. 278. *Volvox.*
A, coenobium; B-E, stages in asexual reproduction.

reached only after several cycles of asexual reproduction, with each daughter coenobium exceeding its parent in size and in number of component cells.

The colonial green algae, of which *Pandorina*, *Eudorina*, and *Volvox* are examples, illustrate one likely course of evolution from the unicellular condition to the multicellular. *Volvox* is the largest type in the series and probably represents the limit of this type of construction. Any further increase in size of the coenobium without some internal strengthening, would produce a more and more fragile structure. Progressive increase in size up to the maximum shown by *Volvox* is accompanied by a trend towards greater division of function in the larger coenobia, with some cells remaining purely

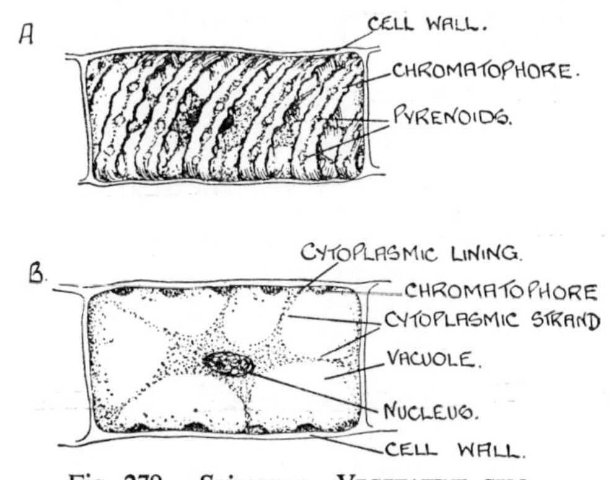

Fig. 279. *Spirogyra*. VEGETATIVE CELL.
A, viewed from outside; B, viewed in optical section. Chromatophore = chloroplast.

vegetative and others, in a restricted area, becoming specialised for reproduction.

Another type of multicellular development whose derivation from a unicellular form can easily be imagined (see p. 17) is the filament, with cells arranged end to end. There are numerous filamentous species among the green algae, some of them comprising the following three genera.

Spirogyra (Fig. 279)

Members of this genus are common in fresh-water streams and ponds, either free-floating or attached to solid objects such as stones or larger plants. The filaments are unbranched and coated with a generous layer of mucilage which gives them a characteristic slimy feel. Each cell is cylindrical in shape, usually not more than three or four times as long as broad. The filaments increase in length by enlargement and division of any cell. An interesting departure from the pattern of cell division normal in higher plants is that the new wall develops as an ingrowth from the parent wall rather than from a cell-plate spreading outwards (Fig. 280, A). There is little or no differentiation between the cells of a filament, though in some species the basal cells develop rhizoidal outgrowths by which the filament is attached to its substratum.

The chloroplasts are the most conspicuous feature of cell structure. There are from one to seven of these in each cell, depending on the species, each one a long ribbon helically coiled

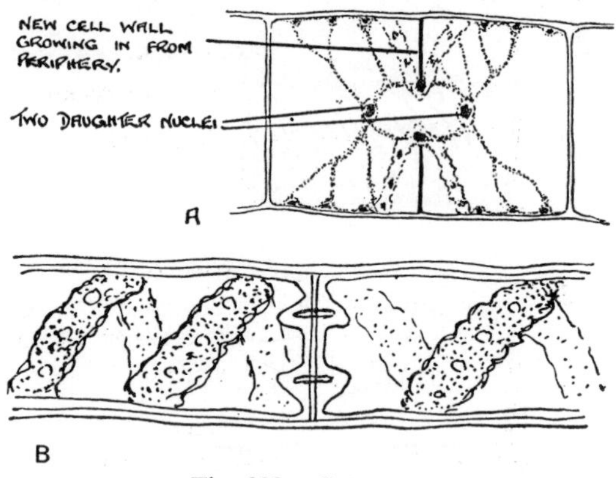

Fig. 280. *Spirogyra.*
A, cell division; B, replicate transverse wall.

from one end of the cell to the other. There may be several prominent pyrenoids in every chloroplast. Encircled by the chloroplast or chloroplasts is a large vacuole and a central nucleus supported by cytoplasmic strands.

Asexual reproduction takes place by fragmentation. Part of a filament may simply break away from the remainder and become an independent individual. Some species have characteristic elaborations of their transverse walls which may assist the detachment of one cell from its neighbour. The replicate condition (Fig. 280, B) is an example of this.

Sexual reproduction involves a process of **conjugation,** that is the joining together of parent cells or individuals and the direct transfer of gametes. Some species are heterothallic. In these cases the two filaments which are to conjugate develop conjugation tubes between opposite cells (Fig. 281, 1 and 2). Then in each pair of connected cells, the protoplast of one passes across the tube and fuses with the protoplast of the other. The product of fusion develops into a thick-walled zygote. In some cases the migration of protoplasts between filaments is strictly unilateral so that it is possible to distinguish male and female filaments. Other species are homothallic, and conjugation tubes may be formed between adjacent cells of the same filament. This does not exclude the possibility of conjugation with other filaments also. In either case meiosis takes place in the zygote, and three of the four resulting nuclei abort. The haploid cell which remains develops a germ tube which grows out from the zygote wall (Fig. 282) and becomes a new filament.

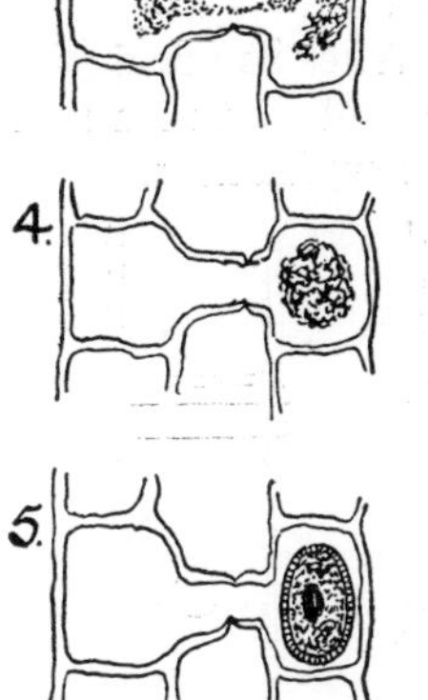

Fig. 281. *Spirogyra*. Conjunction and formation of zygote.

Oedogonium

Like *Spirogyra*, *Oedogonium* consists of unbranched filaments which are widespread in fresh-water streams and ponds, either attached or free-floating. Among its distinctive features are an unusual type of cell division, restricted to particular cells in the filament, and an elaborate type of sexual reproduction.

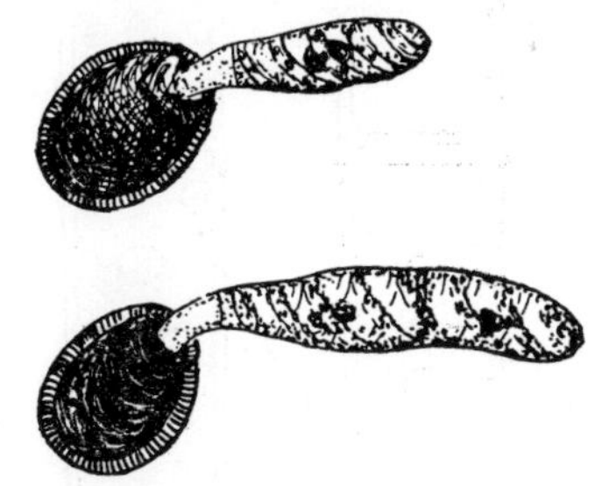
Fig. 282. *Spirogyra*. Germination of zygotes.

Each of the cylindrical cells has one large chloroplast in the form of a network lining the cell wall, with numerous pyrenoids. There is a single nucleus near the centre of the cell. Some of the cells, known as cap cells, have a series of ring-like markings around the wall at one end (Fig. 283). These markings result from previous cell divisions in the following way. Division of the protoplast is

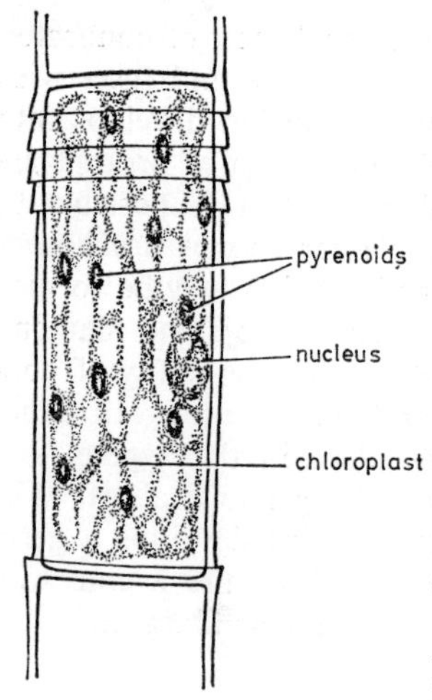

Fig. 283. *Oedogonium*. Cap cell.

accompanied by the formation of a ring of thickening on the inside of the cell wall near one end (Fig. 284, 1). The outer layer of the cell wall then splits around a line corresponding to this ring (Fig. 284, 2), and the cell elongates by stretching of the thickening (Fig. 284, 3). When division is completed, therefore, one cell is enclosed within the original wall, the other in the newly-formed wall to which a cap of the old wall is attached (Fig. 284, 4). By repeated division of this cap cell, a series of four or more caps may be produced.

Asexual reproduction is by zoospores which are generally produced in cap cells. The cap cell swells into a rotund zoosporangium, and its protoplast becomes a single zoospore of characteristic type. The spore is ovoid or spherical, mostly green but with a clear region at one end encircled by a ring of flagella (Fig. 285). There may also be an eyespot. After its release from the sporangium, the zoospore is motile for a while but then settles down, becomes attached, and develops into a new filament.

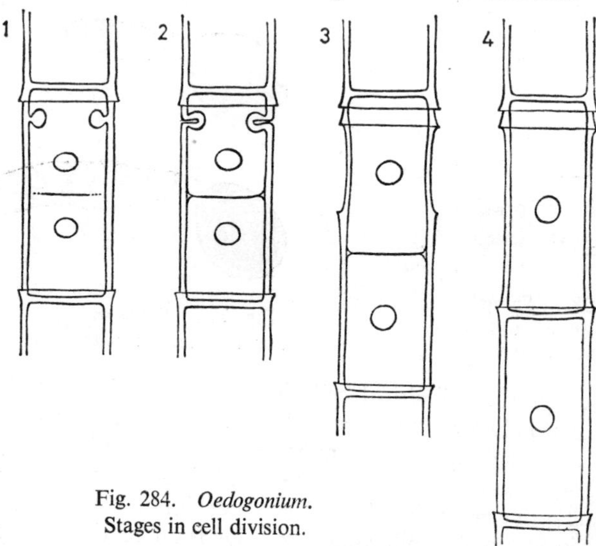

Fig. 284. *Oedogonium*. Stages in cell division.

Sexual reproduction is oogamous and there are important differences between species, mainly concerning the way in which male gametes are produced. In all species the formation of female gametes begins with hitherto vegetative cells acting as **oogonial mother cells**, each of which divides into two. One of the daughter cells then swells into a globose shape and becomes an **oogonium** containing a single egg cell. The nucleus of this cell comes to lie near the wall at a point where a pore or split develops. Shortly

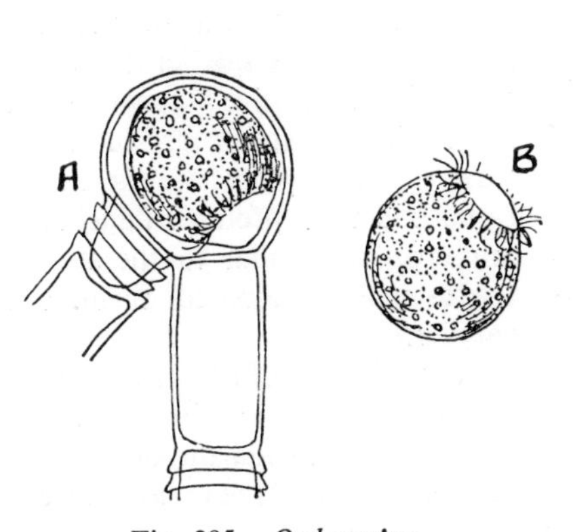

Fig. 285. *Oedogonium.*
ZOOSPORE. A, in sporangium; B, after release.

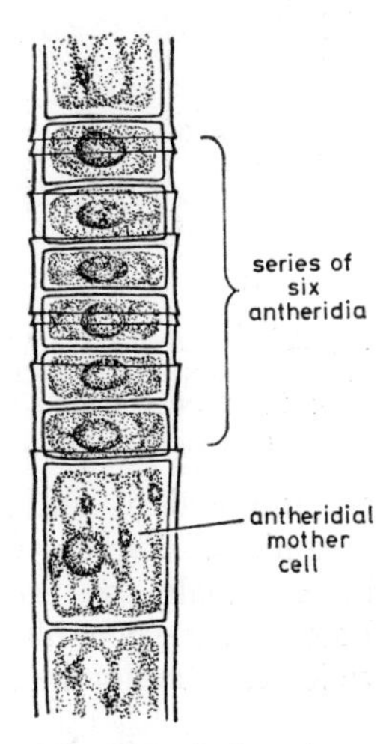

Fig. 286. *Oedogonium.*
Production of antheridia in a macrandrous species.

before fertilisation there is the exudation of a gelatinous substance through this pore.

In some species the male gametes develop directly on normal filaments. These are **macrandrous** species, and the antheridia may be on the same filaments as the oogonia (monoecious) or on different filaments (dioecious). An antheridial mother cell is no different from a vegetative cell at first, but it divides unequally and the short cell produced becomes an antheridium. Division of the mother cell may be repeated, giving a series of as many as forty adjacent antheridia (Fig. 286). The protoplast of each antheridium becomes one or two antherozoids which look like small zoospores. They are released by splitting open of the cell walls, and can carry out fertilisation directly.

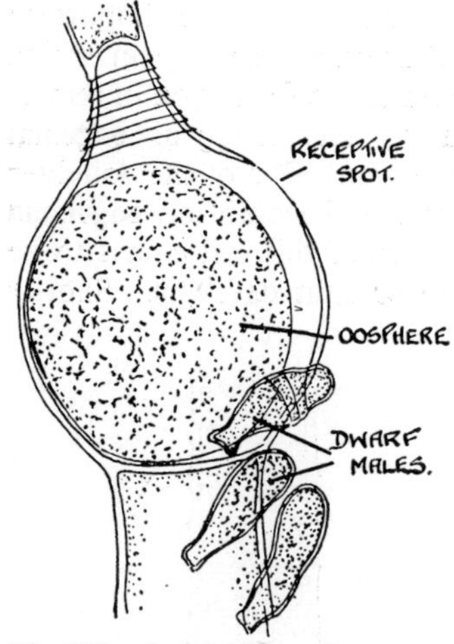

Fig. 287. *Oedogonium.* OOGONIUM OF A NANNANDROUS SPECIES SHOWING ATTACHED DWARF MALES.
Oosphere = egg cell.

In other species, known as **nannandrous** species, the large filaments do not produce antheridia, although vegetative cells undergo similar unequal divisions. Following such a division, the smaller cell releases a flagellated spore known as an **androspore**. This can attach itself to an oogonium or some neighbouring cell and germinate into a short filament of perhaps four cells, much smaller than the cells of a vegetative filament (Fig. 287). The distal cells of these "dwarf male" plants are the antheridia, and they produce flagellated antherozoids similar to the androspores which preceded them, but smaller.

In both sorts of species, egg cells are fertilised by antherozoids which penetrate the pore of the oogonium. Zygotes are retained for a while inside the oogonium, but eventually they are released by breakdown of the oogonial wall. Later, each zygote undergoes meiosis and produces four zoospores which can develop into new filaments.

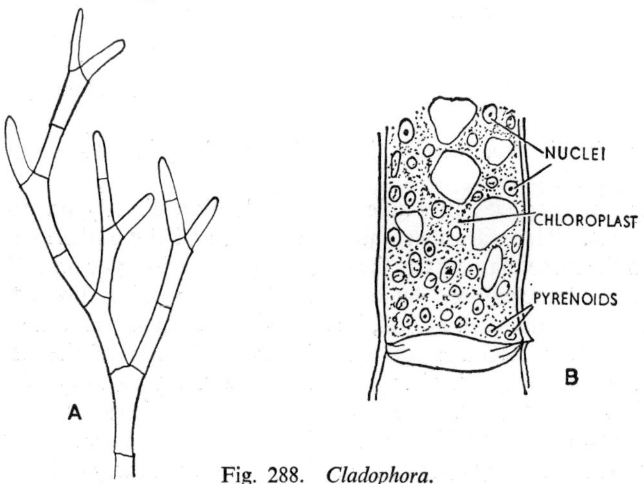

Fig. 288. *Cladophora.*
A, part of plant showing pattern of branching; B, part of one cell.

Cladophora (Fig. 288)

This is another widespread genus of filamentous green algae. It includes both fresh-water and marine species, and there are important differences from the preceding genera both in structure and in reproduction. The filaments are multicellular and branched, and cell divisions are largely or wholly restricted to the apices. Some species are free-floating, but others are attached by branched, multicellular rhizoids. Apart from these rhizoids, each cell has a chloroplast in the form of a network lining the cell wall, and all the cells are multinucleate. The formation of transverse walls is not therefore linked with nuclear divisions in the manner characteristic of many other plants.

Asexual reproduction is by formation of zoospores. Any cell

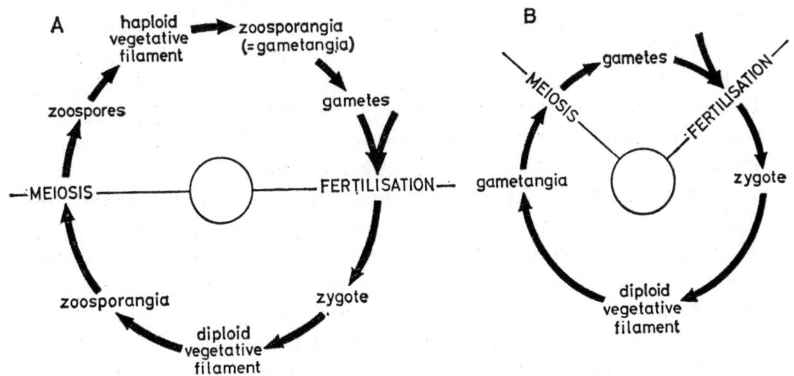

Fig. 289. *Cladophora.* TWO TYPES OF LIFE-CYCLE.
A, with alternation of similar haploid and diploid plants; B, with all plants diploid.

may become a zoosporangium: its protoplast divides into numerous egg-shaped zoospores which have two or four flagella according to the species, and are released through a pore in the sporangium wall.

Sexual reproduction is isogamous. Biflagellate gametes are produced in the same way as zoospores, and fusion occurs only between gametes from different plants. A new filamentous plant develops from the zygote without meiosis occurring. Details of the life-cycle differ between species, but in some species there is an alternation of similar diploid and haploid plants, with meiosis occurring in at least some of the zoosporangia of the diploids (see Fig. 289). In one species, and possibly more, all plants are diploid and meiosis occurs during formation of gametes. In this case, therefore, the gametes are the only haploid phase of the life-cycle.

Desmids

A sample of pond water rich in algae will almost certainly include some desmids, particularly if the water is acid. This collective name is given to a group of genera of green algae showing great morphological variety, but which are related to one another by certain common features of cell structure and reproduction. Most desmids are unicellular, but in some genera the cells are attached to one another in filaments or irregular colonies. Every desmid has a single nucleus, usually centrally placed, and one or two chloroplasts. The cell walls all have an inner layer rich in cellulose and a gelatinous outer pectic layer which is often very thick. The cellulose layer may be plain and smooth, or elaborately sculptured (see Plate 17). In many species the inner wall is made up of two closely fitting halves. The point where the two halves join is frequently marked by a prominent constriction, but several common species show simply a line running round the cell. All these desmids with walls in two parts have an unusual type of cell division. They divide into two so that each daughter cell receives an intact half of the parent wall. The daughter cells develop one new half-wall each, exactly matching the half-wall inherited from the parent.

Sexual reproduction is by conjugation, resembling the process in *Spirogyra* to which desmids are believed to be related. Two desmids which are about to conjugate meet together and become united by coalescence of their gelatinous outer walls. Some species form a conjugation tube between the cells, in which the two protoplasts fuse and form a zygote. In other species the inner walls of the parent cells break open and the two protoplasts fuse in the gelatinous mass. The protoplast may show amoeboid movements before fusion, but there is no truly motile stage. The zygote eventually undergoes meiosis and releases two or four protoplasts which become new individuals.

PHAEOPHYCEAE

In this class the pigments include chlorophyll a and β-carotene, as in Chlorophyceae, but also a substantial quantity of a brown carotenoid called **fucoxanthin**. The class is therefore known as the brown algae. The principal reserves are the sugar alcohol mannitol and a polysaccharide called **laminarin**. The cell walls contain a high proportion of a polymer called **algin**.

With very few exceptions, members of Phaeophyceae are marine. The class includes all the larger seaweeds and many smaller species also. Most species produce flagellated cells at some stage. These cells each have two flagella of unequal length, attached at the side of the cell.

The two genera to be discussed are very dissimilar, and may serve to illustrate the diversity of structure and reproductive method shown by the class.

Ectocarpus (Fig. 290)

Ectocarpus species are among the smaller of the brown seaweeds. There are numerous species in British coastal waters, but only a few are at all common. Each plant is made up of branched multicellular filaments, usually with several main branches and many smaller laterals. As with the filamentous Chlorophyceae described earlier, each filament is only one cell across, but there is a

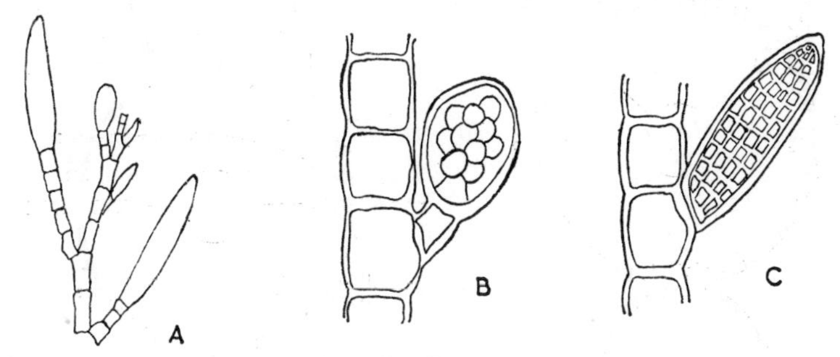

Fig. 290. *Ectocarpus*.
A, branched filament bearing sporangia; B, unilocular sporangium; C, plurilocular sporangium.

tendency in some species for the main filaments to lie closely parallel to one another particularly towards the base, and so become a more substantial axis. A well-developed specimen may be several inches long. The plant is attached at its base by rhizoids. Some species are usually attached to rocks, and others grow epiphytically on larger algae. Most of the epiphytic species are restricted to particular host species.

The shape and number of chloroplasts differ between species. In some, each cell has a single large chloroplast which may be flat, curved, or twisted; in others there are several small disc-like chloroplasts. Each cell is uninucleate.

Two types of sporangia are produced, often on the same plant. Both are borne terminally on lateral branches. **Unilocular** sporangia are ovoid and are not subdivided into compartments. Meiosis occurs in these sporangia, but the products of meiosis may divide several times so that each sporangium liberates numerous flagellated cells. **Plurilocular** sporangia are more elongated, and the contents of each are partitioned off into many compartments, each of which produces one flagellated cell. There is considerable variation in life history between species, and even between members of the same species growing in different places. For example (Fig. 291), all plants of *E. siliculosus* growing on the coast of the Isle of Man appear to be diploid, bearing both sorts of sporangia. The plurilocular sporangia produce diploid spores from which further diploid plants develop asexually. The unilocular sporangia produce haploid

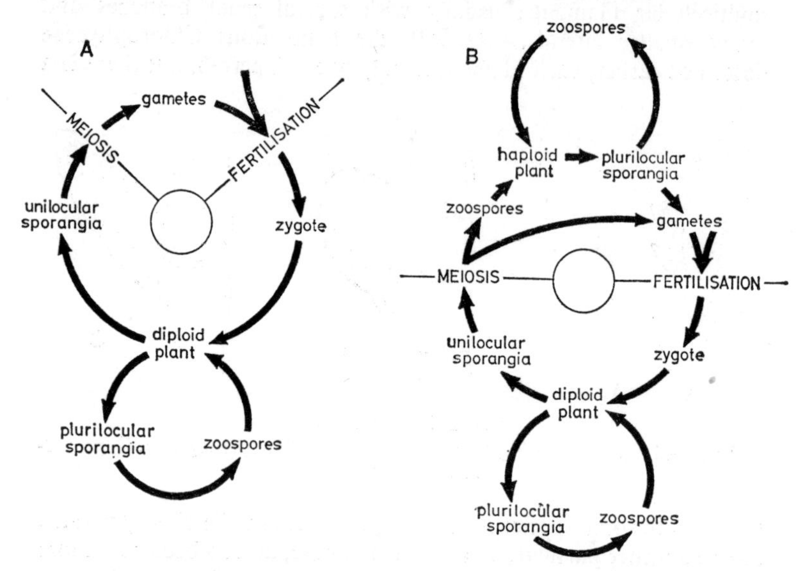

Fig. 291. *Ectocarpus siliculosus.* Two types of life-cycle. A, as on the coast of the Isle of Man; B, as in the Mediterranean.

gametes which fuse in pairs to give zygotes. These germinate to produce more diploid plants. With this arrangement, therefore, the haploid phase is confined to the gametes.

The same species in the Mediterranean, however, produces both diploid and haploid plants which are morphologically similar except for the occurrence of sporangia. Haploid plants have plurilocular sporangia only. Their products either develop directly into further haploid plants or act as gametes and give rise to diploids. Diploid plants have both sorts of sporangia. The diploid spores from plurilocular sporangia produce further diploid plants, while the haploid spores from unilocular sporangia either develop into haploids or act as gametes and restore the diploid condition.

Fucus

Fucus provides a complete contrast to *Ectocarpus* particularly in the advanced state of its structural organisation. *Fucus* species are probably the most familiar of the British seaweeds partly because of their size but also because they grow in the inter-tidal zone and are regularly exposed at low tide. The two most common species, *F. vesiculosus* and *F. serratus* will be found on almost every rocky shore in Britain. These two species differ in the part of the shore

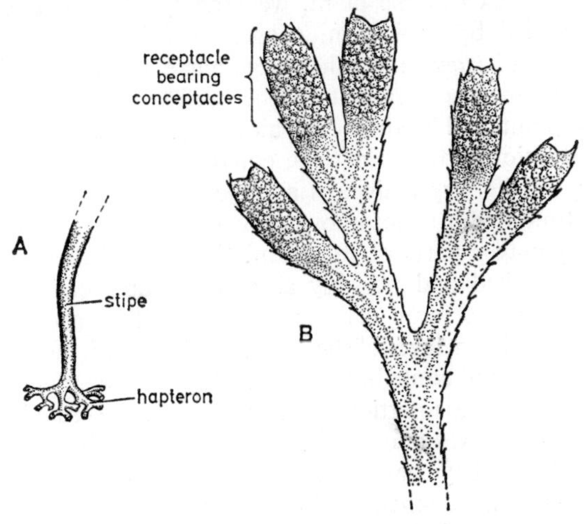

Fig. 292. *Fucus serratus*.
A, hapteron and stipe; B, ultimate branches of thallus.

which they characteristically occupy, probably because of different tolerances to exposure and desiccation. *F. vesiculosus* regularly grows higher up the shore than *F. serratus* though their zones of occupation show considerable overlapping. The description which follows refers to *F. serratus* (Fig. 292).

The plant body is frequently 2-3 ft long and sometimes more. At its base it is attached to a rock by a special organ, the **hapteron,** which grows into crevices and is very difficult to dislodge. Above this is a short cylindrical stalk or **stipe,** and then the thallus expands into the **lamina** which is in the form of a broad, branched ribbon. The species takes its name from the serrated margin of the lamina. Growth of the thallus is partly due to the activity of a single apical cell at the tip of each branch, but other tissues also have meristematic activity. The outermost layer, for example, known as the **limiting layer** continues to undergo cell division and to contribute to the bulk of the plant. This layer has no cuticle, but is covered by mucilage which is important in preserving the plant from desiccation at low tide. Underlying the limiting layer is a parenchymatous cortex. The outermost cells are closely packed, well supplied with small discoid chloroplasts, and constitute the photosynthetic tissue. Further in, the cortex is more loosely organised and has fewer chloroplasts. The cells here probably act as storage tissue. In the very centre is the medulla, consisting of elongated cells lying roughly parallel to the axis of the plant, well separated from one another and surrounded by copious mucilage. The internal arrangement of the thallus of *Fucus* and other large algae, with its mucilaginous matrix, is in marked contrast to the well-ventilated structure of many land plants. The absence of air-spaces must create an entirely different situation with respect to gaseous exchange, but the structural physiology of the larger algae is a subject which has received very little attention, and it is not known how the problems are overcome.

In the younger parts of the plant, the cells of the medulla are mostly thin-walled and possibly carry out translocation. As the tissues grow older, more cells are added to the medulla by cell divisions in the inner layer of the cortex. These new medullary cells have thick walls and contribute to the strength of the plant.

Seaweeds of the intertidal zone are subjected to violent disturbance by the waves and are frequently damaged by being dashed against rocks. They have considerable powers of regeneration. Not only will an attached portion continue to grow in spite of severe damage to its lamina, but detached fragments may also become re-attached as independent individuals. Such re-attachment is probably infrequent, and largely restricted to salt marshes where fragments can gain a foothold more easily than on wave-swept rocks. This is the only form of asexual reproduction known in *Fucus*.

Sexual reproduction is oogamous, with the female gametes released from their parent plant before fertilisation. The *Fucus* plant is diploid. At certain times of the year (autumn and winter in *F. serratus*) the terminal inch or two of the branches of the lamina become conspicuously swollen and are known as **receptacles.** Just below the surface of the receptacles are cavities called **conceptacles**, each opening to the outside by an **ostiole** (Fig. 293). Such cavities are not confined to the receptacles. They are to be found in the vegetative part of the thallus also, but in this position they contain only multicellular hairs and take no part in the reproductive process. These, then, are sterile conceptacles. In the receptacles, however, the conceptacles are fertile, and gametes are produced in them. *F. serratus* is dioecious, but another species, *F. spiralis*, which grows near the high-water mark, is monoecious. In this species, a single conceptacle (Fig. 293) contains structures of three kinds: (*a*) sterile **paraphyses**, which are multicellular, unbranched hairs, seen protruding through the ostiole in Fig. 293; (*b*) fertile paraphyses, which are branched structures some of whose branches bear **antheridia**; (*c*) **oogonia**, each borne on a short stalk composed of one cell. Meiosis takes place in the antheridia and oogonia: each antheridium yields sixty-four flagellated antherozoids, and

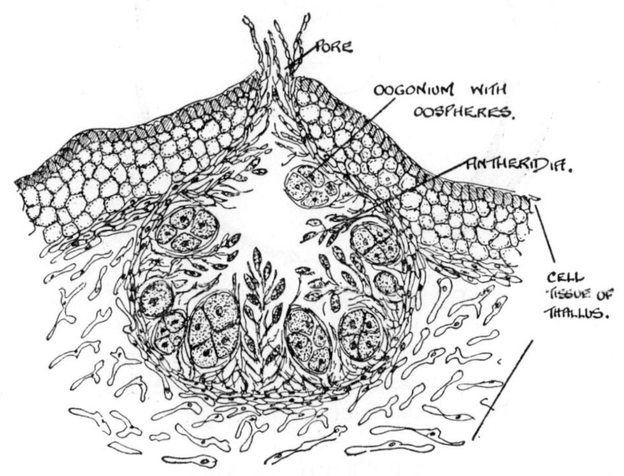

Fig. 293. *Fucus spiralis.*
Section through conceptacle. Pore = ostiole.

each oogonium eight non-motile, spherical egg cells. The gametangia of *F. serratus* are essentially similar, but are produced in separate conceptacles on different plants. Gametes of both sorts are liberated through the ostiole into the sea. Although non-motile, the egg cells are sufficiently buoyant to remain in suspension. Antherozoids are attracted to the egg cells chemotactically, and there follows a period during which the egg cell is surrounded and usually rotated by excited antherozoids seeking to penetrate it. Eventually one does so, and fertilises it. The diploid zygote develops, after settling down, into a new diploid plant.

The life-cycle of *Fucus* (Fig. 294) is remarkable for the extremely restricted haploid phase, which is represented by the gametes and the nuclei which precede them. This arrangement is rare among plants, and the fact that it is here associated with a high degree of structural organisation indicates that in *Fucus* we have the product of two evolutionary trends which have progressed side-by-side. Comparison with a wider range of brown algae than can be mentioned

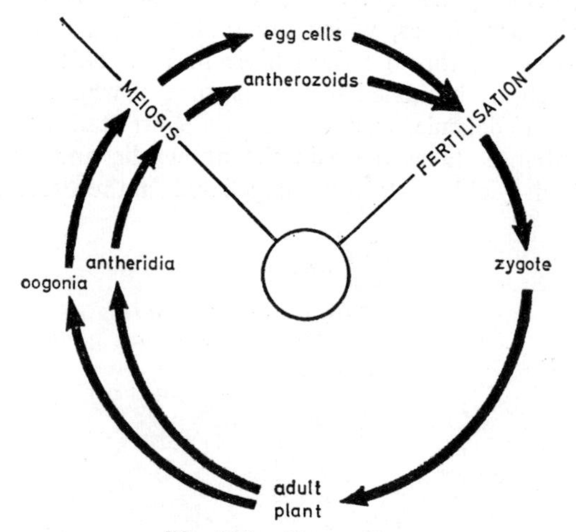

Fig. 294. *Fucus.* LIFE-CYCLE.

in this book would support the belief that increasing size, differentiation, and structural complexity have been accompanied by gradual reduction of the haploid phase of the life-cycle.

RHODOPHYCEAE

In addition to chlorophyll a and β-carotene, members of this class contain two water-soluble phycobilins, **phycoerythrin**, which is red, and **phycocyanin**, which is blue. In the majority of species, phycoerythrin is present in greater quantity, and the plants have a pronounced red colour. In other species, phycocyanin is more plentiful and the plants are bluish-green. The class is referred to as the red algae despite this variation in colour.

Almost all species are marine. Most of them are macroscopic but usually do not exceed a few inches in length. There is a considerable variety of red algae on most rocky shores in Britain, attached either to rocks or to other algae. In the intertidal zone they are commonly found in pools where they remain submerged at low tide, rather than in places where they would be left high and dry.

The Rhodophyceae are a well-defined group showing greater uniformity than either the green or brown algae. Among their characteristic features are:

1. Formation of an unusual type of starch, known as Floridean starch, as the principal reserve.

2. Construction of the thallus in the larger species from aggregation of branched filaments, sometimes approaching a pseudo-parenchymatous condition.

3. Complete absence of motile cells at any stage.

4. A unique type of sexual reproduction, in which non-motile male gametes are passively carried by water to the female structure.

The life history of a red alga always includes a well-developed haploid gametophyte. Fertilisation occurs without the female gamete being released, and subsequent events differ according to the species. In the simplest cases the zygote undergoes meiosis at once, producing haploid spores from which new haploid plants develop. This gives a life history with dominant haploid phase directly comparable with that described for several green algae (e.g. *Chlamydomonas*, *Volvox*, *Oedogonium*). However, other life histories follow a far less familiar pattern. In many of the common red algae of sea shores, the zygote develops into a multicellular diploid attached to the haploid plant. Diploid spores released from this parasitic phase grow into diploid plants which resemble the haploids in general morphology but do not form gametes. They produce haploid spores by meiosis, from which new haploid plants grow. This succession of three generations, one haploid and two diploid, is a type of life history unknown among other algae, or indeed in any other plants.

MYXOPHYCEAE

This class, also known as Cyanophyceae, is commonly referred to as the blue-green algae. The colour results from the presence of phycocyanin in addition to chlorophyll a and β-carotene. Members of Myxophyceae are distinguished by the lack of several features present in most other algae. They have no plastids and no nuclei: their pigments and their nucleic acids are dispersed in the protoplast. Nor is there any central vacuole in the cell. In all these features, blue-green algae show greater affinity with bacteria than with other algae. The principal reserve is a form of starch known as Myxophycean starch. The cell wall contains cellulose and is usually enveloped in a gelatinous layer of a pectic substance.

All blue-green algae are small, many of them being visible only with a microscope. Despite this, most species are multicellular. Many species consist of clusters of cells held together in a mass of mucilage with either a regular pattern or an irregular arrangement of cells. Other species are filamentous, among which a common genus is *Oscillatoria.* This takes its name from the slow, rhythmic movement of the tips of the filaments from side to side. Other filamentous genera show a gliding forward movement. The explanation of these movements is uncertain, though mechanisms which have been suggested include the secretion of mucilage and the alternate expansion and contraction of the filaments.

Because of their small size, blue-green algae are not a conspicuous part of the world's vegetation, though they are extremely widespread and can be found in habitats of many types. They occur in the plankton (see p. 525) of both the sea and fresh water; they occupy many damp terrestrial situations, and they are common in soil. Many species are able to fix atmospheric nitrogen, and some of these play an important part in maintaining soil fertility.

Reproduction is by cell division in the few unicellular species, and by fragmentation in the others. No sexual reproduction has been observed, though there is indirect evidence for a sexual process in one species. No flagellated cells are formed.

XANTHOPHYCEAE

This class is known as the yellow-green algae. Their characteristic colour is the result of a high concentration of β-carotene, often supplemented by yellow xanthophylls. The principal reserve is oil. These biochemical features are shared by a heterogeneous assortment of species, the relationships between which are not close.

Vaucheria

Species of *Vaucheria* are among the commonest representatives of the class. The genus shows great versatility, with some species inhabiting fresh water, others sea-water, and yet others thriving on the surface of damp soil. In all cases the plant body is a long, branched, tube-like filament, which is often 50μ in diameter. There are no transverse walls except following wounding or associated with reproductive structures. The wall has a thin lining of cytoplasm containing many nuclei and numerous discoid chloroplasts, and enclosing a central vacuole. Small droplets of oil in the cytoplasm are often a conspicuous feature. Terrestrial plants may have colourless rhizoidal outgrowths from the main filaments, which penetrate the soil or other substratum.

There is some reproduction by fragmentation, but asexual spores are also produced. Sporangia are formed at the tips of branches, and each is cut off by a transverse wall. The whole contents of a sporangium develop into one spore (Fig. 295, A), which in aquatic plants is a motile zoospore. It is multinucleate, with the nuclei arranged in the periphery and with a pair of flagella opposite each nucleus (Fig. 295, B). This unusual zoospore, with flagella attached over its whole surface, can, after settling down, germinate into a new plant. Terrestrial plants also produce one spore in each

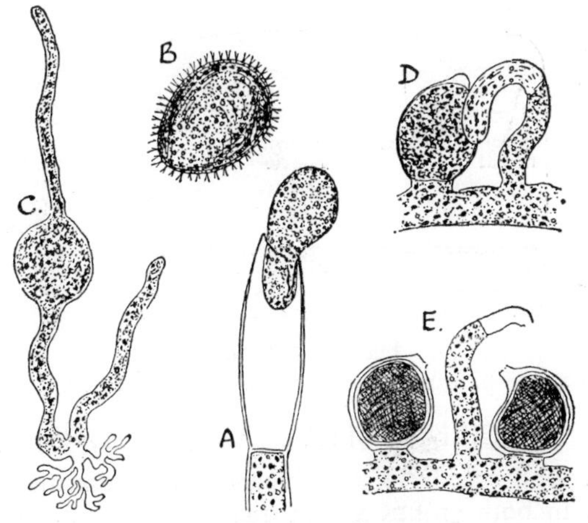

Fig. 295. *Vaucheria.*

A, zoosporangium releasing zoospore; B, zoospore; C, germinated zoospore; D, oogonium and antheridium; E, two oogonia each containing a zygote, with a dehisced antheridium between.

sporangium. The spore is multinucleate but has no flagella and is called an **aplanospore**. In species which can exist either submerged or in a terrestrial habitat, the type of spore produced is governed by the conditions at the time.

Sexual reproduction is oogamous, and all fresh-water species are homothallic with male and female organs developing side by side. The oogonium is a more or less spherical structure attached to a vegetative filament but partitioned off by a transverse wall across the short stalk (Fig. 295, D). The contents become a single oosphere with one nucleus. The wall of the oogonium has a prominent pore. The antheridium develops from a tube-like structure which grows out from the vegetative filament near the point of attachment of the oogonium. The terminal part of this outgrowth is cut off by a transverse wall (Fig. 295, D), and its contents divide into numerous antherozoids, each of which has two flagella. The antherozoids are liberated through a pore or pores in the antheridial wall, and have only a short distance to travel to reach the oogonial pore. Since the oosphere has only one nucleus, it can be presumed that a single antherozoid is sufficient to carry out fertilisation. The zygote develops a thick wall (Fig. 295, E) and is eventually liberated by breakdown of the oogonial wall. When it germinates it undergoes meiosis and develops directly into a new plant.

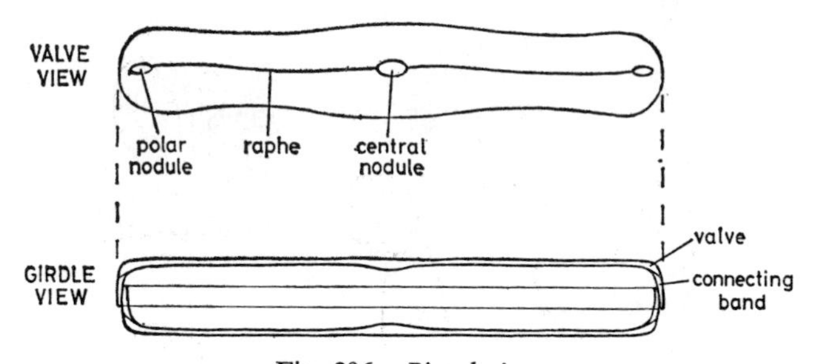

Fig. 296. *Pinnularia.*
A diatom which often comes to rest with valve face uppermost.

BACILLARIOPHYCEAE (DIATOMS)

Bacillariophyceae have some biochemical similarities to Xanthophyceae. In both groups a high quantity of carotenoid pigments gives individuals a yellowish colour, and in both the principal reserve is oil. But thc unique type of cell structure among the diatoms justifies their being placed in a separate class.

All diatoms are fundamentally unicellular, though the cells are sometimes joined into colonies. Each cell is enclosed in a rigid wall consisting of pectic material impregnated with silica. This silicified wall is known as a **frustule**, and there is great variation between species in its shape and construction. In the simplest cases the frustule consists of two closely fitting halves. These may have radial symmetry and resemble the two halves of a Petri dish (Fig. 300). Other species have only bilateral symmetry, and the frustule is more comparable with a date-box (Fig. 296). In both these types of diatom the half-frustule has one face which is more or less flat, known as the **valve** face, with an edge projecting at right angles from it. The edges of the two half-frustules are called **connecting**

bands since they form the connection between the two half-frustules of a complete diatom. The one half-frustule is slightly larger than the other, and their connecting bands overlap, forming the **girdle** of the cell. One therefore distinguishes between the valve view and the girdle view of a diatom, which may be as different from each other as the appearance of a Petri dish seen from above and seen from the side. Many diatoms usually come to rest with the valve face uppermost, so that this is the more familiar aspect. All the diatoms shown in Plate 17, for example, are seen in valve view. However, there are many species where the valve face is small in area and the girdle face much more extensive. This is so in species where the valve of each half-frustule is separated from

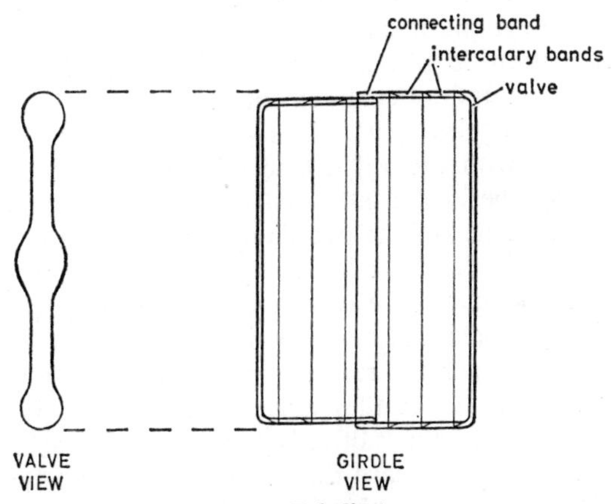

Fig. 297. *Tabellaria.*
A diatom which comes to rest with girdle face uppermost.

the connecting band by one or more **intercalary bands** (Fig. 297). Diatoms of this sort commonly come to rest with the girdle face uppermost.

It will be seen in Plate 17 that in addition to differences in shape, there are differences in the surface markings of the frustules. Every diatom species has a characteristic pattern of ridges, furrows, spots, and other markings which are extensively used in classification.

Outside the silicified wall there is a gelatinous layer. In colonial species it is this layer which joins cells together, and some strictly unicellular forms are attached to their substratum in a similar way.

On the inside, the frustule is lined with cytoplasm containing one or more irregularly shaped chloroplasts, a nucleus, and often droplets of oil. There is a central vacuole.

Some diatoms are capable of slow, rather jerky motion. *Pinnularia* (Plate 17) is a genus which shows this feature. It can be seen that in the centre of the valve face is a pore called the **central nodule** from which a narrow fissure (the **raphe**) extends to either end. At the extreme ends of the raphe are two more pores, called the **polar nodules** (Fig. 296). These are all part of the mechanism of locomotion. Although conclusive evidence is lacking, it appears that a current of cytoplasm moves out from the anterior polar nodule along the raphe and in through the central nodule. The friction of this current with the surrounding medium propels the cell in the opposite direction to the cytoplasmic current. Cells frequently reverse their direction of movement, presumably because polar nodules at opposite ends of the cell act alternately as the source of the cytoplasmic current.

Reproduction is usually by cell division. This begins with nuclear division and an enlargement of the protoplast which forces the two half-frustules apart. The protoplast then divides along a plane parallel with the valve face of the frustule, and each new protoplast synthesises a new half-frustule which fits inside the existing one. Thus, of the two daughter cells, one is the same size as the parent but the other is slightly smaller. If this process were to continue indefinitely, the average cell size would steadily decrease. This tendency is balanced by the periodical formation of **auxospores.** These are sometimes the result of fusion of protoplasts from two cells, but in other cases they are produced from single cells. In either case, the protoplasts of cells which are approaching minimum size for their species discard their frustules completely; if fusion is to take place it does so at this stage. There is then enlargement up to the maximum size for the species, and the synthesis of a new frustule which is not marked in the manner characteristic of normal cells. This enlarged cell is the auxospore, which by subsequent division gives rise to new vegetative cells.

Diatoms are found in a wide range of habitats, including both fresh and salt waters. They are also common in soil and in various other terrestrial habitats. Some species are extremely resistant to desiccation, and soil which has been kept dry for nearly fifty years has been shown to contain living diatoms. The silicified frustule is much more resistant to decay than the rest of the diatom cell, and bodies of water in which diatoms are plentiful accumulate a layer of empty frustules on the bottom, which may grow to a thickness of many feet under suitable conditions. In some places a layer of this sort has been raised above water level by geological changes, giving an accessible deposit of **diatomaceous earth**. This is quarried or mined on a considerable scale for a variety of uses such as heat insulation, the filtration of liquids, and as a mild abrasive.

EUGLENOPHYCEAE

Members of all the other classes of algae which have been described, whatever their biochemical differences, have metabolic systems which are comparable with those of higher plants. Most species possess pigments by means of which they can use the radiant energy of sunlight to synthesise organic compounds from inorganic raw materials. A few exceptional species lack these pigments and lead a saprophytic existence, taking in soluble organic substances from their surroundings. Similar exceptions are found among seed plants (p. 267), and there is no reason to doubt that these colourless organisms, whether among algae or higher groups, are rightly regarded as plants. The Euglenophyceae, however, are a group of flagellated micro-organisms whose status is open to dispute. Many species have photosynthetic pigments closely similar to those of higher plants, and are at least partly autotrophic. Of those pigmented species which have been studied some can, and regularly do, make use of organic substances from outside in addition to those they synthesise. Other species have no pigments and are completely saprophytic. Yet others are able to take in solid particles of organic material and digest them in a manner usually associated with animal life. The Euglenophyceae, therefore, stand on the borderline between the plant and animal kingdoms, and although some species are sufficiently alga-like to be mentioned here, euglenoid organisms are described and discussed, with equal justification, in textbooks of zoology.

Euglena

This genus, from which the class takes its name, includes many species which are common in fresh water, particularly if it is rich in organic matter. As with all members of the class, the individual is a single cell. The outer membrane of the cell is not rigid, so that although in general the organism is elongated (Fig. 298), the shape is not constant. During active movement there is continual change of shape brought about by alternate swelling and contraction of parts of the cell. The absence of a firm cell wall is a feature in which *Euglena* resembles many protozoa rather than plant cells.

At the anterior end of the cell, the membrane is invaginated to give a "gullet" consisting of a narrow neck and an expanded reservoir. Closely associated with the reservoir are several contractile vacuoles which discharge their contents into it. Thus in

Euglena the gullet seems to be primarily concerned with excretion, though in related genera which can ingest solid particles of food it acts as a mouth. A long flagellum, which is the main organ of locomotion, is attached to the wall of the reservoir and projects through the neck of the gullet. It has a swelling near its base, which lies opposite a granular red pigment spot beside the wall of the reservoir. The swelling is called the **photoreceptor**, and together with the pigment spot is believed to be responsible for the phototactic movements of the cell. There is also a second, shorter flagellum attached to the reservoir wall, but it does not extend beyond the gullet.

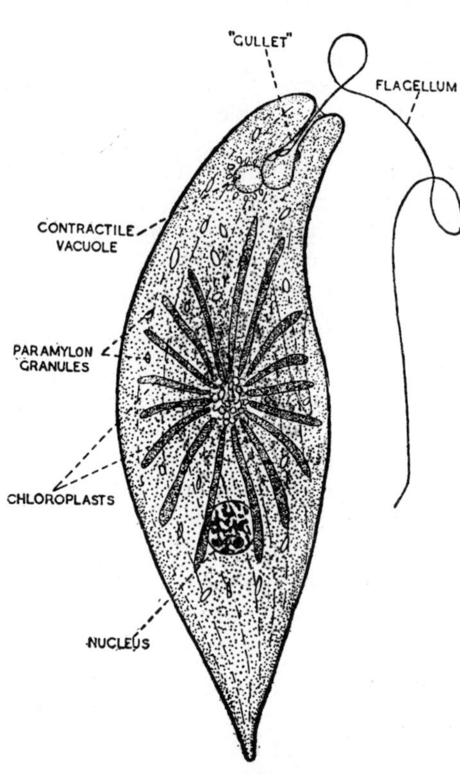

Fig. 298. *Euglena.*

In the body of the cell of a green species are several band- or disc-shaped chloroplasts which may be arranged in a regular pattern. The pigments they contain are almost identical with those of higher plants, but the principal reserve material is an insoluble carbohydrate called **paramylon** not known in any other plant group. Paramylon granules occur in a variety of shapes and sizes, though each species has granules of characteristic form. The cell has a single nucleus which is usually conspicuous.

Reproduction is by cell division. In the motile condition, division begins at the anterior end with duplication of the gullet, flagella, and associated structures, followed by longitudinal cleavage into two separate individuals. Alternatively, division may be preceded by encystment, when the cell comes to rest and secretes a wall around itself. Division occurs inside the cyst, and the release of motile daughter cells may occur only after a temporary palmelloid stage during which further divisions occur in a mass of mucilage. Fusion of cells and other events which might be part of a sexual process have been reported sporadically, but the evidence for sexual reproduction is incomplete.

THE ECONOMIC IMPORTANCE OF ALGAE

Most large bodies of water support the growth of a very considerable algal population. This is particularly obvious on a seashore where seaweeds grow in profusion, but the distribution of seaweeds is generally restricted to the coastline where the plants can be attached to a firm substratum while at the same time near enough to the surface to obtain sufficient light. The most striking exception to this rule is the brown alga *Sargassum natans* which exists in enormous floating masses far out to sea, and creates a navigational hazard near the West Indies in the area known as the Sargasso Sea. In by far the greater part of the sea, and in bodies of fresh water, the algal vegetation is dominated by microscopic species which are either free-floating or actively swimming, and which are collectively referred to as **plankton**. Though individually small, planktonic algae are very numerous and they form an important part of the community of living creatures in these waters. Being photosynthetic plants they have the important quality of adding to the organic content of the water. In this they are distinct from planktonic animals, which are also numerous. It is therefore useful to distinguish between **phytoplankton** (plants) and **zooplankton** (animals), though this classification breaks down in the case of organisms such as *Euglena* (p. 523). Zooplankton is largely dependent upon phytoplankton as a source of food. Both types of plankton are consumed by small fishes, which in turn are preyed upon by larger fishes. In this food-chain the planktonic algae are of fundamental importance since only they can synthesise organic compounds. One can justly claim therefore that the whole fisheries industry depends on phytoplankton, and algae must rank as outstanding contributors to world food supplies.

Plankton algae are not wholly beneficial to mankind, however. To the waterworks engineer, algae can be very troublesome. His task includes the treating of water from reservoirs, lakes, and rivers so that when it reaches the consumer it is fresh, clear, and free of harmful and unpleasant micro-organisms. The magnitude of this task varies greatly according to the source of water used, but whatever the source there is likely to be initially a considerable algal population. Much of London's water is supplied by the River Thames, which drains a large area of agricultural land and is therefore rich in mineral salts. This high salt concentration leads to prolific growth of planktonic algae, much of which must be removed by filtration. One of the most abundant species is the diatom *Fragilaria crotonensis*, and in certain seasons more than one ton by dry weight of this alga alone is removed each day. Other algae, notably members of Xanthophyceae and Myxophyceae, may be far less numerous but can lend an unpleasant taste or smell to the water. In such cases filtration may be ineffective, and chlorination or absorption with activated charcoal may be necessary to make the water acceptable to the consumer.

The difficulties of maintaining water supplies of good quality are increased by the seasonal periodicity of algae. The growth and multiplication of plankton algae are influenced by a number of factors, particularly temperature, light, and the supply of mineral salts. In the spring, for instance, increasing temperature, light intensity, and light duration cause a period of intense productivity which is maintained until the supply of minerals is depleted to the point of scarcity. This limiting factor will affect different types of alga in different ways. Diatoms, for example, with their silicified frustules, may be restricted from multiplying by a shortage of silica while other algae continue to increase in abundance. There is now a considerable body of information on the subject of algal periodicity, from which the waterworks engineer may be able to predict the extent of his problems sufficiently far in advance to take appropriate steps. He may foresee that in an approaching summer season when demands for water will be high, he will be dependent on a source of supply which is likely to be heavily populated with plankton algae. Unless he takes steps to prevent this, his filters will become choked and he will be unable to supply filtered water at the rate needed. One remedy is to treat his reservoir with a suitable algicide such as copper sulphate or potassium permanganate well in advance of the expected peak of algal frequency. This method has been used successfully to prevent the algal population from reaching unmanageable levels.

The direct utilisation of the larger algae, particularly seaweeds, is an attractive proposition since they represent a prolific crop which grows without cost or attention in situations which are not otherwise used. The plants are known to be sources of a great variety of useful products, but with some notable exceptions the enormous potential yield from marine algae has to be largely disregarded. The foremost reason for this apparent waste is that in most coastal waters the algae are very dispersed, extremely bulky and heavy when wet, and often awkward to harvest mechanically. Large-scale collection is therefore expensive, and where alternative sources of the products are available they are generally preferred. Potassium and iodine, for example, are valuable elements which can be extracted from seaweeds in considerable quantity, and local industries based on these processes have thrived in the past. But the discovery of accessible mineral deposits from which the same elements can be obtained more economically has led to the almost complete extinction of these industries.

In many parts of the world algae are collected as food for human consumption or for livestock. In Japan there is even an industry for cultivating the red alga *Porphyra* in a manner comparable with more orthodox agriculture. Special bamboo frames are set up in the shallow waters of sheltered bays and estuaries. The alga grows on these frames, and there is a regular sequence of "seeding" and harvesting. The product is used to make a popular foodstuff. Elsewhere, algae collected for food are mostly naturally occurring plants. Many coastal districts have their characteristic algal delicacies, which vary according to the species available and the local methods of preparation, but there is very little trade in algal foodstuffs. One factor which limits the usefulness of algae as food is that many of the proteins they contain are not easily digestible. Presumably the digestive systems of land animals have never developed enzymes suitable for this purpose.

There are several algal products of some commercial importance for which there appear to be no satisfactory substitutes. Agar, for example, is prepared from a number of red algae, particularly species of *Gelidium* and *Gracilaria*, and is far superior to any other known substance as a gelling agent in solid media for culturing bacteria and fungi (p. 533). This superiority results from the lack, in most organisms, of enzymes capable of decomposing agar. In contrast, there are several micro-organisms which can liquefy solid media made with gelatine. Agar also has a wide range of uses in the food and textile industries. The larger brown algae provide a source of alginic acid, another substance with unusual properties. Salts of the acid are extensively used in the food, pharmaceutical, and cosmetics industries as thickening and stabilising agents in creams, sauces, ointments, and similar products.

A very much longer list could be prepared of the industrial uses of algae and their derivatives. Although each item might be relatively trivial, the total picture would show that the algae have an important part to play in modern living.

19 FUNGI, BACTERIA, AND VIRUSES

Fungi are regarded as forming an important sub-division of the Thallophyta. There are, however, a number of ways in which they differ significantly from green plants and from animals, and it has been suggested that they form a fungal kingdom separate from either plants or animals. Their supposed derivation from algal ancestors, which was the main reason for their being studied by botanists, is *not* now generally accepted. The true fungi, including lichens, number about 100,000 known species.

Somatic Structure

While some fungi, such as yeasts, are unicellular, most have a filamentous somatic structure, the individual filaments being called **hyphae**. The hyphae are usually branched and collectively form the **mycelium**, which is the somatic thallus. This basic filamentous growth habit permits the development of a very wide variety of morphology in the fungal colony, which typically grows at the hyphal apices only and by branching expands the margins so that a more or less circular colony outline results. By a denser branching, and an interweaving of the separate hyphae a compact pseudoparenchymatous structure can result. In form this may be elongated and strand-like as in **rhizomorphs**, hard and compact, as in **sclerotia**, fleshy as in some sporocarps (fruit bodies), or hard and layer-like as in the outer protective wall of other sporocarps.

The hyphae in Phycomycetes, one of the four main classes of the fungi, are mainly **aseptate**, without cross walls, so that large parts of the colony consist of single multinucleate cells. These fungi are considered the more primitive forms. Active protoplasmic streaming can easily be seen in cultures of such fungi. The nuclei are very small and cannot be seen without special techniques. In colonies of such "aseptate" mycelium cross walls may be formed in connection with the development of reproductive structures, at senescence, and after wounding. Such cross walls are without pores and completely delimit one portion of the tubular filament from another. Fungi in other classes are septate from an early stage of hyphal growth. The septa here form at regular intervals behind the hyphal apex, and originate on the inside of the tubular wall as a narrow shelf which increases in width inwards to reduce the diameter of the pore. The septum does not, however,

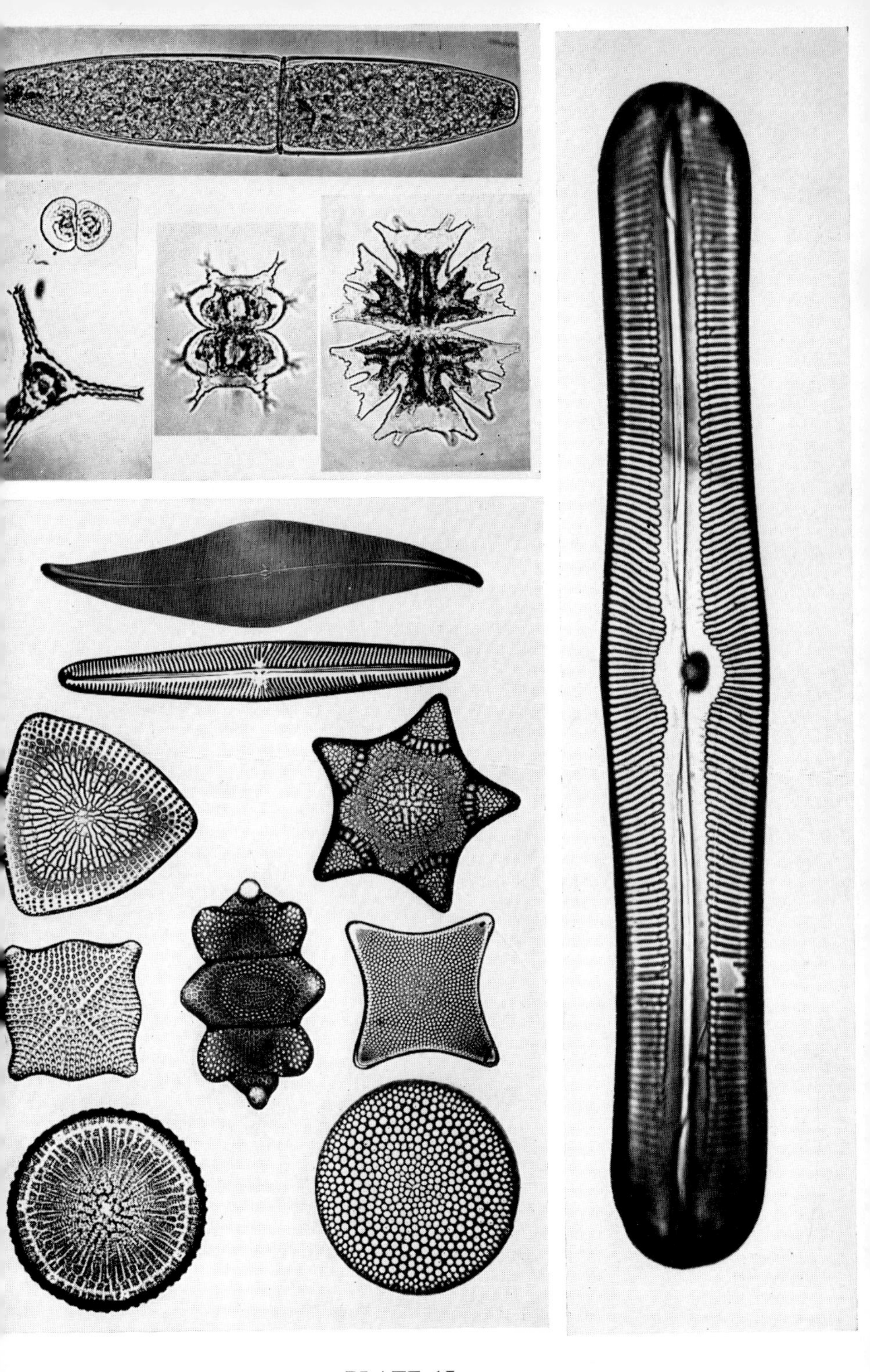

PLATE 17

DESMIDS AND DIATOMS.

Above left: A SELECTION OF DESMIDS (see p. 510).

Below left: A SELECTION OF DIATOMS (see p. 520).

Right: Pinnularia, A DIATOM, IN VALVE VIEW (cf. Fig. 296).

PLATE 18

CULTIVATED FORMS OF *Brassica oleracea*. The wild cabbage (*B. oleracea*) is a plant of no commercial importance, found in coastal districts of Britain. During centuries of cultivation, selection for enlargement of one part or another has led to the forms shown here.

Above: Kohl-rabi, with swollen stem.

Below left: Cauliflower, with swollen immature inflorescence.

Below right: Brussels sprout, with enlarged lateral buds.

(*All the above photographs are reproduced by kind permission of Messrs Sutton of Reading.*)

completely close this pore, which remains so that there is protoplasmic continuity from cell to cell. In Ascomycetes and Fungi Imperfecti, two of the major fungal divisions, the septum remains in this simple condition, but in Basidiomycetes, the fourth class of fungi, further elaboration occurs to produce the **dolipore septum** with its **parenthosomes** guarding the opening on both sides (Fig. 299). The details of this type of septum have only been seen clearly in electron microscope photographs. Perforate septa in the "higher" fungi permit the movement of cytoplasm from compartment to compartment, and even of nuclei in some cases, yet they give added rigidity to the tubular hyphae, and can be quickly plugged to prevent protoplasmic leakage on wounding.

Hyphae of species of both septate and aseptate types can under appropriate conditions break down into yeast-like masses of cells that grow by budding (see p. 559). The factors that induce this so-called **oidial** phase include ageing of the culture, anaerobiosis, and growth in solutions rich in sugars. Many fungi, under unfavourable conditions, show swelling of occasional hyphal cells, which become packed with reserve nutrients, often at the expense of adjacent cells, and produce a thick wall. Such cells are **chlamydospores,** and are more resistant to adverse environmental conditions than normal hyphae. Chlamydospores are very important in the biology of fungi in permitting fungi to withstand desiccation, ageing, nutrient shortage, anaerobiosis, and antagonism from other organisms.

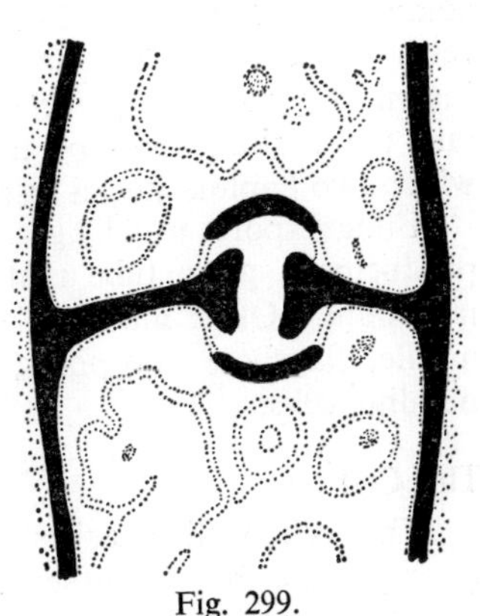

Fig. 299.
DOLIPORE SEPTUM IN SECTION, SHOWING PARENTHOSOMES.

Within the fungal colony there is a certain amount of differentiation of hyphae according to function. Hyphae may be specialised for absorbing nutrients, for translocating substances, for rapidly colonising new areas, or for reproduction.

Reproduction

The reproduction of fungi usually occurs by spores, which are very prolifically produced. Often these are single-celled and colourless, but they can be two- to several-celled, and may have a dark, melanin pigment in the wall (but not in the protoplasm) that helps to protect against damage from ultra-violet and blue light during aerial dissemination. Some are passively detached from their attachment to the mycelium by agencies like wind, rain splash, and vibration, but many fungi possess more or less intricate mechanisms favouring violent spore discharge thus ensuring that the spores get above the still air layer at the surface on which they grow and into turbulent air currents. One of the reasons for the obvious success of fungi in colonising new habitats is their very efficient dispersal of large numbers of spores. In addition to producing dispersal spores most fungi also produce resting spores or resting structures in substrata in which they have grown. In many species such spores are produced at a particular stage in the life-cycle, often before a season unfavourable for activity, and often connected with the sexual process. The sexual spores of Phycomycetes (oospores and zygospores) develop as a direct result of sexual fusion of gametes or gametangia. The ascospores of Ascomycetes and the basidiospores of Basidiomycetes develop from a cell in which two haploid nuclei fuse and then undergo meiosis.

Fungal spores usually germinate by imbibing water, swelling, and producing a germ tube that grows and branches to produce the mycelium. Other modes of germination include the production of motile, flagellate zoospores, of a spore-producing hypha, or of budding cells.

The Cell

The cell wall consists of cellulose in some Phycomycetes (Oomycetes), but in other Phycomycetes (Zygomycetes) and in septate fungi chitin, a polysaccharide based on the nitrogen-containing sugar, glucosamine, is its principal structural constituent. In yeasts the cell wall is largely composed of glucan, a polymer of glucose in which the units are linked differently from those in cellulose, and mannan, a polymer of the hexose sugar, mannose. Irrespective of its chemical composition the wall is built up of long fibrils laid down in layers as is the cellulose in green plants. These layers are mainly of parallel orientated fibrils that confer rigidity on the wall. A more random orientation exists at the hyphal apex where the wall is plastic and extending.

The protoplasm within the cell wall appears rather uniform and homogeneous near the growing tip, but contains small particulate bodies such as nuclei, small vacuoles, mitochondria, and Golgi apparatus that may be detected by phase contrast microscopy or by appropriate staining of fixed, killed material. There is an endoplasmic reticulum and a boundary tonoplast layer. Storage products include glycogen, oils, and the carbohydrate trehalose. Starch does not occur as a storage product in fungi. Further back from the apex the vacuoles become larger, and with age large oily globules appear. A highly vacuolate appearance in fungi indicates a moribund condition. The vacuoles in septate as well as aseptate mycelium probably serve to push cytoplasm and assimilated nutrients towards the growing tips which elongate more rapidly than they are able to produce cytoplasm and thus depend on a supply from older parts of the mycelium. Mycelium more than a few days old is in many fungi senescent, its protoplasm having been used up in supplying younger growing regions or in the production of reproductive bodies.

Nutrition

All fungi, like viruses and most bacteria, are heterotrophic. They do not make any dry weight increase in the absence of organic food substances. No fungi are able to photosynthesise or to use carbon dioxide as their sole source of carbon.

Some yeasts can use materials as simple as acetate as sources of carbon but for most fungi simple sugars are the most readily utilised carbon substrate. Glucose is suitable for almost all fungi, and sucrose and maltose are also generally suitable. Fewer fungi are able to utilise starch, and still fewer, cellulose. A number of fungi are able to make good growth on fats as sole carbon source.

All fungi can utilise an organic source of nitrogen such as protein, peptides, or an amino-acid. Many fungi also find a suitable source of nitrogen in ammonium salts, though fewer are able to utilise nitrates or nitrites, and the last can be toxic quite apart from suitability as nitrogen source. Organic sources of nitrogen can also be used by fungi as sources of carbon.

Some fungi are completely self-supporting (autotrophic) for vitamins, needing no exogenous supply for growth to occur. Others have requirements for particular vitamins and are said to be heterotrophic in this respect, though the term **auxotrophic** is also used to distinguish this disability from carbon heterotrophy. Some fungi, for instance species of *Phycomyces*, are particularly sensitive to the supply of vitamins and are used in the biological assay of small amounts of these materials. In the presence of low concentrations of the deficient vitamin the amount of growth is strictly proportional to the concentration and can give an accurate measure. Thiamin is the commonest vitamin requirement among fungi, though some also need pyridoxine, nicotinic acid, and pantothenic acid.

Mineral nutrition of fungi is in some ways similar to that of higher plants. Fungi need potassium, phosphorus (as phosphate), magnesium, and sulphur (as sulphate) in fairly large amounts. Calcium is not required in large quantities, although some fungi appear to need it as a micronutrient. Iron acts as a minor element, as do manganese, zinc, molybdenum, copper, boron, and cobalt. Fungi that are **obligate parasites** may require some of their nutrients as unstable intermediates. They are unable to find adequate nutrition from a dead host, and are physiologically confined to a strictly parasitic existence. A fungus without such particular requirements can find a dead substratum adequate for growth, and may be a **saprophyte**. Some such fungi are completely unable to tolerate any host defence mechanisms (host resistance) and are consequently obligate saprophytes. Between the two extremes are fungi that can live as saprophytes and also, on some hosts, as parasites. Some of these are very well adapted to parasitic existence and less well adapted to antagonism from other microbes, so that while in isolation they may grow well as saprophytes, in nature after the death of their host they decline and soon cease activity. Such fungi are facultative saprophytes, and have also been described as ecologically obligate parasites, reflecting their role in nature, but not their nutritional characteristics. Still other fungi are in nature mainly saprophytic but may occasionally infect a living host and cause disease particularly when the host is weakly or unhealthy to begin with. Such fungi are called facultative parasites.

Decomposable materials in nature support an ecological succession of fungi that is based in part on nutritional properties of the colonisers. The progression moves generally through the decomposition of easily utilised sugars, then starches, next cellulose, and finally lignin. The later stages progress more slowly, and the whole course of succession may take years in massive plant parts like tree stumps and roots. Other materials show the succession more quickly. The dung of herbivorous animals presents a rapid succession from Phycomycetes in the early stages, through Fungi Imperfecti and Ascomycetes, to Basidiomycetes finally.

Wood decay, both of standing trees and of structural timber, is caused by fungi. **Brown rots** or corrosive rots result from attack by species of fungi that remove the structural cellulose but leave the lignin as a dry, cracked, crumbly material. *Merulius lacrymans*, the cause of the common dry rot in houses, shows this behaviour. The fungus needs damp wood to colonise and begin activity but once it is growing sufficient water is produced in respiration to allow further growth on adjacent, initially dry timber. This fungus, moreover, may by its mycelial strands transport water for several yards through inert masonry to a fresh source of timber which even if dry may be attacked. **White rots** or destruction rots result from the removal of lignin from the timber by fungi. Some of these remove the cellulose as well leaving an ashy powder, while others may only incompletely utilise the cellulose, leaving stringy white strands or pockets in the timber.

Culture Methods

When growing in nature fungi commonly exist as poorly differentiated mycelium and may lack the characteristic structures that are needed to permit identification. For this reason and also for the examination of many aspects of the behaviour of the individual species fungi are best studied growing alone in the laboratory under controlled conditions. This type of growth, without the presence of contaminating organisms, is called an **axenic** or **pure culture**, and may be supported on a chemically and physiologically defined substratum. The earliest method was to grow fungi in liquid or "broth" culture, and this is still the best for accurate biochemical studies where very pure substrates need to be used. For such cultures growth has to be measured as increase in dry weight, and morphological studies are difficult because of the danger of disarranging or damaging the delicate mycelium. It is much more convenient for general work with fungi to use a "solid" or gelled medium. The first gelling agent to be used was gelatine but this has a number of serious disadvantages. Being a protein it is itself decomposed by a number of micro-organisms, mostly bacteria. It also changes to a liquid at temperatures higher than 28° C. which limits its use for many investigations. Agar, or agar-agar, is now almost universally used as a gelling agent in culture media. It is a carbohydrate derived from the tissues of various seaweeds but is fortunately resistant to attack of all micro-organisms except a few uncommon marine bacteria. No fungus is known that can decompose agar. When used at a concentration of about 2 per cent. in nutrient solutions it gives a medium that is more or less solid at normal temperatures, and that does not melt until about 100° C., so permitting incubation at high temperatures. On cooling, the medium solidifies again at about 40° C. and so allows the incorporation in it of spores or cells, where it is desired to prepare a culture by "seeding" or inoculating throughout, without risk of the inoculum being damaged by long exposure to high temperatures. Fungi are commonly grown in agar in a Petri dish (Fig. 300). The melted agar is poured into the base and the lid covers it; the whole is then called an **agar plate.** Plate cultures provide a relatively large surface for the growth of fungi. Agar is also used in test-tubes plugged with cotton wool, or in screw-top phials, the container being slanted during the cooling and setting of the medium, so as to produce an **agar slope.** Slopes take up less space than plates and are less liable to accidental contamination by unwanted micro-

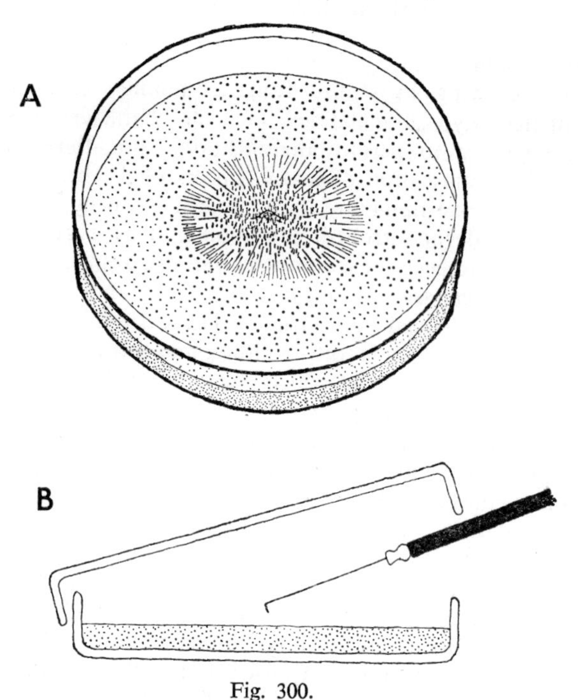

Fig. 300.
A, Petri dish base, with fungus colony on agar; B, Petri dish, inoculating needle and agar.

organisms, and are thus particularly useful for storage of stock cultures in culture collections.

Appropriate precautions must be taken to exclude unwanted organisms from pure cultures. Glassware is sterilised in dry air ovens at 160° C. for four hours. Agar and liquid media are sterilised in large pressure cookers called **autoclaves** at a pressure of 15 lb. per sq. in. (equivalent to 121° C.) for twenty minutes. The inoculum which may be of mycelium or spores is transferred from the parent pure culture to the prepared sterile medium in its sterile container with a needle or loop of platinum or nichrome wire that has previously been sterilised by flaming to redness and then cooled. After inoculation the plate or slope is closed and incubated under the desired conditions to await growth.

Variation in Fungi

Fungi are notoriously variable, both in nature and in the laboratory, and this variation may occur in respect of biological behaviour, morphology, or physiology. This potentiality for variation is of advantage to fungi in nature in their role as versatile opportunists. In culture the variation may appear obvious as a sector of the circular colony that differs from the parent culture in form, colour, sporulation, amount of aerial mycelium, or growth rate. When the genetical basis of the change is not known the process is called **saltation**, and the variant form a **saltant**. Less obvious changes may occur and may be more gradual, taking several to many transfers in pure culture before they are noticed. These may be the result of an unconscious selection during culture. Variants having particular properties such as high growth rate may be favoured by the method of transfer or by the culture medium used, and these properties may be linked with other, sometimes more important, ones. Amount of sporulation or the production of pigments, enzymes, and antibiotics may change in this way in culture.

There are several mechanisms by which variation may occur in fungi. Some types of variation are **environmental** and non-genetic. Changes of this sort, caused by changes in environment, are reversible in new growth produced on return to the original culture conditions. **Mutation** occurs very commonly in fungal cultures. This is not surprising since a fungus colony in culture often contains many more than 10^8 nuclei. At normal mutation rates the fact that variant forms are common in colonies is perfectly explicable. **Sexual recombination** occurs in fungi and permits re-assortment of genetic material with the production of forms different from the parental types. Some members of the Fungi Imperfecti, which are defined as having no known sexual stage in the life-cycle, are now known to possess a mechanism allowing in somatic hyphae diploidisation and subsequent reduction division with exchange of genetic material between the combinant nuclei. This process is called the **parasexual phenomenon. Heterokaryosis** occurs in fungi, and is a process whereby, through fusions between hyphae of different genotypes, nuclei having different genetic properties may occupy a single cell in the mycelium. A heterokaryon constituted in this way from a pool of available nuclei might possess a very wide range of potentialities. The system is unique to fungi, and is an especially labile one since the properties of the mycelium may be altered by a shift in the relative proportions of the different constituent nuclei, or more drastically by the deletion from the new growth of one or more of the nuclear types. A mycelium containing only one type of nucleus is called a monokaryon, and is monokaryotic. Some properties of fungi which depend upon particular metabolic pathways are inherited not directly via the nucleus, but through cytoplasmic particles. Unequal partition of such particles to daughter cells in cell division may lead to an absence of the particles and hence a loss of the associated property in some cells. Limitations in aerobic respiration in the *Neurospora* strain, "poky", and the yeast strain, "petite", have been identified as due to **cytoplasmic variation** in this way.

The surprising rate and degree of variation shown by fungi is partly attributable to their possession of a range of mechanisms for variation greater than that of other organisms and partly to their relatively short generation time. They have been described as a "treacherous and mutable race".

SYSTEMATIC TABLE OF FUNGI DESCRIBED IN THIS CHAPTER

Genus	Group	Class
Saprolegnia	Oömycetes	Phycomycetes
Pythium		
Phytophthora		
Peronospora		
Albugo		
Mucor	Zygomycetes	
Aspergillus	(Fungi Imperfecti)	Ascomycetes
Penicillium		
Erysiphe		
Monilinia		
Saccharomyces		
Puccinia		Basidiomycetes
Agaricus		

SAPROLEGNIA

This is an aquatic genus typically found in fresh, clear water. The species are mainly saprophytes preferring substrata rich in protein, and requiring sulphur and nitrogen in organic form. Some species grow in damp soil, and one is a parasite of fresh-water fish. Species are very easy to isolate and to culture by suspending a suitable bait, such as boiled split hemp seed, dead flies, or ants' "eggs" just below the surface of water from a pond or stream. Rhizoidal feeding hyphae penetrate the substratum and are usually not seen, but very wide, non-septate hyphae extend from the substratum into the water where they branch freely. After several days asexual reproduction (Fig. 301) begins by the tips of some of these hyphae becoming slightly swollen and club-shaped. Each is delimited by a cross wall from its supporting hypha to form a zoosporangium. The dense contents of the zoosporangium consist of a multinucleate mass of cytoplasm that differentiates by cleavage into a large number of uninucleate, naked, pear-shaped zoospores, each with two flagella at the pointed end. The zoospores escape

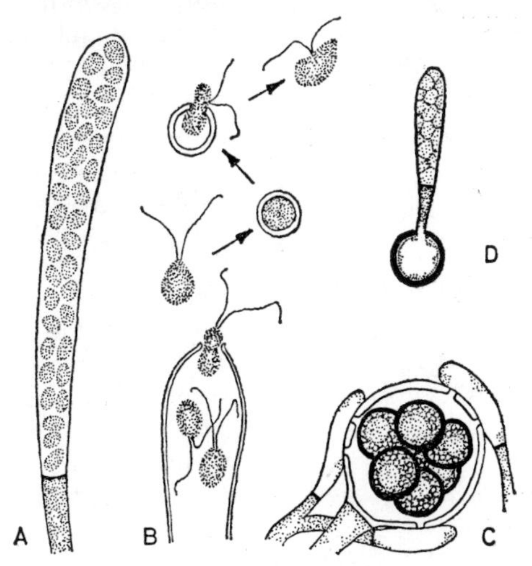

Fig. 301. *Saprolegnia*.

A, sporangium; B, liberation of zoospores, and diplanetic stages; C, oogonium with antheridia and oospores; D, germinating oospore.

from the sporangium through a terminal pore that suddenly develops at maturity. After swimming pointed end forward for a period each zoospore withdraws its flagella, rounds off, and encysts by secreting a wall. It rests for a short period before germinating by the emergence from within the cyst wall of a zoospore that is kidney-shaped, with its two flagella attached at the concave side. One flagellum is orientated forward and one to the rear during this second motile phase (Fig. 301, B). The possession of two types of zoospore is called **diplanetism**, and the process of encystment followed by production of a further motile stage is **repeated emergence**. Both phenomena are characteristic of this group of water moulds. In the absence of a suitable substratum further repeated emergence can occur with successive production of zoospores of the secondary type. When a zoospore makes contact with a substratum it encysts and germinates by a germ tube that branches to colonise the material. Further series of zoosporangia may develop within the discharged one by upward growth of the cross wall at the base.

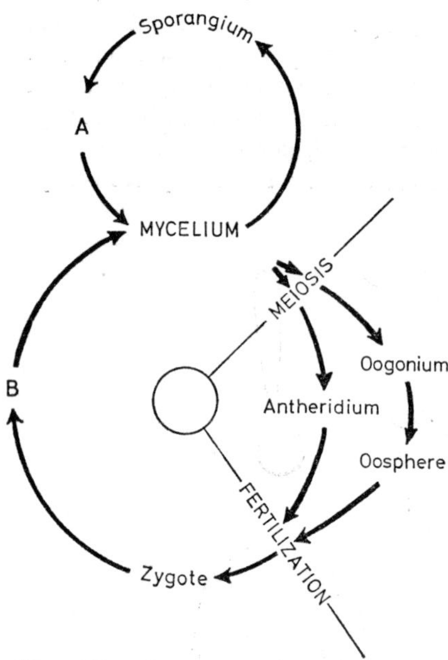

Fig. 302. GENERALISED LIFE-CYCLE FOR OOMYCETES.

At point "A" *Saprolegnia, Pythium,* and *Albugo* give zoospores; *Phytophthora* may give zoospores, or the sporangium may germinate directly; *Peronospora* has the sporangium germinating directly always. At point "B" *Saprolegnia* and *Pythium* produce a sporangium that liberates zoospores; *Albugo* differentiates zoospores within the germinating oospore, and *Phytophthora* may also do this, but may also show direct germination of oospores. *Peronospora* always shows direct germination of the oospore.

Sexual reproduction (Fig. 301, C) occurs in older cultures when the substratum or the surrounding water becomes unsuitable for further somatic growth. Short lateral branches of the hyphae bear spherical female gametangia, the oogonia, which are multinucleate. Several nuclei persist near the centre of each oogonium; the others migrate to the periphery and become disorganised. From five to ten uninucleate gametes, or oospheres, are differentiated by cleavage of the protoplasm about the remaining functional nuclei. The male gametangia, or antheridia, are multinucleate and develop as narrow branches from nearby hyphae from which they are delimited by a cross wall. They grow towards the oogonium and when one makes contact with its wall a very narrow fertilisation tube penetrates the wall and grows towards one of the oospheres where its tip bursts liberating the contents to fuse with those of the oosphere. A single male nucleus fuses with the oosphere nucleus to give a diploid zygote nucleus. Each of the oospheres may be fertilised in this way. A fertilised oosphere develops a thick smooth wall to become an oospore that contains fatty globules of reserve nutrients. **Apogamy**, the development of an oospore from an oosphere without fertilisation, is frequently observed. Some members of the Saprolegniaceae are dioecious, with separate male and female thalli, and the various processes involved in the initiation and development of their gametangia are controlled by a rather intricate system of hormones. The oospores are liberated by decay of the substratum, the mycelium, and the oogonial wall, and may remain inactive for long periods. Eventually the oospore germinates to give a short germ tube bearing a terminal sporangium that produces zoospores (Fig. 301, D). Meiosis has for long been thought to occur on germination of the oospore, the mycelium being regarded as haploid. However, very recent work has indicated that in species of *Saprolegnia* and *Pythium* meiosis occurs during the formation of the oospheres and antheridia, and that the diploid oospore germinates to give a diploid somatic mycelium. If confirmed these observations may result in a complete revision of opinion on life-cycles throughout the Oomycetes.

PYTHIUM

The genus includes both aquatic and terrestrial species. *P. debaryanum* is a much-studied species that lives in soil as a saprophyte but that can cause disease in seedlings or weakly plants. Even as a pathogen it lives on dead tissues, since the invading hyphae secrete toxins that diffuse in advance of the fungal growth and kill the host cells. The mycelium is coenocytic and the hyphae grow intracellularly in and through the dead cells. Several days after infection, particularly under conditions of high humidity or in the presence of free water, asexual reproduction by globose, terminal sporangia occurs at the surface of the host. Each sporangium contains a multinucleate protoplast that discharges through a pore to form a vesicle outside the sporangium where it cleaves into uninucleate, biflagellate, kidney-shaped zoospores (Fig. 303). The vesicle bursts to liberate the zoospores which swim in the water film, then settle down and encyst. Each germinates by a germ tube and can renew infection. Under dry conditions no sporangia develop.

At a later stage in infection sexual reproduction (Fig. 304) takes place deep in the host tissues. The oogonium is globose and contains a single multinucleate oosphere surrounded by a distinct, clear zone of cytoplasm called **periplasm** to which all but one of the nuclei move and there degenerate. An antheridium develops usually on the same hypha as the oogonium and also contains finally only one functional nucleus. The contents of the antheridium pass through a fertilisation tube into the oosphere where the two nuclei fuse. The zygote becomes a thick-walled, smooth, oospore, and after decay of the putrescent host tissues rests in the soil until stimulated into germination by a suitable nutrient material. At temperatures higher than 20° C. oospores may germinate by germ tube, at lower temperatures a vesicle is extruded containing the protoplasm which differentiates into zoospores. As in *Saprolegnia*, it was until recently thought that meiosis occurred on germination of the oospore, but there is now evidence that the mycelium is

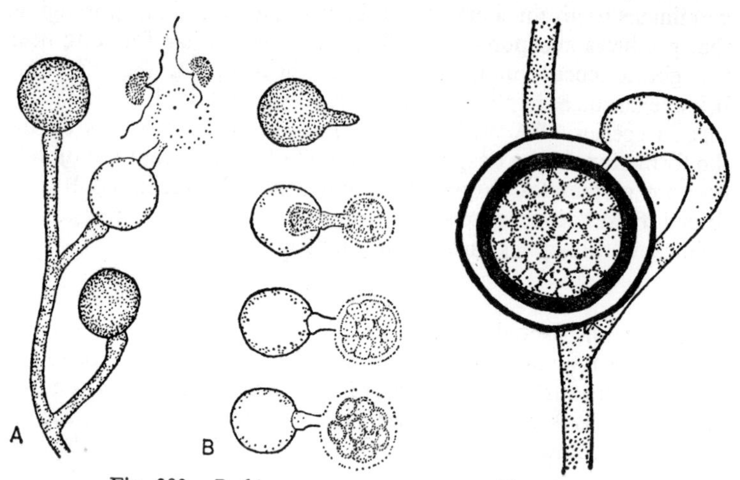

Fig. 303. *Pythium*.
A, sporangium; B, stages in germination of sporangium.

Fig. 304. *Pythium*.
Oogonium with antheridium and oospore.

diploid and that meiosis takes place during the development of the antheridia and oogonia.

PHYTOPHTHORA

Phytophthora is better adapted to terrestrial conditions than *Pythium* being less dependent on free water for reproduction. The genus is mainly parasitic and contains several economically important pathogens. *P. infestans*, the causal organism of late blight of potato, was one of the contributory factors in the potato famine in Ireland from 1847 onwards. It still continues to cause serious losses in potato crops. It is an ecologically obligate parasite that in nature depends on the host for activity. The tissues of the potato plant are parasitised by intercellular aseptate hyphae that have branched, fine haustoria penetrating the host cells and absorbing food from them. Branched sporangiophores are produced at the surface of the infected leaves and stems through stomata (Fig. 305, B). Pear-shaped sporangia are borne on the sporangiophores laterally and terminally. These are lightly attached and easily dislodged. The sporangia are dispersed intact, by splash droplets or by contact with adjacent leaves. They lose their viability if they fail to germinate within a few hours. Germination of the detached sporangium occurs in water. At temperatures around 20° C. the sporangium produces a germ tube, but at lower temperatures, around 12-15° C., the multinucleate protoplasm cleaves into five or six uninucleate zoospores within the sporangium. These are then liberated through a pore that develops in the wall (Fig. 305, C). This mode of germination without an extruded vesicle differentiates *Phytophthora* from *Pythium*. The kidney-shaped, laterally biflagellate zoospores may swim for a few hours in surface films of water before coming to rest and each producing a germ tube. The germ tube attaches itself to the host surface by an appressorium, the underside of which produces a fine tubular infection peg that mechanically penetrates through the cuticle into an epidermal cell before swelling out to normal hyphal diameter. Intercellular hyphae with haustoria are produced by further growth and branching. The lesion resulting from this infection may under warm and humid conditions begin to produce a further crop of sporangia in five or six days. Very rapid spread of the disease is possible under such conditions.

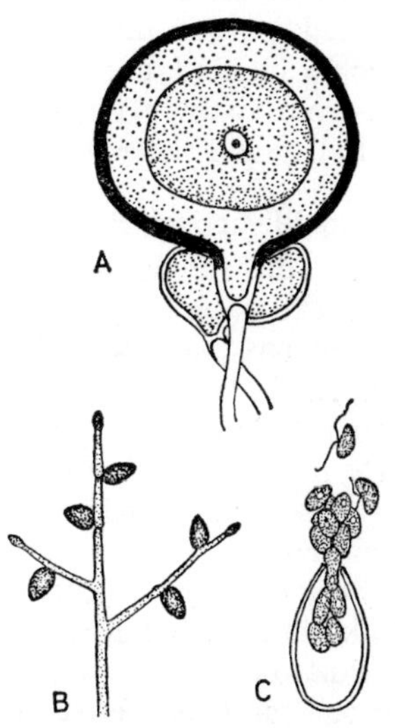

Fig. 305. *Phytophthora infestans*. A, oogonium with amphigynous antheridium; B, sporangiophore; C, Sporangium liberating zoospores.

The sexual stage is rare in most parts of the world but occurs commonly in Mexico. It depends on the meeting of two compatible mating strains. The disease is common in most of North America, in Europe, and in South Africa, and in these countries it seems that only one or the other of these strains occurs in any area and oospores are not produced. Where the two strains occur in a host near together gametangia develop. The more or less globose antheridium arises first and then from the other strain an oogonial branch grows through the centre of this and expands above it to form the oogonium which is thus surrounded at its base by the now collar-like antheridium (Fig. 305, A). Each strain produces both male and female gametangia but mating can only occur between compatible strains. Fertilisation normally occurs by fertilisation tube, although parthenogenetic development has been described. The oospore eventually germinates after decay of the host to produce either a germ tube or a short sporangiophore bearing a sporangium. Over-wintering of the fungus occurs by oospores where these are produced, but the usual mode of survival through winter is as mycelium in infected potato tubers remaining in the ground. The tubers become infected not by growth of the fungus down the haulm but from sporangia that are washed down from infected leaves on to exposed tubers.

Potato Blight and Plant Pathology

The disease resulting from infection by *P. infestans* shows its worst effects on the green parts of the plant which in severe attacks are soon reduced to a brown putrescent mass. In dry or cool weather the fungus does not spread rapidly from plant to plant and there is little loss in yield. If warm humid weather occurs relatively early in the year the disease spreads rapidly if not controlled by the grower and tuber yield may be considerably reduced. When blight conditions first occur relatively late in crop growth the tops may be destroyed by the fungus without interfering greatly with yield, but heavily infected tubers may rot in store.

Potato blight was first recorded in Britain in 1845. It is one of the comparatively few constantly recurring plant diseases of considerable economic importance in the British Isles. Its epidemiology is discussed here as it shows that much more than a knowledge of the bare life-cycle is necessary to help control disease. The severity and importance of the disease is largely dependent on local weather conditions. In south-west England and in Ireland unprotected crops may be severely damaged in almost any year, whereas in south and south-east England this is so only in about four years in every ten. In the north serious damage is rare, although the disease may develop late in crop growth, but without seriously affecting the yield or quality of the tubers.

Blight begins each year in the field in isolated patches starting on stems and leaves arising from lightly infected tubers planted or left in the ground. Only a small proportion of such tubers produces aerial parts that contain the fungus. In one study only twenty-one out of 3,260 infected, but viable, tubers were capable of acting as infection foci. Visible and sporulating lesions appear on such plants about nine to ten weeks after planting, and further infection within the crop and in neighbouring crops depends very greatly on weather. In dry weather and in young plants where the relative humidity around the leaves remains low there is no serious spread. In well-grown plants with luxuriant dense foliage, rainy and dull weather can favour the development in the crop of a relative humidity of more than 90 per cent. that persists for fairly long periods. Two to three weeks after a spell of such conditions obvious field outbreaks may be seen. Similar weather conditions early in crop growth do not give the same results, since the ecoclimate is more important than overall local climate. Plants infected with the virus disease "leaf roll" are more susceptible to blight because of the different microclimate about the leaves. It is remarkable that vigorous growth of the crop favours its most destructive pathogen. During hot, dry summer weather the mycelium can survive in stem lesions for more than forty days, but does not spread or sporulate until conditions become favourable again.

Spraying with Bordeaux mixture, which is copper sulphate and quicklime in water, is effective in preventing epidemic outbreaks of disease. The spray deposit on the leaves slowly releases soluble copper compounds that are more toxic to the sporangia of the pathogen than to the leaves of the host, and they prevent germination and infection. Other copper compounds such as copper oxychloride and cuprous oxide have also been successfully used as sprays. The economic value of spraying is not easy to assess. The cost of the materials and their application, and the damage to the crop by spray and machinery have to be balanced against the value of any increase in yield that may result from control of the disease. In a period or an area where the level of disease is low spraying may easily be uneconomic. In Yorkshire, for instance, it is rarely worth while. In one area near the Wash it was found from a ten-year study that it paid to spray in three only of these years, which were "blight" years; in three other years yields were substantially depressed as a result of spraying. One factor to be considered is that blight weather is also good potato growing weather so that it is possible for a crop to become diseased in a blight year and yet give a better yield than one in the same area in a "no-blight" year.

Spraying becomes more economic when used in conjunction with disease forecasting. If in any disease a good correlation can be found between certain weather conditions and the subsequent appearance of disease then it may be possible on the occurrence of such conditions to give a warning in time for the plants to be protected. In this way spraying can be done only when it appears economically necessary. The correlation is rarely easy, but for some diseases, and potato blight is one, meteorologic and disease data have been analysed and a valid relationship established. For this disease the method that is normally adopted is based on the Beaumont period, a period of forty-eight hours with a temperature of not less than 10° C. and a relative humidity not below 75 per cent. Given a sufficiently advanced stage of plant growth and the presence of an inoculum focus, blight usually appears seven to twenty-one days after such conditions. Since 1950 this system has been the basis of a national collaborative scheme for blight forecasting on a regional macroclimate basis.

The large-scale rotting of tubers by blight during storage is a result of damage allowing infection by *P. infestans* during the harvesting of the tubers. By killing the haulms of an infected crop before the tubers are harvested this loss can be controlled, since the inoculum is then removed before the tubers are lifted. Compounds that have been used include sulphuric acid, copper sulphate, tar acid compounds, and sodium chlorate. In addition to preventing tuber rot haulm killing has advantages in clearing the ground, making harvesting easier, helping to avoid late infection by viruses in tubers saved for seed, and is also used to restrict tuber size for seed potatoes.

Different varieties of potato differ in their resistance to blight, and breeding programmes aimed at producing better and more resistant varieties are being pursued in several countries. There are a number of reactions of plants to infection that can be useful in reducing the damage done to the crop as a whole. **True resistance** directly limits infection and spread in the host, **tolerance** to infection allows an infected plant to continue activity and thus produce a crop, while **hypersensitivity**, in which a diseased plant part, or even the whole plant, is very rapidly killed by the pathogen, limits growth of the pathogen and prevents it forming an effective inoculum for the infection of other plants. **Field resistance** in a crop may incorporate any of these mechanisms.

P. infestans, like some other important disease-causing organisms, exists in different **physiologic races**, and potato varieties differ in their susceptibility to the different physiologic races. This considerably complicates the breeding programmes, particularly since even a low level of cross-fertilisation between different races of the fungus may give rise to new physiologic races with different pathogenic properties.

P. infestans, as well as causing potato blight, can cause a blight of tomato where plants are grown out of doors, but the disease is not usually serious. The fungus has also been observed on wild plants such as species of *Solanum*, *Petunia*, *Lycium*, and *Datura*. The fungus is unable to survive for long as a saprophyte.

PERONOSPORA

Peronospora parasitica, an obligate parasite of members of the Cruciferae, is not an important pathogen of cultivated plants. The

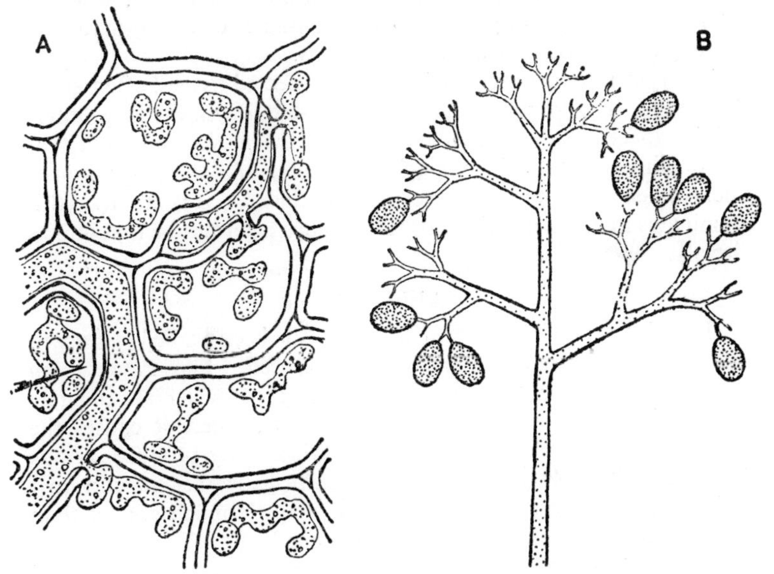

Fig. 306. *Peronospora*.
A, mycelium and haustoria; B, sporangiophore.

somatic mycelium is coenocytic, and intercellular in the host, and produces large forked haustoria that penetrate the living host cells (Fig. 306, A). The fungus does not immediately kill the cells of the host, and may even stimulate them to abnormal growth so that gross distortions of infected stems, leaves, and flowers result.

Branched sporangiophores (Fig. 306, B) are produced externally on the host and often in such large numbers as to give a whitish, cottony appearance to the surface of the infected organ. The term **downy mildews** is applied to diseases caused by this and related pathogens because of this property. The asexual sporangia are produced terminally on the sporangiophores, and are easily detached and dispersed by air currents. When mature the sporangiophores twist jerkily with changes in atmospheric humidity and this helps to dislodge the sporangia. Sporangia of this species are unable to produce zoospores and by analogy with asexual structures in the Fungi Imperfecti some authorities refer to them as "conidia", and to the sporangiophores as "conidiophores". Their homologies, however, are clearly with sporangia and sporangiophores in fungi like *Phytophthora.* Germination occurs in a drop or film of water on the host leaf or stem, and a germ tube is produced that wanders over the surface until its tip approaches an open stoma, which it enters to set up infection. Under suitable conditions further sporangia are produced after several days.

The sexual process occurs deep in the infected tissues, often in the stem pith. The oogonia and antheridia develop in the large intercellular spaces, and are similar to those of *Saprolegnia* except that the oogonium has only a single oosphere. After fertilisation a thick-walled resting oospore is produced. Eventually this germinates in contact with a host to produce a germ tube that infects directly.

ALBUGO

The fungus *Albugo candida* has also been called *Cystopus candidus* and this name is still sometimes used. Like *Peronospora* it is a member of the order Peronosporales, all of which are obligate parasites. It also attacks cruciferous plants, where it causes the "white rust" or "blister rust" disease which may produce serious damage. When *A. candida* and *P. parasitica* together infect a host their action is synergistic, in that the damage is much greater than the sum of that done by the two independently The coenocytic mycelium of *Albugo* is intercellular in the host, but the haustoria here are small and knob-like (Fig. 307, A). After several days growth in the host, pads of mycelium are formed in local areas just below the epidermis, and from these pads arise short, stout, unbranched sporangiophores arranged in a dense palisade-like layer (Fig. 307, B). Each of the club-shaped sporangiophores produces from its tip a series of multinucleate sporangia in a chain, the oldest distal and the youngest near the tip. The mass of sporangia above each mycelial pad accumulates so that the pressure pushes up the overlying epidermis causing a small visible blister. The pressure eventually bursts this to liberate masses of the dry, powdery sporangia which are disseminated by air currents. When a sporangium falls on a moist, susceptible plant surface it may germinate in either of two ways depending on the temperature. At high temperature a germ tube is produced directly. At low temperature from four to twelve kidney-shaped, biflagellate zoospores are liberated. After a short period of motility these encyst, and each produces a germ tube which may penetrate the host.

Oogonia and antheridia develop near each other at the ends of hyphal branches within the host's tissues. Both are initially multinucleate but by the time the antheridium makes contact with the side of the oogonium each has only a single functional nucleus. In the oogonium it is the central nucleus that persists, the others moving to the peripheral periplasm and degenerating. The antheridial contents are injected through a fine fertilisation tube into the

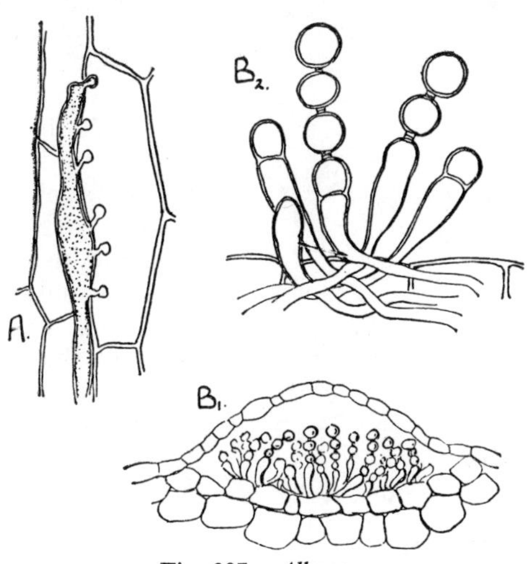

Fig. 307. *Albugo*.
A, mycelium with haustoria; B, sporangiophores and sporangia.

oogonium where nuclear fusion occurs. There then occur several nuclear divisions, and the oospore develops a thick, warty wall. After an over-wintering rest period the protoplast of an oospore near a host plant cleaves into forty to sixty uninucleate segments, each developing into a zoospore. After liberation and a period of swimming each zoospore encysts and can infect by means of a germ tube.

MUCOR

This is a genus of fungi with many species. They are essentially saprophytic, common on dead materials, in soil, and on dung. The broad coenocytic hyphae commonly show unidirectional protoplasmic streaming in culture. This is probably caused by loss of water through transpiration from the aerial mycelium. On removing a Petri dish lid to observe a culture there is a sudden lowering of the humidity above the culture thus increasing the rate of transpiration. The volume of water lost is made good by a movement forward of protoplasm from the older mycelium, giving the visible rapid streaming.

After two or three days of growth the absorptive mycelium in the substratum produces a greyish aerial mycelium that bears the sporangiophores (Fig. 308, A). These are long and fairly stout, and often branched. The tips become spherical and each is delimited as a sporangium by a septum. This septum is curved upwards to form the dome-shaped columella that gives a large surface for the diffusion of nutrients across from the sporangiophore to the developing spores within the sporangium (Fig. 308, B). The protoplast in the sporangium is richly provided with reserve foods and contains many nuclei. It cleaves into a large number of uninucleate spores, each of which secretes a wall. These spores do not have flagella, are non-motile and are called aplanospores. The sporangial wall is coated with closely-set, needle-like crystals said to be calcium oxalate. At maturity the sporangium absorbs water through the columella and most of its wall dissolves in this to produce a **sporangial drop** supported by a short collarette formed from a persistent narrow rim of the sporangial wall where it joins the columella (Fig. 308, C). This behaviour is described as **diffluent**, and because of it one has difficulty finding an intact mature sporangium in aqueous mounts of the fungus. In nature, in humid conditions, the sporangial drop remains fluid and if it touches a surface spores are deposited. On a suitable substratum each germinates quickly to give a germ tube. In dry air the sporangial drop dries down and the spores are cemented

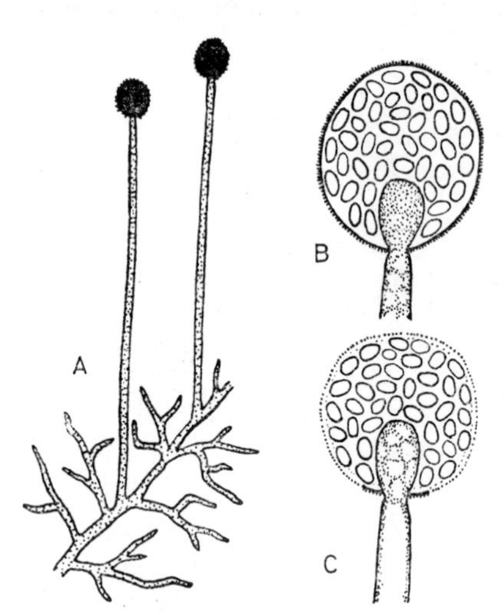

Fig. 308. *Mucor*.
A, sporangiophores; B, sporangium with central columella; C, sporangial drop supported by collarette.

together in a mass and are not disseminated until more moisture is available. Such **slime spore** dispersal mechanisms occur in unrelated groups of fungi and depend upon the presence of ample moisture. Some fungi related to *Mucor* have quite different dispersal mechanisms, some of which depend on dry conditions. *Rhizopus stolonifer* has a sporangial wall that at maturity cracks open in dry air and allows the spores to blow away. Liberation of the spores in this fungus is assisted by a twisting and jerking of the thick-walled sporangiophore on drying.

The sexual phase in *Mucor* is apparently rare in nature and is initiated by the coming together of two morphologically similar but genetically different thalli. The two mating types are given the symbols + and −, and each is self-incompatible. There is here no true sexual differentiation of male and female structures, and the phenomenon is described as **heterothallism**. In some other fungi maleness and femaleness can occur together with heterothallism but as a different phenomenon. This happens in *Phytophthora infestans* as described earlier. Where hyphae of the two strains of *Mucor* lie near each other a short lateral branch is produced from each, and these, the **progametangia**, grow directly towards each other until their tips make contact (Fig. 309). By septum formation a more or less isodiametric, multinucleate gametangium is delimited at the tip of each, and the supporting part of the hyphal branch is now called the **suspensor**. Hormones of a gaseous nature are responsible for the orientated growth and the subsequent differentiation of gametangia. At the point of contact between the two equally sized gametangia the mutual wall is digested and the contents fuse to form a zygote within the gametangial walls. Cytological evidence suggests that the nuclei fuse in pairs at this stage. The zygote swells and accumulates dense oily reserve substances, and the wall thickens and becomes dark and warty in the mature zygospore. After a period of dormancy the zygospore becomes capable of germination to produce an unbranched sporangiophore with a single terminal sporangium (Fig. 310). Because of the dark

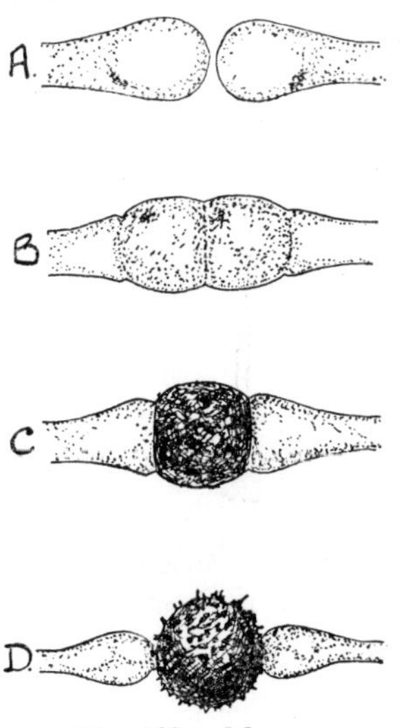

Fig. 309. *Mucor*.
A, progametangia; B, fusion between gametangia; C, young zygote; D, mature zygospore.

wall of the zygospore cytological details during development and germination are difficult to observe, but the evidence indicates that meiosis occurs at or just before its germination. The spores in any one sporangium resulting from germination of a zygospore are all of one mating strain, either "+" or "−". It is believed that the difference between "+" and "−" is controlled by a pair of alleles which separate at meiosis. If this is so then degeneration of some of the nuclei resulting from meiosis must take place to eliminate one of the mating strains.

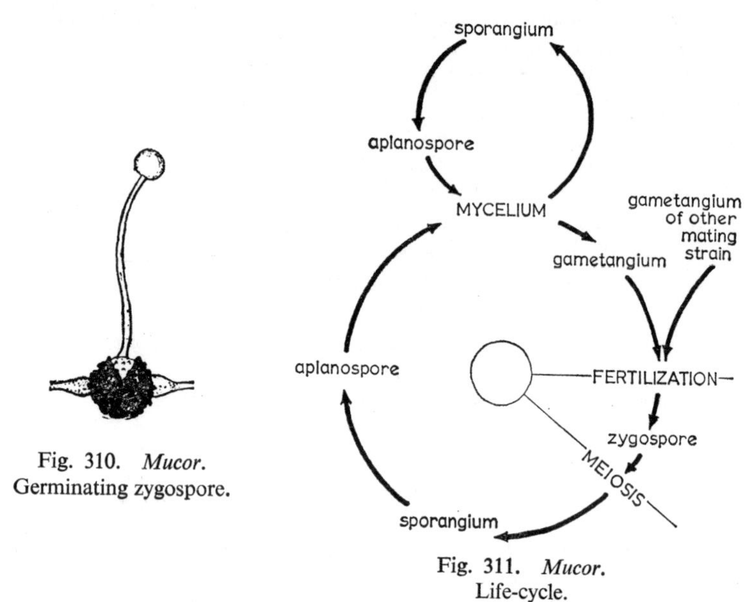

Fig. 310. *Mucor*. Germinating zygospore.

Fig. 311. *Mucor*. Life-cycle.

ASPERGILLUS (EUROTIUM)

Members of the genus *Aspergillus* are predominantly saprophytic Ascomycetes in which the asexual or "imperfect" phase is much more prominent than the sexual or "perfect" stage. In most species the perfect stage is uncommon, while in others it has never been found. *Eurotium* was the name first given to the perfect stage of fungi in this genus, and the name *Aspergillus* that given to the conidial imperfect forms before the connection between the two was fully appreciated. A **form-genus** is the term applied to generic names given to part of an organism when the connection with its other parts has not been established with certainty. For convenience it is now usual to use the generic name *Aspergillus* for both phases, mainly because the conidial stage is that most commonly seen in nature and in culture, and by which species can readily be identified. The species *A. glaucus* (*E. herbariorum*) is an osmophilic saprophyte (preferring substrata with a high osmotic pressure) occasionally found growing on slightly damp substrata like leather, dried fruit, and preserves.

The main characteristic of the genus is the conidiophore (Fig. 312) which arises by a single cell, the **foot cell**, of the septate, somatic mycelium swelling greatly and producing a stout, non-septate, upwardly-growing branch that elongates to a length of 2-5 mm. This swells at the tip to produce a more or less globular vesicle. From sites at the surface of the vesicle grow tubular **phialides**. The whole structure from the foot cell to the tips of the phialides is the conidiophore. The phialides produce from their tip small globose conidia in chains, basipetally, the youngest conidium being that at the tip of the phialide, the oldest being distal. The conidia have a surface that is wetted only with difficulty, and the long chains are unstable so that the conidia are easily dislodged and disseminated in dry air. A linear series of several conidia may adhere together and be dispersed as a unit. The surface of a mature thallus is closely covered with conidiophores and the conidia are thus produced in very large numbers.

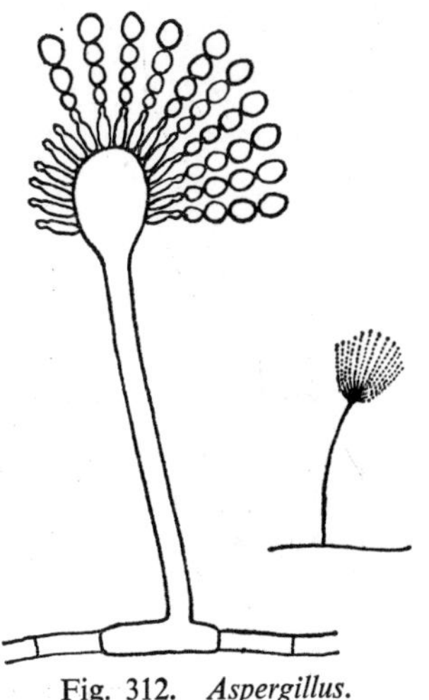

Fig. 312. *Aspergillus*. Conidiophore.

In *A. glaucus* the sexual stage (Fig. 313) is initiated by the development of a small coiled, septate branch of the mycelium called an **ascogonium**. This is the female gametangium. A multinucleate antheridial branch nearby coils around the multinucleate ascogonium and nuclear migration occurs from the antheridium into the ascogonium. Each nucleus in the female gametangium becomes paired with one from the male gametangium, but no nuclear fusion occurs at this stage. The association together of two haploid nuclei in this way and their subsequent co-ordinated division together in succeeding stages of growth constitute the **dikaryotic condition**. A dikaryon in fungi has in every one of its cells two nuclei derived from different parents, and is a preliminary to nuclear fusion and the production of a diploid phase. The dikaryotised ascogonium produces a number of branches called

ascogenous hyphae, these also being dikaryotic. About them grow monokaryotic hyphae from the base of the ascogonium which intertwine to form a pseudoparenchymatous **ascocarp** like a hollow ball roughly the size of a pinhead. This surrounds and protects the developing dikaryotic hyphae which grow and branch within. An ascocarp with this hollow closed form is called a **cleistothecium.** A swollen cell, the **ascus**, develops from each terminal cell of the ascogenous hyphae, numerous asci developing in a scattered arrangement within the cleistothecium. The two nuclei in the dikaryotic

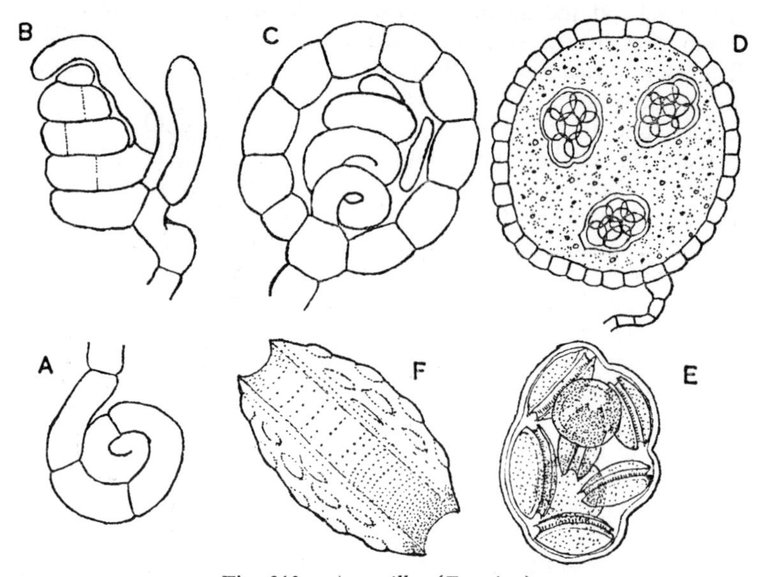

Fig. 313. *Aspergillus* (*Eurotium*).
A, young ascogonium; B, development of antheridial branch and a sterile hypha; C, sterile hyphae investing the dikaryotised ascogonium; D, ascocarp with asci; E, ascus with ascospores; F, single ascospore.

ascus fuse together to give a diploid zygote nucleus which immediately undergoes a meiotic division producing four haploid nuclei. There is then a further mitotic division of each of these giving a final eight nuclei in the ascus. About each of these nuclei some cytoplasm becomes delimited, not by cleavage, but by a process known as **free-cell formation**, in which not all the protoplasm is included in the developing ascospores, some remaining outside as a nutritive substance. The ascospores have a characteristic shape, being more or less lens-shaped with a small groove round the edge, like a pulley wheel. The ascal walls break down and the uninucleate ascospores lie free in the cleistothecial cavity. They are eventually liberated by disintegration of the cleistothecium, and germinate to give a haploid mycelium.

Some species of *Aspergillus* are of economic importance. *A. fumigatus* is able to grow well at temperatures higher than 37° C. and is common in overheated mouldy hay. Workers repeatedly exposed to such materials may develop a disease known as "farmer's lung". "Aspergillosis" of the lung, a disease not uncommon in warm-blooded animals such as rabbits, guinea pigs, and poultry, is caused by *A.*

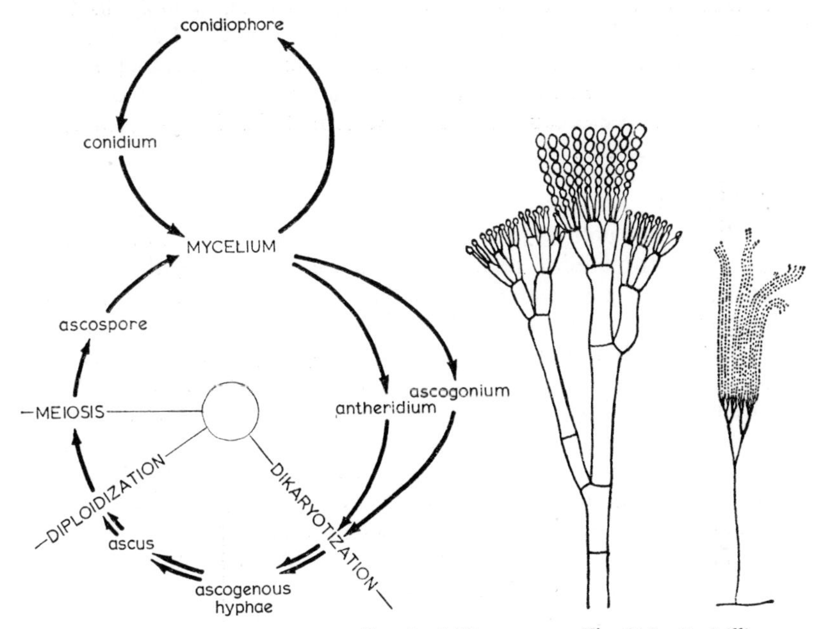

Fig. 314. LIFE-CYCLE OF *Aspergillus*, *Penicillium*, AND *Erysiphe*.

Fig. 315. *Penicillium*. Conidiophore.

fumigatus. A wide range of enzymes used in industrial fermentations is readily obtainable from cultures of *A. niger* and *A. oryzae*.

PENICILLIUM

Very closely related to *Aspergillus*, the genus *Penicillium* resembles it in a number of respects. Like that genus it is a form-genus of imperfect fungi, identified mainly by their conidial stage. Some species may occasionally produce cleistothecia, but most have no perfect stage. The conidiophore has resemblances to that of *Aspergillus*, but differs in some important ways (Fig. 315). It has no distinctive swollen foot-cell, it is not a single cell but is septate, and there is no vesicle at the top—instead there is a compact series of branches, the last degree of which forms the phialides that produce the basipetal chains of conidia. The whole conidiophore with its terminal conidial chains is sometimes called the **penicillus** (= a small brush: Latin).

Species of *Penicillium* are common saprophytes and like *Aspergillus* often able to grow with limited supplies of water. A number of species are of economic importance, notably in the production of therapeutic antibiotics (see below). In addition, *P. roqueforti* and *P. camemberti* are used in cheese-making, some species such as *P. italicum* and *P. expansum* cause plant disease, while other species cause deterioration of materials like jam, leather, paper, and textiles.

Antibiotics

It was not until 1945 that the word antibiotic, now in common use, was introduced to refer to a substance produced by the activity of a micro-organism and that inhibits the growth of other micro-organisms. Penicillin was first demonstrated as a product of *P. notatum*, but is now obtained in highest yields from various improved and selected strains of *P. chrysogenum*. It inhibits Gram positive bacteria (see p. 576) and is available in several forms that differ in their constitution according to the chemical side-chains on the molecule. Unnatural forms of the molecule can be synthesised by alteration of the side-chains, and help to counteract the development of strains of pathogenic bacteria resistant to penicillin.

To be useful in combating disease in animals an antibiotic must show no serious toxicity to animal tissues. Many antibiotics are valueless for therapeutic use since not only are they toxic to pathogenic micro-organisms but also to higher animals. A number of valuable antibiotics have been discovered in soil-inhabiting actinomycetes, a group of filamentous micro-organisms more closely related to bacteria than to fungi. Streptomycin was the first of these, but others have since been discovered. Among these are terramycin (oxytetracycline), aureomycin (chlortetracycline) and chloromycetin (chloramphenicol), all of which are **broad-spectrum antibiotics**, inhibiting not only Gram positive bacteria, but also Gram negative bacteria, the rickettsias (a group of bacteria-like obligate parasites of animals), the larger viruses, and pathogenic amoebae. Chloramphenicol was first isolated from the actinomycete, *Streptomyces venezuelae*, but is now manufactured by chemical synthesis.

Griseofulvin, an antibiotic produced by *Penicillium griseofulvum*, is toxic to some other fungi, and can be used systemically to control ringworm diseases of animals. It has also been used experimentally to control plant diseases caused by fungi.

ERYSIPHE

Members of this genus are obligate parasites of plants and cause a number of economically important plant diseases known as **powdery mildews**. Most species have a very limited host range, some being so specific as to infect only a single species of plant. *Erysiphe polygoni* is unusual in the group in having a very wide host range, and it has been recorded from more than 350 species of host.

Infection occurs by a spore germinating on the host surface. The spores of powdery mildew fungi are unusual in that they are able to germinate in the absence of free water, and at relative humidities as low as 76 per cent. A branched septate mycelium with uninucleate cells is soon produced and although this remains entirely superficial on the epidermis of the host it sinks absorptive, richly branched haustoria into the epidermal cells. The host cells are not much damaged and continue to function apparently normally. The external mycelium soon produces short erect branches, each functioning as a conidiophore and cutting off at its tip an unbranched chain of uninucleate, oval conidia (Fig. 316, A). Because these occur in dense masses, infected areas of the host assume a whitish, floury appearance. The ripe conidia are easily detached and dispersed by wind, and are responsible for fresh infections throughout the growing season. In late summer cleistothecia are produced, and are about $\frac{1}{5}$ mm. in diameter, brown-coloured and hard, and anchored to the host surface by mycelial appendages (Fig. 316, C). They are the culmination of the sexual stage that begins by the development of a club-shaped uninucleate ascogonium. Near this arises a uninucleate, rather narrower antheridium that makes contact with the ascogonium (Fig. 316, B). The male nucleus passes through a pore in the region of contact, and the dikaryon is constituted in the ascogonium. Dikaryotic ascogenous hyphae grow out as branches from the ascogonium, and themselves branch, developing slowly within the cleistothecium through the winter. Eventually from five to twenty asci are produced, each of which is binucleate initially, but by a nuclear fusion followed by meiosis and a single mitosis becomes eight-nucleate. In spring the asci mature to produce ascospores. There are sometimes eight ascospores to an ascus, one developing about each nucleus, but the number may be from three upwards, the remaining nuclei degenerating. When the ascospores are fully formed the epiplasm (the ascal protoplasm not included in the ascospores) undergoes a change that causes an increase in osmotic pressure. The asci absorb water and swell, and the cleistothecial wall is ruptured, the asci protrude, and the internal pressure bursts them so that the spores are shot out into the air and are dispersed. Ascospores start new foci of infection as young host leaves are unfolding.

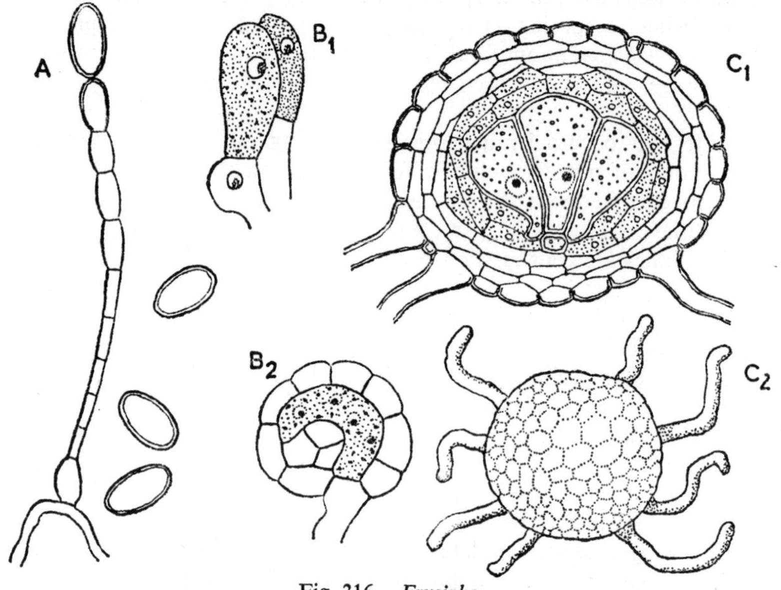

Fig. 316. *Erysiphe*.
A, conidiophore and conidia; B_1, ascogonium and antheridium; B_2, dikaryotised ascogonium and investing hyphae; C, cleistothecium—C_1, section, with young asci; C_2, external appearance.

With powdery mildews disease control is relatively easily effected by the application of fungicidal sprays or dusts before infection is likely to occur.

MONILINIA

Monilinia fructigena belongs to the group of Ascomycetes known as Discomycetes which have saucer- or cup-shaped ascocarps with exposed asci arranged in a hymenial layer. This is a palisade-like layer on the upper concave surface of the ascocarp. An ascocarp of this form is called an **apothecium**. *M. fructigena* is a parasite of stone fruits like plum and peach. An ascospore or a conidium germinates on a young blossom or leaf of the host. The mycelium invades the tissues causing their death and results in either a blossom blight or a leaf and twig blight. Near the surface of the infected host long, branched hyphae soon break through. From the tip

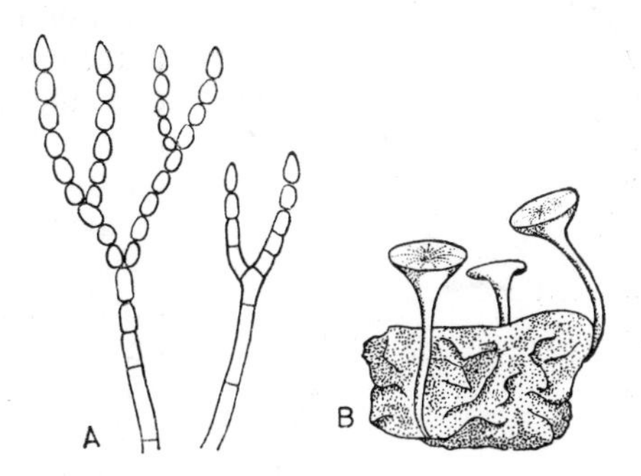

Fig. 317. *Monilinia.*
A, *Monilia* conidiophores; B, *Monilinia fructicola*, peach mummy with apothecia.

backwards these become septate into short cells, each of which separates off from its neighbours and rounds off at the corners to become an oval conidium. In this way conidia are formed in chains that are branched (Fig. 317, A). The conidia are lightly attached, and easily become detached and wind-dispersed to set up new infections on other plants or other parts of the same plant. This is the

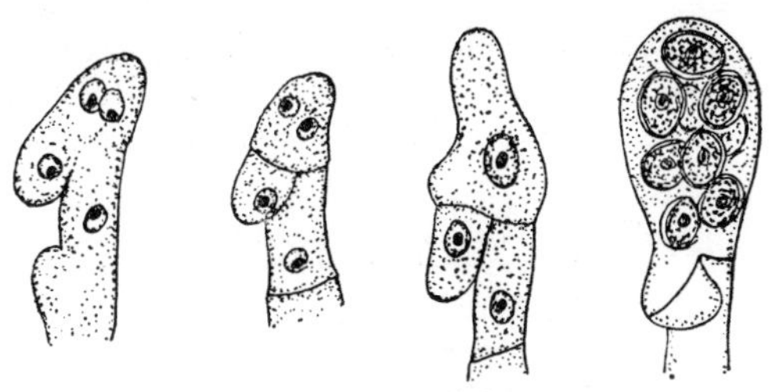

Fig. 318. *Monilinia.*
Cytology of ascus.

Monilia stage of the fungus. *Monilia* is a form-genus in the Fungi Imperfecti.

Infections occurring on developing fruit cause a brown rot of the fruit. In wet years this can result in considerable damage to the crop. Some infected fruits do not completely rot but become shrivelled and hardened into black, mummified structures. All the soft tissues become converted into fungal mycelium, but conidiation as found in the brown rot stage does not occur here. The mummified structures are fungal sclerotia, and may remain on the tree or fall to the ground. In either case the sclerotia may remain viable throughout the winter. Those on the tree may produce conidia on renewal of activity in spring. Those on the ground eventually get buried. Subsequent development has not been determined with certainty for *Monilinia fructigena*, but is probably the same as in related species in which the buried sclerotium remains inactive for a number of years, but finally at springtime germinates to produce a stalked apothecium raised above ground level (Fig. 317, B). Asci develop (Fig. 318) in the hymenial layer and the ascospores are shot into the air. Ascospores that blow to new unfolding leaves and blossoms initiate fresh infections.

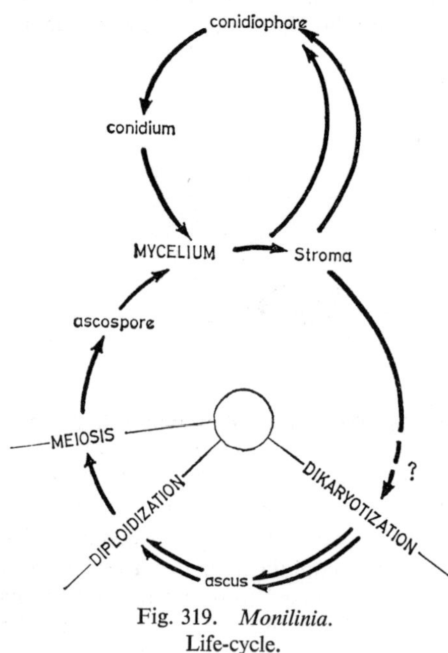

Fig. 319. *Monilinia*. Life-cycle.

SACCHAROMYCES

This genus of yeasts, *Saccharomyces*, when treated in isolation as a type has little to show its relationships with other Ascomycetes, but a detailed study of related forms shows genera of fungi that link yeasts with well-defined mycelial Ascomycetes. The unicellular budding condition which is characteristic of yeasts is connected with their habit of growing in sugary solutions. Similar budding stages can be induced to develop in a variety of normally mycelial fungi by culture in liquids with high concentrations of nutrients or by reducing oxygenation of the culture. In *Saccharomyces* the adaptation has become permanent, but by growing the fungus in the presence of certain chemicals, such as penicillin, a true mycelium may be produced.

S. cerevisiae occurs as a wild yeast but it also has many industrial and domestic strains that have special properties useful to man and that have been selected for particular purposes. Brewers' yeasts, bakers' yeasts, and wine yeasts are all strains of *S. cerevisiae*.

The yeast cell is oval with a firm cell wall. At one side of a large vacuole in the cell is a dense nucleus. Because of staining difficulties the status of this nuclear body was for many years a subject for dispute, and one view was that the vacuole itself was the nucleus proper. It is now known from studies with the electron microscope that the nucleus is in fact the body to the side of the vacuole (Fig. 320, A). Reserve material occurs in the cell as glycogen and oily materials. Growth occurs by an overall increase in cell size, until eventually vegetative reproduction takes place. This begins by a bud blowing out at one end, and when this reaches about half the size of the parent cell, the parent nucleus divides and with it the vacuole. One half of each passes into the bud which becomes pinched off, leaving a scar on both cells. Further growth of the parent cell, which is already at its maximum size, results in the production of another bud at the opposite end to the first. By repetition of this process, known as **bipolar budding**, a spiral series of bud scars is formed at each end of the parent cell and these indicate how many buds it has produced.

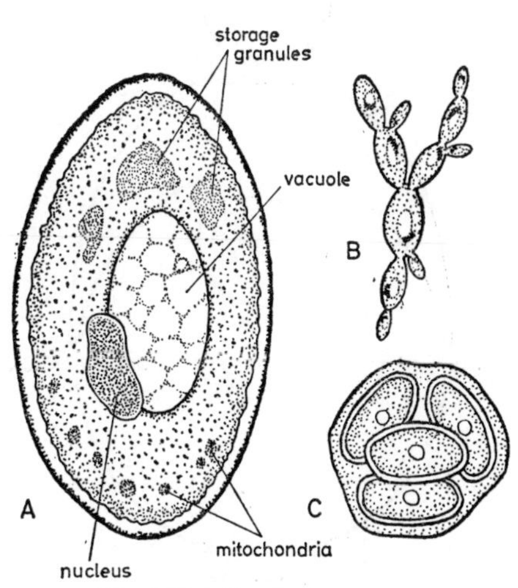

Fig. 320. *Saccharomyces.* A, cell; B, pseudomycelium; C, ascus.

In a well-aerated solution with ample nutrients the yeast multiplies rapidly by budding and has the normal aerobic metabolism that is represented overall by the equation:

$$C_6H_{12}O_6 + 6\ O_2 \rightarrow 6\ CO_2 + 6\ H_2O.$$

With very rapid growth (a cell may duplicate itself about every two hours) the cells may fail to pinch off completely before the daughter cells themselves produce further buds. In this way bead-like, branched chains of cells develop and are called **pseudomycelia** (Fig. 320, B).

In the absence of sufficient oxygen somatic growth is much reduced and vegetative multiplication is negligible. The cells, however, may continue to metabolise anaerobically, the reactions being represented in sum by the equation:

$$C_6H_{12}O_6 \rightarrow 2\,C_2H_5OH + 2\,CO_2.$$

This process is **fermentation** and the two products, ethanol and carbon dioxide, are important for some of the different domestic and industrial functions of yeasts.

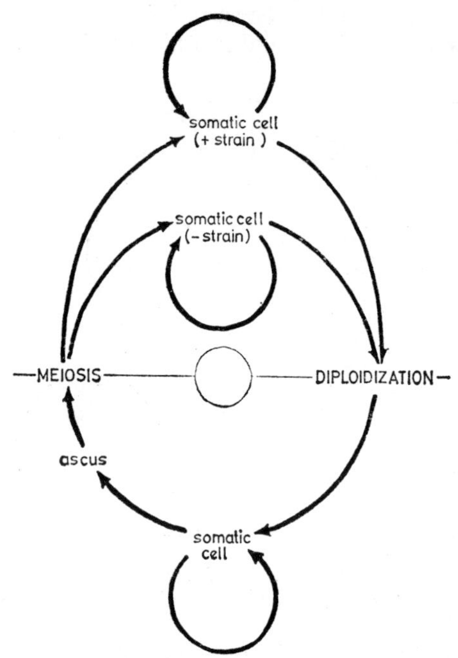

Fig. 321. *Saccharomyces.* Life-cycle.

Well-grown cells of *S. cerevisiae* can be induced to produce ascospores by transfer to a relatively inhospitable substratum. A 0·5 per cent. solution of sodium acetate gelled with 2 per cent. agar serves this end very well. The normally diploid cell produces four, or occasionally fewer, haploid ascospores (Fig. 320, C). These germinate to give small round haploid budding cells that can continue growth but are somewhat less vigorous than the diploid. Contact between haploid cells of compatible mating strains results in cell fusion followed immediately by nuclear fusion to give the diploid condition that has the larger oval cells.

Fermented Beverages

All alcoholic drinks are based on the fermentative activities of yeasts. In the production of wines a fruit juice, usually grape juice, provides the yeast with a source of sugar and other nutrients including suitable nitrogenous compounds and sufficient vitamins and minerals for growth. Suitable strains of yeast normally exist on the skins of the fruit, but wild forms of other species that detract from the flavour of the final product are also often present and in some modern processes the juice, or **must**, is partially sterilised and a suitable inoculum subsequently added. In the early stages oxygen is present and the inoculum grows to produce large numbers of cells. The fermenting liquid has a relatively small surface exposed to the air and when most of the dissolved oxygen is used the anaerobic process takes over, with the formation of alcohol and carbon dioxide. The yeast cells continue to ferment until about 12-16 per cent. by volume of alcohol has been produced, which becomes toxic to the cells and stops their further activity. The actual level of alcohol in a wine depends largely on the initial concentration of sugar, of other nutrients, and on the strain of yeast. A low initial sugar concentration gives a low level of alcohol, but too much sugar can act synergistically with the alcohol to inhibit a high yield of alcohol. When the cells stop producing carbon dioxide gas they settle to the bottom as **lees** and the wine becomes clear, and can be racked off the sediment. Final maturation with the full development of characteristic odour and flavour occurs more slowly and depends partly on a slow oxidation of alcohols to acids, and combination of these acids with alcohols to produce esters. If excessive oxygen is admitted to the wine the bacterium *Acetobacter* can grow and convert the ethanol to acetic acid. The wine may then become vinegar. If under unusual circumstances the yeast is able to ferment to an alcohol level of about 18-19 per cent., or if the wine is fortified to this level by the addition of distilled spirit alcohol *Acetobacter* is prevented from developing, and the wine is self-preserving. Port, sherry, and madeira are fortified in this way.

The raw material for beer is the starch in barley grains. Yeasts do not produce amylase and hence are unable to hydrolyse the starch to glucose. The barley grains are first malted. This is done by allowing the grains to germinate under closely controlled conditions so that their hydrolysing enzymes are activated, but before much of the starch has been altered the germination is stopped by heating to a level which does not damage the enzymes. The grain is then dried and ground when it is called **malt**. The malt is later mashed by mixing with warm water, allowing the amylase to convert the starch to glucose, after which the process is stopped by heating. Hops (the dried fruiting inflorescences of *Humulus lupulus*) are boiled with the clear fluid from the mash, which is then cooled to fermentation temperature in a fermentation tank. Yeast is added in bulk to start the fermentation. Different breweries use individual selected strains of yeast that help to give the product characteristic properties. The hops contain resins that assist in the clearing process by precipitating the proteins that contribute to cloudiness. The resins also have some preservative action against bacterial spoilage, and give to the beer a characteristic astringent flavour.

In saké, an oriental beverage, rice is the starting material, and its starch is converted to glucose by the amylase of the moulds *Aspergillus oryzae* or *Rhizopus oryzae*, before the yeast inoculum is added.

PUCCINIA

Puccinia is one of the lower Basidiomycetes that produce basidiospores without the support of a large toadstool-like fruit body. It is a member of the group of rust fungi. This includes several thousand species, all of them obligate parasites of plants, and many causing enormous economic loss of cultivated plants. *P. graminis* causes black rust or stem rust of wheat and some other grasses. It is of small significance in Britain, but is very important in large wheat growing areas like the U.S.A. and Australia. Its life-cycle is complicated by **heteroecism**, whereby part of the life-cycle occurs obligatorily on one host and the remaining part obligatorily on another. Heteroecism occurs in several groups of animal parasites, but in fungi there are only two or three species outside the rusts that show this behaviour.

In spring a basidiospore settling on the upper surface of a leaf of a plant of barberry (*Berberis* spp. or *Mahonia* spp.) germinates in a drop of water to produce a germ tube that attaches itself to the cuticle by means of a flattened disc-like appressorium. From the underside of this a fine hyphal penetration peg grows downwards and mechanically punctures the cuticle and the epidermal cell wall. Within the epidermal cell the hypha swells out into a vesicle from which branches of normal width are produced. These grow to produce a septate intercellular mycelium having one nucleus per cell. Haustoria penetrate the living host cells and absorb nutrients without causing much damage to the cells. The host cells may in some cases be stimulated to fresh division and growth, and the leaf is often thicker in the infected area. The infection resulting from a single basidiospore is localised in extent, being limited to a few millimetres across. Near the upper surface of the infected area several flask-like **pycnia** (Fig. 322, A) develop with their narrow ostioles or mouths opening at the surface. In the base of each pycnium is a palisade-like layer of cells that abstrict from their tips unicellular, uninucleate **pycniospores** into the interior along with a slimy, sugary solution. This oozes out to form a drop on the surface of the host and is supported by a fringe of stiff bristle-like hyphae round the ostiole. Also from the interior of the pycnium a few long, branched, flexuous hyphae grow into the sugary drop. These structures are all part of the pycnial apparatus. At the same time some of the infecting mycelium grows towards the lower epidermis and just beneath it produces small compact knots of hyphae having uninucleate cells. These are the **proto-aecia**.

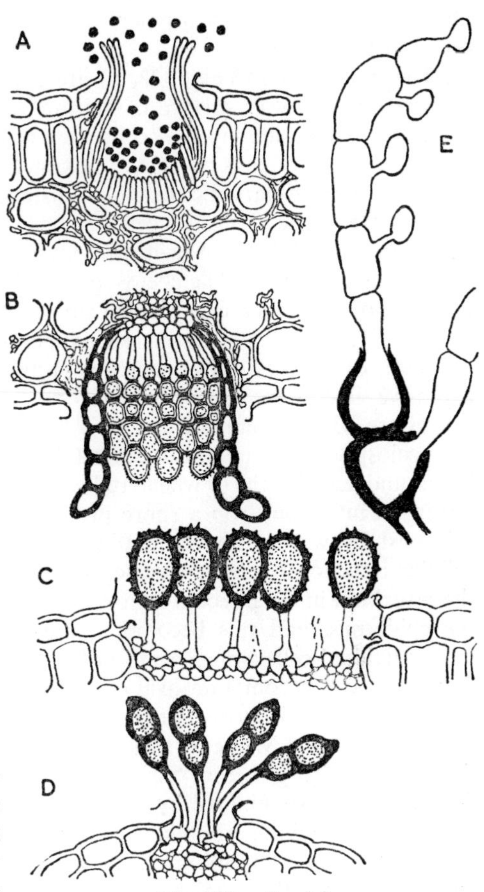

Fig. 322. *Puccinia*.
A, pycnium; B, aecium; C, uredium; D, telium; E, basidium developed from germinated teliospore.

Under natural conditions, with insects visiting the host leaves, the proto-aecia develop into mature, spore-producing **aecia**, but if an infected spot is protected from contamination the proto-aecia do not develop further. Experiments have shown that *P. graminis* is heterothallic. There are two mating strains which are morphologically identical. If some pycnial nectar from the + strain is added to a nectar drop of another + strain or that from − added to − nothing happens. But if nectar from one strain is added to the drop on a pycnium of the other strain the associated proto-aecia of the receptor strain proceed to develop into aecia. It seems very probable that pycniospores from one strain make contact with mycelium of the other strain, probably through the flexuous hyphae, and that the pycniospore nucleus migrates into the mycelium established in the host, dividing on its way, and causing dikaryotisation of the previously monokaryotic cells. Eventually the proto-aecia become dikaryotic and complete their development into aecia, each cell of which contains two nuclei.

The mature aecia (Fig. 322, B) are cup-shaped and grouped in clusters on the lower surface of the infected area. At the base of the cup is a palisade layer of cells each cell of which cuts off from its apex a chain of cells in which isodiametric dikaryotic **aeciospores** alternate with dikaryotic disc-like disjunctor cells, which soon disintegrate. The chains of cells formed at the outer edges of the cup become modified as a protective layer and fuse together to form the pseudoperidium. The aeciospores inside are constricted by the pressure of the other cells, which are continually being produced proximally, and that of the pseudoperidium. At intervals the pressure overcomes the coherence between adjacent cells and explosive liberation of a mass of ripe aeciospores results. The spores are wind disseminated.

Aeciospores are unable to infect barberry, but can infect the leaves and leaf sheaths of wheat and some other grasses. Germinating in an infection drop a spore produces a germ tube that enters this host by way of an open stoma and causes a localised intercellular infection by dikaryotic septate hyphae. After several days the mycelium in the infected area produces a dense mat just beneath the epidermis, and this becomes a **uredium**. From this mycelial mat individual cells elongate upwards and divide once transversely. The upper cell becomes an oval dikaryotic **urediospore** with a thick, warty wall, and is borne on the elongated one-celled dikaryotic stalk (Fig. 322, C). Masses of these reddish urediospores burst through the epidermis to give the "rust" spots. The spores are passively detached and disseminated by wind. Like the aeciospores they are long-lived, containing abundant oily reserves, and can be dispersed long distances. Physiologically and genetically, though not morphologically, the urediospores are identical with the aeciospores and can infect the grass host again. They are a **repeating-spore** stage in the life-cycle, and in nature contribute largely to the build-up of disease to epidemic proportions. The host, however, is rarely killed even by severe attacks, but suffers damage partly by uncontrolled water loss through the ruptured areas and partly by some loss of assimilated food. The uredial cycle of re-infection continues throughout the summer.

As autumn and host maturity approach, a change occurs in the fungus and new lesions instead of producing uredia give **telia** instead. **Teliospores** are produced on these sori. Previously established uredia may also at this stage change over to the production of teliospores. The teliosori on the host are blackish, not red. The teliospore is borne on the same sort of stalk as the urediospore, but the spore itself is two-celled, each cell being dikaryotic and having a thick, but smooth, wall with a thin place, the germ-pore, in each cell (Fig. 322, D). The teliospore is not deciduous but remains attached to the straw, and is dormant, being incapable of germination until over-wintering has occurred, with exposure to weathering and low temperatures.

As the teliospore matures the two nuclei in each cell fuse together, and in spring each diploid cell germinates to give a curved **basidium**. The diploid nucleus undergoes meiosis and the four haploid nuclei migrate into the basidium which then becomes transversely septate to form four haploid uninucleate cells. Each of these cells puts out a narrow peg-like **sterigma**, the tip of which swells out to become a **basidiospore** and the haploid nucleus from the cell supporting it passes in (Fig. 322, E). The basidiospore is asymmetrically attached on the sterigma, and when ripe it is violently shot off into the air by a mechanism like that described for the mushroom on p. 569. The air-borne basidiospores are thin-walled and rather short-lived. They are incapable of infecting wheat, but can infect barberry which unfolds its young leaves at about the time the basidiospores are discharged.

By an international convention each phase in the life-cycle of *Puccinia* is given a number as set out in the system given below. This system applies also to other rust fungi some of which show reduced life-cycles by omission of one or more of the phases. Some authors use variant names for the different stages and these are given here in parenthesis.

Stage 0. Pycnia (spermogonia) + pycniospores (spermatia).
Stage I. Aecia (aecidia) + aeciospores (aecidiospores).
Stage II. Uredia (uredosori) + urediospores (uredospores).
Stage III. Telia (teleutosori) + teliospores (teleutospores).
Stage IV. Basidium (promycelium) + basidiospores (sporidia).

It is significant that the parasitic potentialities of the fungus are strictly related to its nuclear condition, the dikaryon being an obligate parasite of grasses while the monokaryon is an obligate parasite of barberry. The morphology of the reproductive structures, on the other hand, is controlled not by the nuclear condition of the fungus but by the physiology of the host in which growth is occurring.

P. graminis comprises about six **varieties** differing in their host range. Thus *P. graminis tritici* occurs on wheat, barley, and some wild grasses, while *P. graminis avenae* occurs on oat and some grasses, but never on wheat or barley. There are also correlated differences in the detailed morphology of the urediospores. The basidiospores of all varieties, however, infect *Berberis vulgaris*. Within each variety of the pathogen there are further sub-divisions, known as **physiologic races**. *P. graminis tritici* contains more than two hundred of these, distinguished one from the other by differential reaction to infection under closely controlled conditions of twelve specially chosen

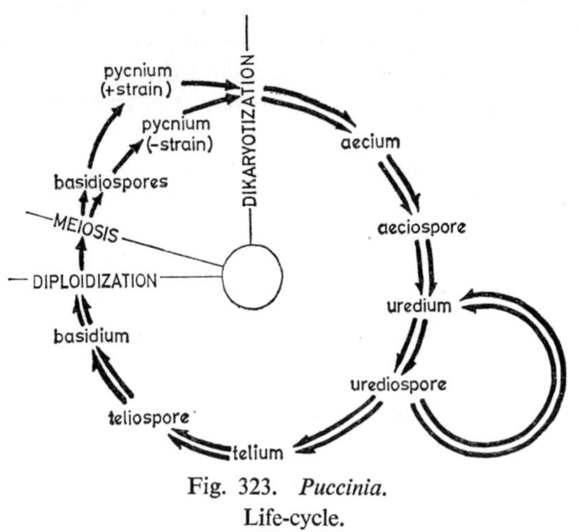

Fig. 323. *Puccinia.*
Life-cycle.

varieties of wheat known as differential hosts. Each race is uniquely designated by a number entered after the varietal trinomial.

A knowledge of the physiologic races present in any wheat growing area assists plant breeders to produce varieties of wheat resistant to those races. Changes occur, however, in the fungus population of an area and new races can arise by hybridisation. The presence of barberry in an area allows this to happen by exchange of genetic material and thus makes more difficult the control of disease, not only by providing new foci of infection in spring, but also by permitting an increased rate and amount of variation in the pathogen. In the absence of barberry effective hybridisation by the normal sexual process is impossible since the basidiospores are unable to continue the life-cycle.

In Britain *P. graminis* would not survive without barberry since the urediospores are unable to survive the cold winters, but in some climates stem rust continues to be an important disease even in areas where barberry does not occur. In U.S.A. barberry has been deliberately eliminated but epidemics commonly move northward to Canada throughout the growing season, having originated in Mexico where the barberry bush still grows. Barberry does not occur in Australia but because of the variation in climate throughout the continent wheat is grown at all times of the year in one area or another and urediospores occur all the year round, migrating from crop to crop.

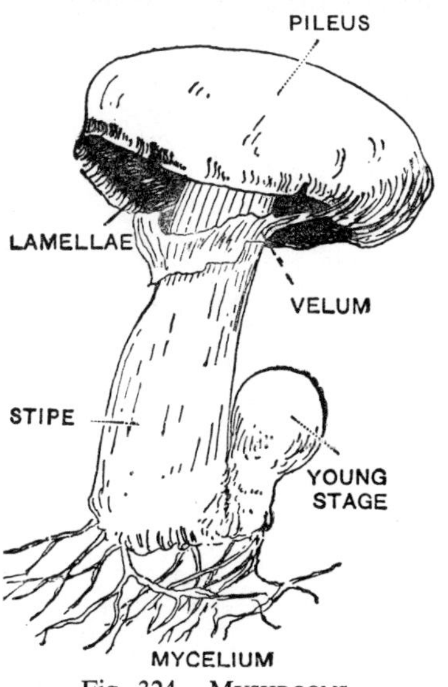

Fig. 324. MUSHROOMS.

AGARICUS

This genus is a member of the group of Basidiomycetes that produce the often massive **sporophores** or fruit bodies that are called mushrooms or toadstools (Fig. 324). Most are saprophytic, occurring in soil or decaying litter on forest floors. *Agaricus campestris*, the edible field mushroom, has the capacity to decompose cellulose and lignin substrata, and in nature usually occurs in soil rich in such material.

The branched septate hyphae of the fungus have the typical Basidiomycete dolipore septa with parenthosomes (p. 529). Each cell of the mycelium contains several nuclei. Mycelial strands, like lengths of string, may be formed by the aggregation of several hyphae into parallel bundles. Such strands are particularly common in species of Ascomycetes and Basidiomycetes that decompose woody tissues. These materials are recognised as being initially difficult to colonise, and the aggregated strands are believed to assist the fungi to concentrate resources at one site during the colonisation process.

The mycelium of *Agaricus* is perennial and exceptionally long-lived and shows numerous fusions between the hyphae. In this way a large and relatively persistent network of mycelium is produced in the soil. This is necessary for subsequent transport of nutrients to the region where developing sporophores arise. The sporophore commences development as a small knot of mycelium attached to a strand. This knot rather rapidly expands by organised mycelial growth to become the sporophore (Fig. 325, A). While the sporophore alone is commonly referred to as "the fungus", it is, in fact, only an ephemeral part of it, and one that is specially modified for the production and dispersal of the basidiospores. The somatic mycelium, although much less obvious, is the most permanent part of the fungus. The sporophore consists of the **stipe** or stalk, the **pileus** or cap, the **lamellae** or gills, and the **annulus** which is a ring around

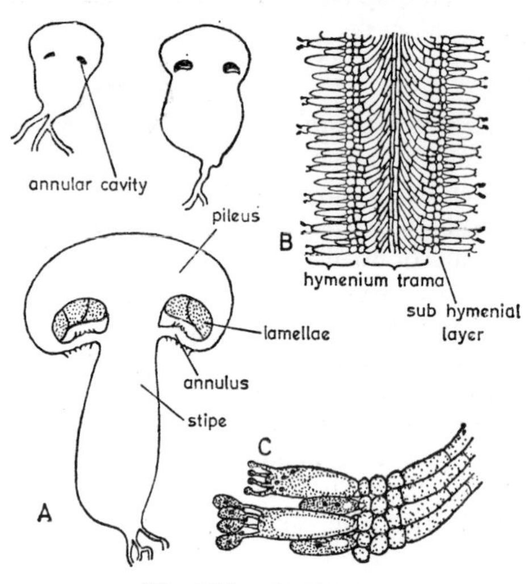

Fig. 325. *Agaricus*.
A, stages in development of the sporophore (longitudinal section); B, part of gill in section; C, basidium development.

the stalk. The narrow gills hang perpendicularly beneath the cap and are attached to it in a radial arrangement. Not all are the same length: the longer ones run all the way across from the stalk to the rim of the cap, and between these are shorter ones near the periphery where the long gills stand further apart. The **hymenium**, which contains the basidia carried at right angles to the exposed surface, covers all the surface of the gills. In a ripe sporophore any area of the hymenium carries basidia in all stages of development, mature ones being separated by young ones or old, discharged ones, so that there is no mutual interference of spore discharge. The innermost part of the gill between the two hymenial surfaces is called the **trama** (Fig. 325, B), and the cells here have fewer nuclei than those in the mycelium of the stalk and flesh of the cap. Further out, in the sub-hymenial layer, there are fewer still—two or three nuclei per cell. Each basidium at the gill surface has initially just two nuclei, and is otherwise packed with cytoplasm. During the development of the basidium these two nuclei fuse to give a single diploid nucleus, which immediately undergoes meiosis to produce four haploid nuclei. Four peg-like sterigmata develop at the apex of the basidium and the tip of each enlarges to become a spore. A vacuole appears at the base of the basidium and enlarges, pushing the protoplasm into the expanding spores, one nucleus going into each spore (Fig. 325, C). At maturity the basidium contains a large vacuole with a narrow cytoplasmic lining, and each of the four uninucleate, protoplasm-packed basidiospores is seated on the tip of its sterigma with the point of the spore, the **hilum**, situated slightly to one side. The hilum secretes a drop of watery fluid that increases in size. Suddenly the spore is shot off the sterigma perpendicularly to the gill surface for a distance of about $\frac{1}{10}$ to $\frac{1}{8}$ mm. into the space between the gills. From there it drops vertically downwards between the gills and out into the turbulent air below the cap. The other three spores are shot off in order soon after, the whole process taking two or three minutes. The basidium remains turgid afterwards, ruling out a squirting mechanism of discharge. One hypothesis is that a collapse of the watery drop occurs from the point of the hilum to the concave side of the spore resulting in a calculable release of surface tension energy. This creates an instability in the attachment of the spore that permits its violent discharge. Recent studies, however, indicate that the drop may be contained in a limiting membrane which, when it ruptures, permits a sudden and localised release of pressure at the base of the spore so that the spore is ejected from the sterigma by jet-propulsion. If a fresh detached cap is placed for several hours on a smooth surface and protected from draughts the accumulation of discharged spores beneath the cap creates a visible deposit of the purple spores known as a **spore-print**. This takes the form of a negative image of the gill pattern. From this description it should be clear that for effective dispersal of the spores an accurately vertical orientation of the gills is essential. The rigid stipe shows in its later stages of growth appropriate geotropic responses, as do also the horizontal cap and the vertical gills. These responses are controlled by growth hormones produced in the gills, and the sporophore is able to accommodate to slight alterations in the position of the base of the stipe.

A fair-sized sporophore can produce about half a million spores per minute over a period of two or three days. Under suitable conditions each spore can germinate to produce a new mycelium, but the chances are very much against the conditions being exactly right. In culture individual spores can be germinated only with difficulty, but if several are placed close together germination soon takes place and hyphal fusions occur to give a heterokaryotic mycelium. The species is homothallic, so that by isolating a single germinated spore the resulting mycelium can be made to produce fertile sporophores. The cultivated mushroom, *Agaricus bisporus*, is characterised by having basidia with only two sterigmata and two binucleate basidiospores.

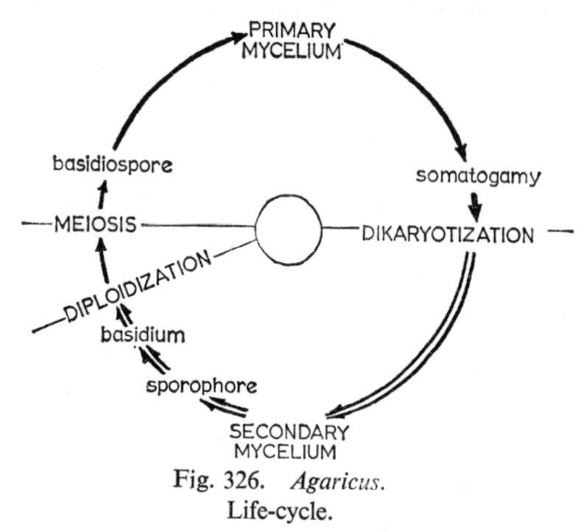

Fig. 326. *Agaricus*.
Life-cycle.

Not all toadstools are homothallic and some produce on a single basidium basidiospores of two or more different mating strains. Each germinates to give a **primary mycelium** that is purely somatic. Fusions between the hyphae of two compatible primary mycelia give a dikaryotic **secondary mycelium** that may grow somatically for long periods and that can also under suitable conditions fructify. A sexual process involving hyphal fusion in this way is described as occurring by **somatogamy.**

Mycorrhizas

Many toadstools are characteristic of woodland, and among these are species of *Lactarius*, *Russula*, *Amanita*, and *Boletus* that tend to be found associated with particular species of tree. These fungi on investigation are found to have a special relationship with tree roots forming a composite structure called a mycorrhiza (= fungus-root: Greek). Most healthy trees show this condition. If the litter layer is moved aside and the roots of the tree uncovered many of the fine rootlets are seen to have a coralloid appearance, being swollen, densely branched, and bearing short stubby branches or being dichotomously branched. A transverse section shows a mantle of fungal mycelium around the root, and the outer cortical cells are radially elongated. Between these cells, and extending intercellularly a little way into the cortex, are some of the fungal hyphae. This arrangement is called a **Hartig net** after the German forest pathologist who first described it. Such a structure is an **ectotrophic mycorrhiza**. The fungus appears to get nutriment from the association, since the particular fungi on isolation are found to require for their growth simple carbohydrates that do not exist in sufficient quantities in forest soils. The tree itself is not apparently harmed except where its vigour is already reduced through other predisposing causes such as overshading, or overcrowding, when the fungus may become pathogenic. By bringing together pure cultures of fungi and sterile seedlings of tree species it has been shown for some combinations that particular types of toadstool mycelium will form mycorrhizas only with certain types of tree. Some trees such as Scots pine will accept association with a variety of toadstools such as species of *Boletus*, *Cortinarius*, and *Russula*.

On poor soils there is evidence that the presence of the fungus assists growth of the tree. Mycorrhizas occur more frequently and are better developed where the tree has a surplus of carbohydrate over that necessary for growth. Thus mycorrhizas are favoured by high light intensity and by a low level of nutrients in the soil. "Infected" tree saplings grow better than uninfected ones and make better and more successful trees. The fungal mantle increases the absorptive area of the roots, and there is also experimental evidence that even for a given root area ectotrophic mycorrhizas are more efficient than uninfected roots at absorbing salts and passing them on to the tree. The association is a controlled one in that active cells in the root keep the fungus growth limited for a long time. Eventually infected roots are shed by the tree and the fungus utilises them as food. The net result is beneficial to both partners.

Not all mycorrhizal associations between fungi and plant roots involve Basidiomycetes. Some mycorrhizas show a different type of relationship with fungal hyphae mainly between and inside the cortical cells, but with no mantle about the root, although hyphal connections go out into the soil. Within the root cells the hyphae may occur as coils or as densely branched structures. Many herbaceous plants show this type of relationship. The hyphae undergo digestion in the deeper layers of cells. This type of association is called an **endotrophic mycorrhiza**. Apportionment of benefits in this relationship is less clear than that in ectotrophic mycorrhizas and all may not be alike. Some endotrophic fungi may be mild parasites barely controlled by the host. But some chlorophyll-less orchids, unable to carry out photosynthesis, possess endotrophic mycorrhizas and somehow obtain their nutriment from the soil, thus being dependent entirely on the associated endotrophic fungi. Such plants are sometimes described as saprophytes, but are in fact parasitic on the fungus. Some pteridophyte prothalli remain subterranean with no photosynthesis for many years, being fed solely by an endotrophic mycorrhizal fungus during this period. There is, then, some good evidence for benefit to the higher plant partner. A variety of fungi is involved in these relationships and not all have been isolated and cultured.

LICHENS

Lichens are composite organisms consisting of a fungus and an alga growing together in a definite arrangement and usually having a definite form, constituting a single thallus. Growth is often very slow, and lichens are characteristic plants of particularly rigorous habitats such as bare soil, rock, walls, and tree trunks, exposed to desiccation and extremes of weather. In some areas, *e.g.* Arctic tundra, rocky mountain tops, and sea shores above the tide zone, they may form the chief vegetation. In a few lichens a Basidiomycete is the fungal partner (**mycobiont**), but mostly, and in all European species, the fungus is an Ascomycete. The algae (**phycobionts**) of lichens are sometimes green species such as the unicellular *Pleurococcus*, and sometimes blue-green such as the filamentous *Nostoc* and *Anabaena*. The algal species are able to grow independently in nature, but the fungi are not found naturally outside associations with algae. The fungus is the predominating partner, however, and gives the form to the thallus. The wide range of growth-form in the group includes species that are filamentous, fruticose (shrubby), foliose (leafy), crustaceous, or endolithic (within rocks). The fungi of endolithic lichens presumably secrete acids that dissolve the rock and allow the fungus to bore into it, and these lichens do not fruit until the surface of the rock is weathered down to the level of the thallus.

The mycobionts appear to be well adapted to the successful parasitism of algal cells, and spores of the fungi if placed near cells of algae characteristically invade them by means of haustorium-like structures that kill the cells and utilise the contents. Cells of some species of algae, however, seem resistant to this infection and survive, becoming enveloped by the hyphae of the fungus and forming the "gonidia" of the lichen thallus. The specificity of phycobiont and mycobiont in lichen species thus seems to depend on resistance of the alga to attack by the fungus. Experimental work indicates that by bringing together an appropriate combination of alga and fungus on a medium unfavourable for the independent growth of either successful lichenisation can result, but if conditions allow either partner to grow independently then lichenisation does not occur. The symbiosis, then, is an enforced one, and is of obvious mutual benefit in that both organisms survive and grow where neither could separately. These facts also help to explain the predominance of lichens on apparently inhospitable substrata. The

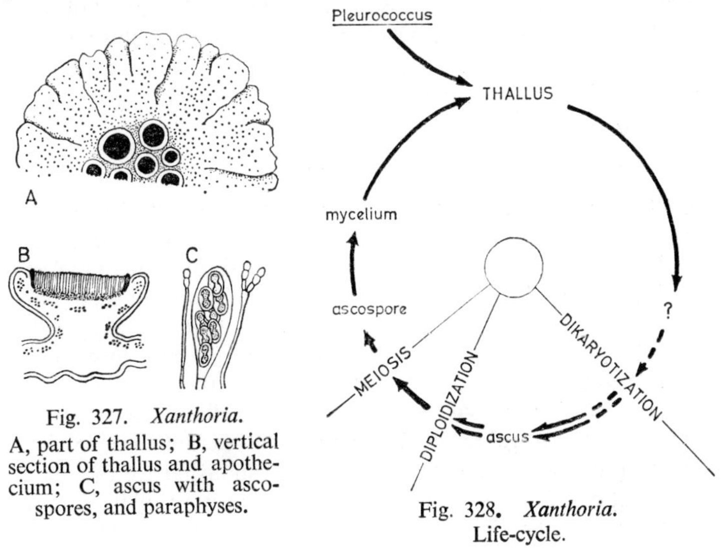

Fig. 327. *Xanthoria.*
A, part of thallus; B, vertical section of thallus and apothecium; C, ascus with ascospores, and paraphyses.

Fig. 328. *Xanthoria.*
Life-cycle.

fungus gets assimilated carbohydrate and vitamins from the alga in return for minerals and protection from high light intensity.

XANTHORIA

Xanthoria parietina (Fig. 327, A) is one of the commonest and best known British lichens. It grows on rock and walls, on roof slates, and on trees and fences. It is particularly common by the sea and on farm buildings. The thallus is foliose and circular, with distinct lobes at the margin, and with deep orange apothecia up to 5 mm. diameter near the centre. In good sunlight it has a bright orange colour, but in shaded situations is yellowish-green.

Three zones can be seen in vertical sections of the thallus (Fig. 327, B). The upper cortical region and the lower cortical region consist of closely interwoven fungal hyphae forming a pseudoparenchyma, while between these is a medullary zone of rather loosely interwoven hyphae that is obviously mycelial in texture. Towards the upper part of the medullary zone cells of the green alga *Pleurococcus* occur in scattered groups. The thallus grows from the margin at a rate of about one or two millimetres a year. The apothecia are similar in construction to those of normal Discomycete fungi, but the outer rim is a **thalline margin**, the compact mycelium containing cells of the alga (Fig. 327, B). The swollen asci each have eight large oval ascospores with a very characteristic waisted lumen (Fig. 327, C). The spores are dispersed without the alga and must fall near *Pleurococcus* cells under appropriate conditions before the synthesis of new thalli can occur. Vegetative reproduction takes place by fragments of the thallus containing both partners being dispersed and under suitable conditions producing new thalli.

BACTERIA

Bacteria are characterised mainly by their small size and an absence of features belonging to other groups of organisms. The range in the group is such that they are difficult to define precisely. There is no evidence for any close relationship between bacteria and fungi. Bacteria have a rigid cell wall that consists of protein, polysaccharides, and lipids, and that is chemically inert to common stains. **Antigens**, substances that stimulate the production of chemically specific **antibodies** by warm-blooded animals, and that are important in serology and in immunity reactions (see p. 582), occur in the cell wall. It is the wall that is responsible for the shapes of bacterial cells, and if it is dissolved by the action of the enzyme lysozyme added to the culture medium, the protoplasts can be cultured without walls. In this condition they assume a spherical shape irrespective of the form of the original cell. In such wall-free cultures the medium must be nearly isotonic for the cell since in nature it is the cell wall that protects the protoplast against osmotic rupture. There are no obvious vacuoles in the cytoplasm. Bacterial cells frequently have two or more nuclei. The bacterial nucleus is a poorly-defined chromatinic body of DNA that has no nuclear membrane separating it from the cytoplasm. The details of nuclear division are still controversial, but there is good evidence for a linear arrangement of genetic characters on a single chromosome that may join up as a circle, and there is equal partition of the genetic material to the two daughter nuclei during division.

Some bacteria move actively by means of flagella. These are long, unbranched, single fibrils consisting almost entirely of a protein that is similar to the contractile protein of animals. Each flagellum is of the same order of thickness (about 12 mμ) as a single protein molecule. The arrangement of the flagella differs in different bacteria; there may be a single polar flagellum at one or both ends, there may be a tuft of flagella at one or both ends, or the flagella may be inserted all round the cell.

Slime is produced by many bacteria, and where it occurs as a fairly firm layer outside the wall it is called a **capsule**. The slimes are usually polysaccharides or polypeptides of high molecular weight, and are sometimes the chemicals responsible for the serological differences between species and strains. They may also protect the cells of some pathogenic strains against phagocytosis, or ingestion by the phagocytic defensive cells of the host.

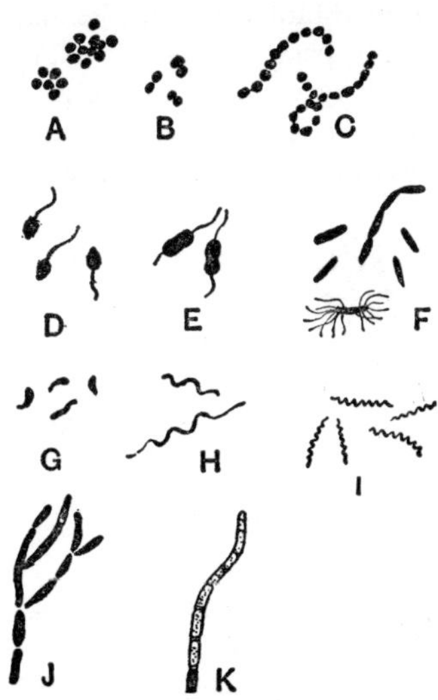

Fig. 329. FORMS OF BACTERIUM-CELLS (× 1,500).

A, *Staphylococcus* from a boil; B, *Diplococcus*; C, *Streptococcus*, of blood-poisoning; D, *Nitrosomonas*; E, biflagellate bacteria; F, bacilli, the flagellated one is *B. typhosus* of typhoid fever; G, commas; H, *Spirillum*; I, *Spirochaeta pallida* of syphilis; J, *Cladothrix dichotoma*; K, *Beggiatoa alba* (the granules are deposited sulphur).

The three main recognised groups of bacteria are the coccal, bacillary, and spirillar forms (Fig. 329). Cocci are more or less spherical, 0·5 — 1·25 μ in diameter, and are almost all non-motile. Bacilli are straight or slightly curved rods. The proportions between length and width vary greatly. Flagella occur in some but not all bacilli. Spirillar forms are strongly curved or twisted rods, usually with flagella. Some bacteria are **pleomorphic**, being able to adopt different shapes and sizes under different environmental conditions or even in different regions of a single colony.

Bacteria reproduce by transverse binary fission of the cells. The chromatinic body divides first during this process, and then a transverse membrane develops separating the protoplast into two nucleated portions. Following full development of a transverse wall from the membrane the cell separates by a median split into two cells. Under some conditions **endospores** are produced by bacteria (Fig. 330). These are highly resistant bodies, being able to survive for many years, and being more tolerant to heat, desiccation, and disinfectants than the somatic cells. Only a single endospore is produced in any one bacterial cell, and it germinates to give a single somatic cell. The process cannot, therefore, be described as reproduction. The envelope of the spore is impervious to simple stains.

Evidence for a true life-cycle is still lacking since it is not clear that any regular cyclical sequence of events occurs. It has, however, been established that sexual processes by which genetic material can be passed from one cell to another exist in some bacterial species.

A very wide range of metabolic function is found in the bacteria and the group has exploited almost every aerobic and anaerobic environment where energy-supplying substrates are available. Bacteria are extremely important economically, and are very common in soil, and in fresh and salt water, where they contribute largely to the breakdown of animal and plant remains. Some are parasites of plants or animals and cause disease.

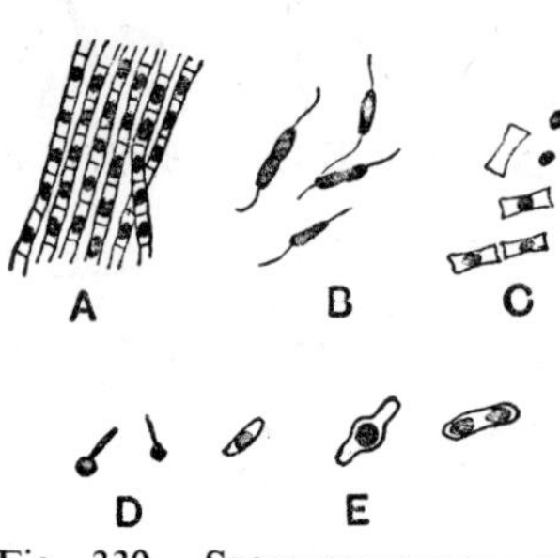

Fig. 330. SPORE-FORMATION IN BACTERIA.

A, zoogloea stage, with spore-formation; B, motile stage of A; C, *Bacillus anthracis*, of anthrax; D, *Bacillus tetani*, of lockjaw; E, *Bacillus mycoides*.

BACILLUS SUBTILIS

This common bacterium is relatively easy to isolate and culture with a minimum of equipment, by preparing an infusion of hay in tap water, decanting the clear fluid into a flask plugged with cotton wool, and boiling for about an hour. Most organisms are killed by this treatment but the spores of *B. subtilis* are resistant and on incubation germinate to produce a film of cells at the surface of the liquid.

B. subtilis is a motile, aerobic rod with eight to twelve flagella inserted round the cell. The cells commonly produce slime copiously, and often remain adhering together end to end after division, forming chains of cells. The cell is Gram positive, which means that cells stained in crystal violet retain the stain when subsequently washed in a neutral solvent such as ethanol or acetone. Old cells may contain endospores that appear as blank areas in normally stained cells.

The Characters of Bacteria in Relation to Disease

Most bacteria have a very high growth rate and an optimum temperature near to 37° C., the temperature of the human body. In order to be parasitic in the human body a species must first of all be able to enter the tissues and then to withstand phagocytosis. The presence of a capsule appears to be important in this respect. Mutant strains of pathogenic bacteria that lack a capsule are usually non-virulent. Not all parasites cause disease. Pathogenic bacteria produce as a consequence of their growth toxins that disturb the host metabolism. A rise in the body temperature of mammals is a common consequence of exposure to these toxins, but tissues may also be damaged.

The unicellular habit is a significant factor in pathogenesis for mammals, since single small cells are readily transported in the blood and lymph systems. Very few fungi are able to cause systemic disease of mammals. The few that are have the property of producing a budding, unicellular phase. Most of these fungi are mycelial in normal laboratory culture, but produce the yeast-like phase in culture at 37° C. on blood agar or cysteine agar, and in the presence of high concentrations of carbon dioxide. The ability to produce two such distinct phases of growth is known as **dimorphism**. Dermatophytes, the fungi that cause ringworm diseases, are always mycelial and are confined to superficial keratinic areas of the body.

The unicellular condition is ill adapted to the production of disease in plants where there is no circulatory system, and there are relatively few bacterial pathogens of plants. Hyphae are much better able to penetrate cell walls and to spread rapidly from cell to cell. Bacteria would have to fill a cell with their own cells and burst it before entering the next cell. Some plant pathogenic fungi show dimorphism in the reverse direction to that in animal pathogens, being yeast-like when saprophytic and mycelial within the plant host.

Nutrition of Bacteria

Most bacteria are heterotrophic and rather unexacting in their requirements, being either obligate or facultative saprophytes, culturable on a range of media containing a sugar, a source of organic nitrogen, and minerals. A few heterotrophs are exacting saprophytes some of which have not yet been cultured in a chemically-defined medium, and which appear to need complex natural substrates. A number of bacteria are, like green plants, autotrophs utilising carbon dioxide as their carbon source and deriving their initial energy from some other source. Light may be the source of this energy as in the **photosynthetic bacteria**, or the energy may be obtained from the conversion of inorganic compounds as in the **chemosynthetic autotrophs.**

The pigments of the photosynthetic bacteria appear under the light microscope to be uniformly distributed through the cell, but the electron microscope shows that very small chromatophores are present. The photosynthetic species are not all alike in their mechanism of photosynthesis but all are able to grow anaerobically in light. They include coccal, bacillary, and spirillar forms. The purple sulphur bacteria contain the pigment bacteriochlorophyll and also carotenoids, and they use hydrogen sulphide as the hydrogen donor in photosynthesis. Sulphur is deposited as globules in the cells. The non-sulphur purple and brown bacteria contain the same photosynthetic pigments as the foregoing group but use organic hydrogen donors and do not deposit sulphur. The green sulphur bacteria contain "chlorobium chlorophyll" which is quite different from other forms of chlorophyll. Hydrogen sulphide is the hydrogen donor here also, but the sulphur is deposited extracellularly, not inside the cell. All these forms occur in mud and stagnant water.

Non-photosynthetic autotrophs obtain their energy by the oxidation of ammonia to nitrate, or nitrite to nitrate, by the oxidation of substances such as molecular hydrogen, carbon monoxide, and methane, by the oxidation of sulphides to sulphur, or sulphur to sulphate, by the oxidation of ferrous or manganous compounds. Some of the reactions mediated by these organisms are important in connection with the fertility of soils.

The transformations of nitrogen compounds in soil have been studied in some detail. The most generally satisfactory form of nitrogenous nutrient for higher plants is nitrate, and it is not present in all soils in amounts sufficient for healthy growth of crop plants. During the decomposition of plant and animal residues the nitrogen of amino-groups is liberated as ammonia. This is oxidised to nitrite by the bacterium *Nitrosomonas*, and the nitrite to nitrate by the bacterium *Nitrobacter*, these processes supplying the energy needed by the organisms for carbon dioxide fixation. These are the only known genera of **nitrifying bacteria.**

Any organism in soil that can assimilate nitrate may also reduce nitrate, since ammonia is the major intermediate in the conversion of nitrate to organic nitrogen compounds. If nitrate reduction proceeds as far as the formation of molecular nitrogen or nitrous oxide the process is described as **denitrification** since these materials, being gaseous, can be lost from the soil into the atmosphere. There are a number of denitrifying soil bacteria.

Molecular nitrogen may be brought into a form available to plants by the activity of the bacterium *Rhizobium* in its association with the roots of leguminous plants. This symbiotic nitrogen fixation has been described in Chapter 10. There is also a wide range of free-living, non-symbiotic, micro-organisms in soil capable of fixing molecular nitrogen. The genus *Azotobacter* is best known in this connection and has been extensively studied, mainly because it is easily grown in large quantities in culture. The bacterium is aerobic and heterotrophic, obtaining its energy for **nitrogen fixation** from the oxidative breakdown of organic carbon compounds. Despite the emphasis that has been placed on *Azotobacter* it is probably much less important in non-symbiotic nitrogen fixation in nature than some other organisms. The genus is rarely common in soils, and in many fertile soils is completely absent. It does not occur at all in soils with a pH lower than 6. The anaerobic heterotrophic genus, *Clostridium*, is much more widely distributed, and probably makes a more important contribution than *Azotobacter* to nitrogen fixation. In tropical soils the bacterium *Beijerinckia*, which is a heterotrophic aerobe, is probably a very important nitrogen fixer, as are also species of the blue-green alga, *Nostoc*. About half the species of blue-green algae that have been tested for the property have been found capable of fixing nitrogen.

The nitrogen transformations resulting from microbial activity are included in the convenient, but simplified, summary known as the **nitrogen cycle** (Fig. 331).

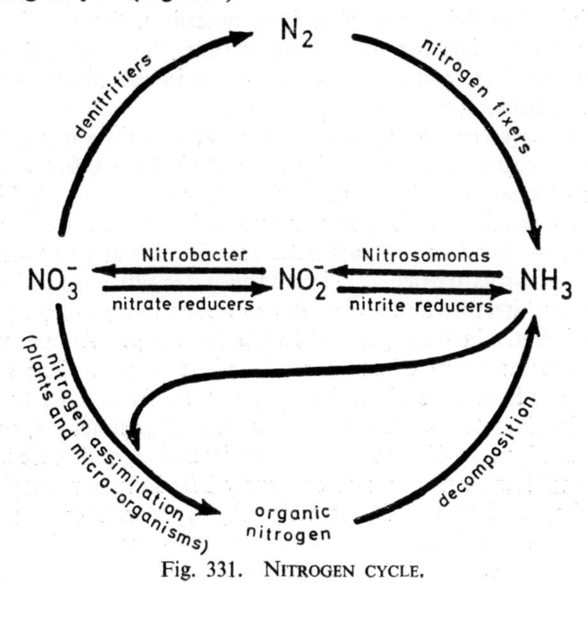

Fig. 331. NITROGEN CYCLE.

Other chemical cycles dependent upon microbial activity and important in maintaining soil fertility are the phosphorus cycle and the manganese cycle, but the processes are as yet less fully understood.

The **carbon cycle** comprises two main phases, one in which autotrophic organisms of all sorts synthesise complex organic compounds from carbon dioxide using light and chemical sources of energy, and a second in which the tissues of dead (and some living) organisms are progressively degraded with the final oxidative production of carbon dioxide. Fertile soils show a reasonable balance between these two phases. Where decomposition proceeds more rapidly than the accumulation of organic debris, as in some tropical soils, the soil becomes largely mineral and lacks the humus which possesses properties desirable for healthy plant growth. Soils in which organic materials decompose more slowly than they accumulate, as in some cool, wet areas, develop a top layer of peat or "raw humus" which is unsuitable for the growth of most plants, being badly drained and aerated, and deficient in mineral nutrients.

VIRUSES

Viruses are the smallest biological structures that contain all the information for their own reproduction. They are unable to metabolise independently, however, and require as an environment for activity the living cell of a host organism, from which they derive the materials for their reproduction. They are, therefore, obligate parasites, and often cause disease in the plants, animals, fungi, and bacteria which they parasitise.

The diseases caused by viruses were at one time differentiated from those caused by bacteria by the fact that the infective agents of virus diseases would pass through a filter designed to hold back cells of bacterial size. The agents were called "filterable" viruses, but it is now possible to construct filters fine enough to hold back the smallest virus particles. Plant viruses are either rod-like, with a helical architecture and a diameter of about 16 mμ, or polyhedral with a diameter in the region of 16 mμ to 22 mμ. Animal viruses show a greater range of size than do plant viruses. The smaller ones usually have a polyhedral shape, and are from 8 mμ to about 100 mμ in diameter, while the larger ones may be spherical, oval, or brick-shaped, up to 450 mμ in smallest dimension, and these usually have a complex structure, not obviously based on any simple geometric shape. Some of the bacteriophages, the viruses that attack bacteria, are polyhedral, others are tadpole-shaped with a polyhedral head about 95 $\times$ 65 mμ and a tail about 100 $\times$ 25 mμ

(Fig. 332). Many plant and some animal viruses can be prepared in a crystalline state and still retain infectivity.

Plant viruses and some animal viruses consist of ribonucleic acid (RNA) and protein. Other animal viruses and bacteriophages contain deoxyribonucleic acid (DNA) and protein. The nucleic acid forms a central core surrounded by an outer coat of protein. The protein may act as a protective layer. Intact particles of TMV (tobacco mosaic virus), for example, are resistant to the action of

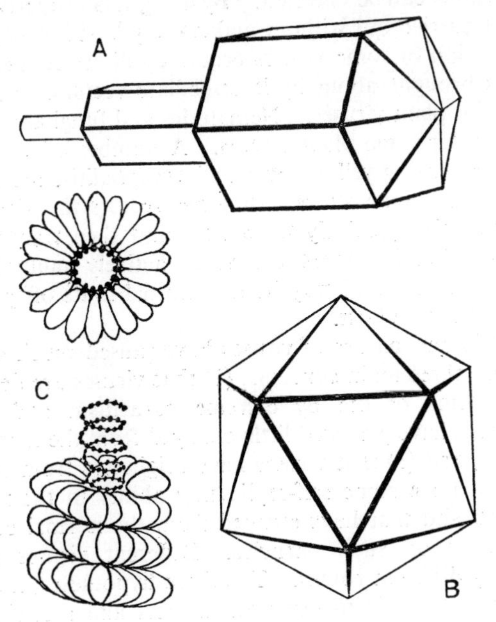

Fig. 332. MORPHOLOGY OF VIRUSES.
A, Coli T2 bacteriophage, form based on hexagonal prism, × about 400,000. B, Bacteriophage Φ X 174 based on icosahedral symmetry, × about 1,400,000. C, Tobacco mosaic virus, part of rod in section and in surface view, helical symmetry, × about 1,400,000.

the enzyme ribonuclease which can bring about the hydrolysis of free RNA. The serological properties of viruses are also determined by the protein coat. The nucleic acid component determines the remaining properties of the virus. With some animal viruses RNA separated from the protein can initiate infection. The RNA carries the coded genetical information which in the host cell is capable of inducing the replication of both the nucleic acid and the protein.

Many viruses have now been investigated in much detail in respect of their fine structure, but viruses are largely identified by physiological properties, either by the symptoms they produce in the host or by serological methods. Because of their protein coats, viruses can act as antigens when present in animals, and thus induce the formation of specific antibodies in the same way as do bacterial pathogens. If blood serum containing antibodies **(antiserum)** is mixed with the corresponding specific antigen characteristic reactions can be detected. By using this property identifications can be carried out without making any host inoculations.

Transmission of some viruses occurs by direct contact, but that of others is brought about by intermediate **vectors**. Some insects are vectors for plant viruses. Nematodes and fungi are also known to be vectors for some plant viruses. A number of animal viruses such as those causing yellow fever and encephalitis, are also transmitted by arthropod vectors. In some vectors the virus particles are merely carried passively for a time and then transmitted to a healthy host, but in others the virus actively multiplies in the tissues of the vector and may be transmitted to its offspring before infection of the main host.

The origin and nature of viruses have caused much speculation and there are three main concepts, (1) that viruses are derived from free-living forms of life by extreme parasitism and reduction, (2) that viruses have persisted little-changed from the most primitive forms of life, and (3) that viruses have originated from cytoplasmic particles that have some self-replicating ability in the normal cell environment, and that have escaped from the normal control that the cell exerts on such particles. Different viruses may have originated by different routes. The three hypotheses, however, are not readily susceptible to experimental test and are, therefore, of limited value.

20 SURVEY OF THE PLANT KINGDOM: EPILOGUE

The reader who has studied Chapters 15 to 19 will now be in a position to visualise more clearly the evolutionary trends briefly referred to in Chapter 14. In the present chapter we shall review the course of evolution in the plant kingdom, drawing together evidence which has been presented piecemeal in other chapters.

If we speculate about the characteristics which were possessed by the earliest organisms recognisable as plants, we are likely to conclude that these organisms were small, simple in construction, and autotrophic; and that they lived in water. These features are possessed by *Chlorella* and other small algae, but it is virtually certain that organisms of smaller size and greater simplicity must have preceded even these humble types of plant. Subsequent evolution appears to have proceeded in three principal spheres.

Firstly, there are those plants which have retained the autotrophic nutrition shown by their ancestors together with the need to live in water. These comprise the series we group together and call algae. At an early stage in plant evolution there appears to have been an offshoot into a second sphere caused by a change from autotrophic to heterotrophic nutrition. From this event onwards it is believed that there has been separate evolution by autotrophs and heterotrophs, though it is likely that the change to heterotrophy has occurred on several independent occasions. The heterotrophs include all the fungi.

The third major sphere of evolutionary activity concerns those plants which have retained autotrophic nutrition but have acquired the ability to grow on land. Although these plants are customarily divided into bryophytes, pteridophytes, gymnosperms, and angiosperms, when the four groups are considered together they show remarkable uniformity in some respects. For instance, they all have identical photosynthetic pigments and hence considerable physiological similarity; there is a large measure of structural similarity also, particularly in the parenchyma which is a tissue common to them all; and they all have a relatively regular life-cycle in which a haploid gametophyte alternates with a diploid sporophyte. The presence of these same features in all the green land plants lends support to the idea that the first colonisers of land possessed a particular, and evidently a successful combination of fundamental features, and there have been no major departures from this basic pattern during subsequent evolution.

By contrast the algae appear to have experimented with many forms of physiological process, structural organisation, and life history, and in each case several alternative systems have been sufficiently successful to have persisted into modern times. A similar claim could be made for the fungi, though here the physiological diversity is not generally recognisable from differences in pigmentation.

Despite the fact that evolution is believed to have occurred independently in the three major spheres described above, there are, nevertheless, some remarkable parallels between them. A comparison of the structural organisation of algae and fungi, for example, shows that in both groups there are many species in which the plant body consists of a long cylinder, sometimes branched, which may be undivided (e.g. *Vaucheria* or *Mucor*), or made up of a filament of cells (e.g. *Ectocarpus* or *Aspergillus*). In both groups, also, there are more bulky species with a structure composed of aggregated filaments (*e.g.* many small seaweeds and the fruiting bodies of many Basidiomycetes). An even more striking case of parallel evolution is evident in a comparative study of life-cycles. The salient points of such a study are given in the following section.

EVOLUTION OF LIFE-CYCLES

Sexual reproduction is a feature of every group which has been described, and all sexual life-cycles can be related to the basic pattern shown in Fig. 217, but there is great variation on this pattern. Some groups (*e.g.* gymnosperms or angiosperms) are relatively uniform in the type of life-cycle shown by their members, but others (algae and fungi) have no such regularity. The variation among algae, for instance, is almost as great as that found among the whole plant kingdom.

Algae

Many species have life-cycles in which the diploid phase is confined to a single cell, the zygote. This cell may have a prolonged existence, but meiosis follows fertilisation without any intervening mitotic divisions. The haploid phase, on the other hand, multiplies extensively by mitosis, giving either a large number of unicellular individuals (e.g. *Chlamydomonas*), or one or more multicellular individuals (e.g. *Spirogyra*). Because of this proliferation, the haploid phase is the more prominent, even though the individual vegetative cells of, say, *Chlamydomonas* may be smaller than the zygotes.

At the other extreme are the large brown algae, where the diploid phase is dominant and the haploid greatly restricted. The limit of this restriction is shown in *Fucus,* where the haploid phase begins with the formation of gametes direct from the products of meiosis and ends with fertilisation.

Between these extremes are many other types of life-cycle, including those described in Chapter 18 for *Cladophora, Ectocarpus,* and Rhodophyceae, among which there is almost every degree of variation in the relative prominence of diploid and haploid phases.

Although it is impossible to arrange the different types of algal life-cycle in any orderly sequence which could represent a single linear succession during evolution, there is some correlation between the type of life-cycle and the size of the individual. Most of the algae which are microscopic at all stages have a dominant haploid phase, whereas among medium-sized and large seaweeds the diploid phase is always well-developed and frequently the dominant phase. If the reasonable assumption is made that large species have evolved from smaller ones, this suggests the conclusion that life-cycles with a dominant diploid phase are more advanced.

Fungi

As with the algae, this is an enormous group of species with an almost endless variety of sexual life-cycles. In many of them, besides the simple alternation of diploid and haploid phases, there is the added complication of a dikaryotic phase. Figs. 302 (Oomycetes), 314 (*Aspergillus,* etc.), and 323 (*Puccinia*) illustrate some of the extremes of variation in life-cycle found among fungi. There appears to be a relationship between size of the individual and prominence of the diploid or dikaryotic phase similar to that in algae. Most of the moulds and other fungi which do not produce structures of much bulk exist mainly in the haploid state. The larger Basidiomycetes, on the other hand, which produce sizeable and conspicuous fruiting bodies are diploid or dikaryotic for most of their life-cycle. Once again the evidence points to increasing importance of the diploid phase at the expense of the haploid as evolution has advanced.

The Green Land Plants

In contrast to algae and fungi, each group of the green land plants can be characterised by a single pattern of sexual life-cycle, and the various groups can be arranged in an orderly succession according to the relative prominence of the diploid sporophyte and the haploid gametophyte.

The average size of individual among the **bryophytes** is smaller than in any other group of green land plants, and as in algae and fungi, small average size is associated with a dominant gametophyte. In no species is the sporophyte reduced to anything like the same extent as in the smaller algae, but it is quite clearly subordinate to the gametophyte. Among both liverworts and mosses, the gametophyte constitutes what one thinks of as "the plant". The sporophyte in liverworts is a temporary structure, smaller than the gametophyte and dependent upon it for both support and nutrition. There is very nearly the same relationship in mosses, though to some extent the sporophyte is nutritionally self-supporting.

The gametophyte in many **pteridophytes** resembles that of liverworts in being small and prostrate and having an independent existence. The sporophyte begins as a parasite upon the gametophyte but vegetative growth continues much longer than in bryophytes, and the fully grown sporophyte is not only larger and more permanent than the gametophyte, but completely independent of it after a short initial period. Thus the sporophyte is unmistakably dominant and there is a reversal of the relationship shown in bryophytes.

Throughout the bryophytes and the pteridophytes the spores, which are the beginning of the gametophytes, are shed from the sporophyte which produces them. In some species of both groups a multicellular gametophyte begins to develop within the spore wall before the spore is shed. This is a tendency which foreshadows the situation in more advanced land plants where the gametophyte not only develops within the spore wall but also, on the female side, remains enclosed within sporophyte tissues throughout its existence. *Selaginella* shows considerable advancement in this direction by comparison with other pteridophytes. Both male and female gametophytes develop inside the spore wall, and the female prothallus with its archegonia is recognisable before the megaspore is shed, though fertilisation is believed to occur always after shedding.

Gymnosperms show further progress in the directions indicated by bryophytes and pteridophytes. The sporophyte is overwhelmingly the more prominent generation. The gametophytes are very small, and on the male side barely multicellular. The female gametophyte is still decidedly multicellular, and as in lower groups it has archegonia in which the female gametes are produced, but it is totally enclosed in the tissues of the sporophyte at all times.

Angiosperms have the most advanced type of life-cycle, judged in terms of the progression we have followed through bryophytes, pteridophytes, and gymnosperms. Size of the gametophytes has reached a point beyond which further reduction is almost inconceivable. The male gametophyte is similar to that in gymnosperms, which is itself extremely reduced. The female gametophyte, however, is of a type unique to angiosperms. Archegonia are completely absent, and the nearest approach to a multicellular prothallus is an embryo sac with no more than eight nuclei incompletely walled off from one another. This structure is usually even more thoroughly enclosed by sporophyte tissues than is the female gametophyte of gymnosperms.

It can be seen that in all three spheres of evolution there is evidence of progress towards a similar type of advanced life-cycle. Such uniformity of direction suggests that there must be some benefit associated with the diploid state. Our knowledge of the probable mechanism of evolution indicates that the diploid state is in fact of great advantage in helping to preserve a species from extinction, so that if the sexual cycle must have both a diploid and a haploid phase it is understandable that the most successful plants are those with the greatest reduction of the haploid phase. The explanation of this requires a knowledge of thc principles of inheritance and their relevance to the mechanism of evolution. These topics, and their relationship to the diploid state, are discussed in Chapter 22.

SIZE, STRUCTURAL COMPLEXITY, AND WATER RELATIONS

These three aspects of a plant are very closely related since change in any one of them will almost certainly have a profound effect on the others. Wherever there are living cells in a plant, these cells must be supplied with water, ultimately from an outside source. For many of the lower plants whose size is small this is no serious problem. They live in or close to their water supply, and their small size means that even their innermost parts are not far from the plant surface. There is therefore no need of special tissues for internal conduction, and the structure of these plants is consequently very simple. The situation is very different for larger plants, particularly in those parts whose direction of growth is away from the source of water. The aerial parts of a tree, for instance, must be supplied with water from the soil, and the vascular tissues responsible for this conduction contribute to an internal structure of great complexity. Other structural features are related to the need to prevent excessive water loss, which is another hazard to be faced by large plants with extensive aerial parts.

The interdependence of these features has meant that they have been inevitably associated during evolution. The groups of green land plants, when arranged in the order indicated by their life-cycles, show a steady progression towards greater maximum size coupled with increasing structural complexity and increasing freedom from the need to have their parts in proximity to their water supply. The algae and fungi have clearly evolved along independent lines, which in this case do not show a parallelism comparable to that in the evolution of life-cycles.

Algae

Since the great majority of algae live immersed in water either continually or for at least part of every day, the water relations of the group are rather special. Water is regularly present over the whole plant surface, and the only conduction needed is from the surface to the inner parts. This situation has permitted the evolution of greater size with very little increase in structural complexity. The characteristic form of the larger seaweeds is a thallus which may be of great length but is never of much thickness at any point. Since no part of the plant is far from the surface, water supplies to all tissues can be satisfactorily maintained by diffusion from cell to cell. No special conducting tissues are necessary.

Protection against excessive water loss does not concern those algae which are permanently submerged. Seaweeds of the intertidal zone of sea shores may be exposed to strong sunshine or drying winds for several hours at a time, and their coating of mucilage protects them from desiccation, but in general algae do not face the risk of prolonged exposure in dry air which many land plants must contend with.

One further feature, which is clearly connected with water relations but not with size or structure is the means of transport for the male gametes. All male gametes in the algae travel by water, either propelling themselves with flagella, or being carried passively as in Rhodophyceae.

Fungi

Fungi have a relationship to water which is something like that of algae, though they show rather more enterprise in growing with at least part of their structure out of water. The water moulds are very like algae in that they are continually submerged: most other fungi are in close contact with a moist substrate at least during active growth. This may be soil, damp wood, the tissues of living hosts, or any of the other substrates which support fungal growth. Increase in size of the vegetative plant body is achieved by growth of the mycelium without much aggregation of the hyphae into bulky structures. Thus no vegetative hypha is far from a supply of water and no serious problems of conduction or structural differentiation arise. The greatest bulk attained by fungi is seen in their fruiting bodies. Some of the Basidiomycetes which parasitise trees produce fructifications which jut out from the infected tree-trunk, and which are not only several inches in thickness but which also persist for months or years. During this time they remain alive and are supplied with water from the host. Unlike the roots or stems of higher plants, however, they do not have a continuous and rapid passage of water through their tissues. They are more like a sponge with an impermeable covering over most of their exposed surface, in which moisture is retained but does not flow. Hence there is no need for special channels of water conduction, and none are found. Other fungal fruiting bodies have similar water relations. They illustrate a rather exceptional type of plant organ in which substantial size is not accompanied by structural complexity.

The Green Land Plants

Of all the groups of green land plants, the **bryophytes** can least be said to have overcome the problems of life on land. They have gained a firm foothold, it is true, but they are very much restricted to a habit where all parts of the plant are close to the supply of water. They illustrate a clear association between small size, simplicity of structure, and the need to be kept moist if they are to show active growth. Like algae, no part of the plant is more than a short distance from the surface, and as a general rule all internal parts receive their water supply by simple diffusion from neighbouring cells. Only in a few mosses is there any differentiation of conducting tissues. Some of the simplicity of bryophytes may be associated with the fact that the "plant" is the gametophyte: perhaps only sporophyte tissues are able to develop a highly differentiated structure.

All bryophytes produce motile male gametes and rely on a film of surface water to achieve fertilisation.

Pteridophytes show a very pronounced advance over bryophytes in their adaptation to life on land. Although most species do not exceed a few feet in height when fully grown, and many are far smaller than this, the group also includes the tree ferns which may reach a height of eighty feet. The structure needed to support a plant of this size and to transport water to its upper parts is far in advance of anything found among bryophytes. There is well-developed xylem and phloem, more primitive in structure than the corresponding tissues in seed plants, but nevertheless adequate to carry out rapid translocation over considerable distances as well as providing strands of strengthening tissue. The vascular tissues of pteridophytes are mostly primary, and the number of species which produce secondary tissues is small. Even in these species the quantity of secondary tissues is not large, and the apparent inability, at least among living pteridophytes, to produce a continuous increase in secondary thickening limits the size to which the plants can grow without becoming mechanically weak.

Although most of the larger pteridophytes show a preference for moist habitats, or at least shaded places where serious drought is unlikely, there are still the problems of avoiding excessive water loss. The epidermal cells are equipped with a cuticle, and there are stomata comparable with those of seed plants. These are both features poorly developed in bryophytes.

The development of large aerial parts must be matched by an appropriate underground system for the collection of water and for anchorage. Most pteridophytes have acquired the ability to produce roots which in size, structure, and function are far more advanced than the rhizoids of bryophytes.

Although in their vegetative features pteridophytes show marked advancement over bryophytes, the reproductive processes of the two groups are very much alike. There are close similarities in the way the gametes are produced and in the mechanism of fertilisation. All male gametes are motile in both groups, so that the gametophytes of pteridophytes are dependent on a surface layer of water to fulfil their function, just as in bryophytes. This feature is in marked contrast to the achievements of the sporophyte in gaining independence of surface moisture.

Since all plants require a supply of water they are bound to be restricted in where they grow, and to what size and shape they grow, by this requirement. The **seed plants**, although as dependent as other plants on water for their existence, have achieved the greatest degree of freedom from the restrictions imposed. This is shown in two particular features. Firstly, size. The seed plants include the largest known plants, some gymnosperm trees exceeding 300 feet in height. Continuous increase of secondary tissues in the trunk provides the massive cylinder of wood which not only supports the weight of the aerial parts but also caters for conduction of water to the topmost branches. The type of xylem found in angiosperms, with vessels which offer little resistance to the flow of water, can be regarded as a factor which contributes to the efficiency of these plants in raising water to great heights. Secondly, the seed plants in general do not rely on water as a medium of transport in the process of fertilisation. Apart from a minority of water plants, pollen is carried by wind, by insects, or by other animals. This feature means that seed plants are able to grow in many dry habitats which would be unsuitable for pteridophytes, whose need for surface water at the time of fertilisation is a severe restriction.

THE SEED HABIT

One further trend, which can be recognised among the more advanced land plants, is that leading towards the production of seeds. In plants which reproduce by seeds, each new individual begins independent life as a multicellular embryo equipped with a protective outer coat to shield it from some of the hazards of climate and biological attack, and a supply of food sufficient to sustain it during germination. The chances of survival for a seed are therefore higher than those for a spore which is smaller, less well protected, and more dependent on an external food supply when it germinates. In consequence, there is a much higher rate of wastage among spores than among seeds, and the evolution of the seed may be regarded as progress towards greater economy of reproductive effort.

Evolution of the seed is closely connected with gradual reduction of the haploid phase, but the one is not an inevitable consequence of the other. The algae, for instance, have undergone progressive reduction of the haploid phase, culminating in the type of life-cycle found in *Fucus*, but none of them produces structures comparable with seeds. It is clear that seed formation is of much greater advantage to a land plant than to one which lives in water and is largely protected from extremes of climate and from shortage of food supply.

During the evolution of the green land plants there has been a transition from propagation by spores to propagation by seeds. Since spores are the beginning of the gametophyte generation whereas seeds contain the beginning of the sporophyte, it follows that there has been a change in the point of the life-cycle at which propagation occurs. Throughout bryophytes and pteridophytes propagation is by spores. The sporophyte of a bryophyte produces only one type of spore, so far as outward appearance is concerned, and the same is true of the homosporous pteridophytes.

These spores are released from the plant which produces them, and each one is potentially capable of developing into a gametophyte. The gametophytes themselves may be monoecious, producing both archegonia and antheridia; or, less commonly, there are separate males and females, as in *Equisetum*. In the latter case, although all the spores are alike in appearance, there is almost certainly a genetic difference between spores which develop into female gametophytes and those which develop into males. This genetic segregation is a necessary preliminary to the evolution of seeds.

The next step in the chain of events is shown by the heterosporous pteridophytes. Here the differentiation between male and female becomes clear at the earliest possible stage of the haploid phase, and the two sorts of spore differ markedly in size. In some genera, e.g. *Selaginella*, there is also a strong tendency for the megaspores to be retained in the sporangium so that the female gametophyte undergoes part of its development while still enclosed in sporophyte tissues. This enclosure of the gametophyte, which becomes more pronounced from the pteridophytes upwards, has already been referred to in describing the evolution of life-cycles. But while it may be interpreted in that context as an indication of the decreasing independence of the gametophyte, it is perhaps more significant as an essential part of the evolution of the seed.

In the gymnosperms there is total retention of the female gametophyte within the sporophyte, where fertilisation takes place. The fertilised egg is the beginning of the next sporophyte generation, but before this new sporophyte is required to embark on independent existence there is further development of the fertilised egg and considerable modification of the surrounding tissues. Together they form the seed, with the young sporophyte as the embryo, the remains of the female gametophyte as the nutritive tissue, and the former integument as the seed coat. But the seed is much more than just a composite structure with the tissues of three generations (two sporophytes and one gametophyte) in association. The embryo, for instance, represents a state of dormancy occurring part-way through the sporophyte generation, which is a most unusual situation. There is also a very specialised nutritional relationship set up between the embryo and its nutritive tissue so that a supply of nutrients is made available to the developing embryo at germination. The seed coat, too, often has a specialised construction related to the mechanism of seed dispersal and the intake of water. Altogether, the seed is a very remarkable structure which, although essentially a development of trends seen in the pteridophytes, sets the seed plants on a different level from that group.

In the angiosperms the female gametophyte has become reduced to a point where it is quite inadequate to become a nutritive tissue for the embryo without substantial development. We therefore find fundamental differences in seed formation between gymnosperms and angiosperms. Outstanding among these differences is double fertilisation, a process confined to angiosperms. One fusion nucleus develops into the embryo, the other into the endosperm which, being derived from both male and female gametophytes, is not homologous with the nutritive tissue of the gymnosperm seed.

EVOLUTION IN THE FUTURE

The span of a human lifetime is almost negligible in terms of a geological time scale, and we cannot expect to witness any but the smallest of evolutionary changes. But fossil remains present in the most recently formed rocks show that evolutionary progress has occurred up to our own times and there is every reason to believe that it will continue far into the future. We can only guess at the directions it will take and the new forms of plant life which will result. Of the trends which have been discussed in the earlier part of this chapter, reduction of the gametophyte has reached a point where further progress is difficult to imagine. It seems doubtful also whether the size reached by the largest of present-day plants will ever be exceeded. Although the enormous *Sequoia* trees continue to thrive in rather restricted regions of western North America they appear to represent an evolutionary sideline, and many of their relatives have become extinct. None of the angiosperms has achieved quite such massive proportions. It is possible that some plants will gain greater independence of their water supply than even the most extreme xerophytes of to-day, and perhaps there will be refinements in methods of propagation to reduce still further the vulnerability of this stage in the life history.

Although no one can predict the future course of evolution with any certainty, it should be remembered that successful new forms will not be found only among the descendants of angiosperms. We may regard the pteridophytes as having reached only moderate levels of advancement, but certain of their members are outstandingly successful plants. *Pteridium aquilinum* (bracken), for example, is an aggressive and widely distributed fern which is firmly established and frequently the dominant plant in its habitat. Similarly we may speak of *Chlorella*, almost scornfully, as being simple and primitive, but we cannot deny that it is vigorous, prolific, and admirably adapted to the habitats it occupies. These, and other successful representatives of lower groups, are just as eligible to be the progenitors of new species as those plants we regard as being highly evolved. In fact, some of the most advanced species are far more likely to become extinct. The orchids, with their elaborate floral structure and methods of pollination, are widely accepted as being among the most highly evolved of living plants, but many of them are extremely rare and seem scarcely able to hold their own in competition with other plants.

Some of the smaller changes which are likely to occur in the foreseeable future can be predicted with some confidence. Man's influence on his environment has led to a number of well-known changes in the fauna around him. Dark-winged moths have become common in areas blackened by soot, and rabbits resistant to myxomatosis have multiplied in response to the spreading of the disease. Similarly there are flies resistant to DDT and bacteria resistant to antibiotics, all representing the evolution of new forms in answer to new situations. Higher plants also show the capacity to adapt themselves to changes in surroundings. Grasses which have colonised the spoil heaps from lead and copper mines tolerate concentrations of these metals which are highly toxic to other individuals of the same species. In a similar way it is to be expected that as towns and industries increase their size and influence, new varieties of plant will evolve with a greater tolerance of the toxic gases and other products which pollute their environment. Such changes are important, though they seem trivial by comparison with those which led to the successful establishment of life on land, or to the production of seeds. Nevertheless, as will be argued in Chapter 22, the greater part of evolutionary progress is made up of small changes which, by accumulating, lead to major advances.

21 PLANT ECOLOGY

Plant ecology is a branch of botany devoted to the relationships between plants and their environment. To a greater extent than is true of most other branches of botany, ecology depends on the study of plants in nature; for whereas one can make a fairly thorough study of the anatomy or physiology or genetics of a plant in the laboratory or greenhouse, there is no substitute for observations in the field if one seeks to understand the conditions under which a plant lives naturally. Plant ecology is a thoroughly scientific discipline which covers the qualitative and quantitative analysis of vegetation, the investigation of why certain habitats are regularly colonised by particular species, why the vegetation of an area may change with time, and many other enquiries of this sort.

The ability to recognise at least a large proportion of the plants which occur in the region where he works is very necessary for a plant ecologist. Indeed, in ecological work it is often essential to make fine taxonomic distinctions, for many species contain varieties and forms which are structurally almost identical but which differ markedly in their habitat preferences.

In this chapter we shall aim to present some of the general principles of plant ecology, with a limited range of examples to illustrate these principles. There is so much variation in ecological circumstances between species and between different areas of vegetation that no attempt can be made in a book of this size to give a comprehensive account of the subject. The chapter has been written with higher plants mostly in mind, since these are most widely known and offer the simplest opportunities for practical work in ecology by the student. Similar general principles apply to all sorts of plants, however, and the reader should recognise that while we may here regard soil fungi as part of the environment of the roots of higher plants, it is just as valid to treat roots as part of the environment of soil fungi.

It is impossible to write about plant ecology, except in the vaguest of generalisations, without mentioning particular plant species. The number of species referred to here has been reduced as far as seems appropriate, and most of them are at least locally common in Britain. The reader who is unfamiliar with these species will find them described in some of the many books devoted to the flora of Britain, of which Clapham, Tutin, and Warburg's

Flora of the British Isles and Ross-Craig's *Drawings of British Plants* are particularly recommended.

The Distribution of Plants

One important generalisation which needs little emphasis is that the distribution of plants is greatly influenced by the environment. On a world scale, this principle is illustrated by maps on which regional variations in vegetation are shown. Most large atlases include a map of the world with the land-masses subdivided according to the dominant type of vegetation. The boundaries of these regions can be related to features of geography and climate, so that regions with similar latitude, altitude, rainfall regime, and other characteristics tend to have similar vegetation. Thus the Amazon basin in South America and the Congo basin in Central Africa are both equatorial regions of low altitude and high rainfall. Both support dense tropical forest. In contrast, parts of south-eastern Australia, central North America, and central Asia are all inland temperate areas with low rainfall and altitudes not exceeding 5,000 ft. All of them are dominated by temperate grassland.

Although the physical features of the environment play a dominant part in determining the *type* of vegetation in a certain area, they do not determine the particular species which grow there. Parts of northern Europe and northern Canada have much in common in being lowland areas with moderate rainfall (or snowfall) and severe winters. They are both covered with coniferous forest, but the species which make up the forests in the two regions are very different. *Pinus sylvestris*, for instance, is the dominant tree species over large areas of northern Europe, but it is absent from the natural vegetation of North America even though in many places conditions are ideal for it to thrive. We may conclude, therefore, that although each species has a limited range of conditions in which it will grow, it will not necessarily be found wherever those conditions occur. In the case of *P. sylvestris* it seems clear that the species has evolved in the Old World where it has become widespread and very successful, but it has been prevented from spreading to the New World by the oceans, and has thus never reached certain habitats well suited to it.

In many cases geographical barriers which are sufficient to defeat the natural dispersal mechanism of a species have been overcome by human intervention. Japanese larch (*Larix leptolepis*) has been planted in many areas of afforestation in Britain, where it grows into fine trees and seems quite at home. As its name implies, the natural home of this species is in Asia, and it is most unlikely that it would have reached this country by natural means.

When studying the distribution of plants, therefore, we must bear in mind several points. The *presence* of a species in a certain habitat means that conditions are suitable for it to grow there. Its presence may be the result of natural events such as evolution and the natural dispersal mechanism of the species, or it may be the result of deliberate introduction by man. The *absence* of a species may mean that conditions are unsuitable, but may equally well mean that the species has not had the opportunity of reaching that habitat, owing to geographical barriers and the historical accident of having evolved elsewhere.

The study of plant distribution on a world-wide scale is recognised as the science of **plant geography** which is introduced briefly on p. 628. Although no clear distinction can be drawn between ecology and ecological geography, the ecologist is generally concerned with the more local and detailed aspects of vegetation. The generalisations about presence and absence of species, given above, are just as valid on a local scale as they are more widely.

Plant Communities

When we come to the detailed study of the vegetation of a single habitat we shall almost certainly find there is a mixture of species showing differences in size, frequency, and life-form. Thus the vegetation of woodland contains many plants which are not trees, and grassland vegetation includes many plants which are not grasses. All the plants in each habitat must be fitted to grow under the prevailing conditions of soil and climate. Equally clearly, they are fitted to live with one another, for plants are very much influenced by neighbouring plants, particularly when competing for light, water, and nutrients. The mixture of species which occupies a habitat represents, therefore, not just a heterogeneous assortment which happen to have become established side by side, but a closely integrated community with balanced relationships between the members.

Succession and Climax

If the relationships between the members of a plant community, and the external factors which affect them, are analysed in sufficient detail it may appear that the community exists in a state of equilibrium and will maintain itself without substantial change in composition. This may be so in the case of some communities, but is far from true in others where observations taken at intervals of, say, twenty years, would show marked changes in vegetation. One common reason for changes of this sort is that when a certain group of species has occupied a habitat for a period, it alters the habitat so as to encourage colonisation by different species. These in turn, having established themselves, make further changes and are then superseded by yet other species. This sequence of events constitutes a plant **succession.**

Successions do not go on for ever. Eventually a point is reached where the equilibrium between vegetation and habitat is such that the species present perpetuate themselves rather than paving the way for others. The succession is then said to have reached its **climax**, and provided that conditions remain the same the climax vegetation will persist.

In an area subject to certain recognised conditions of climate, soil type, and so on, it can be predicted that plant succession will proceed towards a particular climax. Thus in areas of moderate to high rainfall, well-drained acid soil, and strong winds, the climax vegetation in Britain will probably be heathland dominated by heather (*Calluna vulgaris*). But the succession which leads to this climax can be deflected or thrown back by other factors. Heavy grazing, for instance, will prevent the establishment of *Calluna* and result in grassland, while if the vegetation of established heathland is set alight, much of the *Calluna* is destroyed and the succession leading to heathland begins again. Such interference with plant succession is not uncommon.

A complete succession from the colonisation of bare ground to the establishment of climax vegetation usually occupies many years, but there are places where the full sequence of stages may be observed at once owing to neighbouring habitats being at different stages in the same succession. For example, where the coastline consists of a sandy beach which shelves only gently, the vegetation is often spreading gradually towards the sea. As one walks inland from the beach over the sand dunes to whatever type of vegetation is established beyond, one passes across zones which represent a complete plant succession. When one reaches the stable vegetation perhaps half a mile inland, which may be grassland or woodland or something else, depending on the circumstances, one is standing on ground where hundreds of years earlier there was only the shifting, uncolonised sand of the foreshore.

Pollen Analysis. Plant succession of a somewhat different sort is caused by changes in the environment which are not brought about by the plants themselves. Since the glaciers of the last ice age retreated northwards from Britain, about 12,000 years ago, there have been several important changes in the prevailing climate, with associated changes in the vegetation, which can be detected by pollen analysis. This technique depends on the fact that under certain natural conditions the walls of pollen grains do not decompose and may be preserved for thousands of years. Moreover, the pollen grains of particular genera, and even some species, can be recognised by their characteristic pattern of pores, ridges, and other surface markings (Fig. 333). When air-borne pollen settles on a lake or pond it may sink to the bottom and become incorporated into the sediment. Similarly, pollen which falls on an area where peat (p. 612) is forming becomes trapped among its contemporary vegetation and eventually embedded in a layer of peat. In both these situations there is accumulation of layers of solid material in a regular chronological sequence, older layers being below and younger layers above. Both situations also provide water-logged conditions under which pollen grain walls do not decompose. By examining samples from different layers and recording the types and relative numbers of pollen grain present, a picture can be built up of the major changes in vegetation over a long period of time in the district where the samples were collected.

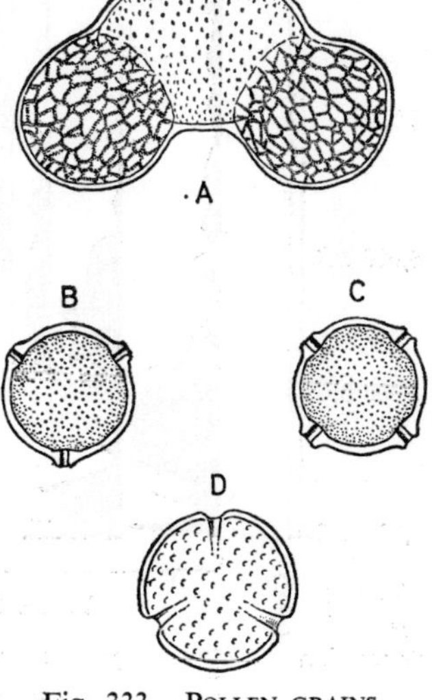

Fig. 333. POLLEN GRAINS. A, pine; B, birch; C, alder; D, oak. All × 500.

Fig. 334 shows a simplified pollen diagram compiled from samples collected near Malham Tarn, Yorkshire. The samples formed a vertical series about ten metres in depth, and were collected with a peat borer—a device which not only drills a hole but can also bring up soil samples from measured depths. The bore hole was made in an area at present covered by peat bog, and the upper six metres passed through continuous peat, representing deposition over about 8,000 years. Below this the hole passed through lake-bed sediments, indicating that formerly the area was covered with open water. Each sample was carefully labelled according to its position in the series and then subjected to a process of chemical treatment, washing, and filtration. This cleans and concentrates the pollen grains and removes as much as possible of other constituents.

With a knowledge of the climatic conditions favoured by particular types of tree, the evidence from pollen analysis can be used to deduce the major climatic changes during the last 12,000 years. Although the evidence given in Fig. 334 applies to the Malham

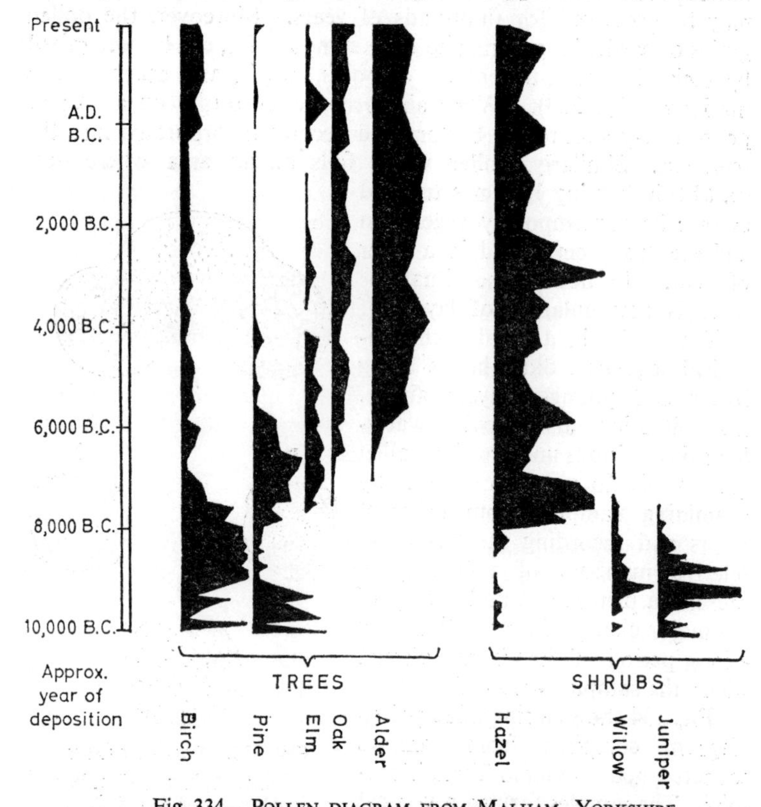

Fig. 334. POLLEN DIAGRAM FROM MALHAM, YORKSHIRE.
Each of the eight plants is represented by a "profile" set against a time-scale. The width of the profile at any point indicates the abundance of that pollen at the corresponding time, *e.g.* in the peat layer deposited in 4,000 B.C. there is a little pollen from birch, pine, and oak, plenty from alder and hazel, but none from elm, willow, or juniper.

area only, it is in keeping with what is known from pollen analysis in other areas in Britain.

From the retreat of the ice of the last ice age up to about 8,000 B.C. birch was usually the most common tree, with some juniper and willow, a little hazel, and a wide range of herbs (not represented in Fig. 334). The native species of birch are more tolerant of cold than most British trees, and do not normally form dense forest. It seems likely, therefore, that in the period immediately following glaciation, the climate was generally cold and the vegetation mainly tundra, such as is still found in parts of northern Europe and Asia. At intervals pine replaced birch as the dominant tree. This probably corresponded with warmer periods when there was some established forest.

A very noticeable change occurred about 8,000 B.C., when birch became much less common, pine increased in frequency, and oak and elm appeared for the first time. Hazel became extremely abundant. This type of mixed forest continued for about 2,000 years, during which the climate must have been reasonably warm and dry. The next major change was the dramatic increase in frequency of alder around 6,000 B.C., accompanied by a sharp drop in frequency of pine. Alder characteristically grows in wet places, and its sudden rise to become the dominant producer of pollen marks a change to a wetter climate. Since that time alder has remained strongly represented in the pollen record, and other trees have maintained more or less constant frequencies, showing that there have been no drastic changes of climate.

Examples of British Plant Communities

In Britain, as in many other countries with an intensive agriculture and a high density of population, very little of the vegetation represents a natural climax. The climate favours the development of a climax vegetation consisting of forest, but areas of existing forest are small and either artificially planted or subject to considerable human interference. Except at high altitudes grassland is never a climax community in Britain, persisting only so long as activities such as mowing and grazing prevent the development of woody plants. Opportunities for studying ecological principles in relatively undisturbed communities are largely confined to areas of rather special terrain, such as marshes, shores, cliffs, and the tops of mountains.

(*a*) **Deciduous Woodland.** Many areas of British woodland are sufficiently "wild" to illustrate some of the biological relationships of a climax community. The great variation in size of the species present makes certain interactions particularly evident. The types of tree present are largely determined by the nature and composition of the soil. If the soil is a deep clay or loam, and especially if it is rich in calcium, the English oak (*Quercus robur*) is likely to be present, perhaps in association with other trees such as ash (*Fraxinus excelsior*) which thrives in similar soils. Given the right soil conditions, these trees will grow to their full size. At maturity they will have tall trunks, sparingly branched below but bearing a crown of smaller branches at the top. During spring, before the leaves are fully developed, plenty of light penetrates to the lower layers of the woodland, but throughout the summer the canopy of leaves produces deep shade beneath the trees. By controlling the light in this way, the trees dominate the vegetation, and all associated species must not only be fitted to the type of soil but must also contend with the shade cast by the trees. These conditions restrict the number of species which are able to grow in an oak wood.

Among the shrubs often present are hazel (*Corylus avellana*), hawthorn (*Crataegus monogyna*), and elder (*Sambucus nigra*), all of which are fairly tolerant of shade though they tend to occur where the trees are more widely spaced apart and the shade is less intense. At a lower level there is a number of herbs which, in one way or another, thrive under the special conditions of the woodland floor. Some of them, such as ground ivy (*Glechoma hederacea*) and wood sanicle (*Sanicula europea*) are shade-lovers and are rarely found in exposed places. They produce their flowers during the summer despite the reduced light intensity. Other herbs flower in the spring before the trees are in full leaf; they include the wood anemone (*Anemone nemorosa*), primrose (*Primula vulgaris*), and dog's mercury (*Mercurialis perennis*). Summer-flowering herbs commonly found in open situations are almost completely absent from woodland.

(*b*) **Calcareous Grassland.** The grassland which develops on well-drained, shallow soil rich in calcium, has a very rich flora judged by the number of species present. There may be a dozen or more grasses all in substantial frequency, other monocotyledons such as species of *Carex* (sedges) and *Luzula* (woodrushes), and a varied assortment of dicotyledons including salad burnet (*Poterium sanguisorba*), clover (*Trifolium pratense*), harebell (*Campanula rotundifolia*), and wild thyme (*Thymus drucei*). It is plain that the conditions here are attractive to a great variety of species, and the competition between them must be intense. Because of the greater uniformity of size of the species present, the inter-relationships here are not as obvious as in woodland, but there can be no doubt that here also the species interact and produce an integrated community. Every square inch of soil is normally occupied by a dense carpet of plants, and soil which is laid bare by some accident is rapidly recolonised. This represents a **closed** community.

(*c*) **Salt Marsh Vegetation.** In contrast to closed communities, there are **open** communities where the ground is not wholly covered by vegetation. The edges of a flat, tidal estuary, for example, usually present an expanse of muddy sand which is periodically covered by the sea and therefore has a high salt content. This type of habitat, known as a salt marsh, is one which very few plants find attractive and it is often difficult to find more than about a dozen species altogether. Conditions are so hostile to plant growth that there may be bare mud or sand which remains uncolonised for long periods of time. In such a community there is far less influence of one species on another.

(*d*) **The Sand-dune Succession.** On beaches where the slope is very gentle the receding tide leaves great expanses of open sand. This dries out and the winds which often blow from the sea tend to dislodge the surface layers of sand and blow them inland. Those parts of the beach which are regularly immersed in sea-water every day have no vegetation unless there are rocks to which algae may be attached. But near the high water mark for spring tides is a zone of sand which is immersed only occasionally, and which is dry, unstable, salty, and subject to high winds. These are conditions which very few British plants can tolerate, but one of the exceptions is the sea couchgrass (*Agropyron junceum*). Like the related *A. repens* which is such a troublesome garden weed, it produces extensive and deeply buried rhizomes, and these help to stabilise shifting sand. The aerial parts can withstand occasional submersion in sea-water and the abrasive action of wind-blown sand. Since they project above the sand surface they also provide patches of shelter from the wind in which small heaps of blown sand are built up. These heaps may then become stabilised by the further growth of rhizomes and roots, and in this way small sand-dunes have their beginning. Because of their position nearest to the sea, they are known as foredunes. *A. junceum* is not a large plant, and the foredunes for which it is responsible are correspondingly small. But they raise the sand level sufficiently to allow colonisation by other grasses which cannot survive submersion in sea-water, notably marram grass (*Ammophila arenaria*). This robust plant is the most conspicuous grass of sand-dunes in Britain, and the binding action of its rhizomes and roots can build up large dunes in a remarkably short time. Dunes ten feet high have been known to develop on the Norfolk coast in fewer than ten years. In regions where *Agropyron junceum* is absent, *Ammophila* may be the pioneer, forming foredunes above the highest tide mark.

Among the youngest dunes, that is those towards the sea, the contours are very irregular, with steep sandy slopes leading up to small plateaux where the vegetation is more dense. Although the surface sand on these plateaux is very dry and mobile, a few inches below the surface there is stable, moist sand in which a little humus is deposited from the decomposition of plant remains. The soil water is almost free from sea-salt, and there is some shelter from the wind. Since *Ammophila* by itself never forms a continuous cover of vegetation, there are therefore opportunities for colonisation by other species which would be quite unable to survive on the exposed sand of the foreshore perhaps only a few yards away. Among species commonly growing on the younger *Ammophila* dunes are ragwort (*Senecio jacobaea*), thistles (*Cirsium* spp.), and spurges (*Euphorbia paralias* and *E. portlandica*). The sand sedge (*Carex arenaria*) is also frequently found on exposed sandy patches nearby, and is of importance because it sends out long rhizomes just below the sand surface and helps to form a stable surface layer.

As *Ammophila* dunes grow older their humus content increases, making it possible for a much wider variety of species to grow, and those dunes which lie a short distance inland from the ridge nearest to the sea usually have quite a rich flora. The actual composition of this varies greatly from one coastal region to another but many of the commoner species (e.g. *Lotus corniculatus* and *Erodium cicutarium*) are not exclusive to sand-dune communities. Prostrate, straggling species such as dwarf willow (*Salix repens*) and rest-harrow (*Ononis repens*) help to provide a more continuous cover of vegetation with fewer patches of uncolonised sand.

Although *Ammophila* is widespread even among the older dunes with a fixed surface layer and a more inland type of vegetation, it does not thrive here so well as on the young dunes. Other grasses such as *Festuca rubra* and *Agrostis* spp. become more abundant, and eventually *Ammophila* is completely replaced.

Subsequent developments depend very much on local conditions, and there is no single type of climax vegetation for the sand-dune succession. Because of the density of population in Britain and the popularity of coastal areas, the succession is rarely allowed to reach a natural climax. In some places the dunes are backed by agricultural land, or by grassland used as a golf course or caravan site. Elsewhere there may be heathland or fresh-water marshes or pinewoods.

(*e*) **The Lakeside Succession.** Another good example of plant succession can often be seen at the margin of a shallow fresh-water lake or pond. There are a few species which can grow completely submerged in water at depths of about ten feet, despite the low light intensity. They include *Elodea canadensis* (Canadian pondweed) and the moss *Fontinalis antipyretica*. These totally submerged plants form a mat of vegetation in which silt and humus can accumulate, leading to a gradual raising of the lake bottom. This allows colonisation by larger plants such as water lilies whose leaves float on the surface. With further accumulation of silt and humus, which is accelerated by the water lilies and similar plants, the water becomes shallow enough for the establishment of other species which need to have their roots and the base of the shoot in standing water but which grow out well above water level. They produce an area of reedswamp. There are numerous species which may occur in reedswamp, and it is remarkable how many of them are reed-like in general appearance in spite of the wide variety of families to which they belong. Common species in Britain are *Phragmites communis* (common reed; Gramineae); *Typha latifolia* (reedmace; Typhaceae); *Iris pseudacorus* (yellow iris; Iridaceae); *Acorus calamus* (sweet flag; Araceae); *Sparganium ramosum* (bur-reed; Sparganiaceae); *Ranunculus lingua* (greater spearwort; Ranunculaceae). Reedswamp is succeeded by marsh as the water gets shallower still, and the reedswamp species are replaced by others which, although thriving on plenty of water, do not require any depth of standing water above soil level. They include *Equisetum fluviatile* (water horsetail), *Menyanthes trifoliata* (bogbean), and *Filipendula ulmaria* (meadowsweet). Later in the succession there may be colonisation by trees such as *Alnus glutinosa* (alder) and *Salix* spp. (willows) which favour marshy ground, and later still, if the progressive drying of the ground continues, by other trees without any special preference for wet habitats.

Quantitative Analysis of Vegetation

In order to make detailed comparisons between the vegetation of different areas at the same time, or of the same area at different times, methods must be devised for the accurate description of vegetation. For very general comparisons there is some value in compiling a straightforward list of species present without attempting to assess the relative importance or abundance of each species on the list. Since many species have rather special limitations on the type of soil or the degree of waterlogging they can tolerate, the mere presence of certain species is some indication of the nature of the habitat. This method is of very little use, however, when a comparison is to be made between two rather similar habitats which have many species in common. Some measure is needed of the proportion of the vegetation which each species comprises. The simplest approach to such measurements is to record each species not only as being present, but as being abundant, frequent, occasional, rare, or whatever other degree of abundance the observer feels is merited. This gives a more vivid picture of the vegetation, but the method is full of pitfalls since the grading of each species is so subjective. What may seem frequent to one observer may be regarded as no more than occasional by another, and there is no certainty that the same individual will apply the same standards on different occasions. Furthermore, a species which is conspicuous may so attract attention that it is given too high a grading, as, for example, in a field with a few tall thistles.

Because of the inadequacy of subjective methods, attempts have been made to standardise techniques for describing vegetation, so that the same plant community gives the same results in the hands of different workers, and a published description from one author can be interpreted in precise terms by his readers. There are several measurements which can be made to assess the status of a species in a community, each one informative but none by itself giving a complete picture. Firstly one may count the number of individuals of a species growing in a certain area. This figure is known as the **density** of the species. Density is usually measured by a sampling technique unless the area being studied is very small. A convenient method is to place on the ground a piece of metal rod bent into a square so that it marks off an area of known size and shape. Both the device and the area it encloses are referred to as a **quadrat.** A square of 25 cm. side is a useful size for many plant communities. The observer counts the number of individuals for each species in the quadrat, and then repeats the operation at other places in the area being surveyed. The results from all the quadrats studied are then assembled and an average density calculated for each species. The method is not without its disadvantages. As with any sampling method, the samples (quadrats) give an imperfect description of the whole area, and deductions from them must be made with caution. Care must be taken to distribute the quadrats at random, so as to avoid over-emphasis on one part of the area which may be untypical of the whole. There is also great difficulty with many species in determining what is a single individual: this is particularly true of species with extensive rhizomes or stolons, where what appears to be a group of separate individuals may in fact be simply different parts of a single one. Finally, in interpreting density records, the average size of the individual must be borne in mind. A density of twenty oak trees to the acre is a very different matter from twenty daisies.

A second type of measurement, which takes into account the different sizes of species, is **percentage cover**. If one imagines a vertical beam of light falling on a plant from above, then the area of shadow cast by that plant, expressed as a percentage of a certain area of ground, is its percentage cover. In practice, cover is not measured from areas of shadow, but by sticking a series of vertical pins into the vegetation, at random, and recording the number of occasions each species is touched by a pin. For grassland which has been grazed and where no plant is more than a few inches high, the "pins" may be steel knitting needles: with taller vegetation, longer pins are necessary. The greater is the cover provided by a species, the higher will be its frequency of contact with the pins. When measured for several species in a community, percentage cover is a useful indication of the relative influence of the aerial parts of each one, irrespective of the number of individuals present. However, a large number of observations must be made before any reliable estimates of cover are obtained, and the work involved is laborious and time-consuming.

A third type of measurement is the easiest to make, and is most widely used in the description of vegetation. Using quadrats of suitable size, one compiles a list of species present in each of many quadrats and then calculates the likelihood of finding each particular species in a quadrat of the size used. Thus a species which occurs in 84 out of 140 quadrats examined has a likelihood of $84 \times 100/140 = 60$ per cent., which is referred to as its **frequency**. Although this method is relatively simple to apply, the results obtained are of limited usefulness. They do not give a measure of the numbers of individual plants present (as in density measurements), nor of the area of ground covered (as in percentage cover). Frequency measurements therefore combine disadvantages of both the other two techniques, and in addition they vary according to the size of quadrat used.

It is clear that no easy method exists for recording quantitatively all the information about vegetation which an ecologist may require. However, a number of well-tried methods are available, each capable of providing accurate information about some aspects of vegetation. By choosing methods appropriate to his special interests, an ecologist can generally raise his work above the purely qualitative and subjective level, and thereby greatly increase its value.

Sampling by quadrats has uses beyond the mere description of vegetation for comparative purposes. It can provide useful information about the pattern of plant distribution within a community. The concept of pattern arises from the frequent observation that members of a species may not be uniformly or randomly dispersed either in relation to one another or in relation to other species. The detection of this non-randomness may require careful analysis of density records from many quadrats, but it is often quite unmistakable. For example, it is sometimes found that the individuals of a species tend to occur in clusters. This can be the result of the way in which the species propagates. Vegetative propagation by rhizomes or stolons, or reproduction by seed with a narrow range of seed dispersal, would each tend to produce a clustered pattern of individuals. This is so with *Juncus effusus*, one of the commonest rushes in Britain, when it has been allowed to colonise land after ploughing or some other disturbance. The plants which first become established disperse their seeds within close range of themselves, and a cluster of seedlings grows up near the parent. Before long the cover of vegetation becomes continuous and there is little chance of subsequent propagation by seed, so the clustered pattern persists.

Other patterns take the form of positive association between species. This is recognised from the joint occurrence of two species in single quadrats more often than their separate frequencies in the area would lead one to expect. For example, if two species have frequencies of 20 per cent. and 40 per cent. respectively, and if they are distributed independently of each other, the likelihood of their both occurring in a single quadrat is 20 per cent. of 40 per cent. = 8 per cent. If the *observed* frequency of joint occurrence were, say, 15 per cent., one would suspect that the presence of one species increased the likelihood of the other occurring in its vicinity. This pattern of distribution may result from local variations in the habitat, sometimes in the soil, or perhaps produced by the plants themselves; for example, established plants of *Juncus effusus* spread vegetatively to give substantial tussocks. The conditions within these tussocks differ from those outside, and appear to be favoured by certain other species such as *Filipendula ulmaria* (meadowsweet) and *Potentilla erecta* (tormentil). The particular features of the tussock which attract these species are not known for certain, but the association is quite clear in some communities.

Alternatively, the presence of one species may decrease the likelihood of some other species being present nearby (known as negative association). Once again this may be the result of local variations in conditions, as is the case in the distribution of buttercups (*Ranunculus* spp.). *R. repens* (creeping buttercup), and *R. bulbosus* (bulbous buttercup) are common species which are frequently found growing in the same meadow, but which occur together in single quadrats much less often than would be expected from their frequencies if they were randomly dispersed. In fact it has been found that these two species are sensitive to slight differences in drainage, so that where there are undulations in the ground *R. repens* is found mostly in the hollows and *R. bulbosus* on the ridges.

Another cause of negative association between species is the secretion by the roots of some plants of toxic substances which are antagonistic to plants of other species. The extent to which this influences the pattern of natural vegetation is uncertain.

Analysis of the Environment

It is easier to study the ecology of a single species than of a whole community, and easier still to study a single plant. But even in a restricted study of this sort the multitude of environmental factors which must be considered is formidable. The list of factors itself gives only a very incomplete understanding of what the plant has to contend with, for the various factors do not act independently of one another: they are very much inter-related. Rainfall, for instance, affects the quantity of water reaching the soil, but wind and temperature affect how much of this water is lost by evaporation. The quantity and movement of soil water affect the texture and chemical composition of the soil, which can directly influence the species of higher plant able to grow there. The physical and chemical conditions of the soil also affect the population of soil micro-organisms, with corresponding effects on mycorrhizas, nitrogen fixation, decomposition of organic remains, incidence of plant diseases, and so on. However, despite these complex interactions it is helpful, as a beginning, to try and recognise separately the more important factors of the environment. They can be classified for convenience under three headings:

(*a*) features of the soil (edaphic factors);

(*b*) features of climate;

(*c*) the influence of other living organisms (biotic factors).

To these might be added features of topography such as altitude, aspect, and slope, but since these are intimately associated with edaphic and climatic factors they will not be treated separately here.

For the purposes of the plant ecologist, each factor must be studied on a local scale. It must be remembered that the water content or acidity or chemical composition of soil may differ markedly in two areas only a few yards apart, and differences of this sort strongly influence the character of the vegetation. Since this book is expected to be used mainly in Britain, the habitat factors of British plants will be given most attention.

Edaphic Factors. In its broadest sense, the word "soil" covers any more or less solid, natural substrate in which the roots of higher plants develop and from which they obtain water and nutrients. Thus it includes not only the mixture of mineral particles, humus, water, micro-organisms, and debris which makes up the soil of agricultural land or a flower bed, but also peat, which consists almost entirely of plant remains in various stages of decomposition with very little mineral matter and a rather sparse population of micro-organisms. Soils vary in depth, texture, chemical composition, acidity, water-holding capacity, and in their microflora and -fauna. They may also be either mature soils, such as are found with climax vegetation, or immature soils which, under the influence of weather, vegetation, and other factors, are undergoing a succession of changes, perhaps corresponding with a succession of plants growing in them. The mixture of sand and a little humus found in young *Ammophila* dunes is an example of a very immature soil.

A few examples of soil types common in Britain will illustrate variation in soil character and in the kinds of vegetation which they support.

(*a*) *Soils which owe their predominant character to the prevailing climate rather than to the nature of the underlying rock.*

Where the soil is deep, and derived from rocks which yield mineral particles of different sizes and with varied chemical composition, the nature of the mature soil reflects the rainfall and average temperature of the region. Thus, similar soils may develop when the parent rocks are impure sandstone or impure limestone, despite the differences between these rocks. Two contrasting soil types are widespread in Britain, the brown earth and the podsol.

Brown earth develops in regions with limited rainfall (20-40 in. per year) and generally warm weather, where there is a fairly balanced relationship in the soil between downward movement of water due to rainfall, and upward movement due to evaporation. The rain washes down the fine clay particles and some of the bases into the lower layers, leaving a surface layer which is well drained and aerated and adequately supplied with bases. Iron salts, which are not easily washed out, remain near the surface and produce the brown colour from which this soil takes its name. These conditions encourage a rich growth both of higher plants and of micro-organisms, and the surface soil develops a good "crumb" structure with mineral particles of moderate size and plenty of humus, which makes the soil slightly acid. The clay particles which accumulate lower down form a layer from which water does not easily drain away. Thus in periods of drought when the surface soil receives no rainfall, there is upward movement of water from the clay layer and the plant cover is protected against extreme water shortage except during the most prolonged droughts. The brown earth type of soil is therefore very productive, and though its natural climax vegetation in Britain is deciduous forest, it has been extensively used for agriculture. It is a common soil type in large parts of southern England.

The **podsol** type of soil develops in preference to the brown earth type where rainfall is heavier and average temperatures lower, so that downward water movement in the soil is much more pronounced than upward. This mainly downward movement leads to severe leaching; that is, the upper soil is washed clear of fine particles and most soluble components. As a result the surface soil is sandy, base-deficient, and often greyish in colour owing to removal of iron salts. What is more, the iron salts combine with other soil constituents to form a hard layer or "pan", perhaps 18 in. down, which plant roots penetrate only with difficulty. This pan largely separates the vegetation from the base-rich lower layers of soil. The base-deficiency at the surface, coupled with the lower average temperature of podsol regions, reduces the speed of decomposition of plant remains, and there is an accumulation of intermediate products which are strongly acid. Altogether the soil conditions in a podsol are very different from those of a brown earth, and the usual vegetation is coniferous forest or heathland. Large areas of upland Britain, particularly towards the west of the country where rainfall is higher, have become "podsolised".

(*b*) *Soils which owe their predominant character to the composition of the parent rock.*

The outstanding British example is **rendzina**, a shallow soil which develops on slopes of soft limestone or chalk. Being near to the surface, the rock maintains a high level of available calcium carbonate and the soil is strongly alkaline. The slope of the ground and porosity of the rocks give excellent drainage. These conditions are favourable to a wide range of species, and the natural vegetation may be either woodland with beech (*Fagus sylvatica*) and ash dominant, or grassland. The rich flora of calcareous grassland has already been mentioned (p. 602).

(*c*) *Soils which owe their predominant character to special water relations.*

The commonest situation under this heading is where water cannot drain away and the soil becomes waterlogged. This deprives the soil of oxygen and largely eliminates the aerobic micro-organisms which play an important part in decomposing plant remains. These remains consequently accumulate and form the purely organic soil we call **peat**. Where the accumulation has gone on for hundreds of years, the peat may be many feet deep.

If the water has drained from alkaline rocks, the waterlogged area is called a **fen**. The fens of East Anglia are the best known example of this situation in Britain, though very few areas remain where the fens are in anything like their natural state. Different fens have different dominant species, among them the common reed (*Phragmites communis*) and purple moor grass (*Molinia coerulea*).

Much more widespread are waterlogged areas where the water is acid, known as **bogs**. These often occur in association with areas of podsol, receiving the water which drains from them. The vegetation is totally different from that of fens. *Sphagnum* spp. (bog mosses) are usually abundant, and for this reason an area of bog is generally spoken of in northern England as "a moss". Another common and conspicuous bog plant is cotton grass (*Eriophorum angustifolium*).

Climatic Factors. The effects of local variations in climate are far more difficult to evaluate than the effects of variation in soil character. For whereas the soil of a certain locality remains more or less unchanged for long periods and can be examined or analysed whenever one chooses, climatic conditions are continually changing. To obtain a detailed picture of the conditions experienced by a single plant over a period of time, one would need to make continuous records of such factors as temperature, rainfall, atmospheric humidity, wind velocity and direction, and the duration and intensity of sunlight. Furthermore, such records would apply only to the immediate neighbourhood of the recording instruments: similar records made a few yards away would often show different measurements, particularly for such locally variable factors as wind velocity and light intensity.

Meteorological records made available by the many weather stations up and down the country give a much more general picture of climatic variation which is useful, however, in helping to explain differences in the types of vegetation in different regions, and the restricted distributions of certain species.

TEMPERATURE AND RAINFALL. By world standards, the whole of Britain has a mild climate without the extremes of heat or cold which produce deserts completely lacking in vegetation. There are, however, distinct differences in temperature regime from one part to another, which are related more to aspect and altitude than to latitude. The mean annual temperature for the south coasts of

England, Wales, and Ireland is above 10° C., whereas for ground above 1,000 ft in Wales, northern England, and almost the whole of Scotland, it is below 8° C., and at the summit of Ben Nevis (4,400 ft) it is below 0° C. Mean annual temperature is less important than the seasonal fluctuation in temperature. The year is clearly divided into a warmer summer season and a cooler winter season, so that the great majority of British plants have a summer growing period alternating with a period of winter dormancy.

Although there is great variation from one district to another in the amount of rain which falls each year, all parts of the country have enough rain to allow good growth by a rich variety of plants. In all districts also, the rain is spread out over the whole year. The vegetation normally remains fresh and green throughout the summer, therefore, in contrast to the situation in countries around the Mediterranean where a comparable amount of rainfall is concentrated into a few months of the year. Annual rainfall is lowest in the south-east of England (about 20 in.), generally higher in western districts, and highest where there are hills and mountains. Parts of North Wales and the English Lake District have well over 100 in. of rain per year. This distribution of rainfall amounts is clearly related to the prevalence of moist winds blowing from the west and south-west. One of the effects of this distribution is the high frequency of bogs and abundant growth of bryophytes in western parts of Britain.

Together with the wind, temperature and rainfall play an important part in controlling atmospheric humidity, and the occurrence of mists and fogs. High atmospheric humidity can be beneficial to some plants by restricting transpiration and so guarding against excessive water loss. On the other hand, industrial fog, in which the water droplets become mixed with suspended particles of soot, can be extremely harmful through depositing a layer of soot on plant surfaces, thereby reducing the transparency of the epidermis and blocking the stomata.

The combined effects of temperature and rainfall in determining soil types have already been referred to (p. 610). Some patterns of plant distribution can be related primarily to soil type, and so indirectly to climate, but with others climatic conditions may be of primary importance. A number of so-called "Atlantic" species are found in Britain only in western regions where the weather is, on the average, wetter and warmer. These include English stonecrop (*Sedum anglicum*) and Welsh poppy (*Meconopsis cambrica*). Other species ("Germanic" species) have an opposite distribution, occurring in the south-east but not further westwards. These species, which apparently prefer drier weather and tolerate more severe winters, include the oxlip (*Primula elatior*) and the pasque flower (*Pulsatilla vulgaris*).

LIGHT. Variation in the intensity and duration of sunlight is another important feature of climate. Reference has already been made when describing woodland vegetation (p. 601) to the differing abilities of plants to tolerate shade, and in a country such as Britain, far removed from the equator, the vegetation as a whole is subject to great seasonal variation in sunshine. The shorter days and weaker light of winter are as important as the lower temperature in reducing physiological activity.

Seasonal changes in the length of day have important photoperiodic effects. Throughout Britain, summer days are too long to allow flowering of short-day plants, and many introduced plants which show good vegetative growth in Britain (*e.g.* some tobacco varieties) are unable to flower unless the days are artificially shortened. Even within Britain itself there is considerable variation in day length due to different latitudes, ranging from less than 16½ hours of light at midsummer in south-western England to nearly 19 hours in the Shetland Islands. The day length characteristic of any region has an important influence on the range of species able to grow and reproduce there.

Apart from the effects of climatic factors on presence or absence of particular species, they also have important effects on the appearance of individual plants. A species which has a wide range of tolerance of light intensities, for instance, shows great differences between its members in plant height, intensity of pigment, and internal structure. These individual differences of appearance will be dealt with later in this chapter (p. 626).

Biotic Factors. Every plant is subject to the influence of other living organisms, which may be classified under three headings: other plants, including micro-organisms, animals apart from man, and man himself. Generally speaking, all three types of organism play a part in shaping the environment, though there are still some remote parts of the world where there are no human settlements and the influence of man is negligible. In a densely populated region like Britain, scarcely any of the vegetation is completely free of human interference.

The biotic factors which affect plants are so diverse that we can only make brief reference to some of them and thereby emphasise this very diversity.

(*a*) *Influence of plants on plants.* Except in rare cases of very open communities or sometimes under cultivation, every higher plant has neighbours with similar requirements to its own. They will compete together for light, water, space, and nutrients. The effects of this competition are clearly shown by the increase in size when a small wild plant from a closed community is transplanted to garden conditions where competition is largely eliminated. Most soils also contain a varied microflora which affects the fertility of the soil and the health of plants growing in it. Micro-organisms are responsible for many of the vital stages in the carbon and nitrogen cycles, and may invade the tissues of higher plants with either beneficial results (*e.g.* mycorrhizas and root nodules) or harmful results (fungal and bacterial diseases). Not all disease-causing plants are soil inhabitants, of course, nor are they all micro-organisms. Many fungal pathogens are air-borne rather than soil-borne, and some plants may act as hosts to other higher plants such as mistletoe (*Viscum album*).

(*b*) *Influence of animals on plants.* Animals are an almost inevitable feature of every plant's environment. Their influence may be either beneficial or harmful (or negligible, but these cases we can disregard). Insects on which plants depend for pollination, and birds which effect seed dispersal are obviously useful. Animals also enrich the soil by their excretions while alive and by decomposition when they die. On the debit side, animals are responsible for widespread injury, disease, and mortality among plants. Nematodes attack their roots, deer and squirrels injure their bark, rabbits eat almost any sort of herbaceous vegetation, insects transmit virus diseases or themselves act as predators and parasites. The list is almost endless.

(*c*) *Influence of man on plants.* No single species has greater influence on plant life than man. He has completely changed the character of the vegetation over vast areas of country, often deliberately, sometimes inadvertently. It is generally accepted that the natural climax vegetation for most of Britain would be forest, deciduous in lowlands, coniferous on higher ground. In fact the present acreage of forest is very limited, and much of what there is has been planted by man himself. As the population has grown, the natural forest has been largely destroyed, partly in order to use the timber for building and as fuel, and partly to use the land for housing and agriculture. Other agricultural land has been acquired by draining fenland, again resulting in a complete change from natural to artificial vegetation. Even the undulating parkland of so many country estates with its apparent naturalness, is usually the result of careful landscape planning, which flourished in the eighteenth century under the influence of Lancelot ("Capability") Brown.

Among the unintentional changes brought about by human activity we can include devastation caused by accidental fires, stunting and withering of vegetation caused by atmospheric pollution, and the rapid spread of plants which flourish on disturbed land, such as rose-bay willow herb (*Chamaenerion angustifolium*) on bomb sites and spoil heaps.

Difficulties of Ecological Interpretation

No matter how completely the characteristics of the habitat may be known, the significance of any particular feature in the life of the plant often remains obscure, and relationships which seem quite obvious often turn out to have unexpected side issues. Take, for instance, the common observation that some species (known as **calcicoles**) seem to prefer, or are actually confined to, soils with a high lime content; while other (**calcifuge**) species are found almost exclusively on soils free from lime. This is apparently a simple matter of chemical preference; but in reality it is a complex situation which is only imperfectly understood. For one thing, the question of competition arises. Many of the species will grow successfully on the "wrong" kind of soil so long as they have it to themselves. It seems clear also that the question of soil preference is linked with climatic conditions, for a number of species which are rigidly confined to limestone soils in Britain are much less selective in the south of Europe. Furthermore, there is experimental evidence that some species are affected not so much by the lime content of the soil as by the availability of other minerals. Naturally-occurring calcareous soils have a low iron content, so that any species with a high iron-requirement will automatically be reported as a calcifuge. This explanation is unlikely to apply to *all* calcifuge species.

In general it is a matter of the greatest difficulty to discover what environmental factor actually determines the limit of distribution of a species at a particular point, and we must expect different factors to be decisive in different places. Observations in Scandinavia leave little doubt that the northern boundary beyond which holly cannot grow is there decided by the severity of winter frosts. It is an exceptionally clear case, and the evidence is massive and convincing. But if we ask why holly does not extend further south into Africa it is certain that quite different considerations apply, that the explanation will probably have to be sought at a different time of year, and that the number of possibilities requiring investigation is likely to be very large.

One important aspect of this matter is the difference in requirements between young plants and adults. An average lawn or playing field is an excellent place for the growth of plantains, daisies, and dandelions. Whether it is even a moderately good place for the growth of the *seedlings* of these species is quite a different question.

Because of all these complications it is unsafe in ecology generally to draw conclusions about environmental influences without having made appropriate experiments. The results of ecological experiments can be surprising. It has, for instance, been demonstrated repeatedly that in a closed and stable plant community (for example, a turf) it is virtually impossible to change the composition of the community by adding seeds of any of the species already present. If a lawn already has a balanced population of plantains and grass, another bucketful of plantain seeds will merely act as a fertiliser, which is not what most people expect to happen.

Especially in the biotic sphere, an ecological effect is often the result of a whole chain of successive causes. In the early part of this century, for instance, it was evident that young oak trees were becoming increasingly uncommon, and over great parts of England the natural replacement of the oak had virtually ceased. Various possible causes were examined: a succession of dry summers, a rise in the frequency of forest fires, a fungus which attacked the seedlings. In the end it turned out that the main source of the trouble was a change in game-keeping methods, leading to systematic shooting of predatory animals such as owls, hence to an increase in the population of ground rodents, especially voles, and so to a situation in which virtually every acorn was bitten open.

Life-forms and Plant Distribution

The association of species with similar morphology in a certain habitat has been referred to in connection with reedswamp plants (p. 605). This is an extreme example, but a comparable situation may be seen elsewhere. As one might expect, the prevailing conditions of each habitat determine, through natural selection, the type of plant which is most successful there, and success is closely related to general morphology. For example, large, leafy trees with their high rate of transpiration and rather vulnerable aerial parts are unable to survive in an arid desert or on an exposed mountainside continually subject to violent winds, and are most often found where water is plentiful and the aerial parts are not subjected to great mechanical stresses. The form of a plant during the most unfavourable period of the year is particularly important in determining survival, and this is taken into account when classifying plants according to their life-forms. The Danish botanist Raunkiaer introduced a system of classification which, so far as land plants are concerned, depends on the position of resting buds relative to the soil surface during the unfavourable season (*i.e.* winter in a temperate climate). The more common life-forms are these:

(*a*) **Phanerophytes.** Tall, perennial plants which hold their resting buds at least 25 cm. above soil level. They include most trees and shrubs, and have the greatest degree of exposure of the buds.

(*b*) **Chamaephytes.** Perennials of small size, whose resting buds are above soil level but not above 25 cm. Common British examples are *Vaccinium myrtillus* (bilberry) and *Helianthemum chamaecistus* (rockrose).

(*c*) **Hemicryptophytes.** Perennials, with resting buds at soil level and therefore partly protected by the soil, unlike those of (*a*) and (*b*): e.g. *Mercurialis perennis* (dog's mercury) and *Bellis perennis* (daisy).

(*d*) **Geophytes.** Perennials, with resting buds below soil level and therefore very well protected. They include plants which perennate by tubers and bulbs (e.g. *Endymion nonscriptus*, bluebell) or by rhizomes (e.g. *Petasites hybridus*, butterbur).

(*e*) **Therophytes.** Annuals, which pass through the unfavourable season as seeds and thereby give their resting buds (in the embryos) thorough and prolonged protection.

The proportions of these five life-forms among the species of a given area are related to the severity of the unfavourable season. The following table shows the estimated percentage of species with each life-form in three contrasting habitats:

	SEYCHELLES IS.: Warm climate with high rainfall	LOWLANDS OF SCOTLAND: Temperate climate	TRIPOLI, NORTH AFRICA: Hot, semi-desert
Phanerophytes	59	10	6
Chamaephytes	7	8	13
Hemicryptophytes	13	60	20
Geophytes	4	8	9
Therophytes	17	14	52

It can be seen that in the Seychelles Is., where the climate throughout the year is generally favourable for plant growth, a large majority of species are phanerophytes. In the semi-desert of North Africa, however, there may be long periods with no rainfall and a correspondingly large number of therophytes is found. The Scottish lowlands are intermediate between these extremes, having winters which are harsh enough to endanger the survival of very exposed buds, but no prolonged periods of cold or drought. The most common life-form here, as in many temperate regions, is the hemicryptophyte.

Specialised Life-forms

The recognition of the importance of the position of the perennating buds was a major advance in the study of life-forms, but for many purposes it is necessary to take other features into account. We may recognise a number of specialised life-form categories; the plants can be assigned places in Raunkiaer's scheme as geophytes and so on, but possess distinctive properties which call for separate consideration.

Hydrophytes are plants which live submerged in water. It is possible to draw finer distinctions between free-floating species and rooted ones, between those with submerged leaves and those with floating ones, and so on. In their manner of perennation hydrophytes are similar to geophytes, with a high degree of shelter from frost. They display marked structural peculiarities (pp. 625-8). Many angiosperms and a few ferns live as hydrophytes, mostly in fresh water. Only a very few vascular plants (all monocotyledons) are marine.

Helophytes are marsh plants, requiring waterlogged soil but not normally submerged. They display similar anatomical features to the hydrophytes, but in much less degree. The distinction between hydrophytes and helophytes is not completely sharp, and there is a restricted group of **amphibious** species, which can live in either manner.

Succulents are plants in which the shoot system is appreciably swollen by the development of internal water-storage tissues. It is most unusual for stem and leaves to be equally affected, so that there is an almost sharp division between **leaf-succulents** with swollen leaves (Fig. 335), and **stem-succulents** with more or less reduced leaves but a swollen stem (Fig. 336). Succulents are characteristic of regions with a particular type of arid climate, stem-succulents being associated, on the whole, with more extreme aridity than leaf-succulents.

Halophytes are plants which can grow in soil with abnormally high concentrations of soluble minerals, especially, though by no means exclusively, sodium chloride. Halophytes naturally tend to occur in coastal marshes and on beaches; it should be remembered, however, that salty soils also occur in many inland areas (Utah, etc.)

and also that many **maritime** plants (that is, those which are found largely in coastal districts) are not significantly tolerant of salt, but owe their special distribution to other factors. A majority of halophytes show some degree (usually quite mild) of succulence, but otherwise their peculiarities are physiological rather than structural.

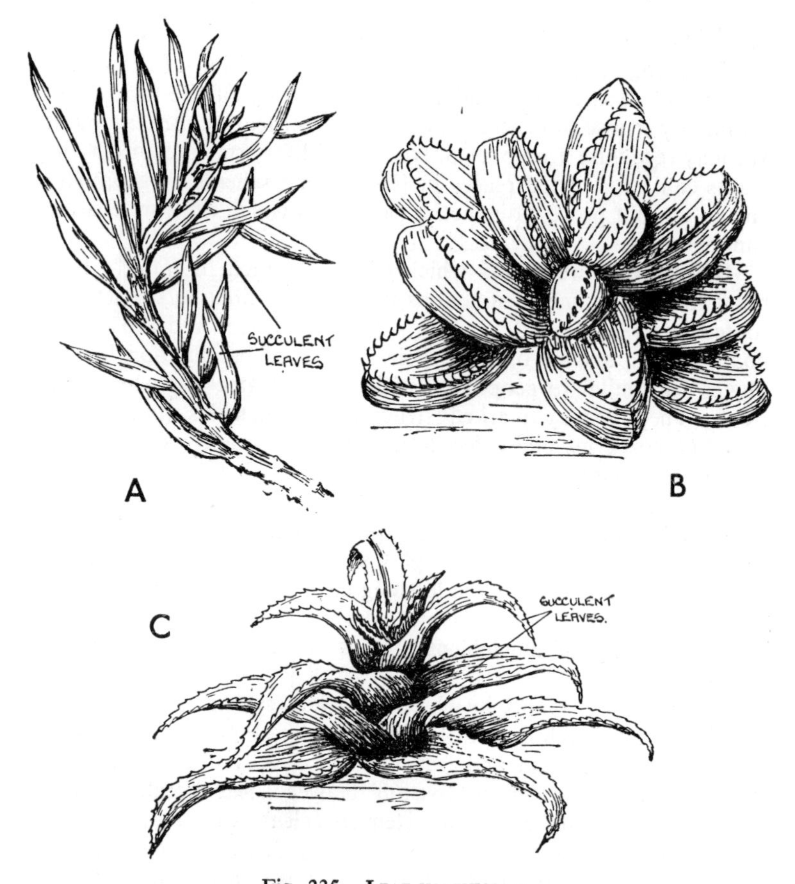

Fig. 335. LEAF-SUCCULENTS.
A, *Kleinia ficoides*; B, *Mesembryanthemum* sp.; C, *Aloe spinosissima*.

Their tissues have high osmotic pressures, for example. The fact that a high proportion of halophytes are drawn from only a small number of plant families (especially Chenopodiaceae and Plumbaginaceae) suggests that halophytic adaptation is not a simple matter.

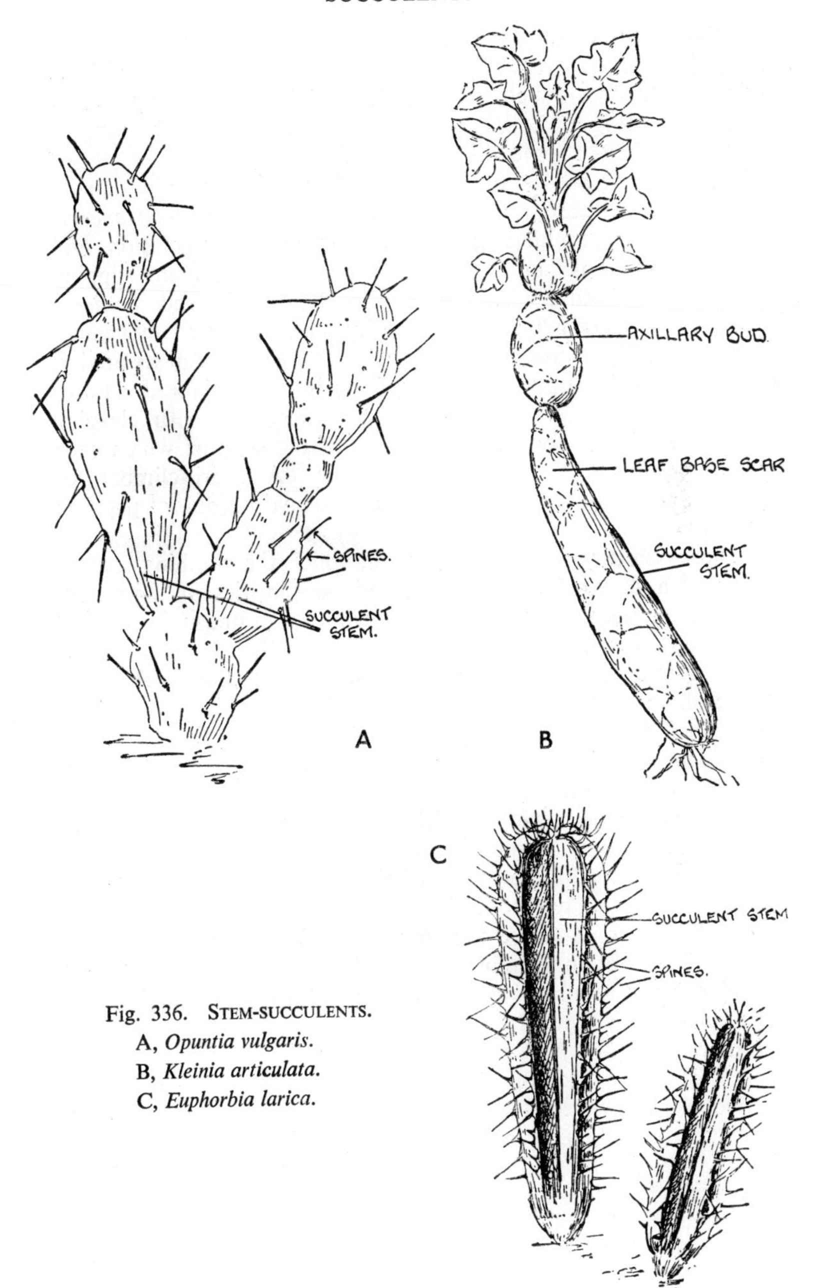

Fig. 336. STEM-SUCCULENTS.
A, *Opuntia vulgaris*.
B, *Kleinia articulata*.
C, *Euphorbia larica*.

Climbers are plants which grow up from ground level to a height which they can only reach by depending for support on other plants or inanimate objects such as walls. They fall into four very distinct groups according to the way in which the attachment to the support is accomplished. Some, like *Hedera helix* (ivy), have means of adhering to any porous or fissured surface, and can grow equally well up a rock-face or a tree-trunk. Some, like *Galium aparine* (cleavers), are scramblers, growing up through the vegetation, and relying upon hooks and prickles to prevent them from slipping back again. Many, like *Convolvulus* (bindweed) and *Lonicera* (honeysuckle), are twiners, climbing by an exaggerated movement of nutation which causes their stems, which have no special sensitivity, to coil round the support. Lastly, there is the specialised class of tendril climbers (e.g. *Lathyrus odoratus*, sweet pea) with clasping organs sensitive to touch. The nature of the support which each species requires is of ecological importance. A tendril climber, for instance, can only grip thin objects, and would be out of place in high forest.

Those climbers, known as **lianes**, in which the climbing stem is perennial and woody, display marked peculiarities in their stem anatomy, the secondary tissues being arranged in unusual ways and broken up into separate masses or strands, so that the stem retains much of its original flexibility. In twining plants the development of the shoot is distinctively modified, with the elongation of the stem running ahead of the expansion of the leaves. In general, the special features of climbers are readily intelligible in terms of adaptation to environment.

An **epiphyte** is a plant which grows upon another, without, however, absorbing materials from it as a parasite would do. Epiphytism is not unknown in Britain; it is common among our coastal algae, we have mosses and lichens on the trees, and in the wetter distics some of the common ferns often grow epiphytically. But we have not in Britain, or indeed anywhere in Europe, any vascular plant which is especially adapted to epiphytic life. In warm climates without a dry season, however, there are many true epiphytes, species which grow in no other way. Some particular groups of plants (notably ferns, orchids, and a family of monocotyledons known as the Bromeliaceae which is *predominantly* epiphytic) contribute a great proportion of the epiphytic flora. There is no absolute distinction between epiphytes and climbers; between the two lie some species which begin as epiphytes and send roots down to the soil (p. 68) and others which begin as climbers but become epiphytes by the death of their lower parts.

Some Ecological Aspects of Anatomy and Morphology

The relationship between life-forms and habitat conditions can often be pursued into matters of detail, and very large numbers of cases can be quoted in which plants in no way closely related to one another, but growing in similar habitats, have assumed life-forms so similar as to suggest some process of mimicry or imitation. Thus the African deserts, which have no true cacti at all, possess stem-succulents, drawn from other families, which resemble cacti not merely in being stem-succulents, but in many other features as well. Similarly the mangroves, stilt-rooted halophytic trees of tropical mudflats, are not all related to each other, though they share a mode of life which calls for a whole series of co-ordinated structural modifications.

Only to a limited extent can these more detailed adjustments of life-form to habitat be understood in the simple terms at present available to us. We can see why a climate with a dry season should be associated with an abundance of geophytes, but not why the Mediterranean type of dry-season climate should be specially linked with the bulb-forming type of geophyte. This lack of explanation, however, does not prevent this kind of study from leading to the concept of an **ecological niche**, the idea of a vacancy which may be filled by any plant with the appropriate qualifications. On high mountains near the equator there seems to be an opportunity for a special type of dwarf, almost unbranched tree. In the Andes the position is filled by *Puya* (a monocotyledon), in Africa by *Lobelia* (a dicotyledon); in life-form the two resemble each other but differ strikingly from their own close relatives. Not every niche is filled; for this particular one suitable candidates have appeared in some of the Pacific islands but not in others. The degree of conformity to pattern varies, and we can never be sure how far resemblances between unrelated species are to be attributed to chance and how far they reflect the formative pressure of environmental factors.

Of all the features of the habitat the one which bears the most obvious relationship to the structure of the plant is the abundance (or scarcity) of water. In general, the plants of dry places have small cells with thick walls, widespread lignification of the tissues, thick cuticle, a relatively small volume of internal air-spaces, and a tendency to cover and enclose their stomata, as by rolling of the leaf, development of hairs, and so on (e.g. *Ammophila*, Fig. 337). Other features which often occur are reduction of the surface:volume ratio, and a high level of secretory activity, with production of resins, gums, and volatile oils. This whole complex of characters constitutes the condition known as **xeromorphy**. Plants can be arranged in a kind of scale, with extreme xeromorphs at one end and hydrophytes, which show the opposite structural tendencies, at the other. The correlation with the measured properties of the environment is so clear that it cannot be seriously questioned.

The interpretation of the facts has, however, aroused a great deal of controversy. At one time there was general agreement that the plants were rather closely adapted to their environments; xeromorphic construction was seen as the result of natural selection, and as a set of devices which tended to reduce transpiration, protect the tissues from excessive sunlight, and in every way to make the plant more successful in its specialised mode of life. Similar

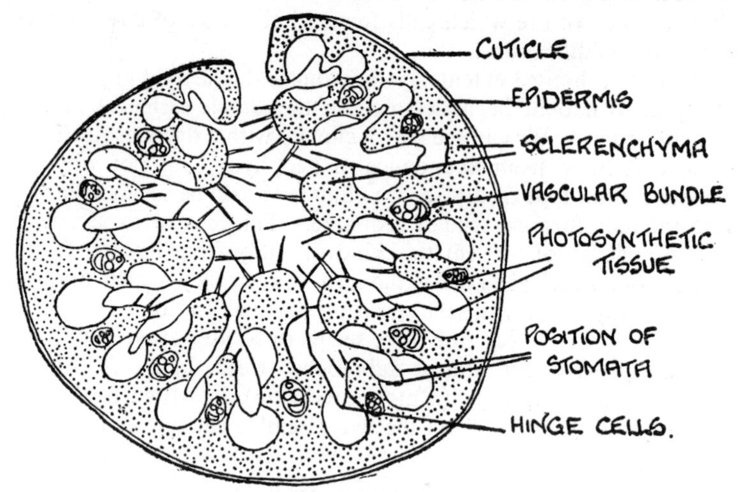

Fig. 337. *Ammophila*.
Diagram of T.S. of leaf. Note that the leaf is rolled with the stomata on the inside.

reasoning was applied to the hydrophyte; its large thin leaves, thin cuticle, and frequent internal air-spaces (see Fig. 338) enabled it to overcome the difficulties of gaseous exchange which were thought to arise in an aquatic environment; its lack of lignified tissue allowed it to yield harmlessly to the movement of the water, and so on.

The whole system of thought was based on little but guesswork, yet contained a core of truth; we need not doubt that a plant in a desert is better with a thick cuticle. Modern botanists, however, with a fuller appreciation of the difficulties, no longer expect any theory of adaptation to provide more than a partial explanation of xeromorphic effects.

In reality it is impossible to justify any claim that xeromorphy is entirely related to reduced water supply. A dry habitat is often hot, a moist one is often shady. Whatever may be accomplished in the laboratory, ecological studies in the open do not enable us to separate the effects of water supply from those of temperature and light-intensity. In some cases the early theorists certainly emphasised the wrong aspect of the environment. From actual measurements it seems unlikely that hydrophytes experience any particular difficulty in obtaining carbon dioxide for photosynthesis, but many of them must be critically short of essential minerals.

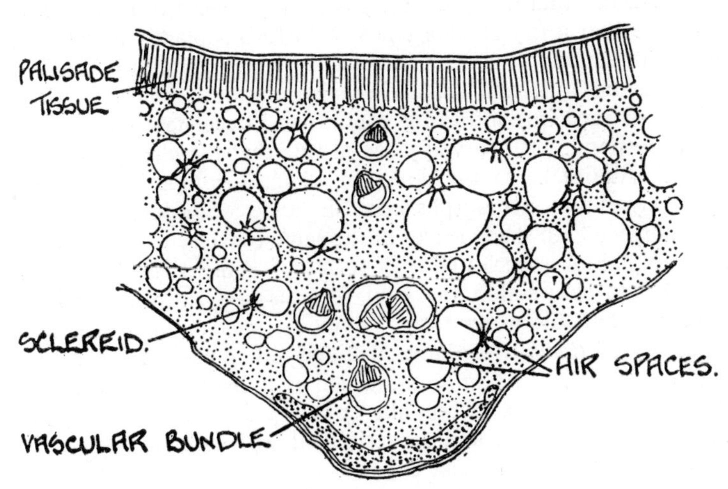

Fig. 338. WATER LILY.
Diagram of T.S. of leaf midrib showing frequent air-spaces.

"Adaptation" theories which presupposed a contrary state of affairs have naturally lost much of their appeal.

Where it has been possible to subject supposed adaptations to experimental test the results have been predominantly unfavourable to at least the more extreme adaptationist position. Some xeromorphs, although endowed with sunken stomata and all the other peculiarities which were supposed to cut down transpiration to the absolute minimum, are not in any way remarkable for specially low transpiration rates. Nor does there seem to be any truth in the oft-repeated plea that the abundance of lignified tissue in a xeromorph would allow it to stand undamaged in a wilted state. Admittedly an extreme xeromorph can usually wilt without falling over, but if the wilting is anything but temporary the plant will die just as certainly as any other. We know from the example of various mosses, lichens, and algae, that some plant cells can be reduced to a very low water content without permanent harm. The tissues of the vascular xeromorphs, however, show no sign of any special resistance to death by drying.

As it becomes less likely that a point of structure can be explained as an adaptation to the environment, so it becomes more necessary to seek another cause. Attention then tends to rest on the possibility of direct action of the habitat on the plant. Xeromorphs are characterised by a high level of secretory activity, yet there is very little evidence that this peculiarity is of any benefit to them. May it not be that a dry climate tends to disturb a plant's metabolism in the direction of greater secretion? Such questions admit of experimental test, and many investigators have placed a single species or race in contrasting conditions to see how its structure would respond. It is a very general rule that the changes induced in such studies lie in the direction which a comparison between hydrophytes and xeromorphs would indicate. Sun leaves are more xeromorphic than shade leaves of the same tree (see p. 151). Work with amphibious species (British forms of *Ranunculus*, *Polygonum*, *Nasturtium*) shows that the land form is less hydrophytic in its structure than the water form. Some of the amphibious species, especially of *Ranunculus*, have strikingly different forms of air leaf and water leaf. In *Sagittaria*, which is a hydrophyte, there are three forms of leaf, a ribbon-like submerged leaf, a floating type with rounded outline, and an aerial leaf with pointed lobes. The behaviour of an individual depends on the depth of water; the further it is below the surface, the more hydrophytic its leaf-structure becomes. Less spectacular examples are just as clear in their indications. *Teucrium scorodonia* (woodsage), for instance, which grows in the open and also in the herb layer of woods, shows differences in internode length, leaf size, hairiness, and other features, differences which usually escape attention until contrasting specimens are laid side by side, but obeying the rule that increased exposure means increased xeromorphy. However, it should not be assumed that such differences will always disappear when conditions are standardised. Apart from the experiments mentioned above in which similar plants are exposed to a variety of different conditions, many experiments of the opposite kind have also been carried out. The results of collecting distinctive members of the same species from different habitats and growing them under uniform conditions are unpredictable. In some cases the plants take on a similar appearance to one another, indicating that the previous differences between them were the direct effects of the environment on the developing plants. In other instances, however, morphological differences persist despite the uniformity of the environment, and can be shown to be inherited. Where this is so, it is less easy to believe that the characteristic morphology associated with a particular habitat has no functional significance. Our knowledge of natural selection (p. 658) suggests that if a certain morphological pattern becomes inherent in members of a species accustomed to a certain environment, then that pattern has a functional advantage in that environment.

Xeromorphy appears in many cases where the existence of any real shortage of water is at least doubtful. Almost all evergreens are somewhat xeromorphic, some of them very markedly so. Xeromorphic features are found also in many plants of acid (but sometimes very wet) soils. Upon a theory of adaptation these would have to be cases in which a plant for one reason or another (low soil temperature, acidity of the soil solution, high wind velocity, inefficient water-conduction in the stem) tended to have difficulty in taking up and retaining sufficient water for full physiological activity. The explanation is plausible in some instances (see conifers, p. 482) but few modern botanists are satisfied with its application to bog plants.

It is, in any case, perfectly clear that one cannot equate the xeromorphic condition with the idea of a **xerophyte**, a plant adapted to life in dry places, for even in deserts there are many plants which in some degree avoid full exposure to drought. Desert ephemerals, which pass the dry season as dormant seeds, are not significantly xeromorphic. Nor are those Saharan species which, by enormous elongation of the tap-root, obtain access to abundant underground supplies of water. Nor are the leaves of some of the desert shrubs, for these plants spread out a new crop of foliage when it rains and drop the leaves as soon as the soil dries again (several times a year if necessary). The succulents also, though many of them are extreme xerophytes, are by no means thoroughly xeromorphic in structure. They have a thick cuticle and a reduced external surface, but there is a striking absence of the external protection for the stomata which is such a feature of typical xeromorphs. The inner tissues of succulents show no trace of xeromorphy.

Because structural features are similar, or associated in some way, it does not follow that we can attribute a common significance to them. Succulence in xerophytes may well be adaptive, a useful provision for survival. That similar considerations apply to succulence in halophytes now seems rather unlikely. Many hydrophytes have large intercellular ventilating canals, much bigger than cells, and easily visible to the naked eye. In some cases (look at shoot-bases of *Typha* or *Sparganium*) each canal is crossed at intervals by a **diaphragm**, a thin plate of parenchyma through which air can pass by very small intercellular holes. Owing to surface tension effects a diaphragm acts like a water-tight bulkhead; when there is water on one side and air on the other only high pressure will burst the surface film across the microscopic pores. Local damage such as the loss of a leaf therefore does not cause general flooding of the canal system. This is generally regarded as a specialised adaptation, for a diaphragm is not a simple structure. Against this we must set our inability to explain the purpose of the canals themselves; it is far from certain that the canal system has anything approaching the value formerly attached to it as a means of storing and transporting gases, or as a source of buoyancy.

Plant Geography

This subject divides rather sharply into two parts. On the one hand there is floristic plant geography which deals with the distribution of species, genera, and families. It is in some ways closely related to taxonomy and has made substantial contributions to our knowledge of the course of evolution. Floristic evidence also plays some part in the discussion of such purely geographical questions as whether the island of Madagascar was ever joined to the mainland of Africa, and so on. Ecological plant geography, on the other hand, is concerned with the distribution of vegetation types, the character of which depends much more upon the life-forms of the constituent plants than upon their taxonomic relationships.

Floristic Plant Geography. In general, the findings of floristic geography present a picture for each group of slow outward spread from a centre of origin. We can be reasonably sure that the cacti arose in Central America and the thistles somewhere between the Adriatic and the Persian Gulf, because these groups are still very far from having filled the space available to them. By contrast, the great family of Leguminosae is spread evenly round the world, being presumably of great antiquity, and its centre of origin can no longer be recognised.

The extent to which a plant group can spread is influenced by the limitations of dispersal mechanisms and the effectiveness of geographical barriers. The amount of difference between the floras of two land-masses thus increases with the length of the sea-crossing between them. This means, among other things, that the floras of the continents become progressively more distinct as one moves from north to south. For similar reasons, a species which originates on an island, or in any region surrounded by barriers to dispersal, is likely to have a restricted range. In most countries a proportion of the species present are **endemics**, that is they occur there and nowhere else in the world. The proportion of endemics is a function of geographical isolation, primarily of isolation by sea. It is greatest in Hawaii (where almost all vascular plants are endemics), smaller in Ceylon, smaller still in mainland Italy (endemism is not found only in islands), and zero in Anglesey.

The flora of Britain has certain peculiar features which are only partly due to the separation from continental Europe, for the English Channel is relatively narrow and, by geological standards, of very recent formation. One outstanding feature is the shortage of species. The British Isles have only about one-third of the number of species which could reasonably be expected on grounds of size, climate, and latitude. This is partly the result of glaciation. The ice sheet which covered most of Northern Europe until about 12,000 years ago greatly impoverished the flora. *Magnolia*, for example, which is common in America, China, and Japan, no longer figures in European vegetation, though fossils of it are found in European rocks. There are many similar examples.

There is also good reason to believe that angiosperms originated in warm climates and only later spread into temperate regions. Many important families, such as the palms, have never progressed very far in that direction. Britain, therefore, is too far north to have a fully representative selection of the flowering plants. The biased sample of the world flora which makes up the British angiosperms has the following features all over-represented: herbaceous habit, deciduous foliage, small leaf-size, wind pollination, and grass-like foliage in monocotyledons. The overall shortage of species also helps to account for the prevalence of plant communities with only one or two dominant species, such as beech wood, heather moor, and so on, and for the success of a single species such as bracken in a wide range of habitats.

Ecological Plant Geography. One cannot hope for any general rules to cover the distribution of all the vegetation types of the world, but it is helpful to keep in mind as a central type the tropical rain forest characteristic of areas where conditions are more or less ideal for continuous growth. There are large trees, usually evergreen but not xeromorphic, belonging to a large number of species with none achieving dominance, accompanied by lianes, epiphytes, and large monocotyledons. Insect pollination prevails, though the flowers are often far from showy.

Passage to any climate in which growth cannot be continuous involves loss of most of the epiphytes and lianes, and replacement of the larger monocotyledons by smaller and more grass-like types.

Seasonal interruption of growth may be caused by drought or by low temperatures, and these agencies differ markedly in their effects. Even a moderate degree of drought, if it occurs regularly, is associated with a pronounced reduction in the general stature of the vegetation. More severe aridity brings xeromorphy and succulence, and the plants cease to cover the whole surface of the soil. In general, the appearance of bare ground in a climax community betokens shortage of water; the bare ground is often not really vacant, because beneath it spreading root systems are in competition for water. Drought alone does not bring any significant shift away from insect pollination, and even severe dry conditions are compatible with a predominantly woody vegetation containing a high proportion of evergreen species.

So long as no question of frost arises it is possible to have a vegetation of luxuriant character, and temperatures well below equatorial level seem to have no dwarfing effect at all. But where there is winter frost, however mild or occasional, many species are totally excluded, and there begins to be a shift towards the herbaceous perennial habit, with regular leaf-fall in many of the woody plants. A winter of any severity is certain also to bring an increase in the prominence of wind pollinated species. It is probably incorrect, however, to attribute to a mere decrease in temperature the more extreme peculiarities which are observed in the vegetation of arctic and alpine regions. Stunted growth, a limited range of species, and a very high proportion of grass-like monocotyledons, are the most obvious features, but these are likely to arise rather from the shortness of the growing season and the presence of permafrost in the soil than from any direct action of low temperature.

22 GENETICS AND EVOLUTION

We have seen in Chapter 8 that when a living cell divides by mitosis, the daughter cells are in many ways replicas of the parent. Each receives a set of instructions which makes it potentially capable of doing all that the parent cell could do. Similarly, when a new individual is produced by sexual reproduction each parent contributes something of its nature to the offspring. These two forms of inheritance, from cell to cell and from generation to generation, together with many associated topics, form the subject matter of genetics. Although genetics is frequently defined as the study of biological inheritance, it is helpful to remember that when William Bateson first suggested the name "genetics" in 1906 he described the subject as the "physiology of descent". This apt phrase clearly emphasises that genetics is closely allied to physiology, and that many, though not all, of the problems of inheritance require biochemical, physical, and mathematical techniques for their solution.

This is so with one of the central and most important features of heredity, namely the similarity between parents and their offspring. When we sow the seeds from a wallflower, we have every confidence that they will grow into more wallflowers, not into cabbages. Similarly we expect that an egg laid by a chicken will hatch into another chicken, not a duck. This regularity with which each species reproduces its own kind is so taken for granted that one may need to be reminded that it presents any problem. A moment's thought, however, makes it clear that parents must be responsible for determining the general developmental pattern of their offspring. One branch of genetics seeks to understand in what form the necessary instructions are transmitted, and some of the achievements of this line of investigation are described in Chapter 8. It is now generally agreed that the irregular sequence of nucleotide pairs in DNA molecules contained in the cell nucleus constitutes a coded message, and that this message is faithfully reproduced at each mitotic cell division. This represents a considerable step forward in the understanding of inheritance, but also emphasises a further problem which is still largely unsolved. If all the cells of an organism receive the same genetic message why do they not all behave in a similar way? Why, in the development of a higher plant, do some cells remain small while others enlarge to great lengths, some retain their living contents while others lose them, some produce chloroplasts and undertake photosynthesis while others do not? Questions such as these can only be answered by an intimate knowledge of the structure and activities of individual cells and cell constituents. The increasing variety of techniques which can be applied to subcellular analysis has already resulted in important discoveries in this field, and further progress can be expected. These aspects of genetics, being dependent upon refinements of technique which are relatively recent, have only a short history. For many years the inheritance of similarities and the paradox of differentiation were topics ignored by most geneticists, who devoted their attention to the differences in detail between related individuals. Such differences are readily observable, and their inheritance can be studied without any elaborate equipment. For example, a group of seeds collected from an orange-flowered wallflower plant may grow into plants some of which have orange flowers and some yellow. Situations like this are very common, and were much more frequently recognised when it was usual to collect one's own seed for raising next year's plants. Such variation among progenies, and between parents and their offspring, was a source of great interest to gardeners in the eighteenth and nineteenth centuries, who quite rightly assumed that cross-fertilisation was generally responsible. Indeed the artificial cross-pollination of related varieties of flowering plants became a popular hobby among enterprising gardeners, and was recognised as a method of producing varieties with new combinations of characters. As a result, information about the inheritance of differences has accumulated over a long period of time, but it is important to remember the nature of that information. If it comes from experimental cross-fertilisation, it may tell us what happens to the differences during several generations, but it does not tell us where the differences came from in the first place. The origin of inherited differences is a subject we shall return to later in this chapter.

Hybridisation

The process of cross-fertilising two dissimilar individuals is called **hybridisation**, and the product is a **hybrid**. The word "hybrid" has sometimes been restricted to the offspring of markedly different parents, such as members of different species, but it is perfectly legitimate to use it in reference to the offspring of any parents between which there is a clear, inherited dissimilarity. In spite of the numerous plant hybrids successfully made during the eighteenth and nineteenth centuries, much of the work was unsystematic and involved parent plants of uncertain ancestry. As a result, few conclusions of any general application could be drawn from this work, though it became clear that, as one might expect, the more distantly related are two plants, the less likely are they to form a viable hybrid. There are no records of successful hybridisation between plants belonging to different families, but a number of intergeneric hybrids are possible. For example, the crosses

Raphanus sativus (radish) × *Brassica oleracea* (cabbage)
and *Triticum aestivum* (wheat) × *Secale cereale* (rye)

both give hybrid offspring which are vigorous but sterile. The fact that hybridisation is successful indicates a fairly close relationship between the two parent genera in each case, but the sterility of the hybrids is an obstacle to further study of their relationships. Other intergeneric hybrids may show considerable fertility. Among the orchids there are plants which are placed in different genera on the basis of morphological dissimilarity, but which produce fertile offspring when crossed together.

Many interspecific hybrids have been produced, some sterile and others with varying degrees of fertility. Hybrids between the primrose (*Primula vulgaris*) and the cowslip (*P. veris*) can be made in either direction (i.e. *P. vulgaris* as seed parent × *P. veris* as pollen parent, or the reciprocal), though when *P. vulgaris* is the seed parent most of the seeds produced have no embryos and will not germinate. In hybrids produced by either of the reciprocal crosses only about 30 per cent. of their pollen is fertile. Thus there are both barriers to formation of the hybrids and reduced fertility in the hybrids which are produced. These features are common in interspecific hybridisation. In fact when two plants which are regarded as members of different species hybridise without difficulty and produce fully fertile offspring there is reason to doubt the validity of giving each specific rank. For example, the red and white campions, widely known as *Melandrium rubrum* and *M. album* will cross-fertilise very readily, giving rise to hybrids which are vigorous and fertile. On the strength of this evidence it has been suggested that the two parental forms should be regarded as merely sub-divisions of a single species. As was mentioned in Chapter 13, there is no generally acceptable definition of a species which can be applied to all cases, but almost all modern attempts to define the species take account of cross-fertility as well as the more traditional criteria of taxonomy such as gross morphology.

Mendel's Experiments in Plant Hybridisation

During the nineteenth century there was a growing belief among biologists that cross-fertilisation did not produce a haphazard mixture of parental or intermediate features in subsequent generations, but that the process was subject to certain laws, knowledge of which would enable predictions to be made of the outcome of particular crosses. It is now known that the belief was well founded. Many of the experiments in hybridisation carried out at the time were inadequate in design or in execution to allow recognition of these laws. Other experiments were of suitable design, but the significance of the results was missed. The earliest man who had the skill both to design suitable experiments and to interpret their results correctly was Gregor Mendel (1822-84). Since the story of Mendel's discoveries makes one of the most significant chapters in the history of biology, a brief historical note is appropriate here before considering the experiments themselves. While living as a monk in the Augustinian monastery at Brünn (now Brno in Czechoslovakia), he conducted experiments in the monastery garden, the results of which were read before the local Natural History Society in 1865 and published by the Society in 1866. Although the publication was received by scientific libraries in various parts of Europe, little attention was paid to Mendel's work at the time. His election as abbot in 1868 curtailed his scientific work and he died in 1884, unknown as a man of science. Not until 1900 was the importance of his work realised and given the publicity it deserved. In that year Correns in Germany, von Tschermak in Austria, and de Vries in Holland, who had all been studying similar problems, simultaneously discovered one of the laws governing inheritance but found that Mendel had forestalled them by thirty-five years. The rediscovery of Mendel's laws generated widespread interest, and gave the study of inheritance an impetus which it has never subsequently lacked. It is interesting to speculate on how much more progress might have been made if Mendel's achievements had been recognised in his lifetime.

Mendel's experiments merit detailed consideration not only because of the importance of the conclusions he drew from them, but also as a model of experimental design and deduction. Although he experimented at one time or another with plants of several species and with animals also, his most thorough and successful work was done with the garden pea, *Pisum sativum*, and it is this work which we will now consider. His aim was to cross-fertilise distinctive varieties and to study the consequences in the succeeding generations. He realised that to give the most conclusive information his experimental material must satisfy several requirements, namely:

(*a*) the chosen varieties must differ from each other in features which are inherited, and each variety must breed true for its characteristic features;

(*b*) it must be possible to control pollination so that the pollen parent of any seed is known;

(*c*) the chosen varieties must be capable of producing hybrids with complete fertility so that experiments can be prolonged for as many generations as necessary.

In all respects *P. sativum* was an ideal species for the experiments Mendel proposed to carry out, largely becausc it is a species in which self-fertilisation is the natural breeding system. As a general rule the anthers burst within the bud and pollination occurs before the flower is fully open. This system has important consequences, since with habitual self-fertilisation each pea plant has only one parent, one grandparent, and so on: there is never any mixture of inheritances. Mendel obtained seed of several varieties, and by growing them side by side for two generations he not only confirmed that each variety bred true, but also showed that the differences between varieties were constant and unmistakable.

The control of pollination in *P. sativum* is also straightforward. As mentioned above, if a flower is left unmolested, it will self-pollinate. However, if the stamens are removed with forceps before dehiscence (a procedure known as emasculation), cross-pollination can be carried out using pollen from any chosen source. Flowers which are emasculated and not deliberately pollinated rarely set seed, and the rare intervention of insect pollinators can be avoided if necessary by enclosing flowers in bags.

Finally, hybrids produced by cross-fertilisation between varieties are fully fertile and can themselves be used for the production of further generations.

Having chosen his material, Mendel then cross-fertilised certain pairs of varieties, paying particular attention in each case to one outstanding difference between the parents. For instance, he crossed a tall variety (plants 6 ft-7 ft high) with a dwarf variety (plants 9 in.-18 in. high), using sometimes a tall plant as seed parent and sometimes a dwarf. These reciprocal crosses gave similar results:

$$\left.\begin{array}{c}\text{tall} \times \text{dwarf}\\ \text{or}\\ \text{dwarf} \times \text{tall}\end{array}\right\} \rightarrow \text{progeny all tall.}$$

[N.B.—(*a*) when describing a cross in writing it is customary to give the seed (or female) parent first; (*b*) the first generation offspring from cross-fertilisation is called the **first filial** generation, usually abbreviated both in speech and in writing to $\mathbf{F_1}$.]

Two points should be noted at this early stage in the experiment:

(1) the F_1 was identical with one of the parents, not intermediate between the parents as one might be led to expect from some popular fancies about heredity;

(2) the reciprocal crosses gave the same result, indicating that in this case at least, the two parents make equivalent contributions to the F_1. This also is significant in view of previous controversy about the relative importance of male and female parents.

Mendel allowed the F_1 plants to produce seed by self-fertilisation and sowed the seeds in the following year. The plants so produced constituted the F_2 generation, which by definition is the product of self-pollinating an F_1 or of cross-pollination among the members of an F_1. Unlike the F_1, the F_2 was not uniform but included both tall and dwarf plants, each type indistinguishable from one of the original parents. Mendel took particular care to record the numbers of each type of plant, which were:

787 tall and 277 dwarf plants.

The attention which Mendel gave to the relative numbers of different types in mixed progenies was an essential factor in enabling him to interpret his results.

Further experiments of similar design but using parents which differed in other features gave comparable results. For example, Mendel crossed varieties which differed in flower colour (purple or white) or in the colour of the cotyledons in ripe seeds (yellow or green), with these results:

(*a*) *flower colour*

purple × white
or
white × purple } → F_1 all purple

F_2 comprised 705 purple and 224 white.

(*b*) *seed* (= *cotyledon*) *colour*

yellow × green
or
green × yellow } → F_1 all yellow

F_2 comprised 6,022 yellow and 2,001 green.

In all, Mendel studied seven pairs of contrasting features in this way, and all of them gave results of this sort, indicating a common pattern of inheritance. Points of importance which should be noted are as follows:

(1) Parental features which are absent in the F_1 reappear in the F_2. This is contrary to the old idea of blending inheritance which compared hybridisation with the irreversible mixing of two liquids such as ink and water. Mendel's results suggest that hybridisation

is more like the mixing of two sorts of particles, each of which retains its identity in the hybrid and can be separated out in the F_2.

(2) In all seven cases, the F_1 resembled one of the parents: if any experiment was repeated it would always be found that the same parental type appeared in the F_1. This led to the recognition of **dominant** and **recessive** features. In the experiment on plant height, for example, tallness was dominant and dwarfness recessive.

(3) In all seven cases the two parental types appeared in the F_2 in a similar numerical ratio. The ratios for the three examples given above were:

height 2·84 : 1 flower colour 3·15 : 1 seed colour 3·01 : 1

—with the dominant feature in the majority each time. This consistent approximation to a ratio of 3 : 1 indicates that inheritance was subject to the same law in each case.

Mendel's interpretation of his results has subsequently been fully confirmed by other workers. The basis of the interpretation is that each feature which is inherited in this way is under the control of particles, now called **genes**, contained in the cell nucleus. Thus there is a gene for tallness which we shall represent by the symbol *T*, and another for dwarfness, *t*. Every gamete contains one or the other (but not both) of these genes, and every zygote therefore has two, which may be alike (*TT* or *tt*) or different (*Tt*). A zygote containing *TT* will grow into a pure-breeding tall plant, all of whose gametes will receive the tallness gene *T*, whereas a *tt* zygote will become a pure-breeding dwarf plant whose gametes all receive *t*. We can now re-write Mendel's cross between tall and dwarf parents in terms of genes, like this:

parents: tall (*TT*) × dwarf (*tt*)
gametes: *T* *t*
↘ ↙
F_1 hybrid: *Tt*

This F_1 hybrid we know to be a tall plant, so just as we recognised dominant and recessive features, we can say that *T* is a dominant gene and *t* a recessive gene. To explain the composition of the F_2 we must consider the gametes produced by the F_1. Since F_1 plants have genes of both sorts, they can produce gametes with either *T* or *t*; in fact the two types are produced in equal frequencies:

F_1 hybrid *Tt*

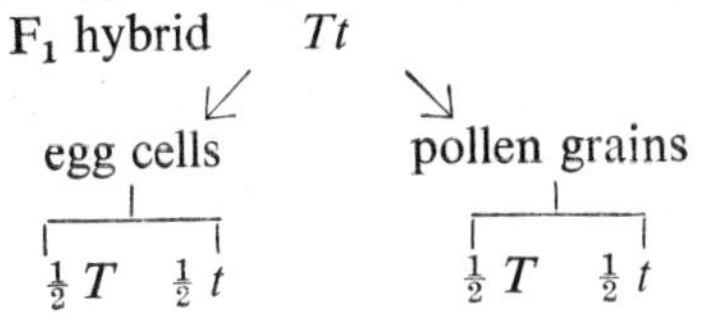

If the F_1 hybrid is self-pollinated, therefore, four types of fertilisation are possible, represented by the four compartments in Fig. 339:

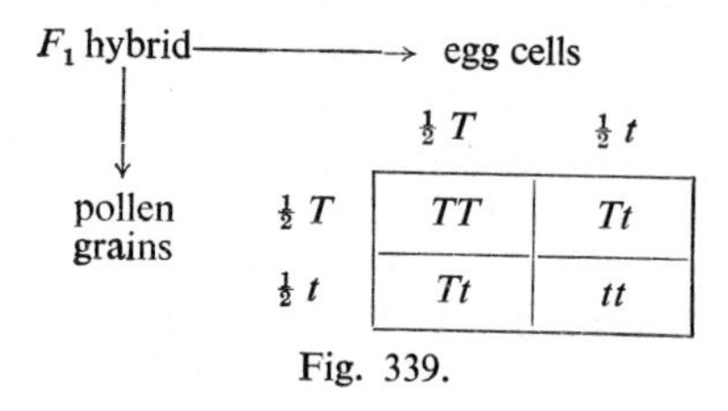

Fig. 339.

If half the egg cells contain *T*, and half the pollen grains also contain *T*, there is a probability of $\frac{1}{2} \times \frac{1}{2} (= \frac{1}{4})$ of any zygote receiving *T* from both gametes. Thus the top left-hand compartment of Fig. 339 represents $\frac{1}{4}$ of the total F_2 progeny. Reckoning up in this way it can be deduced that the F_2 will include plants of three types:

TT plants: pure-breeding tall plants: $\frac{1}{4}$ of total.
Tt plants: tall but hybrid: $\frac{1}{2}$ of total.
tt plants: pure-breeding dwarf plants: $\frac{1}{4}$ of total.

This explains why the F_2 contains three times as many tall plants as dwarfs. It will be noted, however, that the tall plants are not genetically identical: one-third of them are expected to breed true when selfed while the other two-thirds should behave in the same way as F_1 plants. This prediction was tested by Mendel, who took 100 tall F_2 plants at random, allowed each to self-pollinate and grew the 100 lots of seed separately. Twenty-eight lots grew into plants all of which were tall, and all the remaining seventy-two lots included some tall and some dwarf plants. This confirmed the prediction that tall F_2 plants were of two sorts, with the majority behaving like F_1 plants.

The most important point which emerges from this first series of Mendel's experiments is that inheritance can be explained in terms of particulate genes transmitted from one generation to the next. If, as in a hybrid, an individual possesses both genes of a particular pair, the two sorts of gene will be segregated when gametes are produced so that each gamete has one gene or the other. That is to say, each gamete is genetically pure. This principle of **segregation of genes** and **purity of gametes** is sometimes recognised as Mendel's first law.

Before passing on to consider more of Mendel's work, it is necessary to introduce some technical terms which are helpful in describing genetical experiments. Like most branches of science, genetics has acquired a considerable vocabulary of its own which is often bewildering to the beginner, but only the bare minimum of technical terms will be used here. First of all, we have already met the concept of some genes being alternatives of each other. The genes affecting the height of the pea plant, *T* and *t*, are alternatives in the sense that any one gamete may carry only one of them. Two genes which have this relationship are a pair of **alleles**. This term has almost completely superseded its longer synonym "allelomorphs" which will be found in the older books. At fertilisation, a zygote is produced which has two genes for height. If these are similar to each other (*TT* or *tt*) the zygote is a **homozygote**, but if both alleles are present (*Tt*) the zygote is a **heterozygote.** These two terms may be used not only for the zygotes but also for the plants which grow from them, as may the corresponding adjectives **homozygous** and **heterozygous**. Finally we have seen that a plant may be described either in terms of its appearance or in terms of the genes it possesses. Thus the F_2 of Mendel's experiment on plant height consisted of two visibly distinct types of plant, tall and dwarf. These descriptions are **phenotypes**. However, it was demonstrated that genetically there were three types of plant present, homozygous talls (*TT*), heterozygous talls (*Tt*), and dwarfs (*tt*). These descriptions of genetic constitution are **genotypes**. It will be noticed that two (or more than two as we shall see shortly) genotypes may share the same phenotype.

Having established the pattern of inheritance for the varietal differences considered one at a time, Mendel proceeded to consider what was the result of crossing parents which differed in two features. In this experiment he used features of the embryo, thereby economising in both space and time since a progeny could be classified by examining the seeds. The two features by which the parents differed were, firstly, cotyledon colour (see p. 636) and secondly the shape of the ripe seeds, which is also a feature of the embryo since the maternal seed coat adopts the shape of the embryo it encloses. In one variety the embryo remained swollen, giving a smooth, rounded seed surface; in the other the embryo shrivelled as the seed ripened, giving a wrinkled surface. One of the parent varieties bred true for smooth yellow seeds, the other for wrinkled green seeds. When crossed together they produced a uniform F_1 of smooth yellow seeds:

parents: smooth, yellow × wrinkled, green

↓

F_1 all smooth, yellow.

This confirmed the dominance of smoothness and yellowness already established from experiments in which the differences were studied separately. Fifteen of the F_1 seeds were planted the following year and after self-pollination yielded 556 seeds, classified as follows:

smooth, yellow	315
smooth, green	108
wrinkled, yellow	101
wrinkled, green	32
	556

Note the following points about this F_2:

(1) The parental features which were missing in the F_1, namely wrinkled shape and green colour, reappear in the F_2.

(2) Apart from the two parental phenotypes, smooth yellow and wrinkled green, the F_2 includes two new phenotypes with the separate features arranged in new combinations—smooth green and wrinkled yellow. The occurrence of these **recombinant** phenotypes shows that though two features may be combined in one parent variety they are not inseparable. This knowledge has great practical significance. For instance, a plant breeder may possess two varieties of a crop plant each with an inherited quality which the other lacks. By a suitable programme of hybridisation he can produce a recombinant phenotype in which the two qualities are combined.

(3) The four phenotypes occur in frequencies which agree with the known behaviour of seed shape and seed colour considered separately, and which indicate that these features are inherited independently of each other. For instance, seed shape is expected to show a 3 : 1 ratio of smooth : wrinkled, which it does (423 : 133). In other words, three-quarters of the F_2 seeds are smooth. By similar reasoning, three-quarters of the F_2 seeds should be, and are yellow (416 out of 556). If shape and colour are independent, the proportion of F_2 seeds which are both smooth and yellow should therefore be $\frac{3}{4} \times \frac{3}{4} = \frac{9}{16}$ of the total. This proportion of 556 seeds is 312·75, which is very close to the observed frequency of 315.

In a similar way the expected and observed frequencies of all four phenotypes can be compared, as shown below.

	Expected proportion	Expected frequency	Observed frequency
smooth, yellow	$\frac{3}{4} \times \frac{3}{4} = \frac{9}{16}$	312·75	315
smooth, green	$\frac{3}{4} \times \frac{1}{4} = \frac{3}{16}$	104·25	108
wrinkled, yellow	$\frac{1}{4} \times \frac{3}{4} = \frac{3}{16}$	104·25	101
wrinkled, green	$\frac{1}{4} \times \frac{1}{4} = \frac{1}{16}$	34·75	32
		556·00	556

This agreement between observation and expectation is unmistakable, and leads us to examine further what is meant by "independent inheritance" of two features. This can best be done by reconsidering the experiment in terms of the genotypes of the plants concerned, using the following symbols for the two pairs of alleles:

S is the dominant gene for smoothness, and *s* its recessive allele;

Y is the dominant gene for yellowness, and *y* its recessive allele.

The first part of the experiment can therefore be written:

parents: smooth yellow × wrinkled green

S S Y Y *s s y y*

gametes: *S Y* *s y*

↘ ↙

F_1 hybrid: *S s Y y*

The F_1 is heterozygous for both pairs of alleles; it is a double heterozygote. But since it has both of the dominant genes it shows both dominant features. We now need to assume that the F_1 produces in equal frequencies four types of gamete, each of which has one gene for seed shape and one for seed colour:

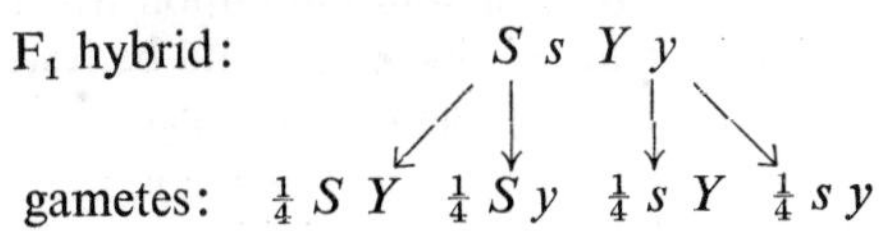

Although at this stage in the explanation this is an assumption, it will be shown a little later that the assumption is fully justified. Since there are four types of egg cell and four types of pollen grain, self-pollination will lead to fertilisations of 16 (= 4 × 4) types, which are represented by the sixteen compartments of Fig. 340.

F_1 hybrid → egg cells (columns); ↓ pollen grains (rows)

	$\frac{1}{4}$ *SY*	$\frac{1}{4}$ *Sy*	$\frac{1}{4}$ *sY*	$\frac{1}{4}$ *sy*
$\frac{1}{4}$ *SY*	1 *SSYY*	2 *SSYy*	3 *SsYY*	4 *SsYy*
$\frac{1}{4}$ *Sy*	5 *SSYy*	6 *SSyy*	7 *SsYy*	8 *Ssyy*
$\frac{1}{4}$ *sY*	9 *SsYY*	10 *SsYy*	11 *ssYY*	12 *ssYy*
$\frac{1}{4}$ *sy*	13 *SsYy*	14 *Ssyy*	15 *ssYy*	16 *ssyy*

Fig. 340.

The sixteen types are all equally probable so that each compartment corresponds to one-sixteenth of the total F_2 progeny. In each compartment is written the genotype of the zygote produced from one of the sixteen types of fertilisation. These genotypes can now be translated into phenotypes in this way:

All genotypes which include both the dominant genes *S* and *Y* give *smooth yellow* seeds. This applies to compartments 1, 2, 3, 4, 5, 7, 9, 10, and 13;

$= \frac{9}{16}$ of total.

All genotypes which include *S* but not *Y* give *smooth green* seeds. This applies to compartments 6, 8, and 14;

$= \frac{3}{16}$ of total.

All genotypes which include *Y* but not *S* give *wrinkled yellow* seeds. This applies to compartments 11, 12, and 15;

$= \frac{3}{16}$ of total.

The genotype with neither dominant gene gives *wrinkled green* seeds. This is found in compartment 16;

$= \frac{1}{16}$ of total.

This scheme provides a satisfactory explanation of the observed F_2 segregation.

We must now return to the assumption upon which the explanation depends. Mendel realised that this could be tested by crossing the F_1 with plants carrying only the recessive genes; i.e.:

S s Y y	×	*s s y y*
F_1 hybrid		wrinkled green variety

The importance of using this "double recessive" variety is two-fold. Firstly, being homozygous, it can produce only one sort of gamete, *s y*. Secondly, since both *s* and *y* are recessive genes they are incapable of concealing any other genes. It follows that any segregation observed in the progeny of this cross must indicate segregation among the gametes of the F_1 hybrid parent. This cross is therefore an example of a **test-cross,** that is a cross between a heterozygote and a corresponding recessive homozygote made in order to *test* the gametes produced by the heterozygote. The results of this test-cross, made reciprocally, were as follows:

	Cross			*Progeny*			
	seed parent		pollen parent	smooth yellow	smooth green	wrinkled yellow	wrinkled green
1.	*SsYy*	×	*ssyy*	31	26	27	26
2.	*ssyy*	×	*SsYy*	24	25	22	27

In each case the progeny included four phenotypes in approximately equal numbers; therefore the heterozygous parent had produced, in equal frequencies, four types of gamete. Similar results from reciprocal crosses proved that segregation into four types of gamete occurred both in the formation of egg cells (cross No. 1) and of pollen grains (cross No. 2). Hence Mendel provided convincing evidence that his explanation of the previous experiment was correct.

These experiments in which two pairs of alleles were involved established the principle which is known as Mendel's second law. Mendel showed that each gamete produced by the F_1 hybrid had one gene for shape and one for colour, but that the way in which the genes were associated in the parent varieties did not affect this. A gamete carrying the *S* gene for shape was equally likely to have *Y* or *y* as the gene for colour, and so on. Expressed more generally, the principle is that in the gametes from an individual heterozygous for two or more pairs of alleles, the segregation of any pair is independent of the segregation of any other pair. This is the principle of **independent assortment**.

Inheritance which follows the pattern demonstrated by Mendel is now known to be widespread, affecting features of various sorts in both plants and animals. It is frequently referred to as **Mendelian inheritance** or simply **Mendelism**. A few examples from higher plants will emphasise the variety of features inherited in this way. We have already considered examples from the garden pea of Mendelian inheritance of

(*a*) plant height;
(*b*) colour of parts of the plant (*e.g.* flowers or seeds);
(*c*) behaviour of the seed during ripening (whether it remains swollen or shrivels).

Further examples from other species include:

(*d*) shape of particular organs;
e.g. in *Antirrhinum majus* (snapdragon) leaves may be broad (dominant) or narrow (recessive), and flowers zygomorphic (dominant) or actinomorphic (recessive);

(*e*) surface of fruits;
e.g. in *Prunus persica* varieties with downy skins to the fruits (dominant) are peaches, and those with smooth skins (recessive) are nectarines;

(*f*) growth behaviour;
e.g. in *Zea mays* (maize) normal varieties grow upright. Another variety of no commercial importance grows horizontally along the ground, and is called "lazy" maize. Normal growth is dominant, laziness recessive;

(*g*) disease resistance;
e.g. varieties of wheat differ in whether or not they resist the fungal parasite *Puccinia glumarum* which can cause a serious disease called stripe rust. Susceptibility is dominant, resistance recessive.

The list of examples could be continued almost indefinitely, but the reader should not be misled into believing that all inherited differences behave in this relatively simple way. Later in this chapter reference will be made to other features whose inheritance can be explained only by a modification or elaboration of Mendel's principles.

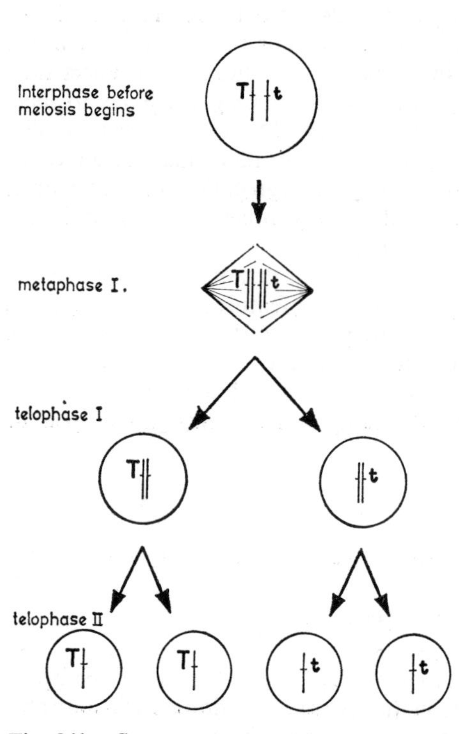

Fig. 341. SEGREGATION OF A PAIR OF ALLELES DURING POLLEN FORMATION. FOR SIMPLICITY, ONLY ONE PAIR OF CHROMOSOMES IS SHOWN.

The diagram illustrates the sequence of events when relative positions of the alleles are not affected by crossing-over (see p. 648), and segregation of *T* from *t* occurs at the first division of meiosis. In other pollen mother cells, crossing-over may result in postponement of segregation until the second division. The final result is similar in the two cases: half of the pollen grains have *T* and half have *t*.

The Chromosome Theory of Heredity

Both the principle of segregation and the principle of independent assortment imply the existence of a mechanism, particularly within the cells which produce gametes, which can distribute the genes in the manner deduced from breeding experiments. Consideration of the nuclear events during mitosis and meiosis (Chapter 8) shows that there is close agreement between the observed behaviour of chromosomes and the inferred behaviour of genes. This led to the suggestion that chromosomes are the carriers of genes and are therefore intimately concerned with inheritance.

This was little more than a suggestion when it was first put forward, and hence it became known as the chromosome *theory* of heredity. However, subsequent work has provided such overwhelming confirmation, that the word "theory" is scarcely necessary any longer. In fact the subjects of cytology and genetics, which were originally quite separate fields of study, are now very closely associated. The branch of genetics which relates observable features of cell structure to the process of inheritance is nowadays called **cytogenetics**.

We will first interpret the principle of segregation in terms of chromosome behaviour. It will be recalled from the explanation of Mendel's experiment on plant height (p. 635) that the heterozygous F_1 produced gametes of two sorts: whereas an F_1 plant carried both T and t, its gametes received *either* T *or* t. This agrees very well with the reduction in chromosome number during meiosis if we assume that the two alleles T and t occur on homologous chromosomes. The sequence of events during meiosis which results in segregation of the alleles is shown in Fig. 341. This shows that the haploid pollen grains have an equal chance of receiving (and transmitting) T or t. The formation of egg cells is comparable and also results in two genotypes of equal frequency.

At fertilisation, two haploid gametes unite to give a diploid zygote with two genes for height in one of the combinations: TT, Tt, or tt. From then on, during development of the mature plant from the zygote, cell division is mitotic, each daughter cell being genetically identical with its parent. Hence, if the zygote had the genotype Tt, mitosis will ensure that every somatic cell of the plant also has this genotype. Only when this plant in its turn begins to produce gametes will segregation of the alleles occur again.

The principle of independent assortment also shows full agreement with the movements of chromosomes during meiosis. Assuming that the genes for seed shape and seed colour are on different chromosomes, the formation of gametes in the double heterozygote $Ss\,Yy$ follows the course shown in Fig. 342.

This diagram shows that there are two possible arrangements of the bivalents at metaphase I, one in which both dominant alleles face the same pole, the other with one dominant and one recessive allele facing each pole. Since the bivalents are quite separate from each other, they orientate themselves independently, and these two possibilities are equally likely. It therefore follows, as the lower part of the diagram shows, that the four types of gamete are formed with equal frequencies. [It will be found on further reading that Fig. 342 is an over-simplification of the true situation since it ignores the effects of crossing-over within the bivalents (see p. 648). This additional factor, however, does not invalidate the principle that independent orientation of bivalents results in independent assortment of the genes they carry.]

The explanation of independent assortment just given makes the assumption that the two pairs of alleles are carried on different chromosomes. However, the garden pea has only seven pairs of

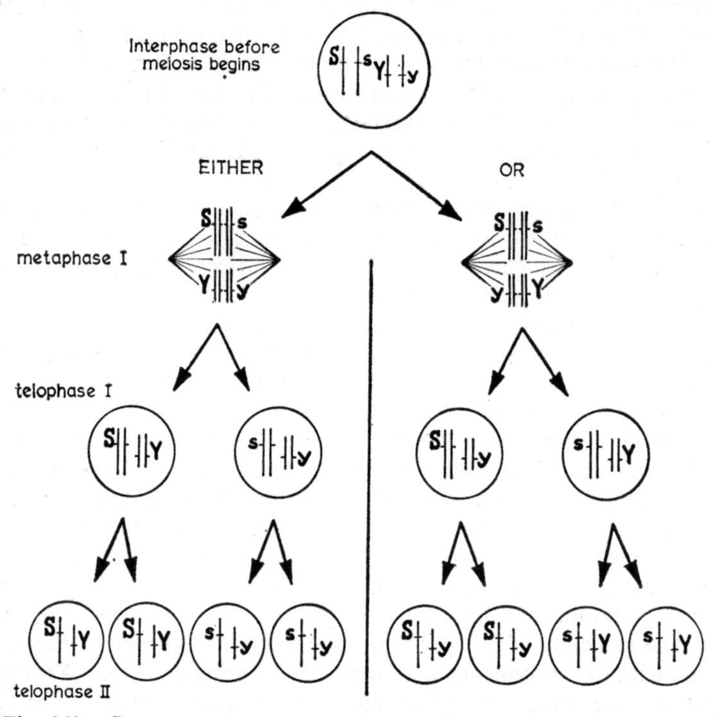

Fig. 342. SEGREGATION OF TWO PAIRS OF ALLELES CARRIED ON DIFFERENT CHROMOSOMES DURING FOLLEN FORMATION.

The effects of crossing-over (see p. 648) have been disregarded. Although crossing-over may postpone the segregation of one pair or both pairs of alleles until the second division of meiosis, the four types of gamete are still produced in equal frequencies.

chromosomes and many more than seven features which, considered separately, follow the rules of Mendelian inheritance. Each chromosome must therefore have at least several genes and the question arises: what pattern of inheritance is shown by two genes both carried by the same chromosome? If location on the same chromosome meant that the two genes were inseparable in inheritance, then one would expect the corresponding features to be permanently associated. In fact this expectation is rarely fulfilled. To illustrate this point we shall consider an experiment which has been carried out with the tomato. The most familiar varieties of tomato have yellow flowers and red fruits, but others are known which have white flowers and yellow fruits. If the inheritance of flower colour or fruit colour is studied separately, the results are in full agreement with Mendel's principle of segregation. But if the two differences are considered together in the same cross the results are as follows:

parents:	yellow flowers red fruit	×	white flowers yellow fruit
F_1 hybrid:		yellow flowers red fruit	

	yellow flowers		white flowers	
F_2:	red fruit	yellow fruit	red fruit	yellow fruit
	68%	7%	7%	18%
	(56%)	(19%)	(19%)	(6%)

The numbers in brackets are the approximate proportions expected on the basis of a 9 : 3 : 3 : 1 ratio. It is clear that in this case there is wide disagreement between the observed F_2 and the result expected if the genes showed independent assortment. There is a marked excess of the phenotypes which resemble the original parents, and a deficiency of the recombinant phenotypes. This sort of result is characteristic of features controlled by **linked genes**, that is genes carried on the same chromosome. Such genes are by no means inseparable, but they do not dissociate with the same freedom as genes on different chromosomes. Again, there is a satisfactory explanation in terms of chromosome behaviour. During prophase I of meiosis, homologous chromosomes pair together. At first there is close pairing along the whole length of the bivalent, but at diakinesis it can be seen that the four chromatids separate into twos, and the bivalent is held together only by one or more chiasmata. These are points where neighbouring chromatids have broken and rejoined into new arrangements. The successive stages of this process and the events which follow are shown in Fig. 343, which also indicates the effect on the positions of two genes if a chiasma forms between them. It will be seen that although the bivalent begins with four chromatids each of which carries either *A* and *B* or *a* and *b*, this arrangement is upset by the chiasma. At anaphase the four chromatids all have different genotypes: two are parental and two recombinant. Each of these four chromatids will pass into a different haploid cell which may function as a gamete.

The breakage and rejoining of chromatids, which leads to chiasmata at diakinesis, is known as **crossing-over**. It explains how linked genes may be separated, and also accounts for the different frequencies with which particular pairs of linked genes combine. These frequencies are related to the physical distance between the genes on their common chromosome. If the genes are situated close together, the chance of a chiasma forming between them is small and they will separate only rarely. Such genes are said to be closely linked. On the other hand, two genes which are

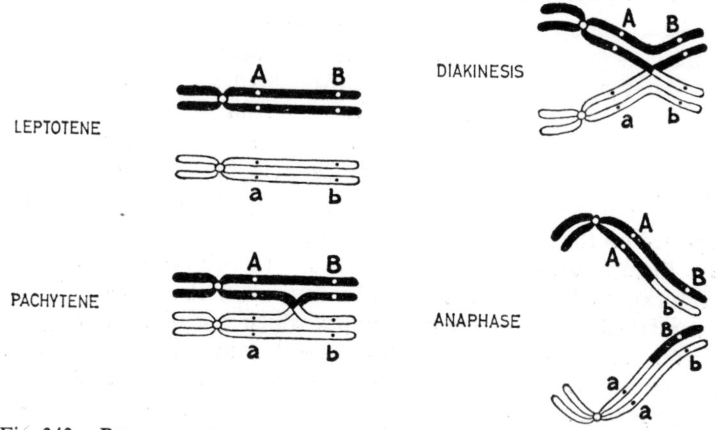

Fig. 343. BEHAVIOUR OF A BIVALENT HETEROZYGOUS FOR TWO PAIRS OF ALLELES (*A*, *a* AND *B*, *b*) DURING FIRST DIVISION OF MEIOSIS. DURING THE SECOND DIVISION, THE FOUR CHROMATIDS SEPARATE AND EACH PASSES INTO A DIFFERENT NUCLEUS. THE FOUR PRODUCTS OF MEIOSIS MAY THEREFORE ALL DIFFER FROM ONE ANOTHER.

far apart on the same chromosome will be separated so often that they will behave almost as though they were on different chromosomes. This relationship between frequency of recombination and the distance apart of linked genes can be used to construct a "map" of the chromosomes on which the relative positions of the genes are marked. For certain plants in which many inherited differences have been studied, such as the maize, tomato, and pea plants, chromosome maps showing the positions of many genes are available.

To conclude this section on the part played by the chromosomes in inheritance, a reappraisal of Mendel's principle of independent assortment is necessary. It has been shown that a completely satisfactory explanation of the principle is supplied by the known behaviour of chromosomes, provided one is considering genes which are not linked. In such a case the principle can be applied to predict with certainty the composition of an F_2 or other progenies of known parentage. The principle does not hold good, however, for linked genes, in which case predictions about the composition of, say, an F_2 can only be made if the degree of linkage has been measured. This limitation of the principle of independent assortment in no way discredits the pioneer work of Mendel, but is a reminder that not all experiments in hybridisation yield results which follow the strict Mendelian pattern.

Quantitative Inheritance

The examples of inherited differences given in this chapter so far have all been chosen for the distinctiveness of one phenotype from another. With the varieties Mendel used, there was no difficulty in distinguishing tall and dwarf pea plants. The difference between red-fruited and yellow-fruited tomatoes is similarly clear-cut. When, as in these cases, a single gene can bring about an unmistakable difference of this kind, it is called a **major gene**. Because their effects are so distinctive, major genes provide the most straightforward material for the study of inheritance. It has already been pointed out that some major genes are of considerable economic importance: the gene for resistance to stripe rust, for instance, is a valuable asset in a variety of wheat. In such a case it is a relatively simple procedure for a plant breeder to incorporate the gene in any chosen variety by a judicious programme of hybridisation. Unfortunately, many of the qualities which a plant breeder may wish to establish in a new variety, though clearly inherited, are controlled by a much more complex genetic system. Of foremost importance in any agricultural crop plant is the yield. This, of course, will mean different things in different crops: weight of root tubers in parsnips, quantity of leaves in tobacco, weight of ripe inflorescences in cereals, and so on. In all these cases the feature is one which must be *measured*, not simply recorded as present or absent. All cultivated varieties of parsnip produce swollen roots, but some produce larger roots than others under identical conditions of cultivation. The differences are therefore inherited. But between the highest and lowest yielding varieties are others whose average yields show all intermediate values. The full analysis of inherited features which show continuous variation between extremes, rather than discontinuous variation into distinct phenotypes, is beyond the scope of this book. But it is known that these features are affected by many genes each with small effects and to some extent supplementary to one another. Such genes are described as **multiple factors** or **polygenes**. A simplified, but not unrealistic explanation of the system controlling root size in the parsnip requires the existence of positive polygenes, each causing a small increase in root size, and negative polygenes whose effect is negligible. The average root size for any variety is related to the number of positive polygenes it possesses. There is evidence that polygenes are essentially similar to major genes except in the magnitude of their effect. They are situated on chromosomes, segregate, and show independent or linked assortment depending on their positions.

An important consequence of a system where many genes contribute to the same feature is that individuals with a complete set of all available positive genes are extremely rare. Two high-yielding varieties may each possess a large number of the appropriate polygenes, but each may have some which the other lacks. In theory, therefore, it should be possible to produce by hybridisation a superior variety with all the best genes from both parents. In practice this is difficult because of the very large progenies which must be grown to give any reasonable chance of all the desired genes coming together by random assortment, though some important varieties of agricultural plants have originated in this way.

Because the individual effects of polygenes are small, there are special difficulties attached to studying their inheritance. In particular, the effect which a single polygene can have on the phenotype is of the same order as that caused by uncontrollable variations in the environment. This is best explained by referring once again to Mendel's experiment on plant height in the pea. As was stated earlier, plants of the tall variety grew to heights of between 6 and 7 ft. That is, in spite of genetic uniformity there was some variation in height, attributable to slight differences in the environment. Nevertheless, there was no question of mistaking a tall plant for a dwarf one: the effect of the gene for tallness was much more pronounced than any effect of variation in climate or soil conditions. In this case, therefore, the phenotype is a reliable guide to the genotype, at least in so far as dominant genes are concerned.

A polygene, on the other hand, is more likely to add half an inch to the height of a plant than 5 ft. If, in a species where height is controlled by polygenes, a group of plants includes all sizes between 3 ft and 5 ft high, it is impossible to say simply by looking at the plants what are the relative contributions of heredity and environment to this variation. The tallest plant might owe its height of 5 ft to a mediocre genotype and fortunate circumstances during development. Another plant only 4 ft 6 in. high might have a superior genotype but have had to struggle in a less favourable environment. This inherent superiority would show only in subsequent generations. In breeding to improve quantitative features controlled by polygenes, therefore, an individual must be assessed more on the quality of its progeny than on its own phenotype. This principle was established many years ago by the experiments of Johannsen on seed weight in the French bean (*Phaseolus vulgaris*), although Johannsen himself did not describe his experiments in terms of polygenes. His work was concerned with the distinction between environmental and genetic variation, and was published in 1903 before the concept of polygenes was advanced. Like the garden pea, *P. vulgaris* regularly self-pollinates itself, so that all the descendants of a single individual have the same inheritance as one another and constitute a **pure line**.

Johannsen took a number of seeds from nineteen bean plants. These beans showed wide variation in weight among themselves, with a mean weight of 0·48 gm. They could be separated, however, into nineteen pure lines corresponding to the nineteen original plants, each of which had a more restricted range of variation and a distinctive mean weight. For example, one pure line had a mean weight of 0·64 gm., and another a mean weight of only 0·35 gm. These observations demonstrated the two types of variation present in the whole collection. The differences in mean weight between different pure lines must represent inherited variation; variation in weight between individuals within a pure line, on the other hand, must be the result of environmental influences.

Johannsen then showed that the environmentally produced differences within a pure line are not inherited. He planted beans representing the extremes of variation from a single pure line, and recorded the weights of their separate progenies. For example, he planted beans weighing 0·40 gm. and 0·70 gm. from a pure line with a mean weight of 0·56 gm. In spite of the difference in weight of the two mother beans, the two progenies were very similar and each had a mean weight of about 0·56 gm.

This experiment has important lessons for breeders of self-fertilising crops. It shows that selecting for high yield in a population which includes a number of pure lines can have an immediate effect, and a variety with improved yield may be established. But once a single pure line has been isolated further selection will be ineffective unless some new inherited variation is produced (see below). The situation in cross-fertilising crops is rather different, but there is the same problem of separating the effects of the environment from those of the genotype.

The Origin of New Inherited Variation

Genetics is a branch of biology which comes close to being an exact science. The regularity with which chromosomes undergo their appointed cycle of changes during nuclear division, the exactness with which they reproduce themselves, and the consequent stability of the genes from one generation to another, all permit confident predictions to be made about the progeny of given parents. But this confidence can never amount to certainty, for neither the regularity of chromosome behaviour nor the exactness of gene reproduction is absolute.

It has been stated earlier that a plant which is homozygous for a certain gene will produce gametes all of which transmit that gene. This seems perfectly reasonable. A factory which makes nothing but motor-cars is not expected to sell anything except motor-cars: it would be surprising if one of its products turned out to be a bicycle. But living things do occasionally produce gametes which seem to be unrelated to the parental genotype; the statement about the gametes from a homozygote has its exceptions. These exceptions are distinctly uncommon, and large numbers of individuals may need to be observed before one is encountered. In some plants special techniques can be employed to detect them without excessive labour. The maize plant, for instance, is particularly well suited to this task for two reasons. Firstly, it is monoecious with quite separate male and female inflorescences, so that emasculation can be carried out very rapidly. The single terminal male inflorescence is simply cut off and the plant becomes exclusively female and incapable of self-fertilisation. Female flowers are in axillary inflorescences which develop into the corn cobs. After fertilisation, each female flower produces one kernel, which is a one-seeded fruit. The second advantage is that there are varieties which differ in the appearance of the endosperm. These make very convenient material for genetical studies, as the following experiment shows. In some varieties the endosperm contains a yellow carotenoid pigment which shows through the transparent pericarp; in others this is absent and the kernels are white. Presence of the yellow pigment is caused by a dominant gene *Y*. If a plant homozygous for white endosperm, *yy*, is pollinated by another plant homozygous for *Y*, one expects that every kernel will receive the dominant gene *Y* and they will all be yellow. This expectation can be tested by growing the two sorts of plant side by side and decapitating all the *yy* plants. It is then a simple matter of observing a large number of kernels on the *yy* plants, each kernel representing fertilisation by a different pollen grain from a *YY* plant. On one occasion when this was done, nearly two million kernels were scrutinised. All were yellow except four, which were white. Any doubt that these four were the offspring of the *YY* plants was dispelled by germinating them and showing that other features were present which could only have come from the *YY* variety.

The conclusion is that out of nearly two million pollen grains from plants of genotype *YY*, four had transmitted not *Y* but its recessive allele *y*. At some stage in formation of these pollen grains there had been **mutation** from one allele to the other. The propensity to mutate into an alternative form is believed to be a property of all genes, though not with equal likelihood. The frequency of 1 in 500,000 for the change $Y \rightarrow y$, measured by the technique described above, is about average for those genes whose mutation rates are known. This explains why changes attributable to gene mutation are met with only infrequently, though they are familiar enough to horticulturists whose daily work involves inspection of large numbers of plants. Mutation can occur at any stage in the development of a plant; the earlier it happens the greater is the proportion of the plant possessing the mutated gene. On several occasions it has been observed that a red-currant bush has produced a branch on which all the fruits are white. This indicates mutation at an early stage in a cell from which much or all of the odd branch has developed. A plant, or part of a plant with unexpected features which arises in this way, is described by gardeners as a "sport". Such sports may be the source of new varieties if they can be propagated. The apple variety "Crimson Bramley" originated as a sport in the better known "Bramley's Seedling". Various physical and chemical agents are known which are **mutagenic**, that is they can induce a higher rate of mutation than is natural. These include ultra-violet radiation, x-rays or the emissions from radioactive substances, and a wide range of chemical compounds. Treatment with any of these agents brings about a general increase in mutation frequency of perhaps 100 times or more, without much discrimination between one gene and another. Some success has been achieved in producing new varieties of crop plants by induced mutation. This work has to be carried out on a large scale since although it is not difficult to induce large numbers of mutant forms, only about one in a thousand is likely to be an improvement on the treated variety. Among the products of this technique is a new variety of garden pea from Sweden, produced by x-irradiation, which has a yield 7 per cent. better than the variety from which it was derived.

The fact that exposure to these radiations can increase mutation rates, and the knowledge that most mutations reduce the fitness of the individual affected are matters of widespread interest and concern. Certain naturally occurring radiations to which almost all living organisms are exposed, such as cosmic rays and the emissions from radioactive minerals in soil, are mutagenic. They are undoubtedly responsible for some so-called spontaneous mutations, though probably for only a minority. Owing to certain recent human activities, particularly the testing of nuclear weapons, there have been considerable increases from time to time in the level of mutagenic radiation to which exposure is unavoidable. The magnitude of the increased mutation rates which must have resulted is a subject of disagreement among experts. Probably the number of additional mutations induced is only a small proportion of what would have occurred in any case, so that the increase in visible mutants is likely to pass unnoticed except in regions which have received an exceptionally high dose of extra radiation.

When speaking of a mutation, one usually means an alteration in a single gene, but the word can also be used in a wide sense to include any change in the chromosomes which is permanent and inherited. Such changes may be far more drastic than the conversion of just one gene into an alternative form. Among the most extreme is a doubling of the entire chromosome complement, which can come about through a disturbance in the normal process of cell division. This produces a cell which is **polyploid**, that is having more than two haploid sets of chromosomes, which will reproduce the increased chromosome number in its descendants if normal cell division is restored. Comparison of chromosome numbers in closely related species or varieties indicates that polyploidy must have arisen on numerous occasions. For example, among the cultivated chrysanthemums there are species with the following chromosome numbers: 18, 36, 54, 72, 90—all multiples of 18. It is difficult to avoid the conclusion that the higher numbers were derived from lower ones by polyploidy.

Like gene mutations, polyploidy can be artificially induced. The most successful technique is to treat meristematic cells with the alkaloid colchicine which is extracted from the autumn crocus (*Colchicum autumnale*). This inhibits formation of the mitotic spindle, without which the cells cannot divide, although the chromosomes do. Under the influence of colchicine, therefore, cells undergo a curtailed mitosis. If there are ten chromosomes to start with, these divide into twenty, but they are not then separated into two daughter cells.

The effects of polyploidy can be assessed by comparing a diploid with a polyploid derived from it. In some cases the increased chromosome number causes an increase in size of either the whole plant or of parts of it, so that the diploid and polyploid are quite distinct from each other. Induced polyploidy has therefore been tried as a method of plant improvement. In some crops the results are disappointing, the polyploids being no better than, and often decidedly inferior to, the parental diploids. But polyploid varieties of rye, sugar-beet, turnip, clover, and other crops, all with increased yield, have either been marketed already or are showing great promise in trials.

Evolution

There has been repeated reference in the preceding sections to the achievements of plant breeders in establishing improved varieties of crop plants. Much of the improvement which they seek depends on two complementary processes: firstly the mutation of genes and chromosomes, either spontaneously or by induction, and secondly the rearrangement of genes and chromosomes into new combinations through cross-fertilisation. By exploiting these two processes breeders are able to supply the market with a succession of new varieties year after year. The best of these have so much more appeal to the grower than previous varieties through their higher yield, or greater disease resistance, or more spectacular flowers or whatever it may be, that they become established as the popular varieties of their time. As a result, some of the older varieties pass out of fashion.

For example, there appeared in 1900 a new variety of sweet pea (*Lathyrus odoratus*) called "Countess Spencer". It originated by spontaneous mutation and was distinguished by particularly large flowers with wavy standards, an attractive combination of features which ensured its success. Waviness of the standard is caused by a single recessive gene which can be, and was, introduced very easily by hybridisation into other varieties with different flower colours. Nowadays all the most popular varieties offered in seedsmen's catalogues have this feature, and it is extremely difficult to obtain varieties which were fashionable in the 1890's with their plain and less showy standards. In this example we see all three of the processes mentioned above: first of all mutation, then recombination, and finally the eclipse of older varieties because of their failure to compete with new ones.

The sequence of events illustrated by the story of the Spencer sweet pea happens repeatedly in all cultivated plants which are of sufficient importance to receive the attention of plant breeders. In another fifty years' time, our gardens and farm land will be growing many varieties which are unknown to us to-day. Although deliberate plant improvement is a type of human interference in the affairs of plants, it should be clearly recognised that the processes involved are essentially natural, that is, capable of happening without human intervention. To begin with, mutation is something which happens spontaneously. Admittedly, the spontaneous frequency seems low, but all the time genes and chromosomes somewhere or other are doing unexpected things, changing their nature or their number. Men may increase the frequency of these events but in doing so they are only copying nature. Secondly, there is abundant cross-fertilisation among plants through natural agencies. Some of the many mechanisms which increase the likelihood of cross-fertilisation have been described in Chapter 12. It is true that natural crossing is more indiscriminate than the carefully planned hybridisations of the plant breeder, but the result is much the same. Genotypes are continually taken to pieces by segregation and reassembled in new combinations. Any new gene which arises by mutation is likely to be incorporated by cross-fertilisation into a wide assortment of different genotypes. Thirdly, there is undoubtedly competition between wild plants just as there is between cultivated ones. The key to success in this case is not the ability to satisfy certain human preferences, but to withstand better than one's neighbours the living conditions of a crowded world where every necessity must be obtained competitively.

Knowing that these three processes of mutation, recombination, and competition are quite natural, it becomes easier to realise that the production of new varieties and the replacement of old ones are not something which man has invented. The capacity to evolve into new forms is a fundamental charactistic of living organisms, and in carrying out his work the plant breeder is simply employing this property for his own ends. By accelerating the frequency of mutation and controlling the otherwise random process of cross-fertilisation, he may achieve results more rapidly and economically than they occur in nature, but he is, nevertheless, directing a programme of artificial evolution strictly comparable with a natural process.

Nowadays it is accepted almost without question that the countless forms of plant and animal life which exist to-day are the products of a long, gradual process of evolution during which one species has led to another, and simple organisms have given rise to more complex ones. But it was not always so. During the early nineteenth century only a handful of advanced thinkers would admit a belief in evolution. Those of their contemporaries who gave any thought at all to the origins of plants and animals were strongly influenced by the Old Testament story of creation which many believed to be literally true. Any who felt doubts about the authenticity of Genesis found only meagre evidence to encourage a belief in a process of gradual change extending over millions of years. But little by little the evidence grew and became more compelling. In particular, studies of fossils (see p. 443) revealed that the flora and fauna of past eras were unlike those still living, though connected with them through time by a series of transitional forms. Despite gaps in the series, the conclusions were inescapable: not only had life evolved over an immense period of time, but the process had been accompanied by the extinction of many forms of life and was not merely a progressive addition to the variety of organisms.

The recognition of evolution as a fact was quickly followed by attempts to explain *how* it had occurred. In 1859 Charles Darwin (1809-82), after many years of painstaking observation and careful thought, published his historic book *On the Origin of Species by Means of Natural Selection*, in which he propounded a theory of the mechanism of evolution. In spite of vigorous opposition at the outset and some vicissitudes since, a substantial part of the theory remains in the explanation of evolution which is most widely accepted to-day. This part of the Darwinian theory which has withstood the test of time and subsequent discovery may be stated briefly as follows.

Firstly, all species of plants and animals tend to produce far more offspring than is necessary simply to maintain their numbers.

Secondly, in spite of this high rate of reproduction, the number of individuals in a species does not normally show a rapid and continuing increase corresponding to the numbers of offspring.

From these two facts it follows that there must be very high mortality in early life which deprives most plants and animals of the opportunity to reproduce and thereby contribute to the future of the species. Darwin visualised this in terms of a "struggle for existence" in which all individuals compete against a variety of hazards, with the prospect of only a minority winning through to reproductive maturity.

A third fact, which may be confirmed as readily as the first two, is that in general offspring of the same parentage are not identical either with one another or with their parents. Diversity among themselves means that competitors in the struggle for existence are not equally favoured or handicapped. Those with superior endowments are more likely to succeed and become the parents of the next generation. Assuming that their superiority is inherited, this has the effect of maintaining the genetic quality of the species: in Darwin's own words, there is "survival of the fittest" in each generation. A logical extension of this argument is that if the offspring include individuals which surpass the parents in competitive efficiency, these will be preserved in preference to the parental types, and the characteristics of the species will gradually change.

It is therefore clear that from the excessive numbers of young plants which come into being, the few which are to survive and reproduce are not picked out by some indiscriminate and random process. On the contrary, the privilege of survival is reserved for those individuals which are most suitably equipped to perpetuate their kind. This selective process was named **Natural Selection** by Darwin. Having stressed the non-random aspect of natural selection, it is only fair to emphasise that there is also, of course, a considerable element of chance in whether a particular individual survives. A forest fire can destroy a complete patch of vegetation, however superior the genotypes of some of the plants may be, and even the most aggressive weed may be eaten by a grazing animal.

The facts given above and the deductions made from them can form a satisfactory basis for a theory of evolution provided there is also a continual supply of genetic variation including new features which can become the characteristics of new species. Darwin's own attempts to complete his theory were hindered by a general lack of knowledge at the time of the principles of inheritance and the sources of genetic variability upon which natural selection can act. There is nowadays very considerable knowledge of both these subjects, which has removed much of the uncertainty from Darwin's original theory. We shall now briefly consider the modern interpretation of Darwinism, often referred to as Neo-Darwinism.

The question of where genetic variation comes from has been discussed earlier in this chapter (p. 652). In addition to the extreme types of mutation mentioned there, namely gene mutations and the occurrence of polyploidy, the genetic mechanism can undergo other types of change. Single chromosomes may be lost or gained; parts of chromosomes may become duplicated or eliminated; and structural changes within the chromosomes may rearrange the genes without any net loss or gain. All these changes can produce phenotypic effects, and probably no species of living organism is exempted from changes of this sort. Here then is a continual and general source of genetic novelty.

But the frequency with which these changes of genotype occur, and the nature of their effects on the phenotype must also be considered. All the events which are recognised as mutations are uncommon (p. 653), and experience has suggested that all but a small minority result in reduced viability or fertility when they are expressed in the phenotype. It is tempting, therefore, to reject mutation as a major factor in evolution on the grounds that it is too infrequent and its results are of the wrong sort. However, this attitude conflicts with direct evidence of the precise differences which do distinguish one species from another. If two closely related species are crossed together and the hybrid analysed, perhaps by further breeding, it can often be shown that the two parents differ by an accumulation of the kind of changes mentioned above. Some are differences in single genes whose individual effects may be large or small; others are structural changes of the chromosomes, or changes of chromosome number. It seems certain that if mutations of the right sort can accumulate, the differences in phenotype are sufficient to warrant the recognition of a new species. We must therefore reconsider the part played by mutation, and in particular take account of two known features of genetic systems. Firstly, most species of plant and animal are diploid or polyploid for the greater part of their life-cycles. Secondly, when genes mutate it is far commoner for a dominant gene to change to a recessive allele than the reverse.

These two facts have an important bearing on the future of a new gene. Let us consider the fate of a recessive gene *a* newly arisen in the pollen grain of a cross-pollinating diploid species. The pollen grain fertilises an ovule which has the "normal" dominant allele *A*, and the seed which is produced grows into a heterozygous plant *Aa*. This plant will not show any phenotypic effect of *a*, which is not therefore exposed to the action of natural selection. In the course of reproduction, the heterozygote will pass the recessive mutant gene to some of its offspring which, because of cross-fertilisation, will also be heterozygotes; *a* is still concealed, but it is now present in several individuals. Further reproduction could involve cross-pollination between two heterozygotes, leading to the production of some individuals homozygous for *a*. The population now includes *AA* and *Aa* plants with the original phenotype, and some *aa* plants with the new phenotype characteristic of *a*. The two phenotypes will be in competition with each other, and there is a high probability (based on the known effects of most mutant genes) that the *aa* plants will compete less efficiently. They may therefore be eliminated fairly rapidly, but this will not mean that the gene *a* is lost from the population. It will be maintained in heterozygotes, perhaps indefinitely, and will constantly reappear in homozygotes as a result of cross-pollination.

This continual reappearance is of profound importance for two reasons which should be considered together since they are closely related. In the first place the system of cross-pollination results in regular reassortment of genes. Two individuals in a cross-breeding species rarely have the same genotype as each other. So each time the *aa* homozygote is produced it is likely to be accompanied by a different residual genotype. The phenotypic effect of *aa*, and its chances of survival, may vary considerably according to which other genes are present. For example if the genotype *aa* increased metabolic efficiency at lower temperatures, the mutant might make a successful coloniser of colder regions, but only if it had other necessary attributes such as frost resistance. Each gene must be thought of not so much as an isolated functional unit but as part of an integrated gene-complex. The potential represented by *aa* can only be realised if the other genes associated with it are harmonious. It is therefore possible that in spite of initial lack of success, *aa* may eventually be incorporated in a genotype which natural selection will preserve.

The second important consequence of the repeated reappearance of *aa* is that although the mutation from *A* to *a* might occur only once, its effects can be tested in a variety of environments. We have spoken above of the *a* phenotype competing less efficiently than the *A* phenotype. This may be true under the conditions of the environment where the mutant phenotype appeared first, but if the species has an efficient dispersal mechanism, *aa* homozygotes will be transferred to a number of different habitats. The relative success of the *A* and *a* phenotypes will not necessarily be similar in all these situations, and it may well be that though in the original habitat *A* ousted *a* elsewhere the opposite will happen. An illustration of this principle is seen in the mutation which produced the tobacco variety Maryland Wonder. This variety first appeared in Washington D.C. as a plant which, unlike its parents, would not flower there under normal field conditions (see p. 313). At the latitude of Washington (39° N.) day length reaches nearly fifteen hours at midsummer, and it was shown that the mutant would flower only if day length were restricted to twelve hours. Under natural conditions at this latitude, therefore, such a mutant would be unable to reproduce and would undoubtedly fail to survive in competition with its parent. With shorter days, however, the mutant was the more successful, and if both types had been planted together in tropical latitudes, the mutant would almost certainly have replaced the parent.

Variation of the environment is a consequence of time as well as of movement in space. It is well established that over long periods of time there are substantial changes in such things as the prevailing climate, the texture, depth, and composition of the soil, and even in the composition of the atmosphere. These changes will also affect the relative success of different genotypes. One which has been well established for many years and which has withstood the challenge of others, may eventually lose its supremacy if the environment in which it achieved its success is significantly altered.

It should now be clear, even from the brief account given, that the emergence of new species during evolution results from the interaction of numerous factors. Those which have been mentioned may be summarised as follows:

1. **Mutation:** an infrequent process providing variations of the genotype, some of which may be the raw materials of new species.

2. **Recessiveness** of many genetic determinants, enabling a species to build up and maintain a store of variability, largely concealed.

3. **Cross-fertilisation:** a breeding system which continually rearranges genotypes, thereby allowing many combinations of genes to be tested.

4. **Variation of the environment** in space and time, which not only gives the opportunity for new species to become established but may force a species to change if it is not to become extinct.

5. **Natural selection:** the selecting from a great number and variety of individuals those whose phenotypes are most advantageous in the struggle for existence.

There is little doubt that a great deal of the mechanism of evolution can be explained in terms of these factors, though it must be stressed that the discussion of gene-mutations in cross-breeding diploids, given above, is to be regarded as an example and not a comprehensive theory. It does not, for instance, cover those plants in which the greater part of the life-cycle is spent in the haploid condition, nor those in which self-fertilisation is the rule. In the former case there is little opportunity for a store of recessive genes to be maintained, and most mutant genes are immediately exposed to natural selection. The establishment of new mutants therefore depends on mutations occurring at precisely the right time and place to allow survival. This will happen only rarely, and it is significant that most haploid plants produce enormous numbers of spores or other propagules, which gives the opportunity for a correspondingly large number of genotypes to take their chance.

The situation in self-fertilising plants seems anomalous at first sight. Here are species which possess all the equipment for sexual reproduction including the capacity for meiosis, the main function of which has been described as the reassortment of genes. But instead of using this to maintain genetic variation in the population by cross-fertilisation, they regularly self-fertilise and thereby perpetuate a standard, homozygous genotype (p. 635). This appears to represent a serious misuse of their natural assets, and might be expected to hinder their capacity to evolve when circumstances demand new genotypes. On the other hand, obligatory cross-fertilisation involves a risk, particularly for annual plants. Survival of the species depends on seed production, which in turn depends on the transfer of pollen from plant to plant by a possibly unreliable agent such as wind or an insect. In a season of bad weather, seed set may fail not through any lack of fertility but because of absence of insects. If the plant is an annual it will therefore have lost its only chance of reproducing itself. This risk can be overcome by self-fertilisation, though at the expense of evolutionary efficiency. It is in fact found that those species which have adopted self-fertilisation as their regular breeding system are predominantly annuals. They can be expected to persist so long as their environment remains the same, but any major change imposes a strong likelihood of extinction.

The important part which cross-fertilisation is believed to play in giving a species the capacity to evolve agrees with the occurrence of sexual reproduction, usually accompanied by devices to ensure cross-fertilisation, in almost all groups of plants and animals. It may seem wasteful, for instance, that many lower plants which can propagate themselves with great efficiency by asexual spores should also be encumbered with a far more complicated sexual process. The explanation almost certainly lies in the long-term advantages which cross-fertilisation can bring. Work done during the last twenty years has shown that even among bacteria and viruses there are mechanisms for genetic recombination similar in effect to the sexual processes of higher organisms.

INDEX

PRINTED IN GREAT BRITAIN BY UNIVERSITY TUTORIAL PRESS LTD, FOXTON
NEAR CAMBRIDGE